Introduction to

Systems Theory

Hinrich R. Martens
Don R. Allen
State University of New York at Buffalo

Introduction to

Systems Theory

Charles E. Merrill Publishing Co.
Columbus, Ohio
A Bell & Howell Company

Standard Book Number 675-09603-0

Library of Congress Catalog Card Number: 69-10631

1 2 3 4 5 6 7 — 73 72 71 70 69

Printed in the United States of America

Preface

This text is the outgrowth of notes developed over the past four years, and is intended to serve as a preparatory text in the subject of system analysis and design. The material has been used effectively by our electrical and mechanical engineering departments as the first of a four-term sequence in the analysis and design of lumped parameter systems. This sequence begins with an introduction to systems concepts and analysis of elementary systems, and terminates with procedures and techniques of design and synthesis of physical systems operating in both continuous and discrete time, with inputs available in analog and digital mode.

The success of such study requires solid footing in the principles of system analysis. Therefore, the orientation of this material is general, and mathematical tools are employed with reasonable sophistication. For the student to deal comfortably and easily with systems of mixed disciplines, he must be exposed to the physical properties and mathematical characteristics of components belonging to many disciplines.

This material has application to a wide range of system disciplines, and is especially appropriate for systems made up of electrical, mechanical, and hydraulic components. Other categories, such as pneumatic and thermal systems, may also be handled by the procedures. The broad orientation of the book makes it useful to students in both mechanical and electrical engineering.

Understanding of *Introduction to Systems Theory* requires a background in (1) a college physics course covering all areas commonly developed in freshman and sophomore physics, and (2) a timely mathematics course in calculus, including an introduction to matrices and determinants, complex algebra, and set theory. A differential equations course is desirable as background, but could be taken concurrently. The differential equations course should include an introduction to the theory and application of the Laplace transform.

Chapters 1 through 4 serve as a general introduction to the subject of system analysis. This subject is presented as a three-step procedure: modeling, formulation, and solution, requiring (1) the formation of a mathematical model of components; (2) the assembly of these models into overall system equations; and (3) the processing of these equations into interpretable information.

The Laplace transform is used extensively in the analysis of simple systems of two and three components (Chapter 5). The immediate application of the Laplace transform aids in both the formulation and solution process. General vertex and circuit postulates are established as the basis of the formulation process.

Mesh formulation, node formulation, and state-variable formulation are presented in Chapter 6. Chapter 7 deals with frequency response, resonance, and steady state periodic analysis. The development through Chapter 7 relies on two-terminal components; Chapter 8 introduces multiterminal components. Linear graph techniques are employed to define terminal variables and their orientation. Two methods of deriving component models are specified: inspection of the physical properties, and analytical procedure. Chapter 9 presents topological concepts pertinent to the study of lumped parameter systems, and treats some important aspects of the theoretical basis of formulation techniques presented in the earlier chapters. (Chapter 9 may be omitted without loss of continuity, as its salient points are presented in other chapters as needed.)

Chapters 10 and 11 consider several examples of more complex systems whose formulation and solution are extensions of the theory already presented. These techniques are particularly applicable to multi-discipline systems; for instance, a mechanism which incorporates electrical, mechanical, and hydraulic subsystems.

The authors recognize that one of the important tools in system analysis is the electronic computer, either analog or digital. The application of the computer to solve equations resulting in the formulation of systems is equally useful for nonlinear, time-varying-parameter systems, or linear systems. Chapter 12 covers a variety of areas where computer solution can be effected in the analysis of problems. The material covered in Chapter 12 may well be used at an earlier time, particularly in conjunction with Chapters 5, 6, and 10.

Acknowledgement is given to the faculties of the departments of Electrical and Mechanical Engineering at the State University of New York at Buffalo, through whose cooperation it was possible to establish the necessary course framework to teach this material. We also gratefully acknowledge the patience and understanding of the instructors who taught from the notes. Their helpful comments and continued interest have been invaluable in the development of this text.

H. R. Martens
D. R. Allen

Contents

Introduction

1

This book develops techniques and procedures useful in the study of elementary systems. The development applies basic laws of physics for the description of systems and utilizes techniques of applied mathematics to investigate the behavior of systems. The material is presented at an introductory level, while still establishing a good foundation for continuing study. The first chapter introduces some underlying concepts and background.

1.1 What Is a System?

The word *system* can be applied to many different kinds of things. Here we use it to denote *a medium which relates a cause to an effect, or an input to an output*. In this context, we will accept the following as systems: an electronic amplifier, with a voltage input and a voltage output; a computer, with data input and data output: a garden hose, with water input and water output; a missile guidance control system, with desired direction as input and actual direction as output.

Obviously the list of systems could become very long. But the few examples cited should adequately illustrate in words the concept of a system which is symbolically represented in Figure 1.1.

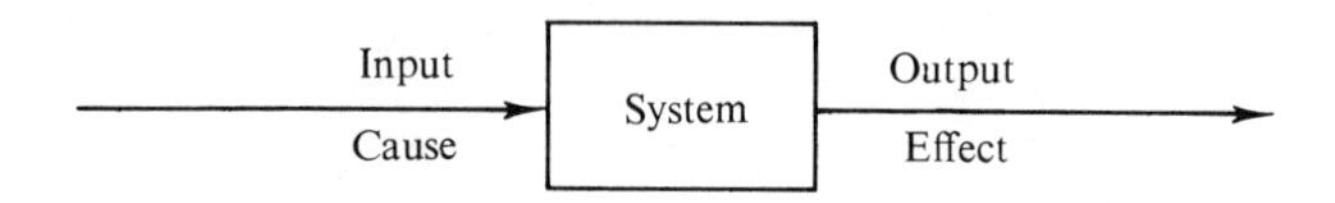

Fig. 1.1. *System.*

An input and an output may be described as a pair of events in time—and the system provides the relationship. The output of some systems may be instantaneously related to the input, in the sense that the input provides certain conditions which specify an output. However, more frequently, systems require a time delay before they react to an input. In any case, the objective of system analysis becomes the study of this interrelationship of input, system, and output.

1.2 System Description

The definition of a system as a medium which provides a relationship between an input and an output is a very general one, giving no indication of the nature of the medium. A need arises for the means of describing a system. There are basically two approaches one might follow in determining the characteristics of a system: *experimental* and *analytical*.

The Experimental Approach

The principle of the experimental approach is simple: The system is subjected to a known input and the output is observed. Then the output and input are paired and an attempt is made to develop a mathematical formula that gives a simple but adequate relationship between input and output. This relationship is normally expressed in terms of a mathematical equation. It may be very precise in its definition of the input-output relationship of the system, or it may be more like an empirical equation with limited applicability.

The experimental approach is probably most useful when the system in fact consists only of one component and the objective is the characterization of the component. In these cases, the mathematical equation is quite precise and very often is a statement of a physical law.

The Analytical Approach

By the analytical approach a system is viewed as an assembly of components, each of which can be characterized independently by a mathematical model. Recognizing the pattern of component interconnection and describing it in mathematical form, the analytical approach then involves a manipulation of the mathematical statements regarding component description and interconnection to generate the desired input-output relationship.

An analytical approach in most cases provides for a very orderly and systematic procedure in the study of systems, and because of that it is naturally preferred to the experimental approach. The techniques to be developed for the analysis of systems will predominantly follow the analytical approach.

To summarize:

a. The system is a connected assembly of components.
b. The pattern of component interconnection is recognizable.
c. Each component can be characterized in a manner entirely independent of any other component connected to it.

These statements form the basis for an orderly procedure in the analysis of a system.

1.3 The Structure of a System

To follow the analytical approach, a mathematical statement of the interconnection of the system's components is necessary. It requires a knowledge of the structure of the system, as it is the structure which identifies the way in which the components are related. This is con-

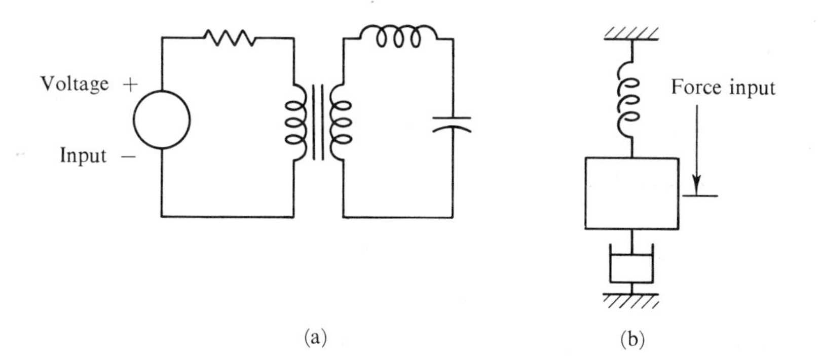

Fig. 1.2. *Schematic diagrams of (a) electrical circuit and (b) mechanical system.*

veniently indicated by a schematic diagram of the system. Thus we may use diagrams such as those shown by Figure 1.2. Although diagrams of this type show the structure of a system once the symbols used are defined, a slightly more abstract interconnection diagram of the type shown in Figure 1.3 is absolutely clear in its interpretation. Furthermore, such a diagram also clearly identifies the " terminals " of the components to which connections are made. For instance,

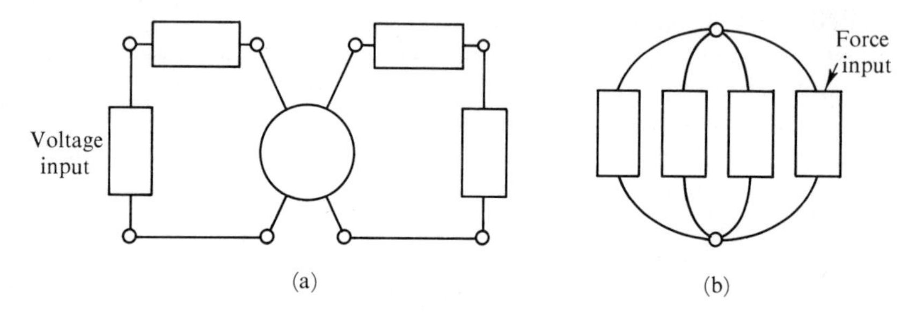

Fig. 1.3. *Interconnection diagrams corresponding to Fig. 1.2.*

Figure 1.3 (b) shows that all components in the mechanical system have two terminals and are connected in parallel. On the other hand, the electrical circuit contains a four-terminal component.

The accurate definition of the structure of a system is an important step in its analysis. There exist many examples which show the definition of the structure to be a simple matter. On the other hand, many problems will be encountered where the structure is obscure and not simply defined. The components frequently overlap one another. Usually, the more realistic the problems, the more complex they are. One of the objectives in studying systems of simple structure is to prepare for more difficult problems.

In conclusion, we will consider that the structure of a system has been defined if we can identify the components of the system and show (perhaps in a diagram) how the components are interconnected.

1.4 Classification of Systems

Systems are classified according to the mathematical equations used to describe them. Since the mathematical model is an approximation of the physical properties and dynamic characteristics of a system, the validity of the classification is limited to the accuracy with which a particular model is prepared. Clearly, a certain amount of judgment is involved, but there is generally little difficulty in making an appropriate choice.

It is not the objective here to discuss all types of classifications, with all their ramifications. Rather we will single out that type of system which is our primary concern. There are essentially five questions to be asked in determining this type of system. With each answer a decision is made in selecting an area of mathematics.

1. Continuous or Discrete Time

If the system variables behave continuously with respect to time the appropriate branch of mathematics is differential equations, whereas difference equations would be used in the case of a system which changes or is observed to change only at discrete moments of time. We will be interested in *continuous time systems* at first. Investigation of discrete time systems is also very important, but is beyond the scope of this book.

2. Lumped or Distributed Parameters

This part deals with the question of whether it is reasonable to assume that the physical characteristics of the individual components are lumped at discrete points, or whether they are distributed over considerable distance, area, or volume. Lumped parameter components and systems are described by ordinary differential equations, while partial differential equations are needed in the description of distributed parameter systems. We will be concerned with the study of *lumped parameter systems*.

3. Linear or Nonlinear

The distinction between linear and nonlinear is probably the hardest of all to make, especially for the uninitiated. Although a precise mathematical test is required for an accurate choice, a simplified physical explanation suffices for now. If the mathematical model developed is valid for all signal levels, such that a change in input level causes a proportionate change in the output, the system is linear. Otherwise the system is nonlinear. This is a very restrictive requirement. Not many systems are truly linear. But a linear approximation is in most cases adequate. On this assumption, therefore, we will limit ourselves primarily to those *systems which can be described by linear equations*.

4. Constant or Time-varying

Another important consideration is whether the system description changes with time. Do the system parameters remain constant over the duration for which we study that system? A system may be either constant or time-varying. Although the mathematical areas used to describe either constant or time-varying systems are identical, the equations of constant systems are considerably more tractable than those of time-varying systems. Our interest will lie in the *constant system.*

5. Deterministic or Stochastic

The last phase in examining the classification of a system consists in determining whether a system behaves in such a way that at any time it is possible to specify the state of the system explicitly. If one can only discuss the system behavior in terms of average values, or if one must attach a certain probability to the value of the system variables or properties, then the system is stochastic. In such a case probability theory is required to study the system. We will limit our activities to those systems for which it is possible to determine the value of each unknown exactly.

In summary, then, the types of systems covered in this text will be restricted to those that are continuous, lumped parameter, linear, constant, and deterministic. Thus the mathematical area is linear, constant coefficient, ordinary differential equations, and the related subject of the Laplace transformation. This area provides the simplest way by which an introduction to the subject of system analysis is possible. Although the five questions are all settled in favor of the simpler mathematical area, the alternatives in the five ways of system classifications are no less important. They are simply to be postponed.

1.5 Procedures of Analysis

An orderly manner of approaching the study of a system in general involves these salient steps:

Modeling: The characterization of components by mathematical models.

Formulation: The development of sets of equations describing the overall system.

Solution: The mathematical procedures of determining solutions to the system equations.

Although system analysis in general is concerned with the complete execution of all three steps, it is entirely appropriate to limit the objective of a study to just one step. Consider now the three major steps.

Modeling

The primary concern of this step lies in the translation into mathematical formulae of physical properties and geometric design specifications of components. Such a formula is a mathematical model of a component. Since our scope is limited at this time to systems describable by ordinary differential equations with constant coefficients, we are making lumped parameter approximations of the physical properties of the components. This assumes all physical properties to be measurable or observable at discrete points of a component to be known as *terminals*.

Symbolically, components are indicated by schematic figures as shown in Figure 1.4. The terminals of the components are clearly shown. Components have at least two terminals. Many important components

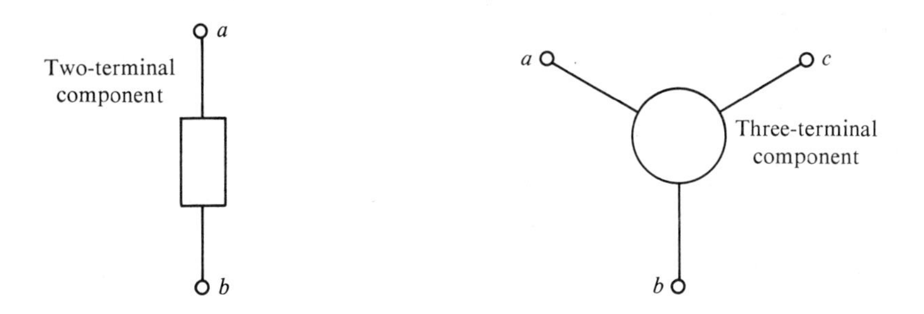

Fig. 1.4. *Schematic figures of components.*

have three and four terminals. Thus, for instance, an electric resistor is a two-terminal component, while a mechanical gear box is a three-terminal component.

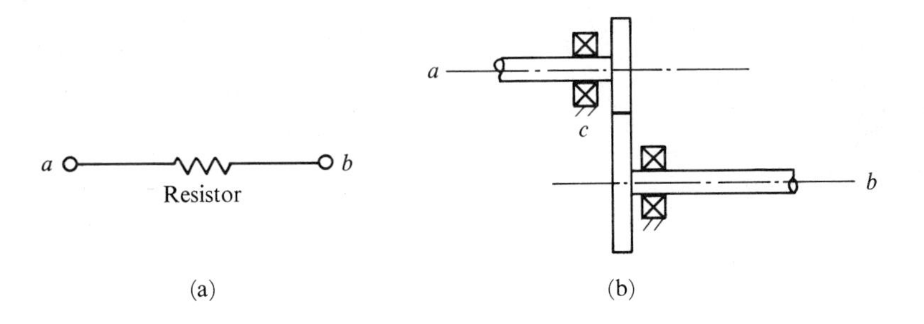

Fig. 1.5. *Examples of two- and three-terminal components.*

Component models are in a format suitable for further processing in the formulation stage of analysis. They consist of two parts: a schematic and an equation. The schematic is of the form shown in Figures 1.4 and 1.5. The equation defines a relationship between physical variables which are appropriate to characterize the component. For instance, the resistor shown in Figure 1.5 (a) is described by an equation involving a voltage and a current, i.e.

$$v = Ri \quad \textbf{(1.1)}$$

An important addition to this equation is the definition of the orientation of the variables. Consider the current i flowing through the resistor from a to b. Is the voltage across the resistor more positive at terminal a or at terminal b? This orientation question can be settled by adopting a convention about signs (polarity). A meaningful convention is shown in Figure 1.6, whereby it is assumed that if the voltage

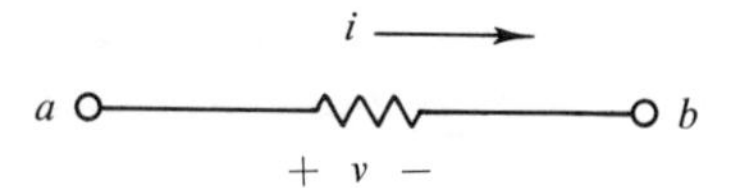

Fig. 1.6. *Sign convention in a schematic.*

is positive from terminal a to terminal b, then the current flows from a to b. Much more about this will be covered later. But the point here is that a mathematical model, to be complete, must include a definition of the orientation of variables used in the equation. Thus a combination of Equation 1.1 and Figure 1.6 constitutes a complete model.

The modeling of components is not a clear-cut procedure. Although mathematical language is used to summarize findings, a great deal depends upon knowledge of the physical principles and properties underlying the design and composition of a component. Even if the physical picture is well understood, it is still difficult to determine what is important. At all times, the mathematical model must be as representative of the component as possible, yet without unnecessary detail. In short, what is required is a simple but complete model of the component.

Formulation

In this stage, the combination of two items of information into complete differential equations is accomplished. These are the component models and the ties existing between the components. The component models are obtained from the modeling stage, while the structure of the system yields information regarding the interconnection of the components. This stage in the analysis is quite systematic, with judgment required mostly in the selection of one of several formulation procedures. Naturally, the selection is guided by a motive of least work.

The basic concern during the formulation stage is illustrated by the following example. Consider a simple mechanical system consisting of a spring, dashpot, and a displacement driver, as schematically shown in Figure 1.7. The displacement driver is generated by an eccentric

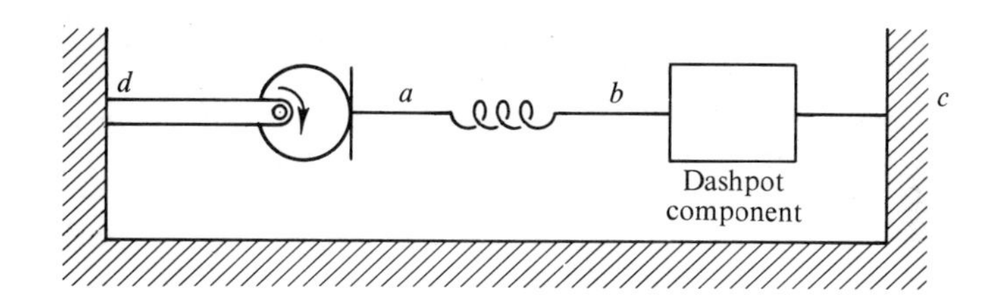

Fig. 1.7. *Simple mechanical system.*

rotating disk driving a follower. From the modeling stage come these three component models:

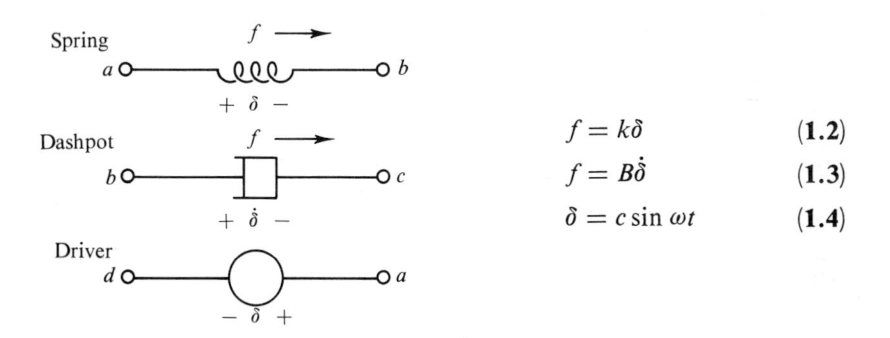

$$f = k\delta \tag{1.2}$$

$$f = B\dot{\delta} \tag{1.3}$$

$$\delta = c \sin \omega t \tag{1.4}$$

All components are two-terminal components and are interconnected as shown by the diagrams of Figure 1.8. In the formulation process a set of equations which represent an overall characterization of the system is derived. This derivation requires knowledge of the component models, which we have already available from Figure 1.8 (b). From terminal *b* of the figure,

$$f_2 = f_3 \tag{1.5}$$

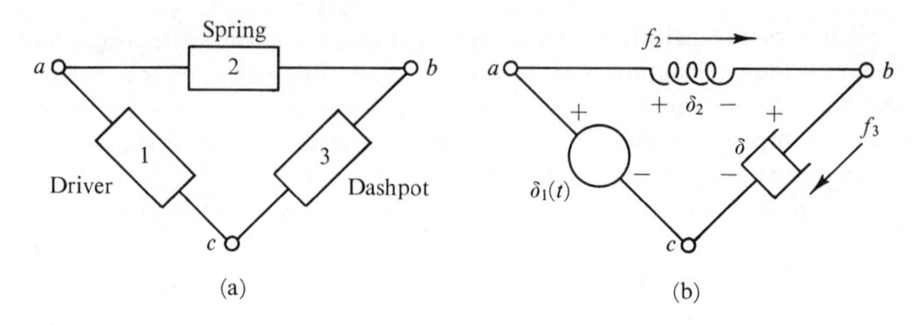

Fig. 1.8. *Interconnection diagrams of mechanical system.*

It is a simple statement of the fact that the forces as defined by the figure are the same in both the spring and the dashpot.

Also,

$$\delta_2 = \delta_1 - \delta_3 \tag{1.6}$$

This shows how displacements of the three components are constrained by their interconnection. The formulation is now concerned with the combination of Equations 1.2 through 1.6.

First we use Equations 1.2 and 1.3 in Equation 1.5:

$$k\delta_2 = B\dot{\delta}_3 \tag{1.7}$$

Then we use Equation 1.6 in 1.7:

$$k(\delta_1 - \delta_3) = B\dot{\delta}_3$$

or

$$B\dot{\delta}_3 + k\delta_3 = k\delta_1 \tag{1.8}$$

and finally, we substitute Equation 1.4 into 1.8:

$$B\dot{\delta}_3 + k\delta_3 = c \sin \omega t \tag{1.9}$$

This result is a first-order linear differential equation whose solution will provide information regarding the behavior of the system.

Solution

The result of the formulation procedures is a set of ordinary differential equations with constant coefficients. A complete study of a system requires a solution to these equations. If all components are characterized by linear mathematical models, the system equations will also be linear. In this case the solution process may be carried out by analytical techniques such as classical differential equations or the Laplace transformations.

If one or several of the components must be characterized by nonlinear mathematical models to accurately represent them, the differential equations are nonlinear. Usually an analytical solution is not possible; then a computer solution must be obtained. Depending upon the nonlinearity, either an analog or a digital computer may be employed. Sometimes it is warranted that the nonlinear equations are approximated by linear equations to obtain an approximate idea of the system through an analytical solution. But computer solutions are so readily available today that a linearization is not justified in all cases. Note that computor solutions are, of course, also available for linear differential equations.

Summary

The first chapter is intended to serve as a general orientation to the objectives of this course in system analysis. It is quite comprehensive. But the subsequent chapters will elaborate at length on the briefly mentioned subjects of modeling, formulation, and solution—the three main steps of system analysis. Possibly the reader will obtain additional benefit from re-reading this chapter after having been exposed to those that follow. Chapter 1 presents the basic approach of system analysis—it points the way. The remaining chapters simply expand upon it and develop the necessary building blocks to carry out the objective.

ADDITIONAL READINGS

Koenig, Herman E., Yilmaz Tokad, and Hiremaglur K. Kesavan, *Discrete Physical Systems,* New York: McGraw-Hill Book Co., 1966.

Sanford, Richard S., *Physical Networks*, Englewood Cliffs, New Jersey: Prentice-Hall, Inc., 1965.

Shearer, J. Lowen, Arthur T. Murphy, and Herbert H. Richardson, *Introduction to System Dynamics*, Reading, Mass.: Addison-Wesley Publishing Co., Inc., 1967.

PROBLEMS

1.1. List several examples of time-dependent systems.

1.2. Classify the following systems according to the criteria of Section 1.4:
  a) Automotive power steering
  b) Radar fire control system
  c) Thermostat control heating system
  d) Hi-fi amplifier

1.3. Identify the structure of the systems of Problem 1.2.

Measurement of Physical Variables

2

The development of mathematical models of components—the process of modeling—requires some facility in the measurement and mathematical representation of physical signals. This is needed because it is through the measurement or observation of these signals at component terminals that an assessment of the component's physical properties can be made. This chapter is therefore devoted to introducing the measurement and instrumentation of physical signals.

2.1 Measurement and Physical Signals

In describing the characteristics of physical components, the need arises for a procedure which is both convenient and useful. At this point acceptance of such concepts as voltages and currents, forces and displacements, pressures and flows (all of which are used to describe the state or present condition of a physical quantity in terms of real numbers) is essential. In fact, when it is said that a physical quantity is equal to x volts, or x newtons, or x meters, the implication is that an appropriately chosen and properly calibrated instrument would give us a precise reading of x volts, newtons, or meters. Thus we identify physical quantities by measurements which could be made using suitable instrumentation.

The various physical quantities whose present value may be determined by a suitable meter will be termed *variables* or *signals*, and the actual numerical values will be termed *measurements*. Thus, we use a voltmeter to obtain a measurement of a voltage which is an electrical variable or signal.

2.2 Two-Point Measurements

The measurements of all physical variables require two points. In order to be able to assign a numerical value to a voltage, pressure, or distance, etc., two points must be chosen between which the measurement is to be made. To speak of a measurement or the value of a signal at a single point is meaningless. All too often a reference is made to a force acting on a point, without recognition that the force requires two points just to be properly defined.

2.3 Electrical Signals and Their Measurement

Voltage and current are probably the most widely used signals in the description of electrical properties and components. They represent a pair of signals—one may speak of one being the cosignal to the other—in terms of which it will be possible to define all other quantities useful in the study of electrical systems. Voltage and current are concepts. They take on practical meaning when, through application of suitable meters, numerical values for them can be measured. It is also quite feasible to use other electrical quantities, such as charge and flux, in the description of electrical components. On occasion this book will employ these concepts, but most of the time voltage and current will be effective.

Physical devices for the determination of voltage or current are called *voltmeters* and *ammeters*, respectively. Voltage and current are not "real things"; they are not directly observable. However, measurements of voltage and current can be obtained by reading or recording an observable reaction of an instrument.

The Voltmeter

The instrument which measures voltage in the most direct manner is the *oscilloscope*. A simple sketch of an oscilloscope is shown in

Figure 2.1, which illustrates the principle of operation but does not show design details.

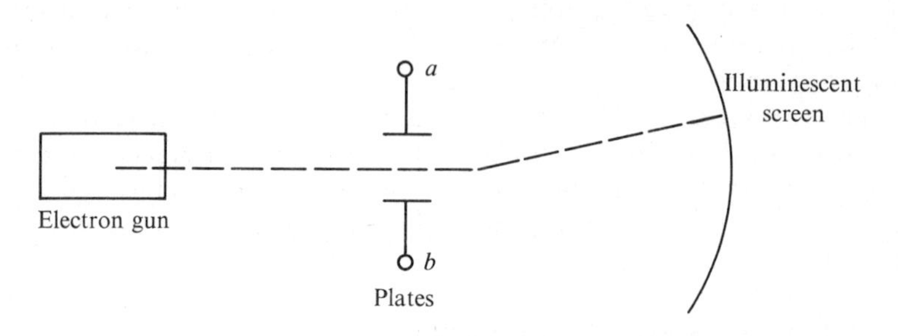

Fig. 2.1. *Oscilloscope.*

In the oscilloscope, a beam of electrons is emitted from an electron gun in a vacuum medium. This beam is accelerated toward an illuminescent screen, which presents an observable indication of the impinging of the beam of electrons. Since electrons are charged particles, the beam of electrons may be deflected when it passes through an electric field. An electric field can be established by the application of a voltage to plates a and b. The amount of deflection of the electron beam depends on the intensity of the field, which in turn depends on the magnitude of the applied voltage. It is therefore possible to establish a correlation between the applied voltage and the resulting deflection. Thus we have a voltmeter which, through a sequence of interrelations between physical phenomena, establishes a connection between the voltage and an observable result. This sequence of interrelations may be effectively depicted by the block diagram in Figure 2.2. To enhance the useful-

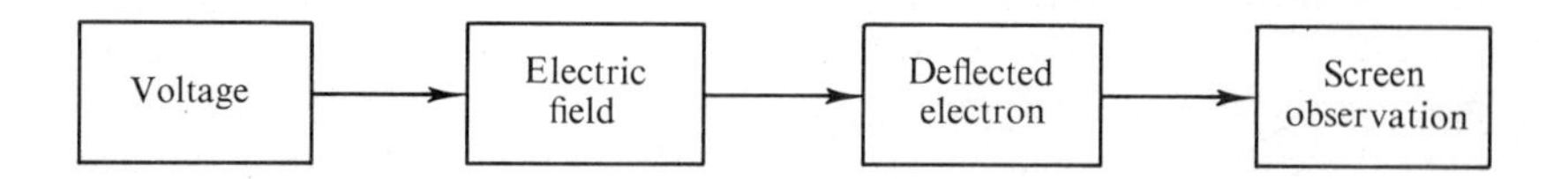

Fig. 2.2. *Functional diagram of voltmeter.*

ness of this meter, the screen is calibrated according to a convenient scale.

The Ammeter

The principle of the ammeter is manifested in the D'Arsonval mechanism shown in Figure 2.3.

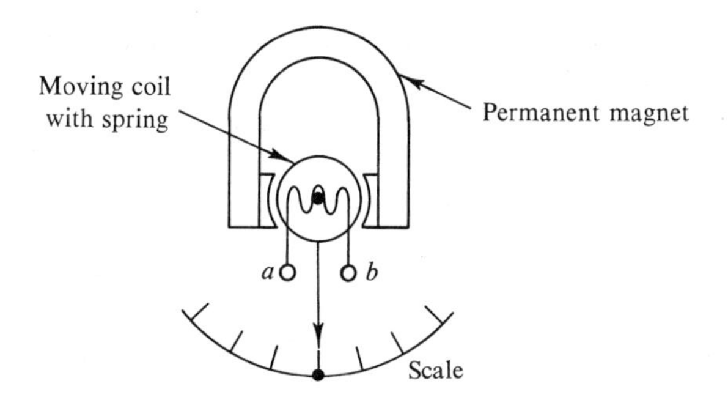

Fig. 2.3. *D'Arsonval mechanism.*

A moving coil is mounted in the field of a permanent magnet. As a current is passed through the coil, a torque is generated on the moving coil, which rotates the coil. The pointer will come to rest when the torque generated by the current balances the spring torque. This rest position is an observable indication, and can easily be related to the current through appropriate calibration. Again, as in the voltmeter, the current is measured indirectly. An instrumentation flow diagram in Figure 2.4 shows this.

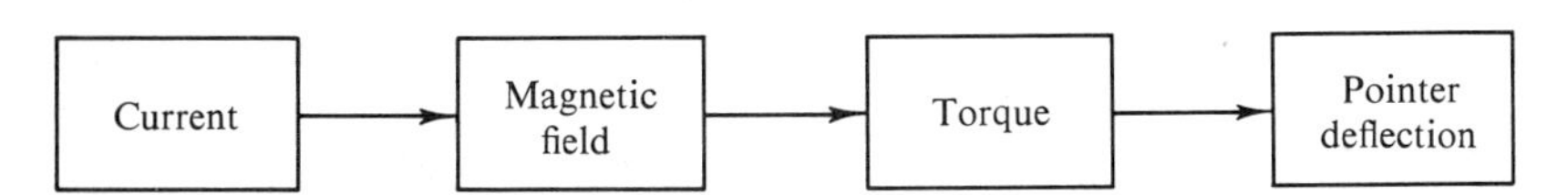

Fig. 2.4. *Instrumentation flow diagram of ammeter.*

It should be noted that a small modification of both the D'Arsonval meter and the oscilloscope will permit them to be used in the measure-

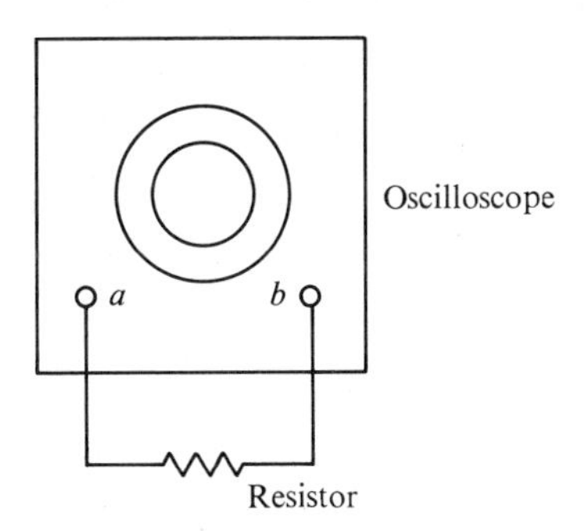

Fig. 2.5. *Connection to measure current with an oscilloscope.*

ment of a voltage or current. For instance, in order to measure current with an oscilloscope, simply connect a resistor in parallel with the terminals of the oscilloscope, as shown in Figure 2.5.
A current flow through the resistor will produce a voltage across the resistor, proportional to the current.

For systems analysis, the design of a particular meter is of no concern; one must only know the right method of connection to effect a particular measurement. Therefore, it is necessary to describe a meter symbolically. Illustrated in Figure 2.6 are three connections for (a) voltage, (b) current, (c) simultaneous voltage and current measurements.

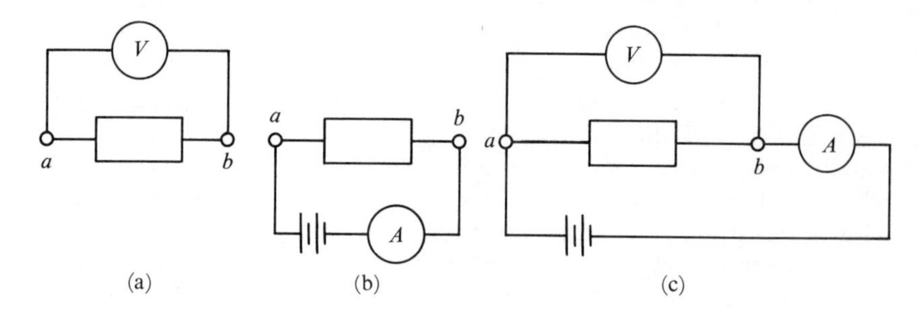

Fig. 2.6. *Symbolic connection diagrams of voltage and current measurements.*

Two important characteristics of electrical measurements should be noted: (1) all measurements are associated with two points; (2) a reversal of the meter connections is accompanied by change in the direction of the indicator; in other words, the meters are polarity-sensitive. Thus, *an electrical measurement is an oriented two-point measurement.* Since, however, the meters are merely an observable indication of either a voltage or current (the actual signals), it must be inferred that these same properties are true of the electrical signals themselves: an electrical variable is defined by two points, the points of measurement, and it possesses orientation. One would expect that a change in direction of current flow, for instance, would change the deflection of the meter measuring the current. Thus this important observation: *electrical variables are oriented and measured at two points.* In fact, the two-point oriented definition is a basic property of all physical variables in the realm of system analysis.

2.4 Mechanical Variables and Their Measurement

In mechanical systems, we are concerned with the signals of force and translational velocity, or with torque and rotational velocity.

Mechanical variables seem to be more " real " than electrical variables. Velocity may be observed; force or torque take on physical significance through action of acceleration forces (weight). Displacement and acceleration also are useful mechanical variables. As in the case of electrical variables, the mechanical variables will be defined in terms of their measurements, the manner in which they are related to the real number system.

Mechanical variables must be viewed as vectors, having both a magnitude and direction. In order to manipulate the variables conveniently, it is useful to define mechanical variables by components in the Cartesian coordinate system. Thus, to specify completely a translational velocity relative to two points, one must make three mutually perpendicular measurements using the following systems:

Force	f	(f_x, f_y, f_z)
Translational velocity	$\dot{\delta}$	$(\dot{\delta}_y, \dot{\delta}_y, \dot{\delta}_z)$
Torque	τ	(τ_x, τ_y, τ_z)
Rotational velocity	$\dot{\varphi}$	$(\dot{\varphi}_x, \dot{\varphi}_y, \dot{\varphi}_z)$

Our present discussion considers measurements in only one direction.

Measuring Instruments for Velocity

Perhaps the simplest way to measure translational velocity is to use a meterstick and a stop watch. It is obvious that this measurement requires two points and that its numerical outcome is dependent on the orientation of the stick, so here again is a two-point oriented measurement. In modern instrumentation practice, it is frequently desirable to record velocity measurements as functions of time. Then it is necessary to transduce the velocity measurements into a proportional voltage signal. This can easily be accomplished by means of a velocity transducer, as shown in Figure 2.7.

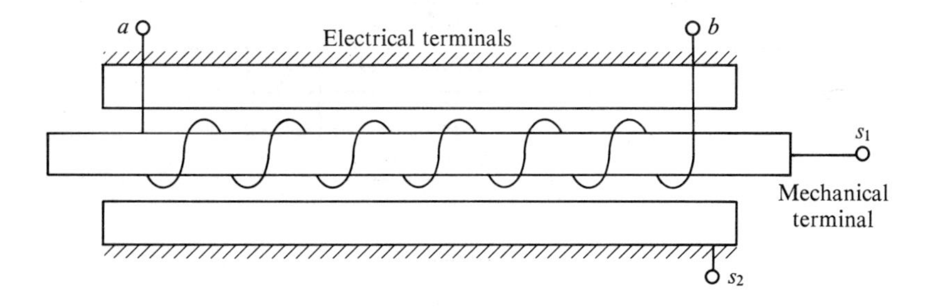

Fig. 2.7. *Velocity transducer for translational velocity measurement.*

Here a voltage which is proportional to the relative velocity $\dot{\delta}$ between the stem S_1 and coil housing S_2 is induced in the coil and measured at terminals a and b.

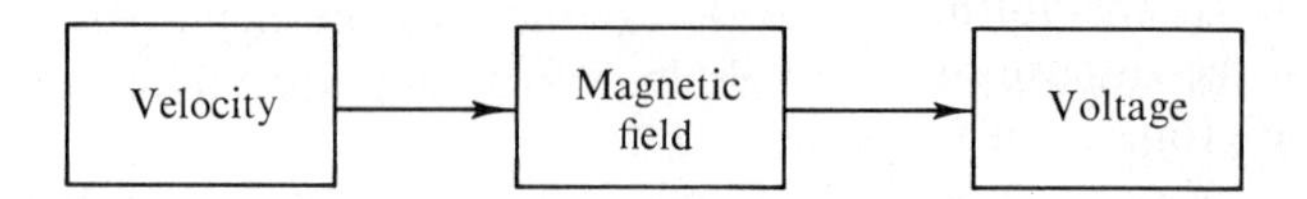

Fig. 2.8. *Instrumentation flow diagram of velocity transducer.*

Meters for the Measurement of Force

The measurement of force depends upon the utilization of elastic materials which change dimension in an observable manner under the action of the force. The simplest forcemeter is the springscale, shown in Figure 2.9.

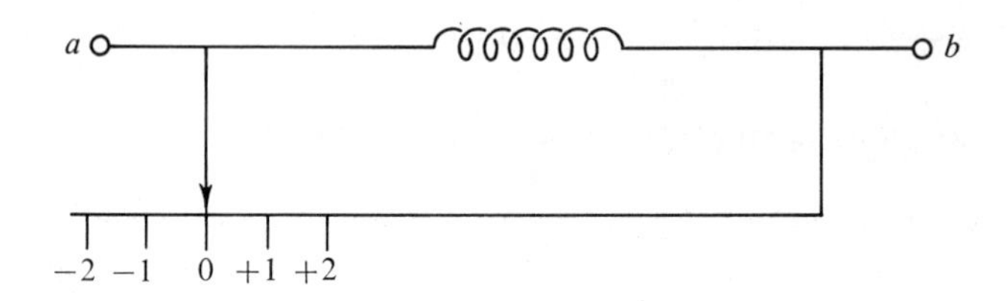

Fig. 2.9. *Springscale.*

A more sophisticated meter and, from an instrumentation point of view, a more practical one is the straingage force transducer. In this

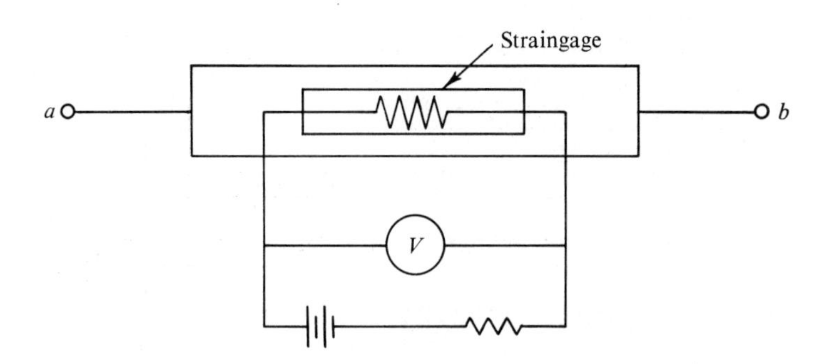

Fig. 2.10. *Straingage force meter.*

design a straingage is mounted on an elastic material and electrically connected to a metering circuit. As the elastic material changes dimensions under the action of the force to be measured, the resistance of the straingage changes its electrical characteristics. This is detected and indicated by the voltmeter. A change in the direction of the force will produce the opposite effect, which is characteristic of the orientation-sensitive property of the meter.

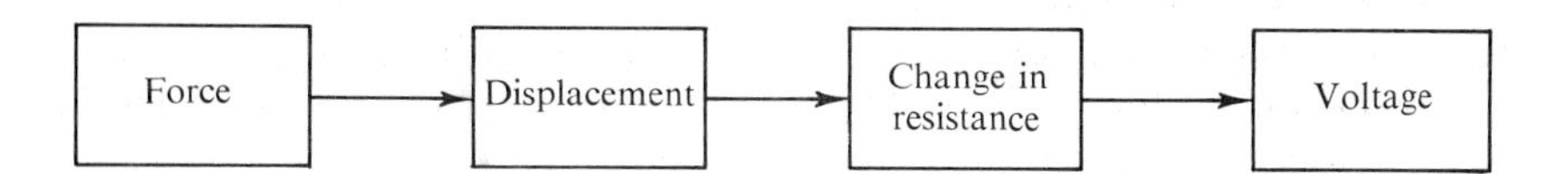

Fig. 2.11. *Instrumentation flow diagram of an electrical force meter.*

Torque may be measured in an identical fashion. It is left to the student to prepare a suitable electrical torquemeter.

Of primary interest in the measurement of physical variables is the numerical result obtained in the measuring process. Thus, as in the case of electrical variables, we may use symbols to indicate the meters. For instance, we might indicate (1) torque, (2) rotational velocity, or (3) simultaneous torque and velocity measurements on a component as shown in Figure 2.12.

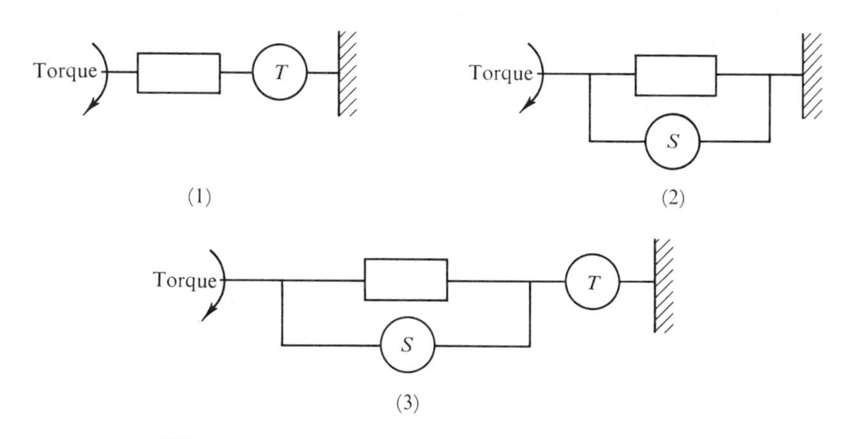

Fig. 2.12. *Symbolic rotational measurements.*

2.5 Across and Through Variables

An interesting observation may be made at this time by comparing the symbolic connection diagram of Figure 2.12 with Figure 2.6. Both the voltmeter and velocity meter appear in a parallel or " across " connection, while the torquemeter and ammeter appear in a series or " through " connection. If this comparison were extended to translational measurements, one would identify the measurement of translational velocity as an across connection and the measurement of force as a through connection. This pattern of meter connection is extremely significant in attaching the following useful properties to the concepts of the variables discussed so far. Certain types of variables are identified as *across variables* and constitute one class of variables, while the other class of variables comprises the *through variables*. Voltage, translational and rotational velocity—variables discussed so far—are across variables, while their co-variables are through variables. These across and through properties are entirely established as a result of the manner in which the variables are measured. However, through their measurements these properties are reflected on the variables themselves. We will find that the across and through properties will be of great important in procedures of system analysis.

2.6 Hydraulic Variables and Their Measurements

Two variables, pressure and flow, denoted by the symbols p and $\dot{g}$, will be used in the study of hydraulic systems. As in electrical and mechanical system, these variables are defined by the process by which they are measured.

Pressure is measured by a pressure gage when sight readings are satisfactory. To record pressure as a function of time, a pressure transducer is required. Such a transducer is shown in Figure 2.13. It measures pressure through the deflection of an elastic membrane

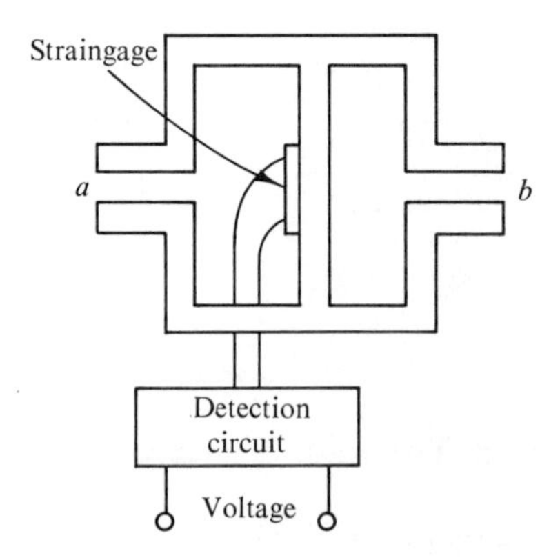

Fig. 2.13. *Pressure transducer.*

separating the two chambers (points) between which the pressure is to be measured. The membrane deflection can easily be sensed by a straingage.

In principle, the pressure transducer is a modified force transducer: through the area of the membrane the pressure is first transduced into a force. An instrumentation flow diagram points this out very clearly. The manner in which the pressure transducer is connected to the two points establishes a pressure measurement as an across measurement.

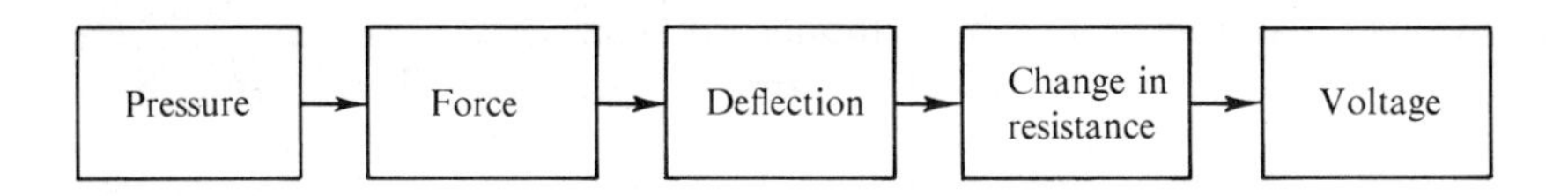

Fig. 2.14. *Pressure transducer, instrumentation flow diagram.*

The through measurement in hydraulic systems is the volumetric flow rate. It can be measured by means of a straingage flow transducer as shown in the Figure 2.15. In this design, a reed flexes under the

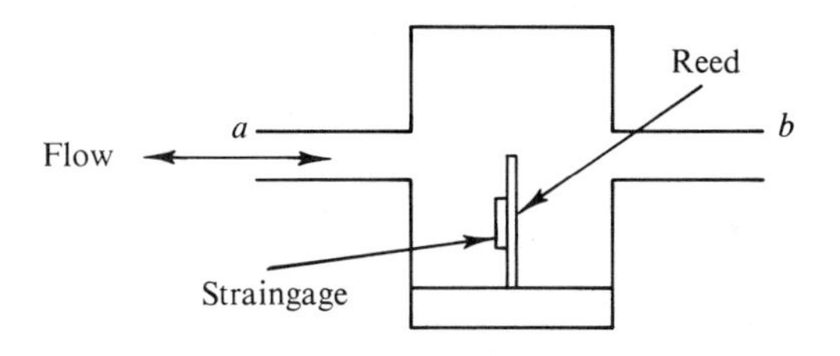

Fig. 2.15. *Schematic of flow transducer.*

action of the flowing fluid. The read deflection, being proportional to the flow rate, is sensed by a straingage, to allow electrical recording of the flow rate as a function of time.

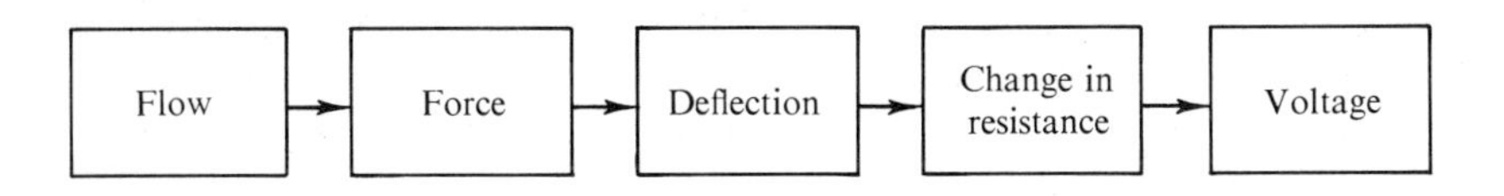

Fig. 2.16. *Instrumentation flow diagram of flow transducer.*

2.7 Other System Variables

The areas of electrical, mechanical, and hydraulic systems have emerged as the more important ones in system analysis. This is a consequence of the major role electrical, mechanical, and hydraulic components play in the design of practical systems. However, other areas take on significance occasionally. It will suffice here to mention them and to define the variables useful in their study.

Thermal Systems

The concepts of *temperature* and *heat flux* serve here as the co-variables, where temperature is the across variable and heat flux is the through variable. The measurement of temperature is easily accomplished by use of a thermometer or thermal junction. The measurement of heat flux, however, presents considerable practical difficulties. At best, it can be deduced from observation of related physical phenomena.

Pneumatic Systems

In the study of pneumatic systems, pressure and mass flow rate are the appropriate across and through variables. In many respects, pneumatic systems have properties identical to hydraulic systems. For instance, there is no difference between hydraulic and pneumatic pressure. In flow, there exists a difference, since pneumatic media, gases, are generally subjected to considerable compression, while hydraulic media, fluids, are generally compressible only to a negligible extent. Pneumatic variables may be measured in a comparatively straightforward manner by pressure and mass flow transducers.

Related System Variables

Two variables each, one across and one through, have been specified for the study of electrical, mechanical, hydraulic and other systems. These are the principle variables. Now it is appropriate to recognize that a number of other system variables may be used equally well.

Usually these variables are related to those discussed above by being time derivatives or time integrals of them. For instance, displacement is the integral of velocity. Volume in hydraulic systems is the integral of flow. Voltage is the time derivative of flux. In general, all time derivatives or time integrals of the principal variables define the variables. However, only a limited number of variables thus formed are of engineering significance. If the principal variable is a through variable, then a related variable is also a through variable. The same holds true for the across variables. This assertion may easily be supported by devising a suitable meter for the measurement of a secondary variable. All variables are summarized in Table 2.1.

TABLE 2.1. *Classification of system variables*

System \ Variable	Derivative	Principal	Integral
Electrical	—	v voltage	$\int v = \lambda$ flux
Mechanical translational	$\ddot{\delta}$ acceleration	$\dot{\delta}$ velocity	δ displacement
Rotational	$\ddot{\varphi}$ acceleration	$\dot{\varphi}$ velocity	φ displacement
Hydraulic	—	p pressure	—

(a) *Across variables*

System \ Variable	Derivative	Principal	Integral
Electrical	—	i current	$\int i = q$ charge
Mechanical translational	—	f force	—
Rational	—	τ torque	—
Hydraulic	—	$\dot{g}$ flow	g volume

(b) *Through variables*

2.8 Units

In studying systems on an interdisciplinary basis, it is a great advantage to use a system of units in which the conversion of units from one discipline to another is simple. Such a property is inherent in the MKS (meter-kilogram-second) unit system. All conversion factors are

TABLE 2.2. *Rationalized MKS units*

Symbol	Name	Unit
$v(t)$	voltage	volt
$i(t)$	current	ampere
R	resistance	ohm
P_e	electrical power	watt
W_e	electrical energy	watt-second
L	electrical inductance	henry
C	electrical capacitance	farad

(a) *Electrical quantities*

$\lambda(t)$	magnetic flux	volt-sec
$M(t)$	magnetomotive force	ampere

(b) *Magnetic quantities*

$\delta(t)$	translational displacement	meter
$\varphi(t)$	rotational displacement	radian
$f(t)$	force	newton
$\tau(t)$	torque	newton-meter
M	mass	newton-second^2/meter
k_t	spring constant	newton-meter
B_t	damping constant	newton-second/meter
P_m	mechanical power	newton-meter/second
W_m	mechanical energy	newton-meter
J	inertia	newton-meter-second^2
B_r	damping constant (rot.)	newton-meter-second
k_r	spring constant (rot.)	newton-meter

(c) *Mechanical quantities*

Symbol	Name	Unit
$p(t)$	pressure	newton/meter^2
$\dot{g}(t)$	fluid flow	meter^3/second
R_h	hydraulic resistance	newton-second/meter^5
M_h	hydraulic inertia	newton-second^2/meter^5
C_h	hydraulic capacitance	meter^5/newton
P_h	hydraulic power	newton-meter/second
W_h	hydraulic energy	newton-meter

(d) *Hydraulic quantities*

TABLE 2.3. *Selected conversion constants*

Symbol	Name	To obtain value in MSK units	Multiply value in English units	By
$\dot{\delta}(t)$	translational velocity	m/sec	in./sec	0.0254
$f(t)$	force	newt	lb	4.448
$\dot{\varphi}(t)$	rotational velocity	rad-sec	rpm	0.10429
$\tau(t)$	torque	newt m	ft-lb	1.3558
$p(t)$	pressure	newt/m^2	lb/in.^{2}	0.689×10^4
$g(t)$	volume flow rate	m^3/sec	gal /min	0.6309×10^{-5}
$p_m(t)$	mechanical power	w	ft-lb/sec	1.356
$p_h(t)$	hydraulic power	w	in.-lb/sec	0.113

set equal to unity. This is accomplished by suitable calibration of the meter scales. The MKS system of units is consistent since energy and power functions can be used interchangeably in the various system disciplines without the introduction of numerical conversion factors. Table 2.2 presents the MSK unit definitions for the most common physical quantities and Table 2.3 shows some selected conversion constants.

Occasionally the numerical values of system variables become very large or very small. It is then convenient to use certain abbreviations. For instance, for a current $i = 0.001$ amperes, we would say $i = 1$ milliampere, or for a pressure $p = 2 \times 10^{-6}$ newton/meter^2, we would say $p = 2$ micronewton/meter^2. The standard abbreviations presently in use are listed in Table 2.4.

TABLE 2.4. *Scale factor*

pica	10^{-12}
nano	10^{-9}
micro	10^{-6}
milli	10^{-3}
centi	10^{-2}
kilo	10^{3}
mega	10^{6}
giga	10^{9}

ADDITIONAL READINGS

Boast, W. B., *Principles of Electric and Magnetic Circuits,* New York: Harper & Row, Publishers, 1950.

Fano, R. M., L. S. Chu, and R. B. Adler, *Electromagnetic Fields, Energy and Forces,* New York: John Wiley & Sons, Inc., 1960.

Firestone, F. A., "A New Analogy between Mechanical and Electrical Systems," *J. Acoust. Soc. Am.*, 4, 1932–33.

Halliday, D., and R. Resnick, *Physics for Students of Science and Engineering*, New York: John Wiley & Sons, Inc., 1962.

Holman, J. P., *Heat Transfer*, New York: McGraw-Hill Book Co., 1963.

Koenig, Herman E., and William A. Blackwell, *Electromechanical System Theory*, New York: McGraw-Hill Book Co., 1961.

Koenig, Herman E., Y. Tokad, and H. K. Kesavan, *Discrete Physical Systems,* New York: McGraw-Hill Book Co., 1966.

Sanford, Richard S., *Physical Networks,* Englewood Cliffs, New Jersey: Prentice-Hall, Inc., 1965.

Shearer, J. Lowen, Arthur T. Murphy, and Herbert H. Richardson, *Introduction to System Dynamics*, Reading, Mass.: Addison-Wesley Publishing Co., Inc., 1967.

Skilling, H. H., *Electromechanics*, New York: John Wiley & Sons, Inc., 1962.

Vennard, J. K., *Elementary Fluid Mechanics*, 4th ed., New York: John Wiley & Sons, Inc., 1961.

PROBLEMS

2.1. Show by means of a sketch the design of a torquemeter suitable for electrical recording.

2.2. Show by means of a sketch the design of an angular displacement meter suitable for electrical recording.

2.3. Why is heatflow not a suitable choice for the through variable in thermal system? (Consider the units of heatflow.)

2.4. Name suitable choices for the across variable and through variable in the study of systems dealing with magnetic phenomena.

2.5. Draw an instrumentation flow diagram for an accelerometer capable of electrical output.

2.6. Show that the following equations are dimensionally consistent:

a) $Ri + L\dfrac{di}{dt} = v$

b) $k\delta + B\dot{\delta} + m\ddot{\delta} = f$

2.7. Suggest a way in which
a) a voltmeter may be used to measure current;
b) an ammeter may be used to measure voltage;
c) a pressuremeter may be used to measure flow.

Mathematical Representation of Signals

3

3.1 Time Functions

All physical systems behave in some defined manner as a function of time. *Time is therefore the independent variable to which all system variables are correlated;* the system variables, including inputs and outputs, are all functions of time in a mathematical sense. In order to analyze a system, then, one must consider the different kinds of time functions which are characteristic of system variables and system inputs.

3.2 Deterministic and Random Time Functions

The physical systems with which this book is concerned are deterministic; for every input there is a unique output which is determined by the system properties. The input to the system, however, may be deterministic or random in its nature. Random inputs cannot be predicted in advance as can deterministic inputs; however, there are certain properties of random inputs which are known. The system output in response to random inputs is no longer deterministic, but is also random in a predictable manner.

Functions of time may be represented analytically or graphically. Figure 3.1 (a) shows a deterministic function of time and the equation $x(t) = 5 \sin \frac{1}{2}t$ is the mathematical representation of this plot. Figure 3.1 (b) illustrates a random function of time which could, for example, be the record of a typical day's temperature. This function cannot be completely predicted and defined from day to day, but certain properties such as average temperature, the rapidity of temperature variations, and the average amplitude of these variations can be determined.

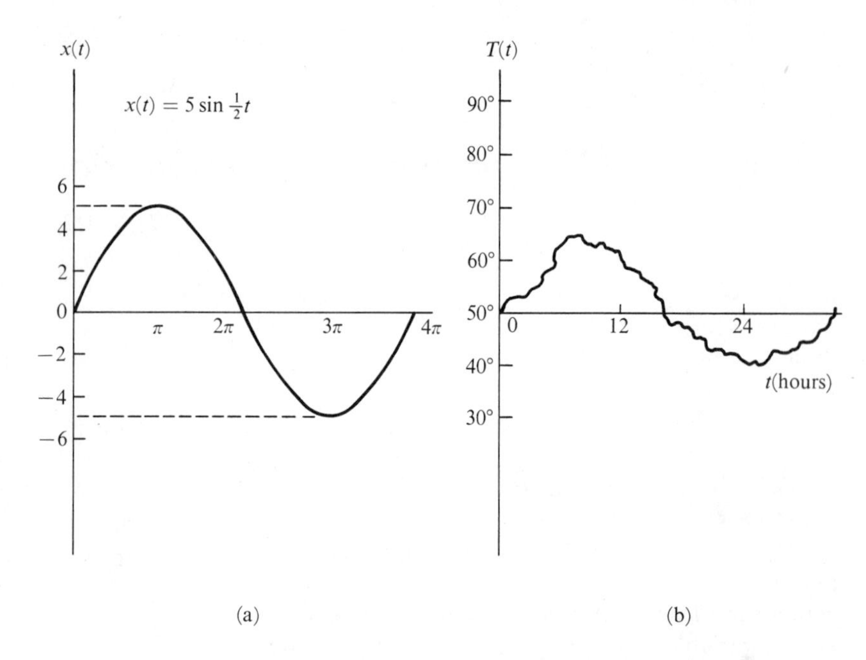

Fig. 3.1. *Deterministic and random functions of time.*

The functions of time shown in Figure 3.1 are continuous functions of time. For every instant of time there is a unique real number value associated with that time. Discrete functions of time, on the other hand, are functions whose value is given only at certain (usually equally spaced) instants of time. Figure 3.2 illustrates the discrete equivalent of the function shown in Figure 3.1 (a). This discrete time function could be obtained from the signal function $x(t) = 5 \sin \frac{1}{2}t$ by placing a switch between the signal and the measurement point. The switch closes periodically for a short instant of time and the measurement consists of discrete samples of the continuous signal. Systems which contain a digital computer either in the input, the output, or as an

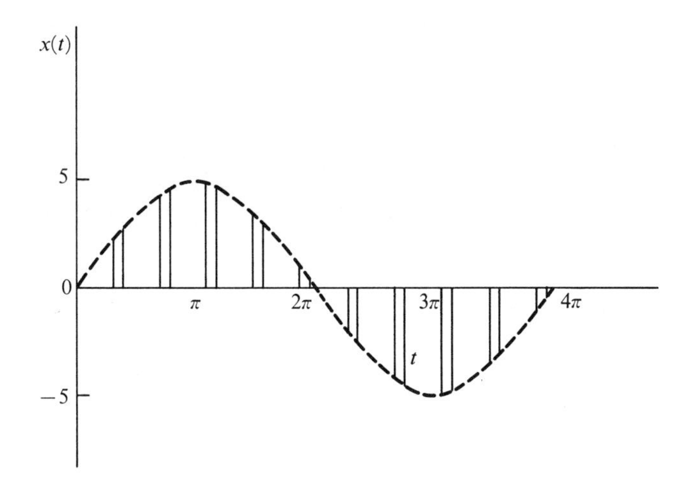

Fig. 3.2. *Discrete equivalent of* $x(t) = 5\sin\frac{1}{2}t$.

integral part of the system, require sampling devices in order to communicate with the computer.

Deterministic Functions of Time

A class of elementary deterministic time functions which can be expressed in equation form is useful for two reasons: (1) In many physical systems, the actual inputs approach these functions and the output time response of the system can therefore be calculated analytically. (2) These time functions can be used as input testing functions to establish the quality of a system either analytically or experimentally. This class of functions includes the sinusoidal function, the step function, the ramp function, and the parabolic function. These are illustrated in Figures 3.3 (a), (b), (c) and (d). These time functions are assumed to start at time 0, but in a practical system may occur at any time. For system testing, the input functions starting at $t = 0$ represent no loss in generality. The equations for these functions are

$$\begin{aligned} x_1(t) &= \sin(\omega t + \phi) && t \geq 0 \; [\text{or } \cos(\omega t + \phi)] \\ &= 0 && t < 0 \\ x_2(t) &= 0 && t < 0 \\ &= 1 && t > 0 \end{aligned}$$

$$
\begin{aligned}
x_3(t) &= 0 & t &< 0 \\
&= t & t &\geq 0 \\
x_4(t) &= 0 & t &< 0 \\
&= t^2 & t &\geq 0
\end{aligned}
$$

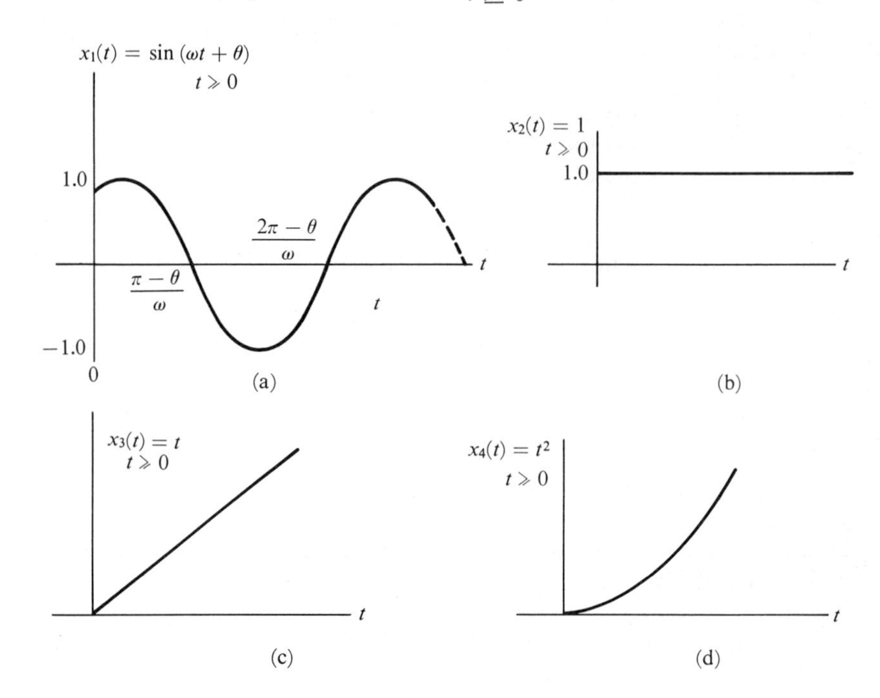

Fig. 3.3. *Elementary functions of time.*

3.3 Exponential Functions of Time

In a general lumped parameter system, there are many variables which are functions of time. One or more of these variables is the desired output. The output functions of time, in general, are not the same as the input functions of time, but depend on the properties of the system. Consider a linear, lumped parameter system with one input and one output. The solution for the output response in terms of the input can always be expressed as a differential equation of the following general form:

$$
\begin{aligned}
a_n\frac{d^n y}{dy^n} + a_{n-1}\frac{d^{n-1}y}{dt^{n-1}} + \cdots + a_k\frac{d^k y}{dt^k} + \cdots + a_1\frac{dy}{dt} + a_0 y \\
= c_m\frac{d^m v}{dt^m} + c_{m-1}\frac{d^{m-1}v}{dt^{m-1}} + \cdots + c_k\frac{d^k v}{dt^k} + \cdots + c_1\frac{dv}{dt} + c_0 v
\end{aligned}
\tag{3.1}
$$

where $v = v(t)$ is the input and $y = y(t)$ is the output. The a_k and c_k are either constants, if the system is time invariant, or are functions of time, if the system is time variant. Linear time-invariant systems represent the class of systems which are of greatest concern in this text. The input-output relationship is therefore expressible as an ordinary differential equation with constant coefficients. The solution of an ordinary differential equation consists of two parts: the complementary solution and the particular-integral solution. The complementary solution consists of terms like $y(t) = Ke^{rt}$ where K is a constant, t is time, and r is a root of the equation:

$$a_n r^n + a_{n-1} r^{n-1} + \cdots + a_1 r + a_0 = 0 \tag{3.2}$$

In an nth order system there are n roots. Therefore, the complete complementary solution is

$$y(t) = \sum_{i=1}^{n} k_i e^{r_i t} \tag{3.3}$$

The roots may be real or complex, but if there are complex roots they must occur in complex conjugate pairs because the a_k's in the differential equation are real. Consider a second-order system with the complex pair of roots

$$r_1 = b + j\omega$$
$$r_2 = b - j\omega$$

Then the general complementary solution is

$$\begin{aligned} y(t) &= k_1 e^{(b+j\omega)t} + k_2 e^{(b-j\omega)t} \\ &= e^{bt}(k_1 e^{j\omega t} + k_2 e^{-j\omega t}) \end{aligned} \tag{3.4}$$

From Euler's equation

$$e^{\pm j\theta} = \cos\theta \pm j\sin\theta \tag{3.5}$$

then

$$y(t) = e^{bt}[(k_1 + k_2)\cos\omega t + j(k_1 - k_2)\sin\omega t] \tag{3.6}$$

In a real system when the arbitrary constants k_1 and k_2 are evaluated from boundary conditions, $k_1 + k_2$ and $j(k_1 - k_2)$ must be real; therefore, k_1 and k_2 are also complex conjugates. Let $C = k_1 + k_2$ and $D = j(k_1 - k_2)$. Then

$$y(t) = e^{bt}(C\cos\omega t + D\sin\omega t) \tag{3.7}$$

From the addition laws of trigonometry

$$\sin(\omega t + \theta) = \sin\omega t\cos\theta + \cos\omega t\sin\theta$$

and (3.8)

$$\cos(\omega t - \phi) = \cos\omega t\cos\phi + \sin\omega t\sin\phi$$

then

$$C \cos \omega t + D \sin \omega t = \sqrt{C^2 + D^2} \sin (\omega t + \theta)$$
$$= \sqrt{C^2 + D^2} \cos (\omega t - \phi) \qquad \textbf{(3.9)}$$

where

$$\tan \theta = \frac{C}{D}$$

$$\tan \phi = \frac{D}{C}$$

Using the sine function

$$y(t) = Be^{bt} \sin (\omega t + \theta) \qquad \text{where } B = \sqrt{C^2 + D^2} \qquad \textbf{(3.10)}$$

When all the roots are real and distinct, the general solution is

$$y(t) = A_1 e^{r_1 t} + A_2 e^{r_2 t} + \cdots + A_n e^{r_n t} \qquad \textbf{(3.11)}$$

If there are repeated roots, the general solution is modified. Let any root, say r_1, be repeated i times; then

$$y(t) = A_1 e^{r_1 t} + A_2 t e^{r_1 t} + A_3 t^2 e^{r_1 t} + \cdots + A_i t^{i-1} e^{r_1 t}$$
$$+ A_{i+1} c^{r_2 t} + \cdots + A_n e^{r_n t} \qquad \textbf{(3.12)}$$

The solution may have more than one term of each type, depending on the order of the system. One order of the differential equation is associated with each term Ae^{rt}, and two orders are associated with each term $Be^{bt} \sin (\omega t + \theta)$. For example, the general complementary solution

$$y_c(t) = A_1 e^{r_1 t} + A_2 e^{r_2 t} + A_3 e^{r_3 t} + B_1 e^{b_1 t} \sin (\omega_1 t + \theta_1)$$
$$+ B_2 e^{b_2 t} \sin (\omega_2 t + \theta_2) \qquad \textbf{(3.13)}$$

is of order seven; that is, $n = 7$ in Equation 3.1.

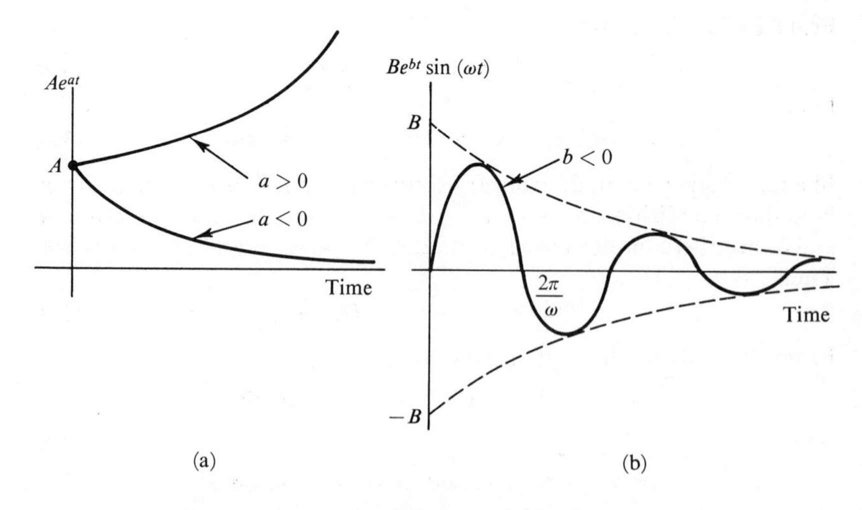

Fig. 3.4. *Plots of Ae^{at} and $Be^{bt} \sin \omega t$ versus t.*

Figures 3.4 (a) and (b) show plots of the two types of exponential functions of time. The coefficient of t in the exponent may be either positive or negative, but in a stable system the exponent must be negative in order that the complementary solution decays with time.

Associated with the exponential time function is the time constant. The time constant is defined as that time $t = \tau$, when $a\tau = 1$ or $\tau = 1/a$. If a is negative, the value of $Ae^{a\tau}$ when $a\tau = -1$ is $Ae^{-1} = 0.368A$. Similarly, in the exponential sine function of Figure 3.4 (b), the dashed lines represent the " envelope " of the sine function of time which decays exponentially if $b < 0$. The time constant of the " damped sinusoid " is also defined as that time $t = \tau$ when $b\tau = -1$.

The particular integral part of the solution for $y(t)$ is always of the same form as the input $v(t)$ or its derivatives. *Any meaningful input in a physical system is a continuous function of time and will not contain exponential time functions.*

3.4 General Periodic Functions of Time

The sinusoidal function of time shown in Figure 3.1 (a) is a periodic function; that is, $f(t + T) = f(t)$ if T is the time of one period. There are other useful periodic functions of time such as the square wave, the triangular wave, the sawtooth wave, and the pulse train. These are illustrated in Figures 3.5 (a), (b), (c), and (d).

The square wave is a periodic alternating step function which is useful for systems testing. Similarly, the triangular wave is a periodic alternating ramp function. The sawtooth function combines the ramp function with the step function. This waveform appears in many systems, such as the driver for the electron beam deflection of an oscilloscope or television set. The pulse train also appears as an input in systems, and is useful as a testing function if the response of the system to a short impulse is required.

Properties of Periodic Functions of Time

There are three properties of periodic functions which are useful in the analysis of systems. These are (1) the average value, (2) the root mean square value (rms), and (3) the peak (or peak-to-peak) value.

Average Value of a Periodic Time Function

The average value of a periodic function is defined as

$$\overline{f(t)} = \frac{1}{T}\int_0^T f(t)\,dt \qquad \textbf{(3.14)}$$

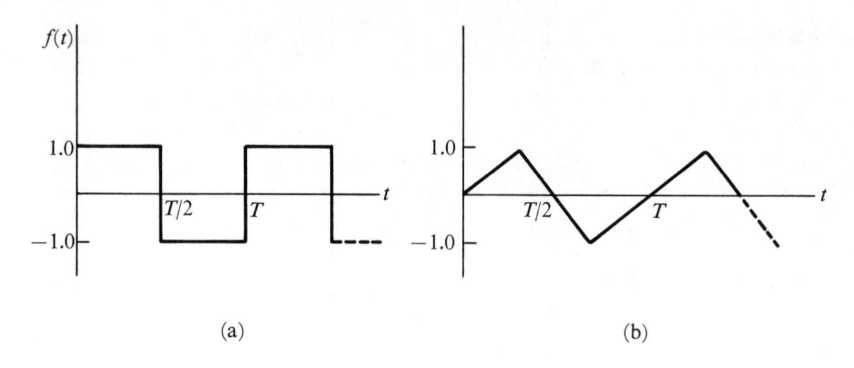

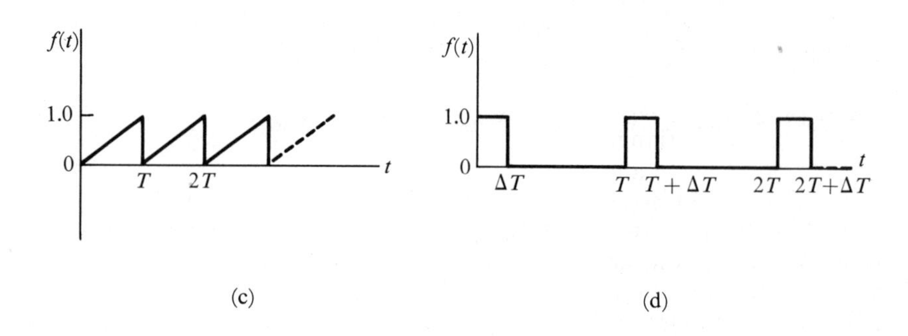

Fig. 3.5. *Useful periodic functions of time.*

This is $1/T$ times the area under $f(t)$ for one cycle of its variation. The average value of Figures 3.5 (a), 3.1 (a), 3.5 (b), for example, is zero. The average value of the sawtooth function of Figure 3.1 (c) is

$$\overline{f(t)} = \frac{1}{T}\int_0^T \frac{t}{T}dt = \frac{1}{2} \tag{3.15}$$

Root Mean Square of a Periodic Time Function

The root mean square (rms) of a periodic function is defined as

$$F = \left[\frac{1}{T}\int_0^T [f(t)]^2 dt\right]^{1/2} \tag{3.16}$$

This is the square root of $1/T$ times the area under $[f(t)]^2$ for one cycle. The rms of the sinusoid of Figure 3.1 (a) is

$$F = \left[\frac{1}{T}\int_0^T \sin^2(\omega t + \theta)\, dt\right]^{1/2} \tag{3.17}$$

where $T = 2\pi/\omega$.

Letting $x = (\omega t + \theta)$,

$$dt = \frac{1}{\omega} dx$$

When $t = T$, $x = 2\pi + \theta$,

$$t = 0, \; x = \theta$$

$$F = \left[\frac{1}{2\pi} \int_{\theta}^{2\pi+\theta} \sin^2 x dx \right]^{1/2} = \frac{1}{\sqrt{2}} \tag{3.18}$$

Peak Value of a Time Function

The peak value of a time function is the maximum value of the function during each period. This description is most useful when the average value of the function is zero and the wave form is symmetrical about the time axis. The $\sin \omega t$ function of Figure 3.1 (a) and the square wave and triangular wave of Figures 3.5 (a) and (b), respectively, have a zero average and are symmetrical above and below the time axis.

A more useful description of a time function which applies to any waveform is the peak-to-peak value, the difference between the maximum and minimum of the wave form. For example, the peak-to-peak value of the triangular wave of Figure 3.5 (b) is 2 units and the corresponding value of the pulse train of Figure 3.5 (d) is 1 unit.

3.5 Energy and Power

As discussed in Chapter 2, there are two types of variables associated with each component of a system: the across and through variables. The energy or work added to or expended on each element is a function of the across and through variables associated with that element. Energy is a scalar quantity, and the total energy in a system is the sum of the energy of all elements in the system. The unit of energy in the MSK system is the joule. If energy is expended, by convention it is positive, and if it is generated, energy is negative. In time T, the energy of an element is

$$\text{Energy} = W = \int_0^T x(t)\, y(t)\, dt$$

where $x(t)$ is the across variable and $y(t)$ is the through variable measured at the terminals of the element.

For example, for the capacitor element let a voltage be the simple sine wave time function of Figure 3.1 (a). If impressed across the capacitor, then

$$v_c = 5\sin\frac{1}{2}t \qquad \text{and} \qquad i_c = C\frac{dv_c}{dt} = C\frac{d}{dt}\left[5\sin\frac{1}{2}t\right] = \frac{5C}{2}\cos\frac{1}{2}t$$

If the capacitor has zero energy initially, then in time T

$$W_c = \int_0^T \frac{25}{2}C\sin\frac{1}{2}t\cos\frac{1}{2}t\,dt = \frac{25C}{4}[1-\cos T] \qquad \textbf{(3.19)}$$

Figure 3.6 shows a plot of energy of the capacitor as a function of T.

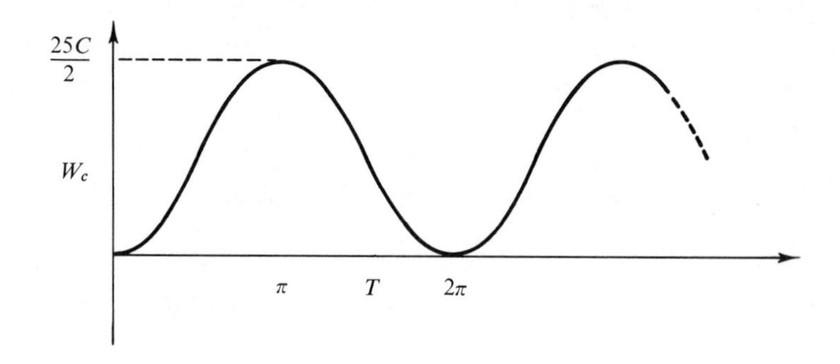

Fig. 3.6. *Energy of a capacitance C.*

Power is defined as work per unit time, and in the MKS system it is the watt unit. Power is therefore the time derivative of the energy, and in terms of the across and through variables of an element

$$P(t) = x(t)\cdot y(t) \qquad \textbf{(3.20)}$$

For example, let the force applied to a mass element be the unit ramp function of Figure 3.3 (c); then

$$f(t) = M\frac{d\dot{\delta}(t)}{dt} = t$$

for $t > 0$.

$$\dot{\delta}(t) = \frac{1}{M}\int_0^t f(\tau)\,d\tau$$

where τ is a dummy variable and $\dot{\delta}(t)$ is the mass velocity.

$$\dot{\delta}(t) = \frac{t^2}{2M},$$

then

$$P(t) = \dot{\delta}(t)f(t) = \frac{t^3}{2M}$$

for $t > 0$.

Power is basically defined as an instantaneous quantity, but in actual practice we are usually interested in average power over a certain time period. We define average power in time T as

$$P_{ave} = \frac{1}{T}\int_0^T x(t)y(t)\,dt \qquad (3.21)$$

Power measurements are particularly useful when the through and across variables are constants or periodic. For Figure 3.6, the average power expended in a capacitor in time T is $25C/4T(1 - \cos T)$, and if T is a multiple of 2π, the average power is zero. Referring to Figure 3.1 (a), a multiple of 2π is a multiple of the half period of the impressed voltage.

In resistance-type elements, the average power over a period of a cyclic waveform is not zero. Let $p(t) = 5 \sin \frac{1}{2}t$ be the pressure impressed across a length of hydraulic line which has resistance to fluid flow as illustrated in Figure 3.7.

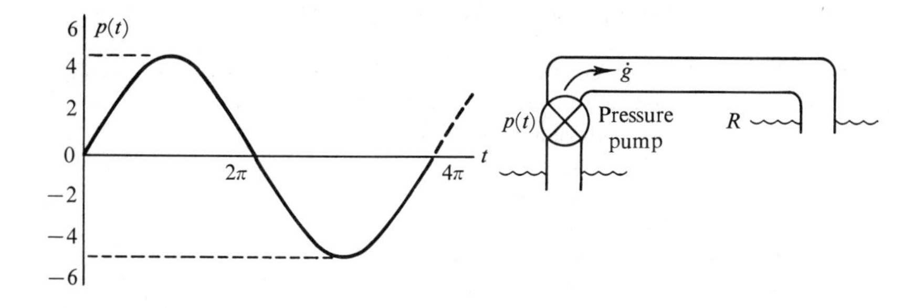

Fig. 3.7. *Hydraulic line.*

The instantaneous power expended in this hydraulic resistance is

$$P(t) = p(t)\,\dot{g}(t)$$

where

$$\dot{g}(t) = \frac{p(t)}{R}$$

$$P(t) = \frac{[p(t)]^2}{R} = \frac{25 \sin^2 \frac{1}{2}t}{R} = \frac{25}{2R}[1 - \cos t] \qquad (3.22)$$

since $\sin^2 x = \frac{1}{2} - \frac{1}{2}\cos 2x$.

The average power in time T is

$$P_{ave} = \frac{1}{T}\int_0^T \frac{25}{2R}(1 - \cos t)\,dt = \frac{25}{2R}\left[1 - \frac{\sin T}{T}\right] \qquad (3.23)$$

If T is a multiple of π seconds or if T is very large compared to one cyclic time period,

$$P_{\text{ave}} = \frac{25}{2R} \tag{3.24}$$

If we compute the root mean square of the pressure and the flow, we have

$$p_{\text{rms}} = \left[\frac{1}{T}\int_0^T 25\sin^2\frac{1}{2}t\,dt\right]^{1/2} = \frac{5}{\sqrt{2}} \tag{3.25}$$

$$\dot{g}_{\text{rms}} = \left[\frac{1}{T}\int_0^T \frac{25}{R^2}\sin^2\frac{1}{2}t\,dt\right]^{1/2} = \frac{5}{\sqrt{2}R}$$

Then

$$p_{\text{ave}} = p_{\text{rms}}\,\dot{g}_{\text{rms}} = \frac{25}{2R}$$

This illustrates the usefulness of the rms value of a time function.

The following example illustrates these concepts.

Example 3.1 The current through R in the electrical resistor of Figure 3.8 (a) is plotted in Figure 3.8 (b). We wish to find

1. the time plot of voltage across R
2. the average value of current in R
3. the average value of voltage across R
4. the rms value of current in R
5. the rms value of voltage across R
6. the average power dissipated in R

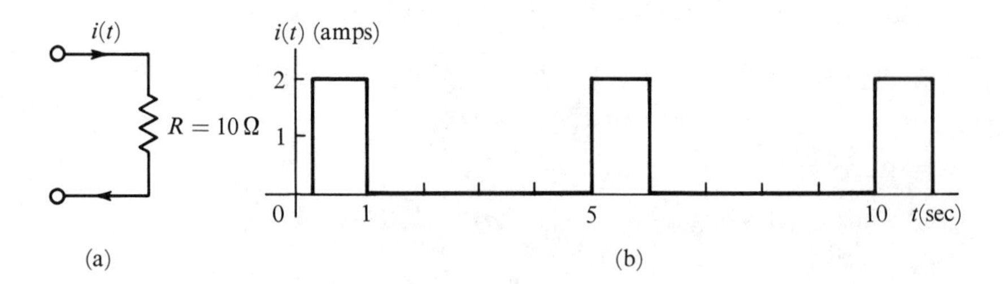

Fig. 3.8. (a) *Electrical resistor* (b) *resistor current.*

The defining equation of the resistor is

$$v(t) = Ri(t)$$

Therefore, the time plot of voltage across R is proportional to the plot of

Figure 3.8 (b) and the pulse amplitude is $10(2) = 20$ volts. The waveform period, T, is 5 seconds; then the average values of current and voltage are

$$\overline{i(t)} = \frac{1}{5}\int_0^5 i(t)dt = \frac{2}{5}\int_0^1 dt = \frac{2}{5} \text{ ampere}$$

$$\overline{v(t)} = \frac{1}{5}\int_0^5 v(t)dt = \frac{20}{5}\int_0^1 dt = 4 \text{ volts}$$

The rms value of current and voltage are

$$I_{\text{rms}} = \left[\frac{1}{5}\int_0^1 (2)^2 dt\right]^{1/2} = \frac{2}{\sqrt{5}} \text{ ampere}$$

$$V_{\text{rms}} = \left[\frac{1}{5}\int_0^1 (20)^2 dt\right]^{1/2} = \frac{20}{\sqrt{5}} \text{ volt}$$

The average power in R is

$$P_{\text{ave}} = \frac{1}{5}\int_0^1 2(20)dt = 8 \text{ watts} = I_{\text{rms}} V_{\text{rms}}$$

ADDITIONAL READINGS

Gupta, Someshwar C., *Transform and State Variable Methods in Linear Systems,* New York: John Wiley & Sons, Inc., 1966.

Koenig, Herman E., Y. Tokad, and H. K. Kesavan, *Discrete Physical Systems,* New York: McGraw-Hill Book Co., 1966.

Kuo, Benjamin C., *Linear Networks and Systems,* New York: McGraw-Hill Book Co., 1967.

Seely, S., *Dynamics Systems Analysis,* New York: Reinhold Publishing Corp., 1964.

Shearer, J. Lowen, Arthur T. Murphy, and Herbert H. Richardson, *Introduction to System Dynamics,* Reading Mass.: Addison-Wesley Publishing Co., Inc., 1967.

PROBLEMS

3.1. Show that the product of an across variable with a through variable of a given discipline represents power.

3.2. Make a plot of the following functions:

a) $x(t) = 5 \sin (2t - \pi/2)$

b) $\begin{cases} x_1(t) = -2\cos t \\ x_2(t) = +3\cos(3/2t + \pi/4) \end{cases}$

c) $x(t) = 5/2t \qquad 0 < t < 2$
$\quad\;\; = 5(t-3)^2 \qquad 2 \leq t < 4$

d) $x(t) = e^{-t/2} \sin 5t$

3.3. Express $5 \cos \omega t - 12 \sin \omega t$ in the two forms

$$A \sin (\omega t + \phi_1)$$
$$B \cos (\omega t + \phi_2)$$

What are ϕ_1 and ϕ_2 in degrees?

3.4. There are three formulas which can be used to calculate the power in a resistive element. Derive them.

3.5. A sine wave of voltage whose peak amplitude is 160 volts is impressed across a 60 watt light bulb. What is the peak amplitude of current flow through the bulb?

3.6. The average value of a function is defined as

$$x(t)\Big]_{\text{ave}} = \frac{1}{T}\int_0^T x(t)\,dt$$

where T is the period. Calculate the average value of the following functions:

a) $x(t) = \sin 5t$
b) $x(t) = x_m \sin \omega t$

Calculate the average value of the functions shown in Figure P 3.6.

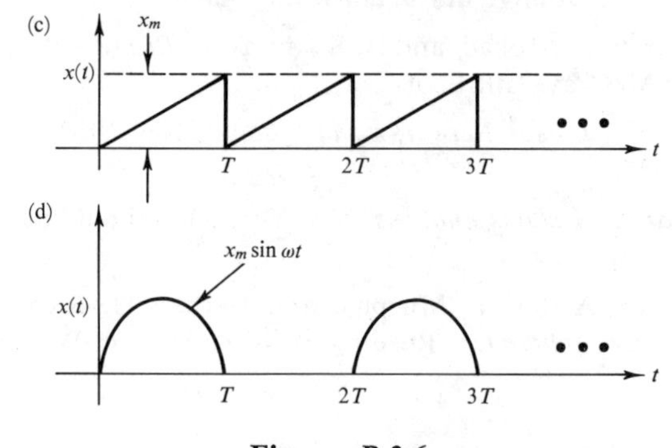

Fig. P 3.6.

3.7. The root mean square value of a function is defined as

$$x(t)\Big]_{\text{rms}} = \sqrt{\frac{1}{T}\int_0^T x^2(t)\,dt}$$

T period. Calculate the rms values of the functions listed in Problem 3.6.

3.8. Determine the rms value of

$$f(t) = 10 \sin 2t + 10 \sin (2t + 45°) + 20 \cos 4t$$

3.9. Find the average and rms values of the waveform shown in Figure P 3.9.

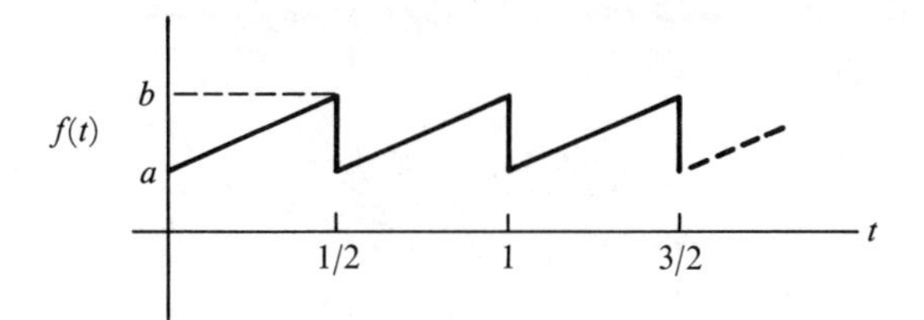

Fig. P 3.9.

3.10. Derive a general expression for the average power in a resistor if the impressed voltage is

$$v(t) = v_0 + v_1 \sin(\omega_1 t + \phi_1) + v_2 \sin(\omega_2 t + \phi_2) + \cdots + v_n \sin(\omega_n t + \phi_n)$$

3.11. If the voltage waveform sketched in Figure P 3.11 is impressed across a coil with an inductance of 1 henry and a resistance of 10 ohms, find the value, b, such that the current waveform through the coil is a linear function of time. Plot $i(t)$ versus t.

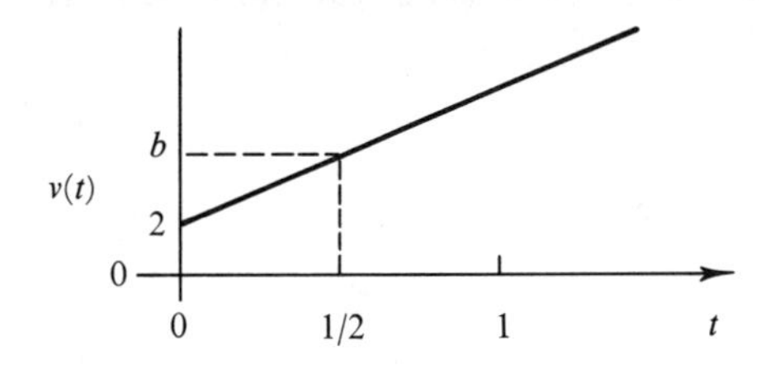

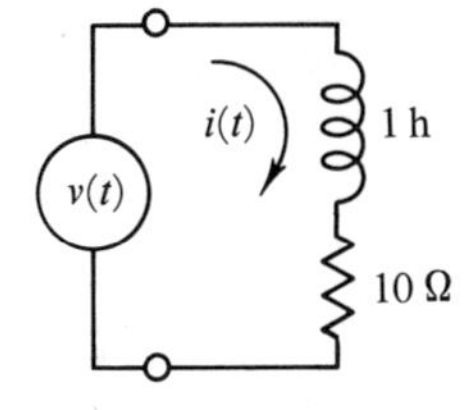

Fig. P 3.11.

Two-Terminal Components

4

4.1 Introduction

Physical systems may be viewed as an assembly of components which range in complexity from electrical or mechanical components with two terminals to those with many terminals of mixed system disciplines. Initially we will limit the description of component characteristics to two-terminal components, which are the least complex.

A two-terminal component has two points to which other components may be connected. Such a component may be represented symbolically, as shown in Figure 4.1. A component is a mathematical model of a

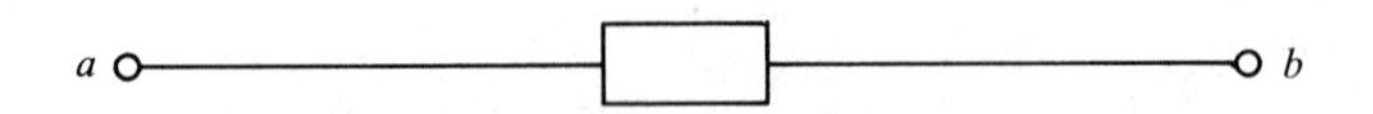

Fig. 4.1. *Symbolic representation of two-terminal component.*

single physical property, i.e., the characteristics of the component are related to a single physical property. To a certain degree, a component is a mathematical abstraction—the physical equivalent of the component may or may not exist with the same precision used in describing the component. In some cases, it may exist only as a system property.

It will be useful to begin the derivation of component characteristics with a discussion and description of system properties, which will then serve as a basis for the proper definition of two-terminal components. It is not intended that this section will suffice as the sole introduction to the physical nature of properties; a basic physics course is assumed as background.

4.2 Electrical System Properties

Capacitance

Voltage and current electrical variables were previously defined. Charge was also defined as a variable. Stationary charges generate an electric field in their neighborhood. Two physical phenomena can be related to this field: (1) Through interaction of the fields of two charges or assemblies of charges, forces are generated that attract unlike charges or repel like charges. (2) When two conductors are placed into an electric field generated by the charges, a potential difference, or voltage, is established between these conductors. The second phenomenon leads to the electric property called *capacitance*.

Consider the two plate-conductors charged as shown in Figure 4.2.

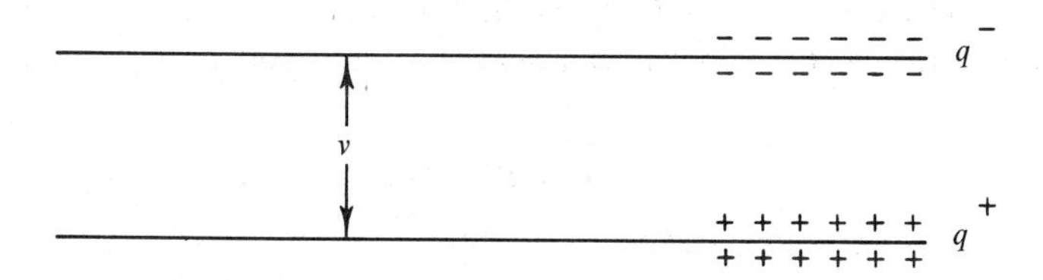

Fig. 4.2. *Charged plates and voltage.*

A voltmeter connected to the two plates would show a voltage proportional to the charge difference on the plates. This relationship can be expressed by the equation

$$v = \frac{1}{C} q \qquad \textbf{(4.1)}$$

where C is electrical capacitance and is given in coulombs/volt, or farads. The voltage-charge phenomenon is reversible; by connecting a voltage source of magnitude v to two uncharged plates, a charge difference q will be generated according to Equation 4.1.

If the voltage v is varied at the rate $\dot{v}$, the charge on each plate varies at the rate $\dot{q} = C\dot{v}$.* But this changing charge results in a current i flowing in the wires.

$$i = \dot{q}$$

or

$$i = C\frac{dv}{dt} \tag{4.2}$$

Both Equations 4.1 and 4.2 define capacitance as an electrical property. Equation 4.1 applies to a static environment, while Equation 4.2 includes time-varying conditions.

Resistance

When charges are to be transported from one point to another in an electrical system, as was the case for the time-varying conditions leading to Equation 4.2, a *conductor* is employed. The ability of a conductor to carry current is determined by the *resistivity*, ρ, of the material of the conductor. If a uniform conductor of length l and cross-sectional area A has a resistivity ρ, its *resistance* R is

$$R = \rho\frac{l}{A} \tag{4.3}$$

A conductor with low resistivity carries current well.

The resistance R is directly related to voltage and current by Ohm's Law:

$$v = Ri \tag{4.4}$$

Figure 4.3 defines v, R, and i.

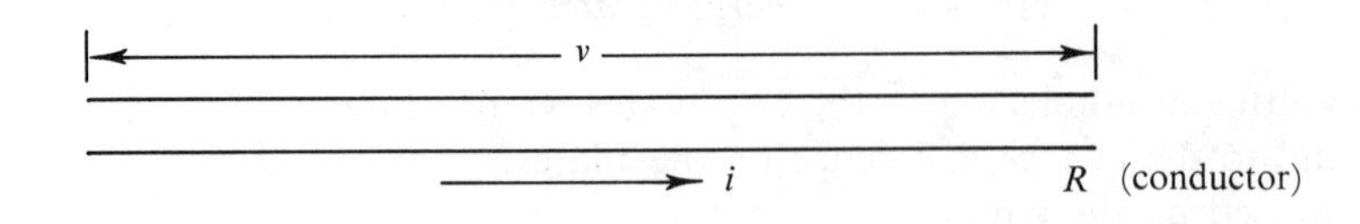

Fig. 4.3. *Resistance.*

* The notation $\dot{q}$ means differentiation with respect to time.

Inductance

Inductance is a third property of interest in the study of electrical systems. It is a phenomenon occurring primarily in conductors wound in coils. Moving charges (current) induce a magnetic field around a conductor. Associated with the magnetic field is a magnetic flux, λ. The magnitude of the flux, of course, is related to the current i flowing in the conductor. The relationship between the flux and the current depends mainly on whether or not the coil is wound on a ferromagnetic core. If not, the flux will vary linearly with the current, as shown in Figure 4.4.

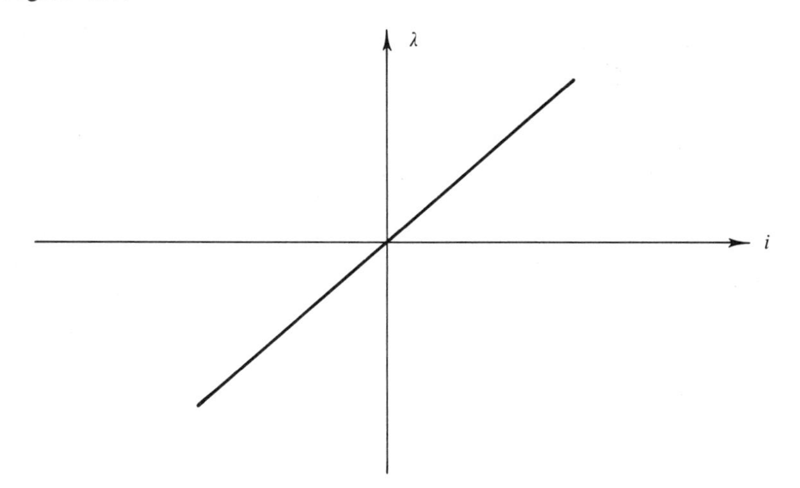

Fig. 4.4. *Flux-current relationship—linear case.*

We then have the linear relationship

$$\lambda = Li \tag{4.5}$$

where L is the *inductance* of the coil.

Where the core is ferromagnetic, the flux current relationship is nonlinear and can best be expressed only graphically, as shown in Figure 4.5. In such a case, the inductive property of the coil is greatly enhanced, but is subject to saturation and hysteresis.

To account properly for inductance in an electrical system, it is desirable to relate it to the variables voltage and current. As a result of experimentation, one can establish that a time-varying flux induces a voltage in a conductor. This voltage can be measured most conveniently at the endpoints of the conductor, and is related to the flux simply by

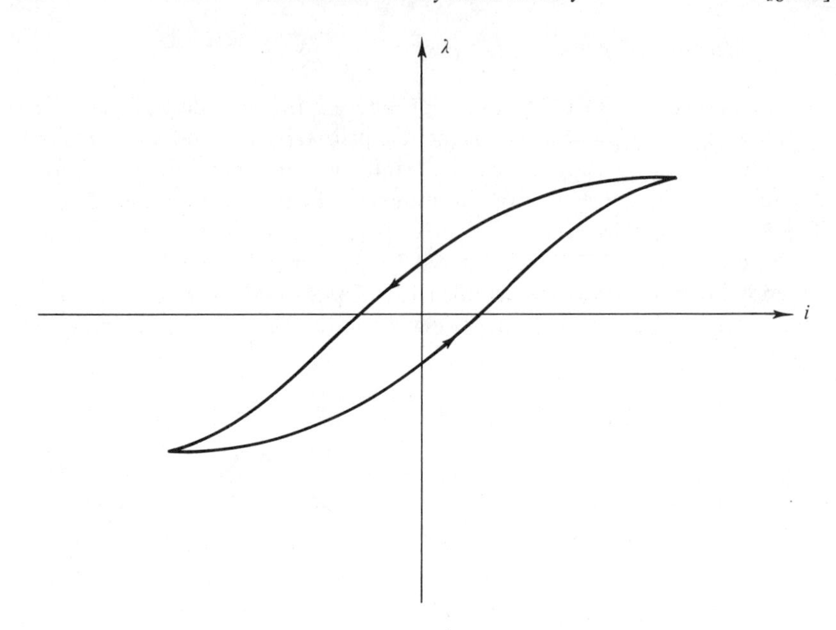

Fig. 4.5. *Flux-current relationship—ferromagnetic core.*

$$v = \dot{\lambda} \tag{4.6}$$

Substituting Equation 4.5 into 4.6, we have

$$v = \frac{d}{dt}(Li) \tag{4.7}$$

or when L is constant,

$$v = L\frac{d}{dt}i \tag{4.8}$$

This is the desired relationship expressing inductance in terms of voltage and current. For a single coil we speak of self-inductance. Frequently we will encounter a situation in which a second coil is in close proximity to the first; they may even be wound concentrically, or may be mounted on the same ferromagnetic core, as shown in Figure 4.6. Then the magnetic fields of the coils may interact with a flux common to both coils.

If a current i_1 now produces a time-varying a flux, voltage is measured at the terminals of the first coil:

$$v_1 = L_1\frac{di_1}{dt} \tag{4.9}$$

L_1 is called the self-inductance.

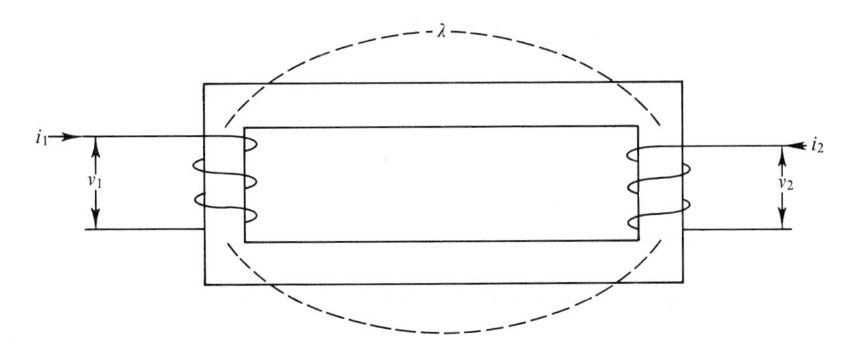

Fig. 4.6. *Two inductively coupled coils.*

Since the second coil is under the influence of the flux of the first coil, a voltage v_2 is induced in the second coil also. This voltage is related to the current i_1 by

$$v_2 = M\frac{di_1}{dt} \tag{4.10}$$

where M is called the mutual inductance.

In the MKS system, inductance has the units of volt-second/ampere or *henry*.

4.3 Mechanical System Properties

Force (torque), velocity, and displacement have been defined as variables for mechanical systems. In terms of these variables, we will now define three system properties: *elasticity*, *friction*, and *inertia*. These three properties exist in both translational and rotational systems. The discussion of the properties will be limited to the translational mode. Extension to the rotational mode is obvious.

Inertia

We know from experience that an object at rest will never start to move of itself. This property is called *inertia*. An external force is required to move the object. More accurately, a force is required to change the velocity of the object. An experiment will show that the rate of change of the velocity is directly proportional to the force applied.

$$f = m\frac{d\dot{\delta}}{dt} \tag{4.11}$$

The constant of proportionality, m, is a measure of the inertia of the object, and is called the *mass*.

Quite frequently it is advantageous to write Equation 4.11 in terms of force and acceleration:

$$f = m\ddot{\delta} \tag{4.12}$$

Mass is expressed in the units of newton-second²/meter, or *kilogram*. An ever-present reminder of the inertia of a body is the weight of the body. The acceleration of gravity is acting on any object in its field. If we know the mass of a particular object, then we can calculate its weight by Equation 4.12,

$$w = mg \tag{4.13}$$

where w is weight of the object and g is the acceleration of gravity. Weight is a force, and is expressed in newtons.

The rotational equivalent to mass is the mass moment of inertia. This is expressed as

$$\tau = J\frac{d}{dt}\dot{\varphi} \tag{4.14}$$

where J is the mass moment of inertia expressed in newton-meter-second²/radian, or kilogram-meter².

Friction

When two objects are in sliding contact, a force is required to move one object relative to the other. It can easily be observed that this force

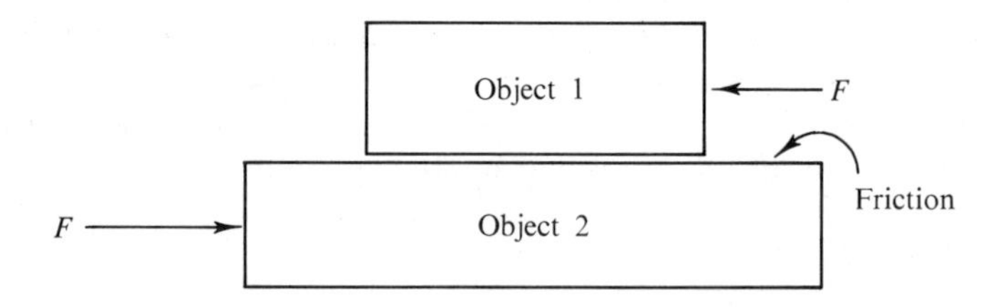

Fig. 4.7. *Friction between two objects.*

is a function of the relative velocity between the objects. The property that relates the force to the velocity is called *friction*.

Friction may be broken down into four major effects.

(a) *Stiction*, or break-away friction. If the relative velocity is zero for any duration, the contact surfaces are allowed to settle into one another. This causes some material bonding which will have to be broken before relative motion will result. This effect is called stiction.

(b) *Dry friction,* or Coulomb friction. Dry contact surfaces, or surfaces in direct material contact, produce a constant force independent of the magnitude of the velocity but dependent on the direction of the velocity. This is expressed as

$$f_c = F_c \operatorname{sign} \dot{\delta} \tag{4.15}$$

where F_c is the magnitude of the dry friction and the sign function is defined as

$$\operatorname{sign} x = \begin{Bmatrix} +1, & x > 0 \\ -1, & x < 0 \end{Bmatrix} \tag{4.16}$$

(c) *Wet friction,* or viscous friction. When the contact surfaces are separated by a fluid medium, the force required to produce relative motion is directly proportional to the velocity. This effect is called viscous friction and is expressed mathematically as

$$f_v = B_v \dot{\delta} \tag{4.17}$$

where B_v is the coefficient of viscous friction measured in newton-seconds per meter.

(d) *Windage friction.* Occasionally, friction effects are encountered between wet or lubricated surfaces that are best described by the relation

$$f_w = B_w \dot{\delta}^2 \tag{4.18}$$

This is called windage friction.

The four effects defined above are illustrated by an experimental *x-y* recording of a general friction characteristic.*

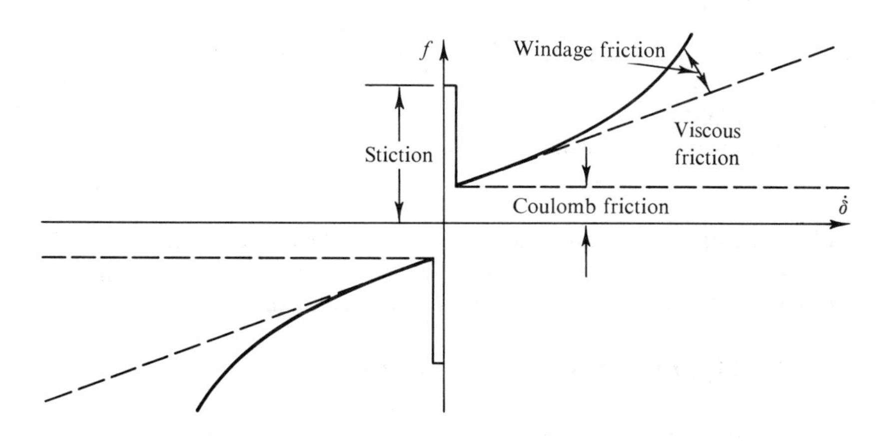

Fig. 4.8. *X-Y recording of general friction.*

* The velocity is assumed to vary slowly in magnitude from maximum forward to maximum reverse, and vice versa.

Exactly the same four friction properties are exhibited in rotational systems. They are defined in equivalent manner with appropriate modification to rotational variables in Equations 4.15 through 4.18.

Elasticity

Consider a longitudinal bar subjected to a slowly time-varying force, as shown in Figure 4.9. Under the action of this force, the length of the bar will change in proportion to the magnitude of the force. The

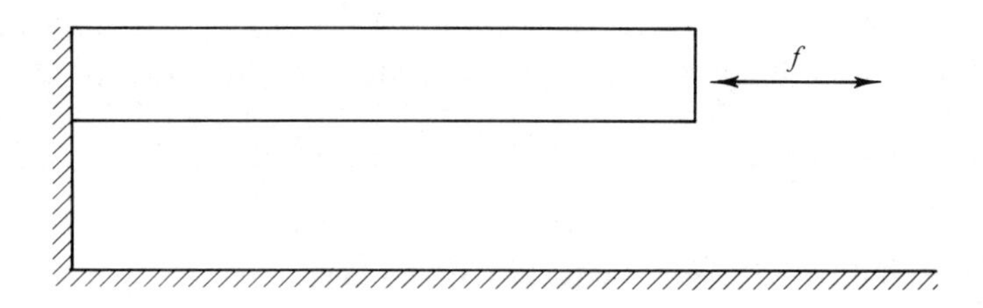

Fig. 4.9. *Elastic bar.*

relationship between the force and displacement is expressed quantitatively as

$$f = k_t \delta \tag{4.19}$$

where k_t is the elastic coefficient and δ is the net deformation of the bar.

This elastic property is of great use in engineering applications when the elastic body is designed as a spring, either a leafspring or a coilspring. In such applications, the elastic coefficient is called the spring constant.

The rotational equivalent to Equation 4.19 reads

$$\tau = k_r \varphi \tag{4.20}$$

and the elastic body is designed as a torsion bar or coil spring.

The units for the translational spring constant are newtons/meter, and for the rotational constant are newton-meter/radian.

4.4 Hydraulic System Properties

There are three hydraulic systems properties: *capacitance*, *resistance*, and *inertance*. They are associated with the characteristics of fluids, and directly derived from the mechanical properties elasticity, friction, and inertia.

Capacitance

Any fluid is compressible to a certain degree. The behavior under compression is perfectly elastic. To describe this property quantitatively we need only modify Equation 4.19 such that f is changed to pressure p and δ is changed to volume g by the following relations:

$$\left.\begin{aligned} f &= Ap \\ A\delta &= g \end{aligned}\right\} \tag{4.21}$$

where A is the area of the cross-section, so that we have

$$p = \frac{k_t}{A^2} g$$

or

$$p = \frac{1}{C_h} g \tag{4.22}$$

where C_h is called the *hydraulic capacitance* in units of meter^5/newton.

Inertance

Fluids, like solid objects, have inertia. Fluid inertia, or *inertance*, is effective in both the rotational and translational mode. In applications to system design, the translational mode is of primary importance. Again by use of Equation 4.21, Equation 4.12 may be modified to obtain

$$p = \frac{m}{A^2} \ddot{g}$$

or

$$p = I\ddot{g} \tag{4.23}$$

where I is the inertance in units of kilogram/meter^4 or newton-second^2/meter^5.

Resistance

The third hydraulic property, *hydraulic resistance*, is obtained by extending the considerations leading to the definition of viscous friction to the fluid medium. Consider a pipe through which a fluid is flowing with a given velocity, as shown in Figure 4.10. The cross-section of the pipe is constant so that the flow may be determined by measuring the flow rate $\dot{g}$. If the pressure difference is now measured at two points along the pipe, it will be found to be a function of the flow rate.

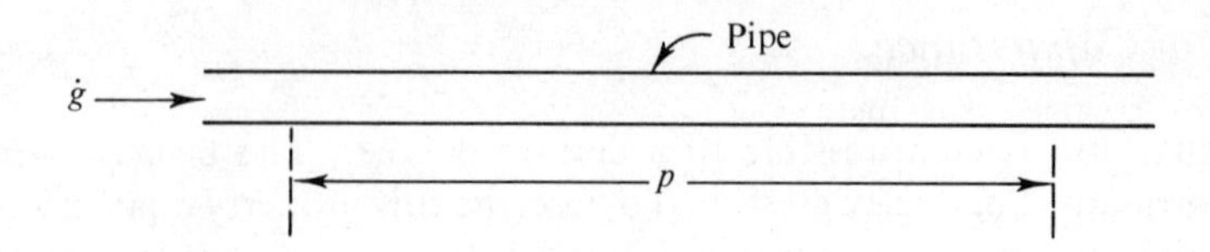

Fig. 4.10. *Schematic for hydraulic resistance.*

If the flow through the pipe is smooth, or laminar, the pressure is linearly related to the flow. If, however, the flow is rough or turbulent, the relationship is more nearly a quadratic, as shown in Figure 4.11.

For the linear case, we may write

$$p = R_h \dot{g} \tag{4.24}$$

where R_h is the hydraulic resistance measured in newton-second/meter^5. Equation 4.24 is found to be related to Equation 4.17 through application of Equation 4.21.

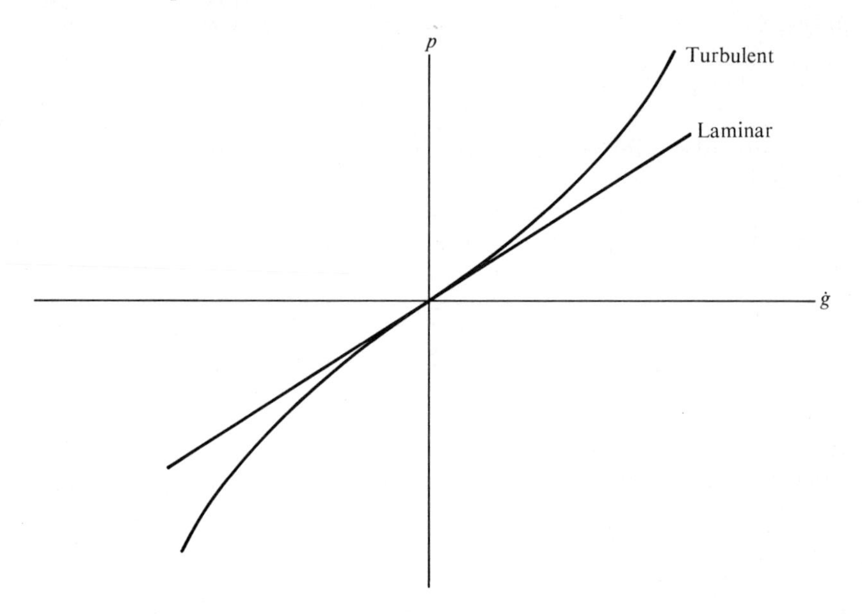

Fig. 4.11. *Pressure-flow relationships for a pipe.*

4.5 Mathematical Models of Two-Terminal Components

All physical components (systems building blocks) exhibit the various physical properties discussed previously in one form or another. The manner in which inductance appears in an electrical circuit, or friction in a mechanism, for instance, is not always well-defined and recognizable. One of the objectives of system analysis, therefore, is to define unambiguously how physical properties are embodied in a system. The attainment of this objective makes necessary the definition of components. A component is an idealization in that it defines exactly where one physical property ends and another begins. It is based on the assumption that physical properties may appear singly and discretely. There exists a great deal of evidence in the physical world to the contrary, yet without this simplifying approximation of a physical system, a mathematical analysis might be all but impossible.

It is convenient to define components according to the various system properties discussed. It will be observed that all these properties have been expressed in terms of an across variable and its associated through variable. In other words, we would require two meters, an across meter and a through meter, to measure the numerical values of the variables; and we require two points to make these measurements. These points will be called *terminals*, and a component exhibiting exactly one system property as the relationship between the across and through measurements will be called a *two-terminal component*. In this section we will present the mathematical models of a number of two-terminal system components.

Electrical Components

Resistor

The component exhibiting resistance is called a *resistor*, and is defined by the relationship

$$v = Ri \tag{4.25}$$

Fig. 4.12. *Schematic of a resistor.*

Equation 4.25 defines the mathematical relationship between the voltage and the current. However, some essential information is still missing. The required information is suggested by the following questions: Is the voltage positive or negative at a with respect to b? or, Is the current, when specified as a positive quantity, flowing from a to b or from b to a? In other words, the *orientation* of the variables must be known. The orientation that has proved to be most useful and consistent with intuitive thinking that the current i is taken to be flowing from a to b through the resistor if the voltage is greater at a than at b. That is, the current is flowing from the higher potential to the lower potential. We are now able to define the orientation as shown by the schematic of Figure 4.13 (a) or 4.13 (b).

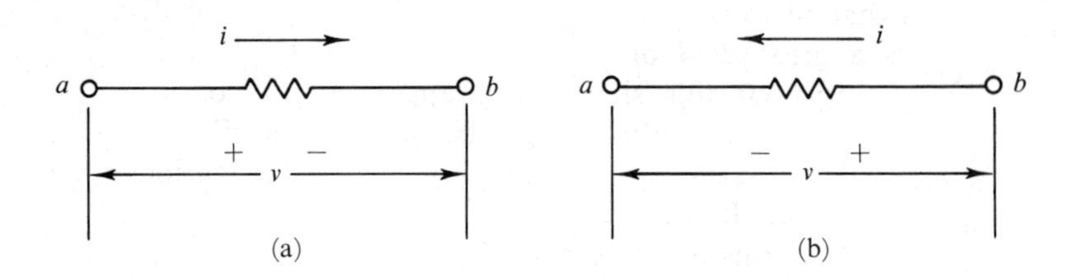

Fig. 4.13. *Orientation of variables.*

As can be seen from the schematic, once this convention is adopted the polarity of the voltage and current correspond to one another: if one is given, the other follows. For this reason, it is also useful to show the orientation by means of a somewhat more abstract symbolism called a *linear graph*. This is shown in Figure 4.14. The linear graph serves to show the orientation of the variables. The use of the linear graph has several advantages: (1) it frees the schematic to be used exclusively to show the location and manner in which a component is

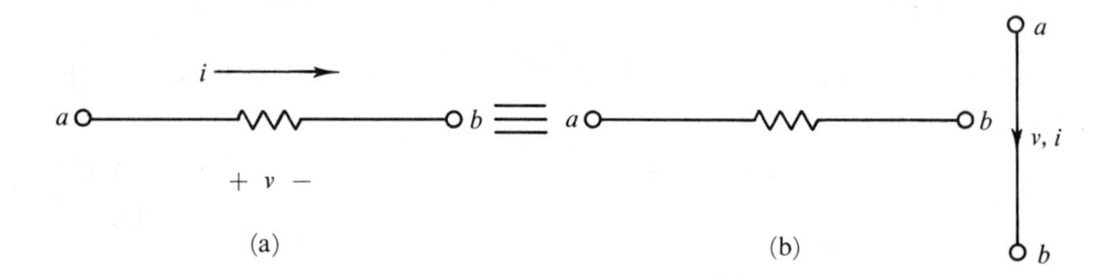

Fig. 4.14. *Schematic of resistor:* (a) *schematic with orientation;* (b) *schematic without orientation and linear graph.*

used in a system; (2) the linear graph will be seen to be the same symbol for all components; and (3) inasmuch as the linear graph specifies the variables used in a component equation, it will offer a convenient way of investigating the interrelations between variables corresponding to components connected together. The full significance of the graph will be realized in a later chapter.

In summary, the mathematical model of the resistor will consist of an equation and a linear graph showing the orientation of the variables used in the equation. It is convenient to show these two parts together.

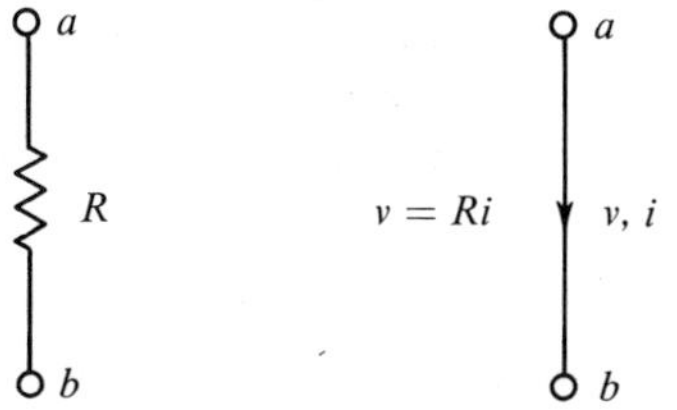

a

R

b

$$v = Ri \qquad (4.26)$$

a

v, i

b

Fig. 4.15. *Schematic and mathematical model of resistor.*

One may also refer to this model as a *component representation*, consisting of a *component equation* and *component graph*.

Capacitor

The capacitor is a component predominantly exhibiting capacitance. Following the same convention as for the resistor, the mathematical model is given in Figure 4.16. Two versions are presented, one involving voltage and current, the other voltage and charge.

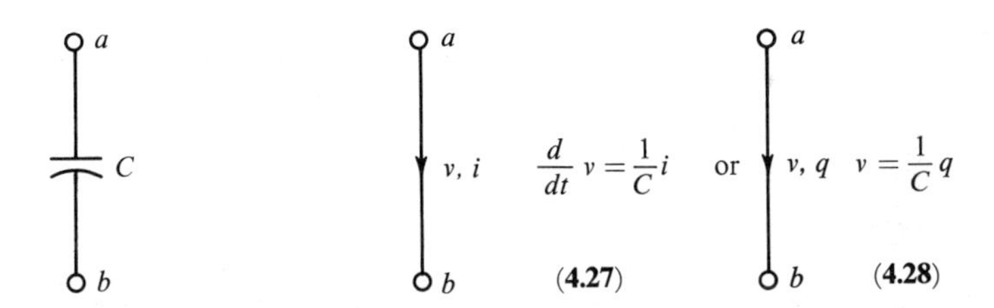

Fig. 4.16. *Schematic and mathematical model of capacitor.*

Inductor

There are also two versions for the inductor.

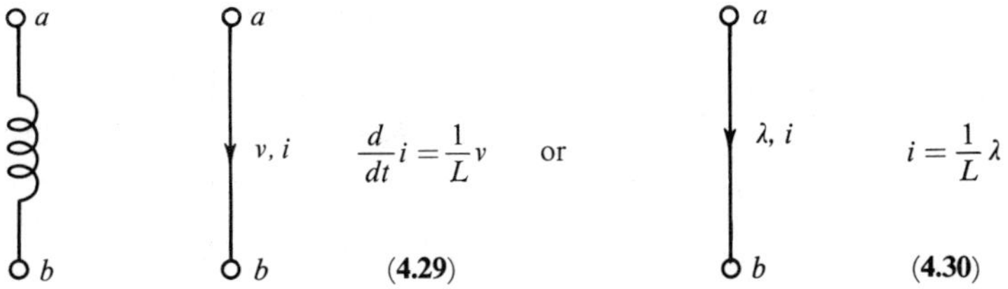

a

b

a

v, i

b

$$\frac{d}{dt} i = \frac{1}{L} v \qquad (4.29)$$

or

a

λ, i

b

$$i = \frac{1}{L} \lambda \qquad (4.30)$$

Fig. 4.17. *Schematic and mathematical model of inductor.*

Example 4.1 Develop a mathematical model for a conductor wound in a coil. It is assumed that the coil has both resistance and inductance.

This example illustrates that many physical properties appear simultaneously in a component. A useful construction of a model for this component when it is treated as a two-terminal component is to superpose the characteristics of the resistor and inductor and suggest this component equation:

$$v = Ri + L\frac{di}{dt} \tag{4.31}$$

with the variables defined by the graph of Figure 4.18 (c). Figure 4.18 (b) suggests that the compound component be viewed as a "series" combination of a resistor and an inductor.

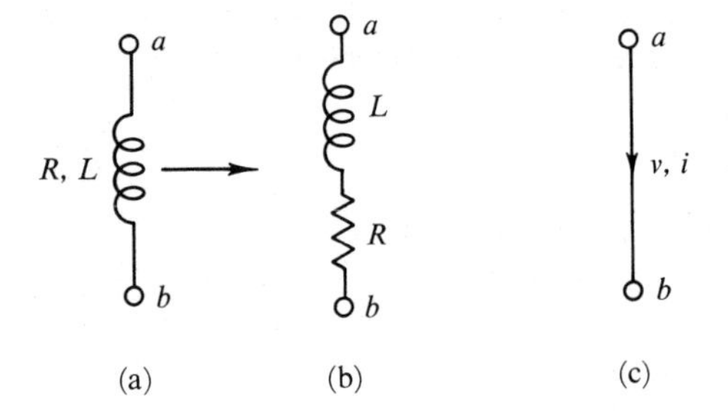

Fig. 4.18. (a) *Schematic of component with compound resistance and inductance;* (b) *equivalent lumped parameter approximation;* (c) *linear graph.*

Hydraulic Components

For the study of hydraulic systems it is useful to introduce two two-terminal components.

Pipe

The pipe is characterized by the mathematical model in Figure 4.19.

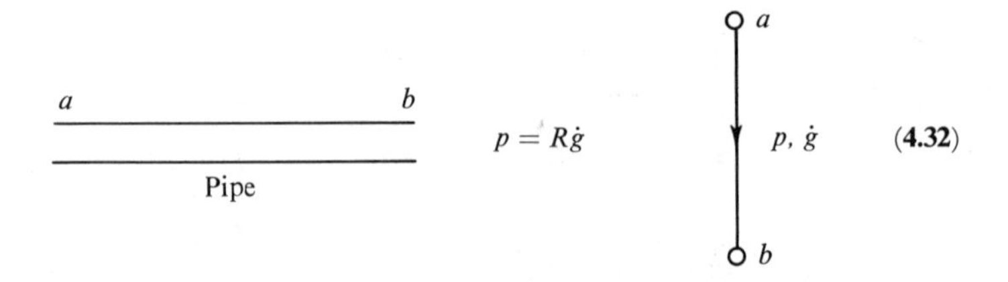

$$p = R\dot{g} \tag{4.32}$$

Fig. 4.19. *Schematic and component model of pipe.*

The orientation of the pressure p and flow $\dot{g}$ follows a convention similar to the electrical variables: the flow is in the direction of decreasing pressure.

Usually the pipe must be viewed as a compound component since, in addition to the hydraulic resistance, the property of inertance is present because of the mass of the fluid. Then the model for the pipe is

$$p = R\dot{g} + I\frac{d}{dt}\dot{g} \qquad \text{(terminals } a, b;\ p, \dot{g}) \tag{4.33}$$

Hydraulic Capacitor

The hydraulic capacitor can be derived from two different physical properties: (1) the compressibility of the fluid, and (2) gravitational effects. In the latter case, the pressure-volume relationship is entirely due to the gravitational forces acting on the fluid and producing a pressure at the bottom of the tank which is proportional to the height (volume). Thus the model is that shown in Figure 4.20.

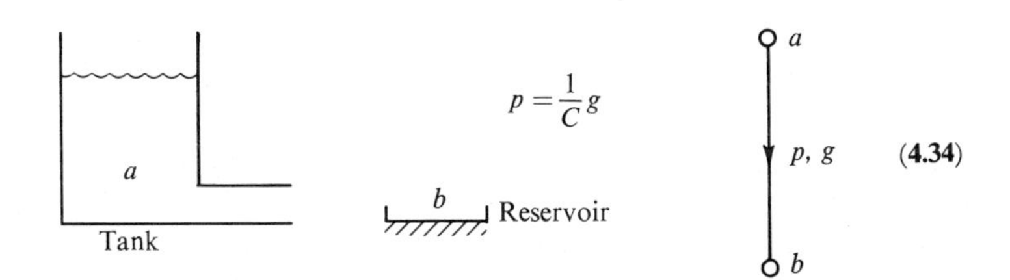

Fig. 4.20. *Schematic and component model of capacitor.*

Notice that the variables can be measured between the bottom of the tank and a convenient external reference point such as a reservoir.

Mechanical Components

There are six mechanical two-terminal components which are of interest in the study of systems. These are three translational components—spring, dashpot, and mass—and their rotational equivalents.

Spring (Translational)

The spring is the component corresponding to the physical property of elasticity. The component model along with the schematic is shown in Figure 4.21.

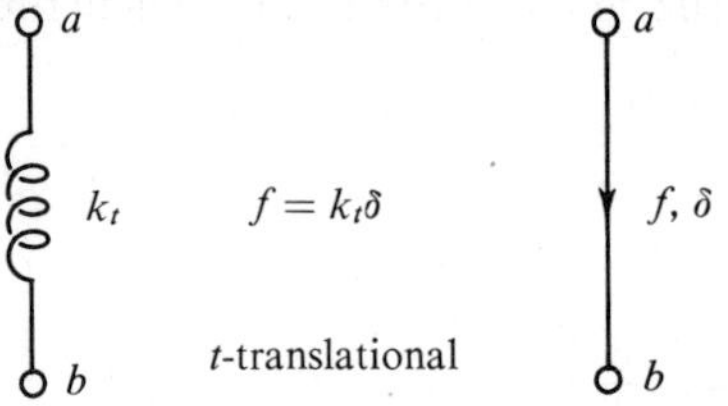

$$f = k_t \delta \qquad (4.35)$$

t-translational

Fig. 4.21. *Schematic and component model of spring.*

The convention is that the displacement δ is positive when the force acting through the spring causes an elongation of the spring. Even though this convention appears intuitively acceptable, it requires some elaboration. Suppose we have a force acting through the spring in the direction $a \rightarrow b$. As Figure 4.22 shows, this may be interpreted in two

Fig. 4.22. *Two interpretations of force acting on spring.*

ways. If the force is applied at a with b fixed, then compression occurs; on the other hand, if the force is applied at b with a fixed, then elongation occurs. This ambiguity is difficult to avoid. As a possible solution, one could accept only one of the interpretations as valid. Since it is inconsequential which is used, we might arbitrarily define the meaning of the variables as indicated by the linear graph according to Figure 4.23. Here the force is in the direction $a \rightarrow b$, but applied

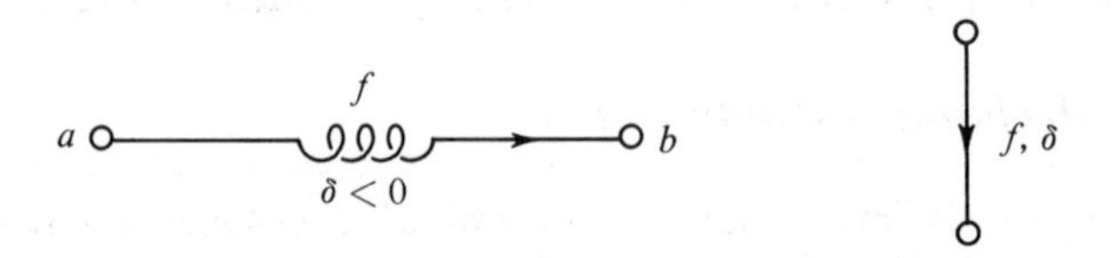

Fig. 4.23. *Orientation of mechanical variables.*

such that terminal b moves away from a, causing δ to be positive. However, the following example illustrates that little is gained by the introduction of the additional convention.

Example 4.2 For the springs connected as shown in Figure 4.24, investigate their displacements under the action of the constant force applied at point a. The two springs and the force form a simple system composed of three two-terminal components; the two springs and the force. The diagram shows

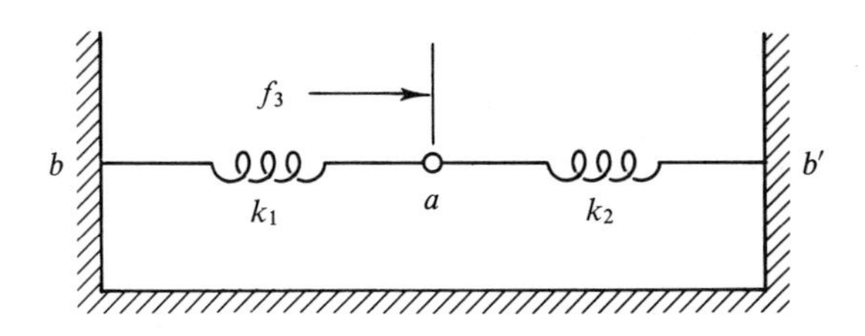

Fig. 4.24. *Simple spring system.*

the force acting from left to right. Now consider two ways of viewing the interconnection of these components according to the schematics of Figure 4.25. We assume the existence of an additional two-terminal component, a constant displacement driver δ_4 between b and b', with the understanding that $\delta_4 = 0$.

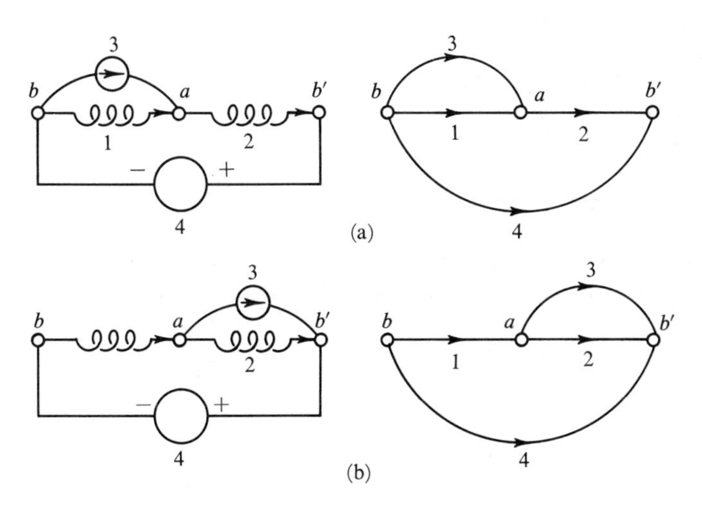

Fig. 4.25. *Two ways of showing the application of the driver.*

For the schematic of Figure 4.25 (a) we state the following relations:

$$f_3 + f_1 = f_2 \tag{4.36}$$

since

$$f_1 = k_1\delta_1$$

and

$$f_2 = k_2\delta_2$$

we obtain

$$k_1\delta_1 + f_3 = k_2\delta_2 \tag{4.37}$$

It is also clear from the same diagram that

$$\delta_1 + \delta_2 = \delta_4 \tag{4.38}$$

Combining Equation 4.37 with Equation 4.38,

$$f_3 = k_1\delta_2 + k_2\delta_2 - k_1\delta_4$$

and solving δ_3 yields

$$\delta_2 = \frac{f_3 + k_1\delta_4}{k_1 + k_2} \tag{4.39}$$

Following the same development but using Figure 4.25 (b), one obtains that

$$\delta_2 = \frac{-f_3 + k_1\delta_4}{k_1 + k_2} \tag{4.40}$$

These results differ in the sign on f_3. Yet they appear to describe the same physical situation, as in both cases the force f_3 is applied from left to right and $\delta_4 = 0$ and the terminals b and b' are identical. The results of Equations 4.39 and 4.40 contradict one another in that one indicates compression while the other indicates tension. Only one can be correct. Although it is perfectly possible to adopt a convention that by definition resolves this contradiction, it remains doubtful whether such a convention would be useful.

It will be shown in Chapter 6 that orientation problems illustrated by Example 4.2 will be easily resolved by solving for the displacement of all terminals relative to a common reference point.

Dashpot (Translational)

The dashpot is the embodiment of the linear friction property, viscous friction. Its component model and schematic is given in Figure 4.26.

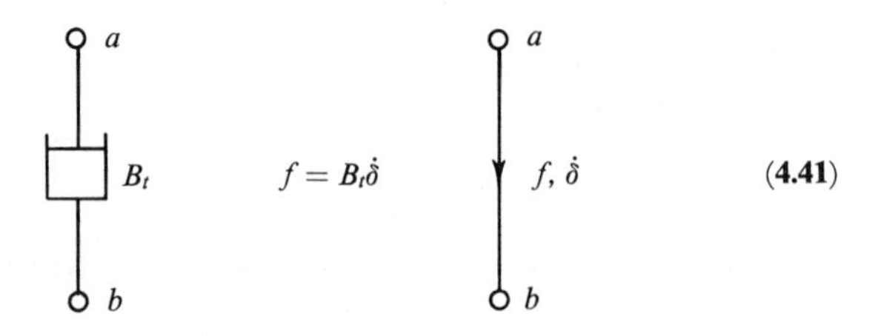

Fig. 4.26. *Schematic and mathematical model of dashpot.*

It is usually immaterial to the study of a system containing a dashpot, or a friction component capable of being approximated by the above linear component model, whether the dashpot is elongated or compressed. It therefore suffices to associate a positive force with a positive velocity, and let the direction of both variables be dependent on the nature of the system under study.

A dashpot, in the more general sense, may not necessarily be characterized by a linear component model. It is possible to encounter a friction component representing other friction properties such as coulomb friction or windage.

Mass (Translational)

The mass is probably the most important mechanical component, since anything that is comprised of some kind of material has mass. For the discipline of the system analysis that we wish to present here, it is necessary to view the mass as a two-terminal component. Thus the component model of Figure 4.27 is adopted.

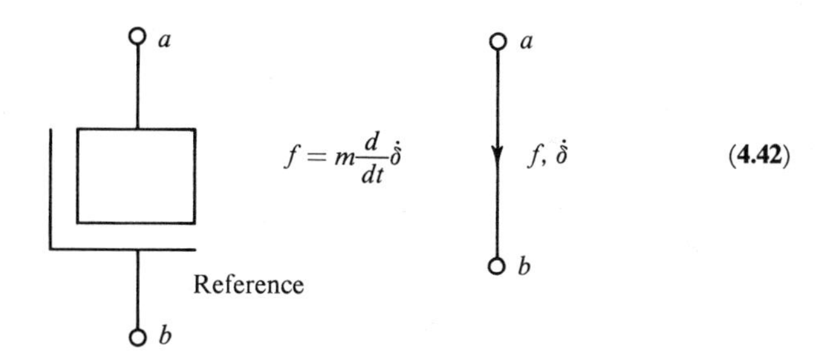

Fig. 4.27. *Schematic and component model of mass.*

The two terminals of the mass are the mass itself and a useful reference point. Then the force f is that force acting between the mass and the reference which produces a rate of change in the velocity of the mass. From Newton's laws of motion, the reference is necessarily an inertial one. However, for most practical cases, the reference is the earth or a structure fixed to the earth.

Viewing the mass as a two-terminal makes it possible to treat the mass like any other two-terminal component, an advantage to be substantiated later.

Each of the three components just presented has a rotational equivalent. These are presented in Figure 4.28.

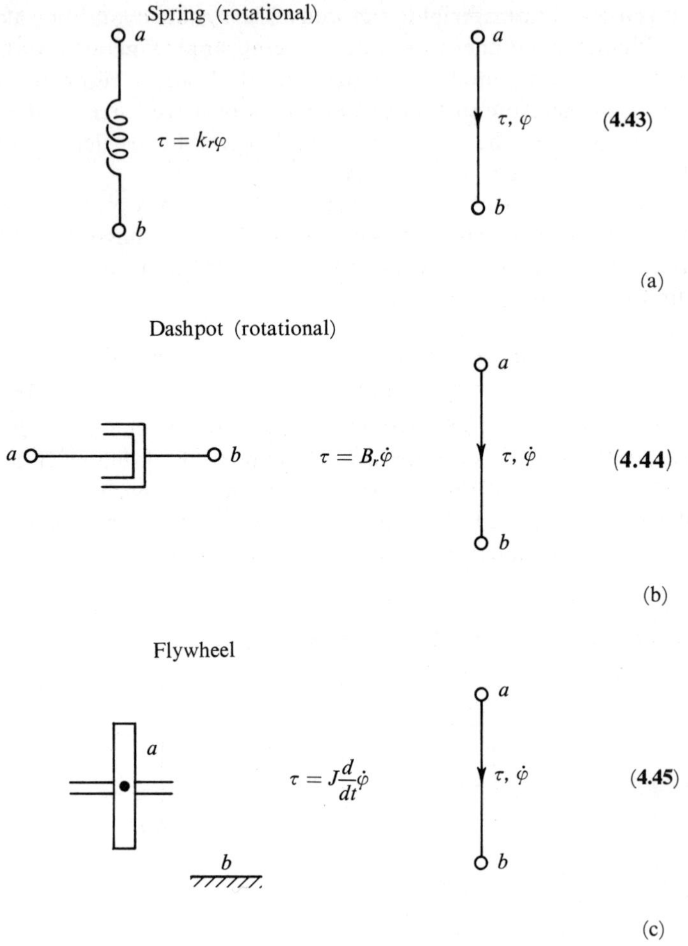

Spring (rotational)

$$\tau = k_r\varphi \qquad \tau,\ \varphi \tag{4.43}$$

(a)

Dashpot (rotational)

$$\tau = B_r\dot{\varphi} \qquad \tau,\ \dot{\varphi} \tag{4.44}$$

(b)

Flywheel

$$\tau = J\frac{d}{dt}\dot{\varphi} \qquad \tau,\ \dot{\varphi} \tag{4.45}$$

(c)

Fig. 4.28. *Schematics and component models of rotational components.*

4.6 Storage Components and Initial Conditions

A number of the two-terminal components defined in the previous section are capable of storing or releasing energy. We will call these components *storage elements*. The energy that may be stored by storage elements appears in various forms; different descriptions will be used to identify it. Thus, in electrical systems there is electromagnetic energy stored in inductors and electrostatic energy stored in capacitors. In mechanical and hydraulic systems there is kinetic energy stored in components characterized by inertial properties, and potential energy stored in elastic components. Potential energy storage may also result from the action of the gravitational force field, due to a difference in elevation.

We have defined an energy function by

$$W(t_2) - W(t_1) = \int_{t_1}^{t_2} P(\tau)d\tau \tag{4.46}$$

where $P(t)$ is the power function defined by

$$P(t) = x_p(t)\, y_p(t) \tag{4.47}$$

and x_p and y_p are system variables of a particular discipline whose product is in units of power. Equation 4.46 specifies the change in energy states from time t_1 to present time t_2. Energy is a point function; that is, the energy state of a system at any given time is dependent exclusively on the variables of the system at that time. Consequently, the integrand of Equation 4.46 will be an exact differential. The sign of Equation 4.46 will indicate a change in the energy state. If we wish to calculate the present energy state of a system, we simply consider the value of the integral at $t = t_2$.

Example 4.3 Energy State of a Capacitor.

The system variables are

$$x_p = v$$
$$y_p = i$$

The component equation of a capacitor is given as

$$i = C_e \frac{dv}{dt}$$

so that the energy function is given as

$$\begin{aligned} W_2 - W_1 &= \int_{t_1}^{t_2} i(\tau)\, v(\tau)\, d\tau \\ &= C_e \int_{t_1}^{t_2} v(\tau) \left(\frac{dv(\tau)}{d\tau}\right) d\tau \end{aligned} \tag{4.48}$$

The integrand is seen to be an exact differential. The parameter t may be eliminated so that Equation 4.48 reads

$$W_2 - W_1 = C_e \int_{v_1}^{v_2} v dv = \tfrac{1}{2} C_e (v_2^2 - v_1^2) \tag{4.49}$$

Hence, the energy state of a capacitor at a given time is seen to be

$$W = \tfrac{1}{2} C v^2 \tag{4.50}$$

In a similar fashion, we may evaluate the energy states of other storage components. The results are compiled in Table 4.1.

TABLE 4.1. *Energy states*

Component	Energy state
Electrical capacitor	$\frac{1}{2}C_e v^2$
Inductor	$\frac{1}{2}Li^2$
Mass	$\frac{1}{2}m\dot{\delta}^2$ or $\frac{1}{2}J\dot{\varphi}^2$
Spring	$\frac{1}{2}k_t\delta^2$ or $\frac{1}{2}k_r\varphi^2$
Hydraulic capacitor	$\frac{1}{2}C_h p^2$

An interesting relation exists between the various storage components: the terminal equations are all expressible equations of identical format.

$$x_p(t) = A\dot{y}_p(t) \tag{4.51}$$

or

$$y_p(t) = B\dot{x}_p(t)$$

where A and B correspond to the appropriate component parameters.*

The terminal equations of all storage components may also be written in integral form, as compared to the derivative form indicated by Equation 4.51. We may write

$$y_p(t) = \frac{1}{A}\int_{-\infty}^{t} x_p(\tau)\, d\tau \qquad \text{(a)}$$

and

$$x_p(t) = \frac{1}{B}\int_{-\infty}^{t} y_p(t)\, d\tau \qquad \text{(b)} \tag{4.52}$$

It is important to know the significance of the limits on the integrals of Equation 4.52. We must consider the possibility of signals existing for all time prior to the time t, the upper limit of the integral. Since we are dealing with time functions that are known only from $t = 0$, we write Equation 4.52 (a) in the form

$$y_p(t) = \frac{1}{A}\int_{-\infty}^{0} x_p(\tau)\, d\tau + \frac{1}{A}\int_{0}^{t} x_p(\tau)\, d\tau \tag{4.53}$$

The first term on the right hand side is a constant, and has the significance of an initial condition on the storage component. We write Equation 4.52 (a) as

$$y_p(t) = y_p(0) + \frac{1}{A}\int_{0}^{t} x_p(\tau)\, d\tau \tag{4.54}$$

A similar relation may be established for Equation 4.52 (b).

Example 4.4 Write the terminal equations for a transitional spring in integral form. In derivative form, we have

* Note that those variables whose product is power are involved in the terminal equations, with one variable appearing as a time derivative.

$$\dot{\delta}(t) = \frac{1}{K_t}\frac{d}{dt}f(t) \tag{4.55}$$

When inverted to integral form, the terminal equations read

$$f(t) = f(0) + k_t \int_0^t \dot{\delta}(\tau)\,d\tau \tag{4.56}$$

A storage component has an initial condition in its integral form terminal equation whenever its energy state at $t = 0$ is non-zero. Thus, energy states and initial conditions are intimately related.

Example 4.5 Determine the energy state at $t = 0$ of the spring of the previous example. The initial condition is given as $f(0)$. Hence,

$$\begin{aligned} W(t) - W(0) &= \int_0^t f(t)\,\dot{\delta}(\tau)\,d\tau \\ &= \int_0^t \frac{1}{k_t} f(\tau)\cdot\frac{df(\tau)}{d\tau}\,d\tau \\ &= \frac{1}{k_t}\int_{f_0}^{f_t} f d\tau \end{aligned}$$

The integral evaluated at the lower limit is the desired result

$$W(0) = \tfrac{1}{2}\frac{1}{k_t} f^2(0) \tag{4.57}$$

The terminal equation for the spring may be written in the form

$$f(t) = k_t\,\delta(t)$$

from which

$$f(0) = k_t\,\delta(0)$$

Hence, Equation 4.57 can be expressed as

$$W(0) = \tfrac{1}{2}k_t\,\delta^2(0) \tag{4.58}$$

It is usually more convenient to express the initial condition and energy state of a spring in terms of an initial displacement.

It is common practice to specify the initial conditions on the various system components under discussion, in terms of the variables, as stated in Table 4.2.

TABLE 4.2.

Component	Initial condition
Electrical capacitor	v_0, q_0
Inductor	i_0, λ_0
Mass	$\dot{\delta}_0$, $\dot{\varphi}_0$
Spring	δ_0, φ_0
Hydraulic capacitor	g_0

4.7 Dissipative Components

Certain components cannot store energy of any form. On the contrary, these components convert system energy (electrical, mechanical, etc.) into thermal energy. These components are identified as the electrical resistor, mechanical components representing any kind of friction, and the hydraulic resistance. The process by which energy from the system is converted into heat is irreversible—the energy is lost. Hence, we call these components *dissipative*.

The rate at which energy is dissipated by any of these components is calculated by the power function

$$P(t) = X_p(t) \cdot Y_p(t)$$

The energy state of dissipative components cannot be defined since the integral energy for such a component is *not* a point function.

4.8 Sources (Drivers)

All components discussed so far are related by one common characteristic: their terminal equations express a functional dependence between an across and a through variable. From the point of view of instrumentation we can say that a non-zero measurement of one variable implies an excitation of the component by a physical quantity corresponding to the associated variable. Consider the resistor in Figure 4.29. In order to measure a non-zero voltage, it is necessary to cause a current to flow through the resistor, since $v = Ri$. If $i = 0$, the resistor will not, on its own, " generate " a voltage.

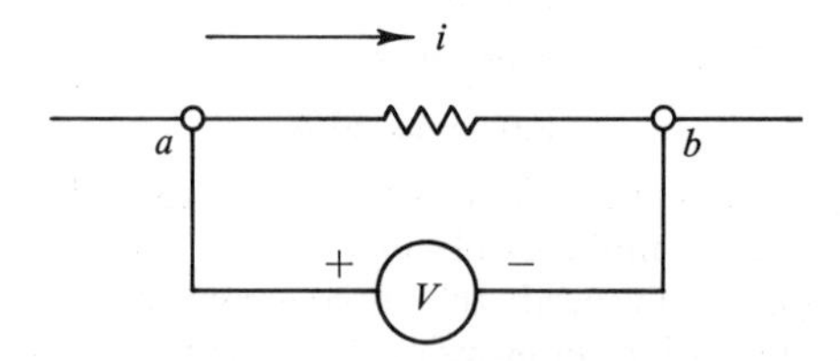

Fig. 4.29. *Voltage across resistor.*

Components which yield a non-zero measurement at their terminals only when excited externally are called *passive* components. Components which fail to exhibit this characteristic are *active* components. A special class of active components consists of *drivers* or *sources*. They are two-terminal components, and their characteristics are summarized in the following statements.

1. An across driver is a two-terminal component whose across variable at any time is independent of the through measurement at its terminals.

2. A through driver is a two terminal component whose through variable at any time is independent of the across measurement at its terminals.

The drivers are represented schematically in Figure 4.30, with definition of orientation.

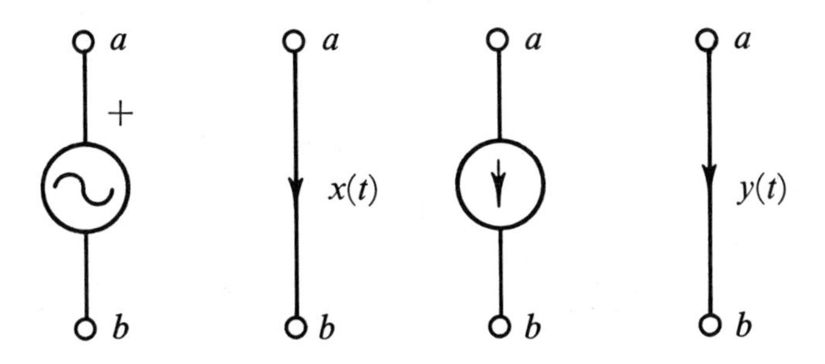

Fig. 4.30. *Across driver—through driver.*

The terminal characteristics of a typical constant voltage driver are illustrated by the x-y plot of Figure 4.31. The plot indicates that the

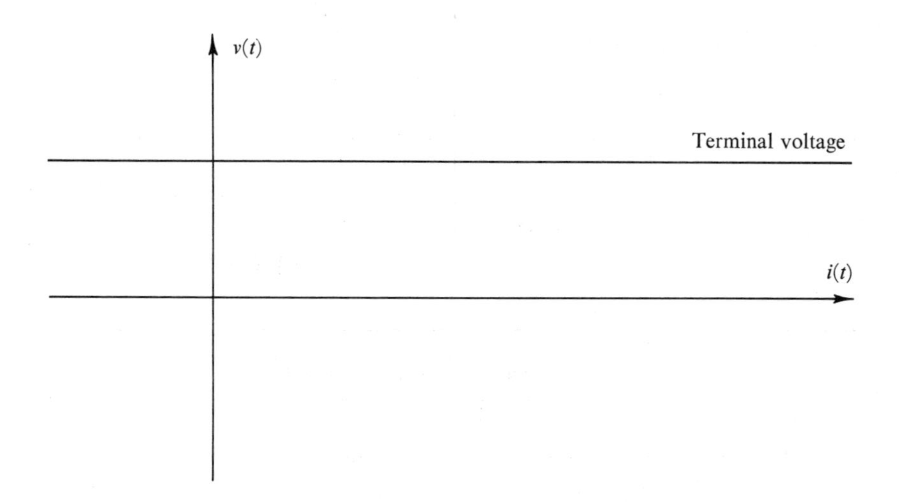

Fig. 4.31. *Voltage driver.*

voltage is constant, independent of the current flowing through the driver. It illustrates the impossibility of establishing a relationship between voltage and current. It will later be seen that the current can be related to the voltage, but only indirectly through a system connection made to the driver.

Tables 4.3 and 4.4 show component representations and mathematical models for two-terminal electrical, hydraulic, and mechanical system components.

TABLE 4.3.

Two-terminal electrical Components

Primary variables $v(t)$—voltage, $i(t)$—current	Orientation of variables: $a \circ \xrightarrow{v,\, i} \circ b$
Component	**Terminal equations**
Resistor R (a to b)	$v(t) = Ri(t)$
Inductor L (a to b)	$v(t) = L\dfrac{d}{dt}i(t) \qquad \lambda(t) = Li(t)$ $i(t) = I_0 + \dfrac{1}{L}\displaystyle\int_0^t v(\tau)d\tau$
Capacitor C (a to b)	$i(t) = C\dfrac{d}{dt}v(t) \qquad q(t) = Cv(t)$ $v(t) = V_0 + \dfrac{1}{C}\displaystyle\int_0^t i(\tau)d\tau$

Two-terminal hydraulic components

Primary variables $p(t)$—pressure, $g(t)$—flow	Orientation of variables: $a \circ \xrightarrow{p,\, \dot{g}} \circ b$

Component	Terminal equations
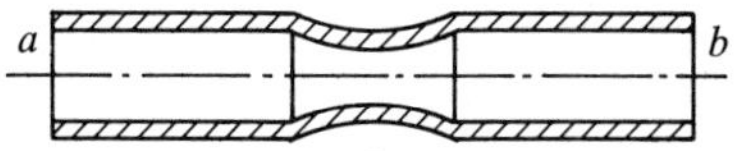 a, b — Restriction	$p(t) = R_h \dot{g}(t)$
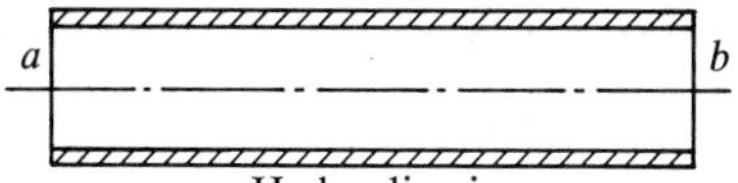 a, b — Hydraulic pipe	$p(t) = R_h \dot{g}(t) + M_h \frac{d}{dt}\dot{g}(t)$
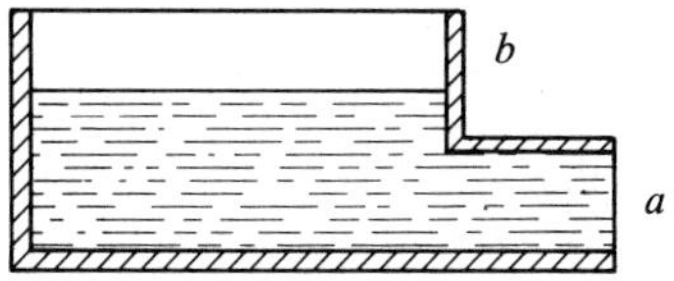 b, a — Hydraulic capacitor	$\dot{g}(t) = C_h \frac{d}{dt} p(t)$ $p(t) = p_0 + \frac{1}{C_h}\int_0^t \dot{g}(\tau)\, d\tau$

Two-terminal mechanical components

Primary variables: $\dot{\delta}(t)$—velocity, $f(t)$—force, $\dot{\varphi}(t)$—rot. velocity, $\tau(t)$—torque	Orientation of variables: 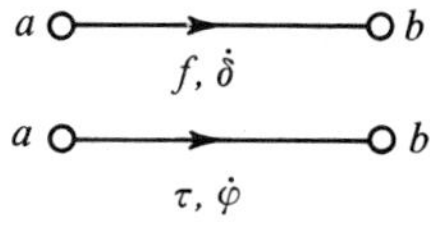 a → b $f, \dot{\delta}$; a → b $\tau, \dot{\varphi}$

Component	Terminal equations
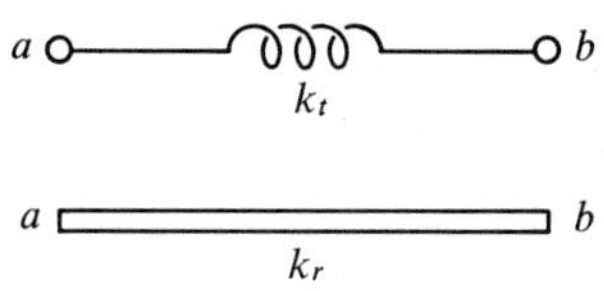 a, b, k_t; a, b, k_r — Spring-torsionbar	$f = k_t \delta_0 + k_t \int_0^t \dot{\delta}(\tau)\, d\tau = k(t)\, \delta(t)$ $\tau = k_r \varphi_0 + k_r \int_0^t \dot{\varphi}(\tau)\, d\tau = k_r \varphi(t)$

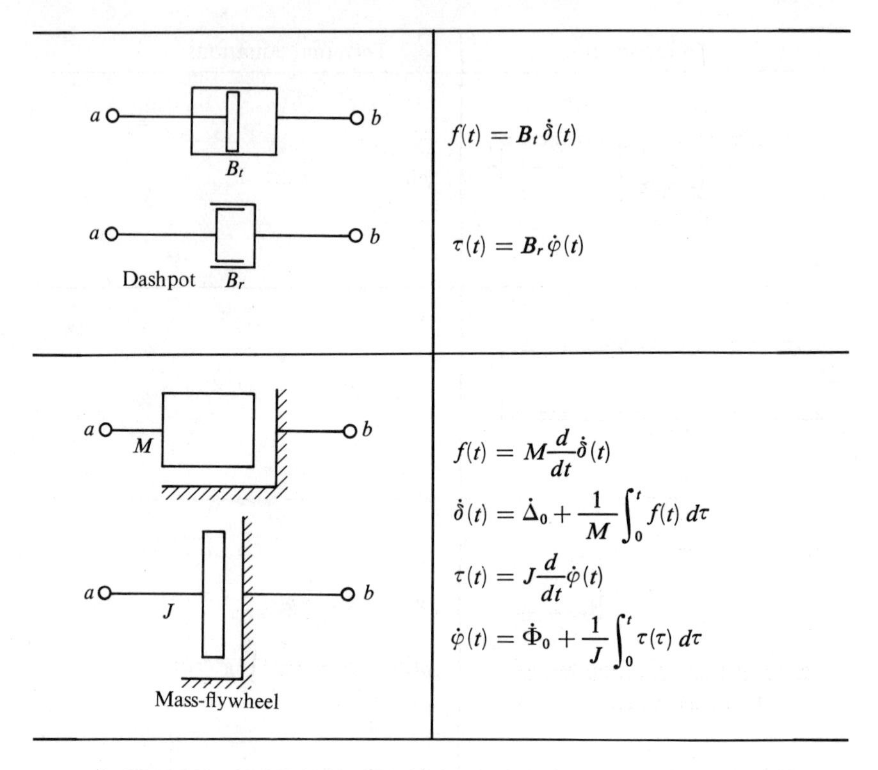

a — B_t — b	$f(t) = B_t \dot{\delta}(t)$
a — Dashpot B_r — b	$\tau(t) = B_r \dot{\varphi}(t)$
a — M — b	$f(t) = M\frac{d}{dt}\dot{\delta}(t)$ $\dot{\delta}(t) = \dot{\Delta}_0 + \frac{1}{M}\int_0^t f(t)\, d\tau$
a — J — b Mass-flywheel	$\tau(t) = J\frac{d}{dt}\dot{\varphi}(t)$ $\dot{\varphi}(t) = \dot{\Phi}_0 + \frac{1}{J}\int_0^t \tau(\tau)\, d\tau$

Drivers can be further classified into independent and dependent drivers. The across and through drivers in Table 4.4 are independent. The $x(t)$ and $y(t)$ are specified functions of time and do not depend on any other variables in a system of which they may be a part. Dependent drivers are also either across or through drivers, but the $x(t)$ or $y(t)$ are proportional to or a function of one or more other system variables. Dependent drivers appear in the equivalent circuits of amplifier devices. The output circuit of a transistor, for example, usually includes a current driver, but this current is proportional to the input current of the transistor. The transistor is a three-terminal component, and a discussion of multiterminal components is reserved for Chapter 8.

TABLE 4.4.

Across driver	$x(t)$-specified
a + (~) b Symbol	a → b Orientation

Electrical	$v(t)$	Voltage positive a to b
Hydraulic	$p(t)$	Pressure positive a to b
Mechanical	$\dot{\delta}(t)$	Displacement a-b increasing
	$\dot{\varphi}(t)$	Angular disp. a-b increasing clockwise

Through driver	$y(t)$-specified
a — b, Orientation	a — b, Symbol

Electrical	$i(t)$	Current flowing a to b
Hydraulic	$\dot{g}(t)$	Fluid flowing a to b
Mechanical	$f(t)$	Tensile force between a and b
	$\tau(t)$	Clockwise torque between a and b

4.9 System State and State Variables

The close correspondence between the energy state of a component and initial conditions constitutes the basis for an important concept in system analysis. We may interpret energy storage components as carriers of the full informarion about the *state* of a system. At any time during the transient of a system (the reaction of the system to an input) only energy storage components may give an indication of the state of a system. Consider, for instance, the situation in which a system containing a typical collection of energy storage components, dissipative components, and drivers is suddenly stopped in motion—all energy storage components are separated from the system and the driver is stopped—it is held constant. Restarting the system, without any noticeable effects except for the time lapse, requires reconnection of the components. The energy states of the storage components contain all the information; they represent the initial conditions. Thus the state of the system is directly dependent on the storage components of the system.

In general, the energy states of the storage components are functions of time and may be expressed in terms of such systems variables as voltage (capacitor), current (inductor), pressure (hydraulic capacitor), velocity (mass), etc. System variables that are related to the state of the system through the energy storage components are called *state variables*. A more formal definition may be stated: The state of a system is the set of variables, the state variables, which contain sufficient information about the present condition of the system to permit the determination of all future time history of the system, provided that all future inputs to the system are known.

The subject of state variables will be considered later, when it will be formally introduced as a procedure of formulation.

ADDITIONAL READINGS

Cannon, Robert H., Jr., *Dynamics of Physical Systems*, New York: McGraw-Hill Book Co., 1967.

Firestone, F. A., " A New Analogy betweenMechanical and Electrical System," *J. Acoust. Soc. Am.*, 4, 1932–33.

Halliday, D., and R. Resnick, *Physics for Students of Science and Engineering*, New York: John Wiley & Sons, Inc., 1962.

Koenig, Herman E., and William A. Blackwell, *Electromechanical System Theory,* New York: McGraw-Hill Book Co., 1961.

Olson, H. F., *Dynamical Analogies,* New York: D. Van Nostrand Co., Inc., 1943.

Sanford, Richard S., *Physical Networks*, Englewood Cliffs, New Jersey: Prentice-Hall, Inc., 1965.

Seely, S., *Dynamic Systems Analysis*, Reinhold Publishing Corp., 1964.

Shearer, J. Lowen, Arthur T. Murphy, and Herbert H. Richardson, *Introduction to System Dynamics*, Reading, Mass.: Addison-Wesley Publishing Co., Inc., 1967.

PROBLEMS

4.1. A square wave current is passed through a capacitor. Sketch the voltage across the capacitor as a waveform.

4.2. Repeat Problem 4.1 with the current as a sinusoidal waveform.

4.3. A triangular wave current is passed through an inductor. Sketch the voltage across the inductor as a waveform.

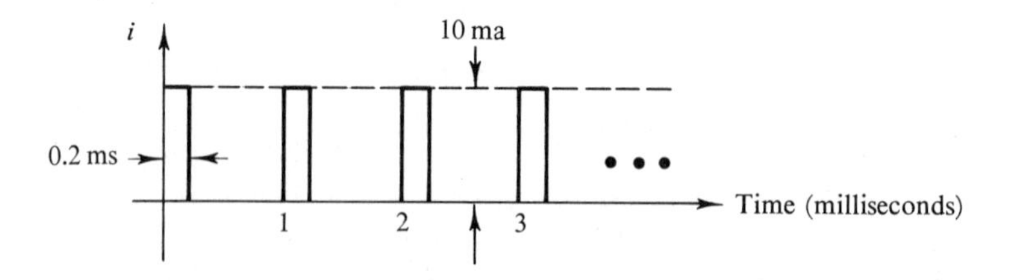

Fig. P 4.5.

4.4. Repeat Problem 4.3 with the current as a sinusoidal waveform.

4.5. A capacitor ($C = 1 \times 10^{-6} f$) receives a pulse train current as shown in Figure P 4.5.

Plot the voltage across the capacitor as a function of time.

4.6. A current of the waveform indicated in Figure P 4.6 is passed through a capacitor ($C = 10^{-6} f$). Determine the waveform of the voltage across the capacitor.

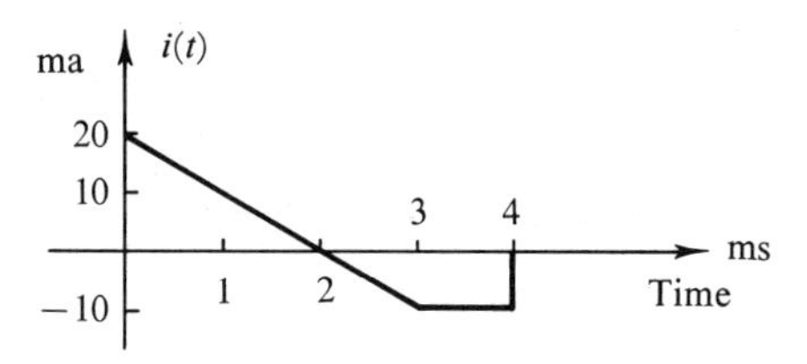

Fig. P 4.6.

4.7.

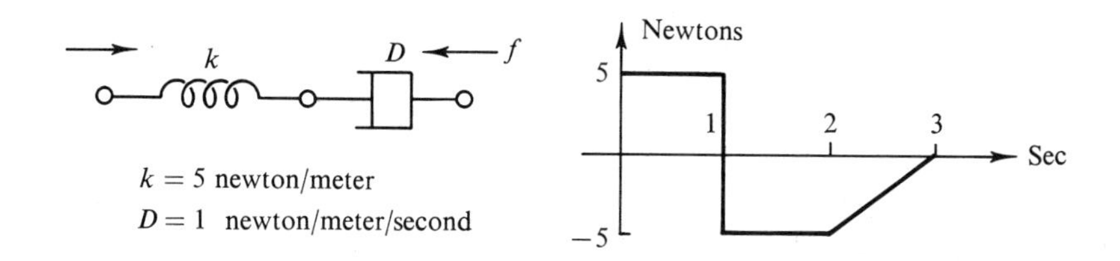

Fig. P 4.7.

A force as shown in Figure P 4.7 is applied to a series combination of a spring and a dashpot. Plot the displacement and velocity of the spring and dashpot as a function of time.

4.8. An inductor usually has a certain amount of inherent resistance such that its terminal equation is

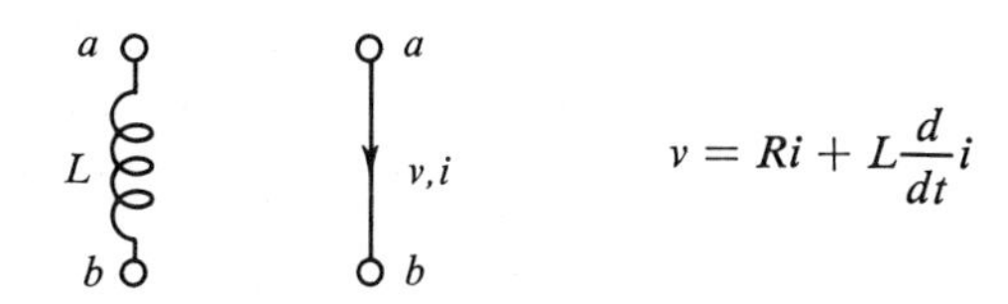

$$v = Ri + L\frac{d}{dt}i$$

Sketch the voltage waveform on an *x-y* plot when a triangular current wave is passed through the inductor as shown in Figure P 4.8. Explain

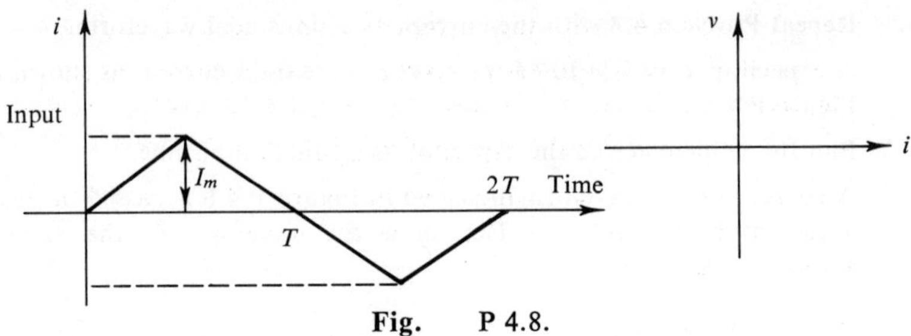

Fig. P 4.8.

how the above results may be utilized to measure L when R, I_m, and T are known.

4.9. Utilize the results of Problem 4.8 to determine the inertia and friction of a component of the terminal equation

$$\tau = J\frac{d}{dt}\dot{\varphi} + B\dot{\varphi}$$

when experimental results as shown in Figure P 4.9 are available.

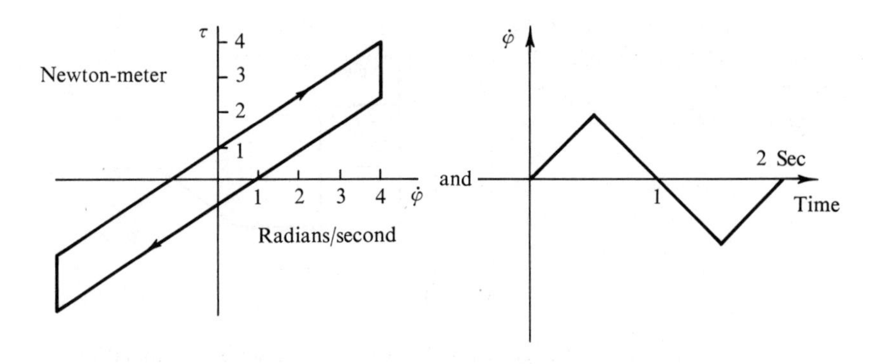

Fig. P 4.9.

4.10. Repeat Problem 4.9 when the τ-$\dot{\varphi}$ plot is as shown Figure P 4.10.

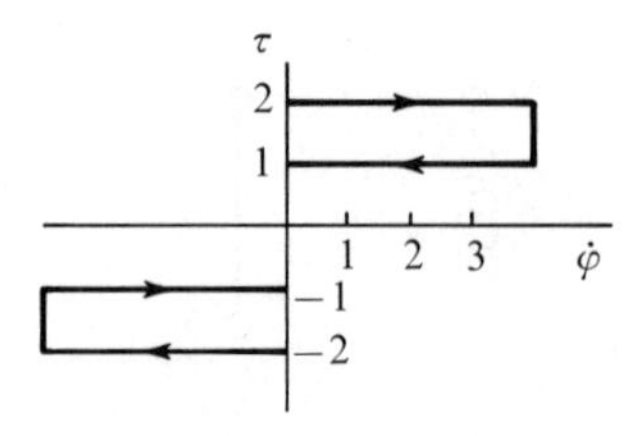

Fig. 4.10.

$\dot{\varphi}$ is still the same triangular waveform.

4.11. By means of a diagram, show how you might demonstrate through suitable instrumentation (force meter, displacement meter) that one spring is being compressed while the other is being elongated under the action of a force as shown in Figure P 4.11.

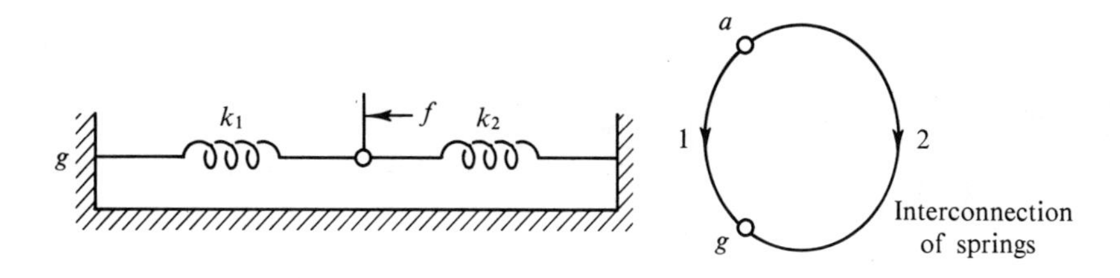

Fig. P 4.11.

4.12. For a two-terminal component having the terminal equation

$$x(t) = Ay(t) + B\frac{d}{dt}y(t)$$

the ellipse shown in Figure P 4.12 is obtained as an x-y plot when $y(t) = Y_m \sin 5t$. Calculate the numerical coefficients A and B.

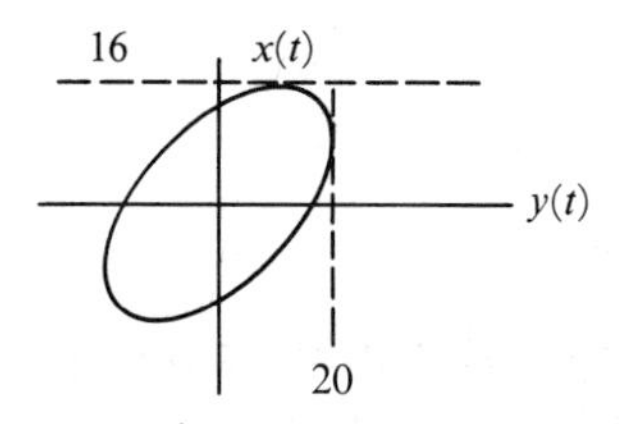

Fig. P 4.12.

4.13. Derive the expressions listed in Table 4.1.

Analysis of Simple Systems

5

5.1 The Solution of Simultaneous Differential Equations

A physical system consists of a collection of components interconnected in an orderly fashion. A mathematical model of the system depends on a mathematical description of the components and a description of how they are interconnected. In the following chapters several procedures for the solution of linear, time-invariant systems will be illustrated; in general, each procedure leads first to a set of simultaneous ordinary differential equations. A solution using classical methods requires first a reduction of the set of equations to one higher-order ordinary differential equation with one dependent variable. The solution of this equation by classical techniques is cumbersome, and complications result when initial conditions on the variables in the original set of differential equations are to be translated into initial conditions on the one variable and its first $(n - 1)$ derivatives in the resulting differential equation (n is the order of the differential equation).

Example 5.1 Consider the following two first-order equations in two dependent variables x_1 and x_2.

$$2\frac{dx_1}{dt} + 3x_1 + 3\frac{dx_2}{dt} + 4x_2 = 2t^2 + \sin t$$

$$3\frac{dx_1}{dt} + 2x_1 + 4\frac{dx_2}{dt} + x_2 = 0 \tag{5.1}$$

Solving the second equation for x_1 in terms of x_2, and letting $d/dt = p$, we have

$$3px_1 + 2x_1 = -4px_2 - x_2 \tag{5.2}$$

$$x_1 = \frac{-(4p + 1)}{3p + 2}x_2 \tag{5.3}$$

Substituting in the first equation,

$$\left[(2p + 3)\left(\frac{-(4p + 1)}{3p + 2}\right) + 3p + 4\right]x_2 = 0 \qquad t < 0$$

$$= 2t^2 + \sin t \qquad t \geq 0 \tag{5.4}$$

or multiplying by $3p + 2$ we obtain a second-order differential equation in x_2,

$$\frac{d^2x_2}{dt^2} + 4\frac{dx_2}{dt} + 5x_2 = 12t + 4t^2 + 3\cos t + 2\sin t \qquad t \geq 0 \tag{5.5}$$

The complete solution requires values for the initial conditions $x_2(0)$ and $dx_2(0)/dt$ where

$$\frac{dx_2(0)}{dt} = \frac{dx_2(t)}{dt}$$

evaluated at $t = 0$. From the original two first-order equations, the initial values of x_1 and x_2 are normally known, but it is necessary to relate the value of $[x_1(0)]$ to $dx_2(0)/dt$ when $t = 0$.

5.2 The Laplace Transform in the Solution of Simultaneous Differential Equations

A much more practical approach to the solution of simultaneous differential equations is provided through the Laplace transformation. The most immediate gain to be realized is the transformation of the differential equations to algebraic equations, shifting the solution process as a mathematical problem from the field of differential equations to the field of algebraic equations. The latter may be readily solved through application of matrix and determinant theory.

It is convenient to refer to the mathematical model of a component or a system as the t-domain model or the s-domain model, depending on whether it is expressed in terms of differential equations with t as independent variable, or in terms of algebraic equations with s as parameter.

The Laplace transform may be applied at two stages in the formulation process: at the component model level or at the system model level. For the first, one transforms the component models into the s-domain, while for the second the system model is first generated in the t-domain and then transformed. The overall result, of course, is the same. For the sake of convenience, the first method is preferred.

5.3 Component Models in the *s*-Domain

It was mentioned that it would be convenient in a formulation process to apply the Laplace transform to the terminal equations of the components making up a particular system. It is therefore appropriate to consider the s-domain models of the terminal equation of the two-terminal components previously discussed. We reproduce here the pertinent transformations as found in Appendix B.

$$\mathscr{L}\left\{\frac{d}{dt}f(t)\right\} = s\,F(s) - f(0)$$

$$\mathscr{L}\left\{\int_0^t f(\tau)\,d\tau\right\} = \frac{F(s)}{s}$$

$$\mathscr{L}\{A\} = \frac{A}{s}$$

Consider, for instance, the terminal equation of a capacitor. The two versions in the t-domain are

$$v = V_0 + \frac{1}{C}\int_0^t i(\tau)\,d\tau \tag{5.6}$$

and

$$i = C\frac{dv}{dt}, \qquad v(0) = V_0 \tag{5.7}$$

The s-domain models are found simply by taking the Laplace transform of Equations 5.6 and 5.7. If we represent variables in the s-domain by upper case letters we obtain, respectively,

$$V = V_0/s + I/sC \tag{5.8}$$

and

$$I = sCV - CV_0 \tag{5.9}$$

Notice that Equation 5.8 is identical to Equation 5.9. In the t-domain an obvious difference exists between the derivative form and the integral form in the way the initial conditions are introduced in the mathematical model, while no such differences exist in the s-domain. It is therefore necessary to consider only Equation 5.8 or Equation 5.9, not both. The student may easily verify that the same equivalent relationships may be established for all other storage components when their terminal equations are expressed in terms of the primary system variables. A complete list of the s-domain models of all two-terminal components is presented in Table 5.1.

TABLE 5.1. *s-domain models of two-terminal components*

Component	Model
Capacitor	$V = I/sC + V_0/s$
Inductor	$I = V/sL + I_0/s$
Resistor	$V = RI$
Mass	$F = Ms\dot{\Delta} - M\dot{\Delta}_0$
Flywheel	$T = Js\dot{\Phi} - J\dot{\Phi}_0$
Transl. dashpot	$F = B_t\dot{\Delta}$
Rot. dashpot	$T = B_r\dot{\Phi}$
Transl. spring	$F = F_0/s + \dfrac{k_t}{s}\dot{\Delta}$
Rot. spring	$T = T_0/s + \dfrac{k_r}{s}\dot{\Phi}$
Hydraulic capacitor	$P = P_0/s + \dot{G}/sC$
Restriction	$P = R\dot{G}$

In many engineering applications, the initial energy states of all components in a system may be considered to be zero. This condition is particularly applicable when a system is under the influence of external drivers, and only the response to these drivers is of interest in the study of a system. In such cases, the s-domain models of two-terminal components reduce to an extremely simple format. Note the following definitions:

1. *Impedance*. The impedance $Z(s)$ of a component is the ratio of the across variable to the through variable as obtained from its component equation, that is

$$Z(s) = \frac{X_p(s)}{Y_p(s)}$$

initial condition zero.

2. *Admittance*. The admittance $Y(s)$ of a component is the reciprocal of the impedance, that is

$$Y(s) = \frac{Y_p(s)}{X_p(s)}$$

initial condition zero.

The impedances and admittances of the two-terminal components may easily be obtained from Table 5-1 by deletion of all initial conditions. We list them in Table 5-2.

TABLE 5.2. *Impedances and admittances of two-terminal components*

Component	*Impedances*	*Admittances*
Capacitor	$1/Cs = D/s$	Cs
Inductor	Ls	$1/Ls = \Gamma/s$
Resistor	R	$1/R = G$
Mass	$1/Ms$ or $1/Ms^2$	Ms or Ms^2
Flywheel	$1/Js$ or $1/Js^2$	Js or Js^2
Transl. dashpot	$1/B_t$ or $1/B_t s$	B_t or $B_t s$
Rot. dashpot	$1/B_r$ or $1/B_r s$	B_r or $B_r s$
Transl.	s/k_r or $1/k_t$	k_t/s or k_t
Rot. spring	s/k_r or $1/k_r$	k_r/s or k_r
Hydraulic capacitor	$1/C_h s$	$C_h s$
Restriction	R_h	$1/R_h$

For mechanical components it is often convenient to relax the above definitions for impedance and admittance and distinguish instead between a displacement impedance as the ratio of displacement to force (or torque) and velocity impedance as the ratio of velocity and force (or torque). Correspondingly, the displacement admittance and velocity admittance are obtained through the reciprocals of the impedance. Both the displacement impedance (admittance) and the velocity impedance (admittance) are listed in Table 5.2; the velocity impedance is shown first, since is is defined in terms of the primary system variables.

5.4 Time Functions in the *s*-Domain

The Laplace Transform of the Elementary Time Functions

In Chapter 3, four elementary functions of time were defined. They were

(1) the sine function,

$$x_1(t) = 0 \qquad t < 0$$
$$x_1(t) = \sin(\omega t + \phi) \qquad t \geq 0 \tag{5.10}$$

(2) the unit step function,

$$
\begin{aligned}
x_2(t) = u(t) &= 0 \qquad t < 0 \\
u(t) &= 1 \qquad t > 0
\end{aligned}
\tag{5.11}
$$

(3) the unit ramp function,

$$
\begin{aligned}
x_3(t) &= 0 \qquad t < 0 \\
&= t \qquad t \geq 0
\end{aligned}
\tag{5.12}
$$

(4) the parabolic function,

$$
\begin{aligned}
x_4(t) &= 0 \qquad t < 0 \\
&= t^2 \qquad t \geq 0
\end{aligned}
\tag{5.13}
$$

In Table 5.3 the Laplace transforms of these elementary functions are shown. These are derived from Table B.1 in Appendix B.

TABLE 5.3.

$f(t)$	$F(s)$
1. $\sin(\omega t + \phi)$	$\dfrac{s \sin\phi + \omega \cos\phi}{s^2 + \omega^2}$
2. $u(t)$	$\dfrac{1}{s}$
3. t	$\dfrac{1}{s^2}$
4. t^2	$\dfrac{2}{s^3}$

The Laplace Transform of Periodic Time Functions

The Laplace transform of the square wave, the triangular wave, the sawtooth wave, and the pulse train are simply extensions of the unit step and unit ramp functions. Since the waveforms are repeating, it is necessary to use the time displacement theorem derived in Appendix B:

$$
\mathscr{L}[f(t-b)] = e^{-sb}F(s) \tag{5.14}
$$

The square wave of Figure 3.5 (a), for example, consists of a unit step at $t = 0$, a negative step of two units at $t = T/2$, and a positive two-unit step at $t = T$, etc. Since $F(s) = 1/s$ for a unit step, the Laplace transform is therefore

$$
\begin{aligned}
&\frac{1}{s} - \frac{2}{s}e^{-(T/2)s} + \frac{2}{s}e^{-Ts} + \frac{2}{s}e^{-(3/2)Ts} + \cdots \\
&= \frac{2}{s}[1 - e^{-(T/2)s} + e^{-Ts} - e^{-(3/2)Ts} + \cdots] - \frac{1}{s}
\end{aligned}
$$

$$= \frac{2}{s(1 + e^{-(T/2)s})} - \frac{1}{s}$$

since

$$1 - x + x^2 - x^3 + \cdots = \frac{1}{1 + x} \tag{5.15}$$

Using this procedure, the Laplace transforms of the four periodic functions are given in Table 5.4.

TABLE 5.4.

$f(t)$	$F(s)$
1. Square wave	$\frac{1}{s}\left[\frac{1 - e^{-(T/2)s}}{1 + e^{-(T/2)s}}\right]$
2. Triangular wave	$\frac{4}{Ts^2}\left[\frac{(1 - e^{-(T/4)s})^2}{1 + e^{-(T/2)s}}\right]$
3. Sawtooth	$\frac{1}{Ts^2} - \frac{1}{s}\left[\frac{e^{-Ts}}{1 - e^{-Ts}}\right]$
4. Pulse train	$\frac{1}{s}\left[\frac{1 - e^{-\Delta Ts}}{1 - e^{-Ts}}\right]$

The Laplace Transform of an Ordinary Differential Equation of nth Order

Let a system with an input $v(t)$ and output $y(t)$ be defined by the differential equation

$$a_n \frac{d^n y}{dt^n} + a_{n-1}\frac{d^{n-1}y}{dt^{n-1}} + \cdots + a_1 \frac{dy}{dt} + a_0 y$$
$$= b_m \frac{d^m v}{dt^m} + b_{m-1}\frac{d^{m-1}}{dt^{m-1}} + \cdots + b_1 \frac{dv}{dt} + b_0 v \tag{5.16}$$

Taking the Laplace transform of this equation we have

$$\begin{aligned}(a_n s^n + a_{n-1}s^{n-1} + \cdots + a_1 s + a_0)\, Y(s) \\ = (b_m s^m + b_{m-1}s^{m-1} + \cdots b_1 s + b_0)\, V(s) \\ + a_n[s^{n-1}y(0) + s^{n-2}\dot{y}(0) + \cdots + sy^{(n-2)}(0) + y^{(n-1)}(0)] \\ + a_{n-1}[s^{n-2}y(0) + s^{n-3}\dot{y}(0) + \cdots + sy^{(n-3)}(0) + y^{(n-2)}(0)] \\ + \cdots + a_1 y(0)\end{aligned} \tag{5.17}$$

where $y^{(m)}(0)$ is the mth derivative of $y(t)$ evaluated at $t = 0$. The right-hand side consists of two parts. The first part results from the input, and the second results from the initial conditions on y and its first $n - 1$ derivatives at $t = 0$.

Example 5.2 Find the solution for the second-order differential equation

$$\frac{d^2y}{dt^2} + 4\frac{dy}{dt} + 5y = 2t \tag{5.18}$$

for $t > 0$.

Taking Laplace transforms, we have

$$(s^2 + 4s + 5)Y(s) = \frac{2}{s^2} + sy(0) + \dot{y}(0) + 4y(0) \tag{5.19}$$

The solution for $Y(s)$ is

$$Y(s) = \frac{2}{s^2(s^2 + 4s + 5)} + \frac{(s + 4)y(0) + \dot{y}(0)}{s^2 + 4s + 5} \tag{5.20}$$

Expanding the first term by the partial fraction expansion technique,

$$\frac{2}{s^2(s^2 + 4s + 5)} = \frac{2}{s^2[(s + 2)^2 + 1]} = \frac{k_1}{s^2} + \frac{k_2}{s} + \frac{k_3(s + 2) + k_4}{(s + 2)^2 + 1)} \tag{5.21}$$

From Appendix B

$$k_1 = \left.\frac{2}{(s + 2)^2 + 1}\right|_{s=0} = \frac{2}{5}$$

$$k_2 = \frac{d}{ds}\left[\frac{2}{(s + 2)^2 + 1}\right]\Bigg|_{s=0} = \left.\frac{-4(s + 2)}{[(s + 2)^2 + 1]^2}\right|_{s=0} = \frac{-8}{25}$$

To obtain k_3 and k_4 it is easier to multiply Equation 5.21 by $[(s + 2)^2 + 1]$ to obtain

$$\frac{2}{s^2} = \left(\frac{2}{5s^2} - \frac{8}{25s}\right)[(s + 2)^2 + 1] + k_3(s + 2) + k_4 \tag{5.22}$$

Letting $s = -2$,

$$\frac{1}{2} = \left(\frac{1}{10} + \frac{8}{50}\right) + k_4$$

then

$$k_4 = +\frac{6}{25}$$

Letting $s = 1$ or any other value,

$$2 = \left(\frac{2}{5} - \frac{8}{25}\right)(10) + 3k_3 - \frac{6}{25}$$

then

$$k_3 = \frac{8}{25}$$

Then

$$Y(s) = \frac{2/5}{s^2} - \frac{8/25}{s} + \frac{(8/25)s + 22/25}{s^2 + 4s + 5} + \frac{(s + 4)y(0) + \dot{y}(0)}{s^2 + 4s + 5}$$

$$= \frac{2/5}{s^2} - \frac{8/25}{s} + \frac{22}{125}\,\frac{5[1 + (4/11)s]}{s^2 + 4s + 5} + \frac{(s + 4)y(0) + \dot{y}(0)}{s^2 + 4s + 5} \tag{5.23}$$

Using Equations (1), (2), and (12) in Table B. 2 (Appendix B) and letting $y(0) = \dot{y}(0) = 0$,

$$y(t) = \frac{2}{5}t - \frac{8}{25} + \frac{22}{125}\omega_n\sqrt{\frac{1 - 2a\zeta\omega_n + a^2\omega_n^2}{1 - \zeta^2}}e^{-\zeta\omega_n t} \sin \omega_n\sqrt{1 - \zeta^2}(t + \phi) \tag{5.24}$$

where

$$\phi = \tan^{-1}\frac{a\omega_n\sqrt{1 - \zeta^2}}{1 - a\zeta\omega_n}$$

and where we can make the identifications

$$\omega_n^2 = 5$$
$$2\zeta\omega_n = 4$$
$$a = \frac{4}{11}$$

then

$$\omega_n = \sqrt{5}$$
$$\zeta = \frac{5}{\sqrt{5}}$$
$$\sqrt{1 - \zeta^2} = \frac{1}{\sqrt{5}}$$
$$a\zeta\omega_n = \frac{8}{11}$$
$$a^2\omega^2 = \frac{80}{121}$$
$$\phi = \tan^{-1}\frac{4/11}{1 - 8/11} = \tan^{-1}\frac{4}{3}$$

Finally,

$$y(t) = \frac{2}{5}t - \frac{8}{25} + \frac{2}{5}e^{-2t}\left(\sin t + \tan^{-1}\frac{4}{3}\right) \tag{5.25}$$

If $y(0)$ and $\dot{y}(0)$ are not zero, we have added terms. For example, let $\dot{y}(0) = 2$, $y(0) = 0$, and $y_1(t)$ be the response to the initial value of $\dot{y}(t)$.

$$Y_1(s) = \frac{2}{s^2 + 4s + 5} = \frac{2}{5}\frac{5}{s^2 + 4s + 5} \tag{5.26}$$

Using equation (8) in Table B. 2,

$$y_1(t) = 2e^{-2t}\sin t \tag{5.27}$$

This example shows one procedure for finding the solution of a differential equation using Laplace transform techniques.

5.5 Formulation and Solution of Systems

Following is a discussion of techniques to determine the time-varying behavior of systems of two-terminal components. We have previously established mathematical models in both the t-domain and s-domain for a variety of two-terminal components. In order to obtain an insight into the behavior of systems made up of these components we need further information regarding the interconnection of these components, for the behavior of a system will depend not only on the individual components, but also on the component interaction. A mathematical model describing the interconnection is provided by a *system graph*.

The System Graph

As an introduction to the system graph, consider the electrical circuit of Figure 5.1. It consists of four two-terminal components.

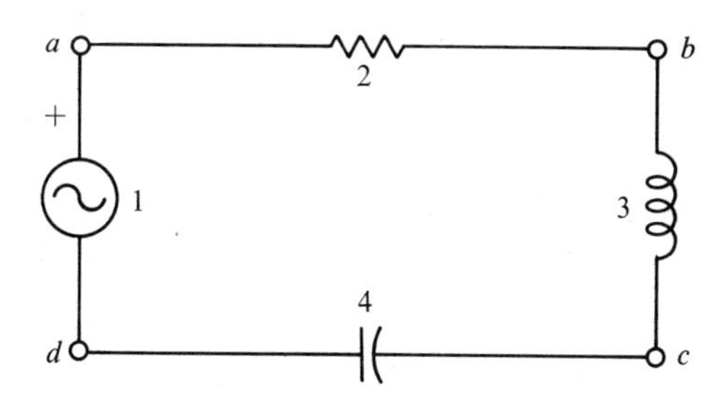

Fig. 5.1. *Physical schematic of electrical circuit.*

These components are represented schematically along with their terminal characteristics in Figure 5.2.

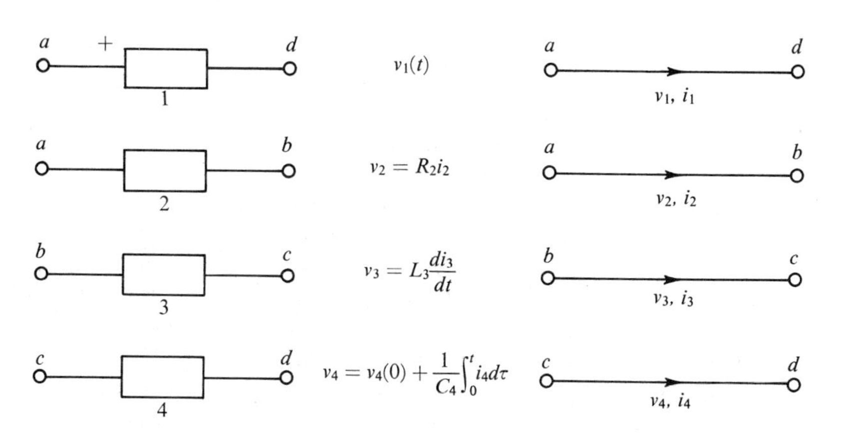

Fig. 5.2. *Circuit components.*

Let us connect the schematic representations in the same manner as their corresponding components are interconnected.

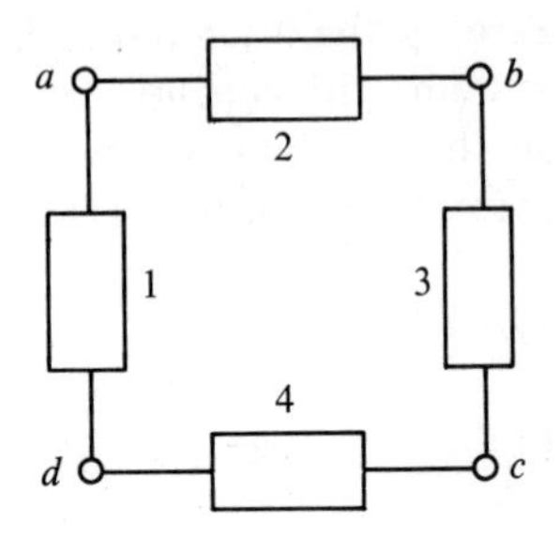

Fig. 5.3. *Schematic interconnection diagram.*

Let us also take the terminal graphs of the four system components and interconnect them in a one-to-one correspondence with the physical component interconnection. The result is a collection of oriented line segments called the *system graph* of the electrical circuit, shown in Figure 5.4.

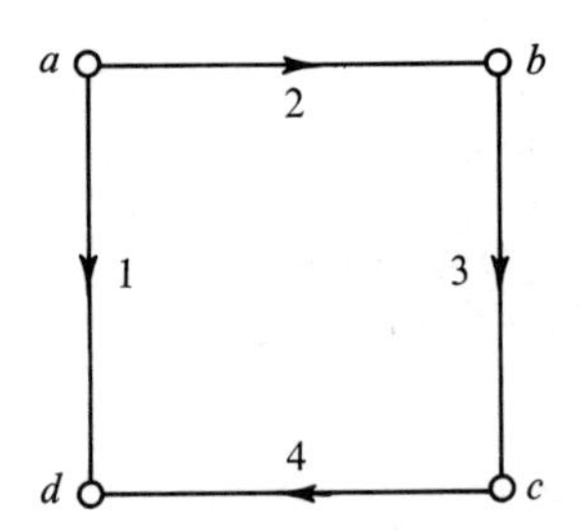

Fig. 5.4. *System graph of electrical circuit.*

Note that the components are clearly identified in the system graph by their appropriate numbers as originally defined in the physical schematic. It is obvious that the system graph could have been established directly from the circuit, since the system graph and the physical system appear, in our diagrammatical representations, topologically similar. To emphasize, consider the circuit and its system graph of Figure 5.5.

The ease with which system graphs are constructed is not always the same. Consider, for instance, the mechanical system shown in Figure 5.6. As before, we establish schematic representations, shown in Figure 5.7.

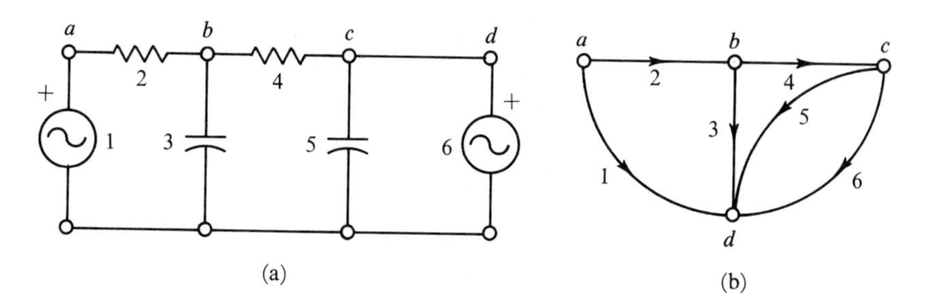

Fig. 5.5. *Electrical circuit:* (a) *physical schematic;* (b) *system graph.*

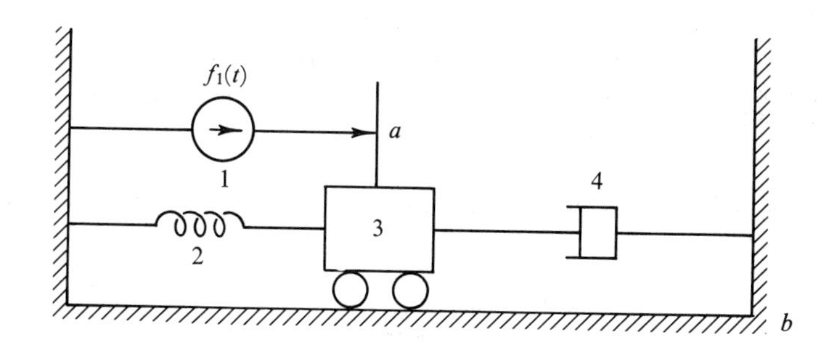

Fig. 5.6. *Physical schematic of mechanical system.*

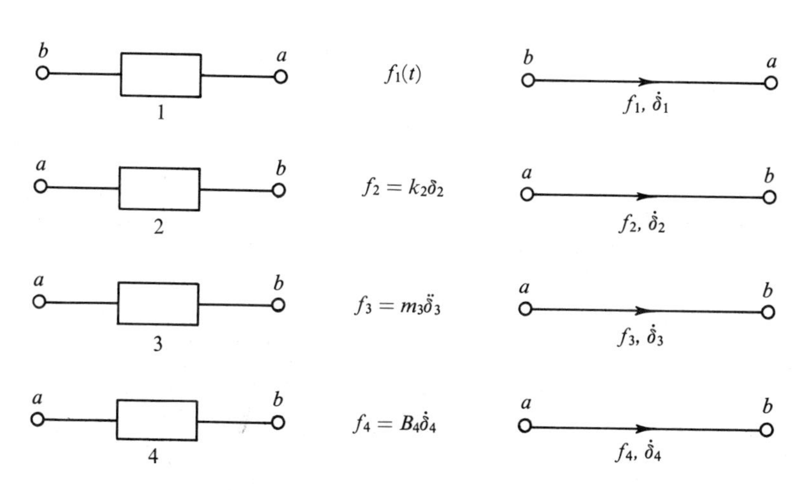

Fig. 5.7. *Circuit components.*

However the resulting system graph, shown in Figure 5.8, has quite a different topological appearance.

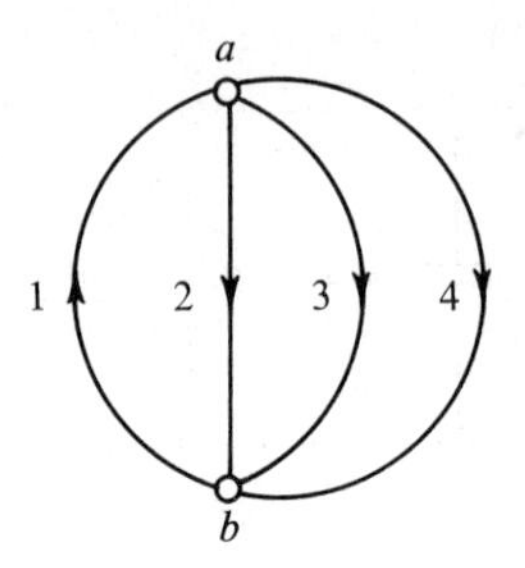

Fig. 5.8. *System graph of mechanical system.*

The system graph of the mechanical system can of course be obtained directly by observing the requirement that the interconnections of the terminal graphs be in a one-to-one correspondence with the interconnection of the components they represent.

Example 5.3 Construct the system graph for the torsional system of Figure 5.9.

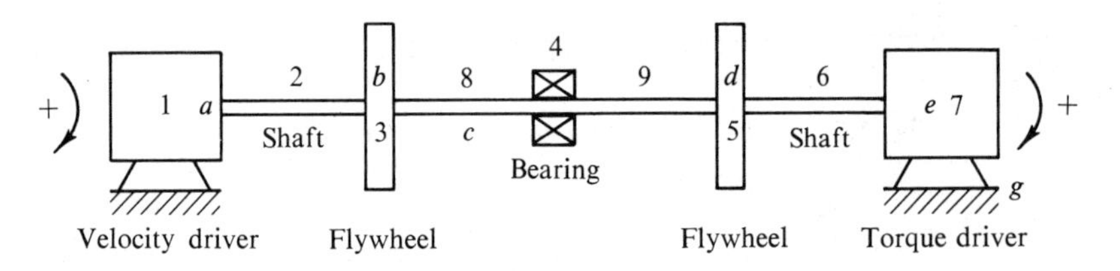

Fig. 5.9. *Rotational system.*

An investigation of the physical dimensions of the system leads to the conclusion that the following system properties should be included in the analysis of the performance of the system:

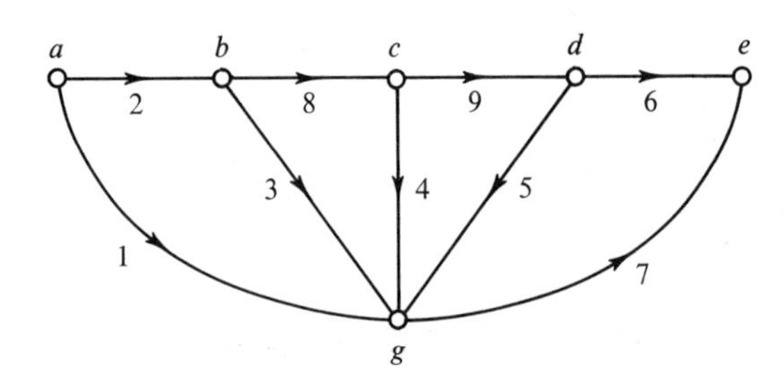

Fig. 5.10. *System graph of rotational system.*

(a) Spring constants of shafts 2, 6, 8, and 9
(b) Inertias 3 and 5
(c) Frictional effects of bearing 4
(d) Two drivers, 1 and 7

Consequently, the system graph is constructed as shown in Figure 5.10.

As will be shown shortly, the system graph will serve as the basis for obtaining the mathematical information of the interconnection pattern of the components. Before this is discussed, a number of definitions are in order:

1. An *element* is any one of the oriented line segments in a system graph. They are numbered 1, 2, 3, $\cdots$.

2. A *vertex* is a point at which at least two elements are incident. (It is also called a node.) Vertices are designated a, b, c, $\cdots$.

3. A *circuit* is a closed path. (It is also called a loop.)

The Vertex and Circuit Laws

Consider the electrical circuit of Figure 5.1 again. For each of the four components, terminal representations have been established. The component characteristics were established by making appropriate across and through measurements on the individual components, all being disconnected. When these components are interconnected as specified, and the same measurements under "live" operating conditions are made, we will find that exactly the same relations exist between a pair of across and through variables: *the component characteristics are preserved.* In fact, we will observe the following experimental results:

(1) The four instantaneous voltages will add to zero.
(2) The four currents are identical.

If we carried out similar experiments for the other system, similar results would be obtained, which are summarized in the following two important statements:

Vertex law: $\sum$ through measurements vanish at vertices.

Circuit law: $\sum$ across measurements vanish around circuits.

These measurements are the observable representations of their associated physical variables, which are conceived to exist in the system. The experimental results on the variables are stated in the form:

Vertex equations:

$$\sum^{e} y_i = 0 \quad \text{at vertices; } i = 1, \cdots, e \tag{5.28}$$

Circuit equations:

$$\sum_{i}^{e} x_i = 0 \text{ around circuits; } i = 1, \cdots, e \tag{5.29}$$

where x, y are the across and through variables of the individual components and e is the number of elements contained in a system graph. The summations do not necessarily involve all elements, since not all elements are in a given circuit or incident at a given vertex.

The information contained in Equations 5.28 and 5.29 is readily available from the system graph, since the system graph was constructed with terminal graphs of the individual components, signifying the orientation and definition of the component variables. Each one of the oriented line segments defines, exactly, one across variable and one through variable, together with their orientations.

The following rules are needed to write the vertex equations and the circuit equations conveniently.

1. Through variables will be summed positively when their orientation is away from a vertex, and negatively when their orientation is toward a vertex.

2. Across variables will be summed positively when their orientation is clockwise in a given circuit and negatively when their orientation is counterclockwise.

Example 5.4 Obtain the vertex and circuit equation for the system of Figure 5.1. We recognize *one* circuit, hence

$$-v_1 + v_2 + v_3 + v_4 = 0$$

There are four vertices, yielding

at a

$$i_1 + i_2 = 0$$

at b

$$-i_2 + i_3 = 0$$

at c

$$-i_3 + i_4 = 0$$

at d

$$-i_4 - i_1 = 0 \tag{5.30}$$

Example 5.5 Obtain the vertex and circuit equations for the system of Example 5.3. We count exactly six vertices, so we can make six statements in the form specified by Equation 5.28.

at a

$$\tau_1 + \tau_2 = 0$$

at b

$$-\tau_2 + \tau_3 + \tau_8 = 0$$

at c

$$-\tau_8 + \tau_4 + \tau_9 = 0$$

at d

$$-\tau_9 + \tau_5 + \tau_6 = 0$$

at e

$$-\tau_6 - \tau_7 = 0$$

at g

$$-\tau_1 - \tau_3 - \tau_4 - \tau_5 + \tau_7 = 0 \tag{5.31}$$

The total number of circuits that can be constructed from the system graph is not easily determined. To appreciate this fact, one should try to write down all possible element combinations that form a circuit. Here are just a few for which circuit equations are written according to Equation 5.29.

1. elements 1, 2, 3 $\quad -\dot{\varphi}_1 + \dot{\varphi}_2 + \dot{\varphi}_3 = 0$
2. elements 3, 8, 4 $\quad -\dot{\varphi}_3 + \dot{\varphi}_8 + \dot{\varphi}_4 = 0$
3. elements 4, 9, 5 $\quad -\dot{\varphi}_4 + \dot{\varphi}_9 + \dot{\varphi}_5 = 0$
4. elements 5, 6, 7 $\quad -\dot{\varphi}_5 + \dot{\varphi}_6 - \dot{\varphi}_7 = 0 \qquad$ (**5.32**)

There are many more.

The vertex and circuit equations are mathematical statements of the interconnection pattern of the components. To be of use, they must contain all, but no more than, the necessary information. As can be shown, this requirement is satisfied by *exactly* any $v - 1$ vertex equations and $e - v + 1$ circuit equations where v — number of vertices in a graph and e — number of elements in a graph.

For instance, we need a total of five vertex and four circuit equations to completely specify the interdependence of *all* the system variables of Example 5.5.

Systems of One Dissipative and One Storage Component

Consider the electrical system of Figure 5.11 (a). It consists of a resistor and a capacitor connected in parallel. The capacitor is charged to a voltage V_0 at the time the switch is closed. Let it be our objective to study the voltage across the capacitor as a function of time.

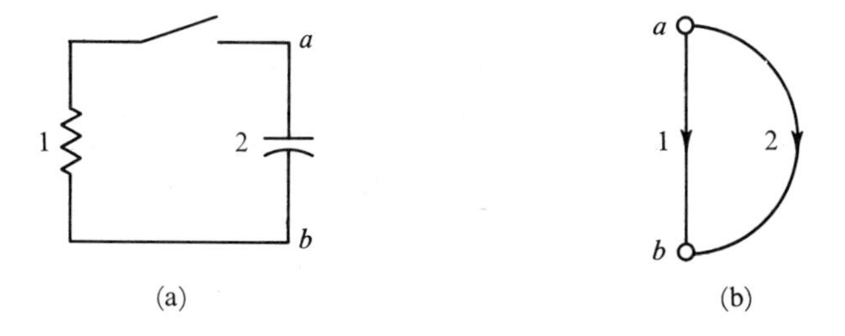

Fig. 5.11. *RC circuit:* (a) *schematic;* (b) *system graph.*

The terminal representations of the components are given as

Resistor:

$$v_1 = Ri_1 \tag{5.35}$$

Capacitor:

$$v_2 = V_0 + \frac{1}{C}\int_0^t i_2 d\tau \tag{5.36a}$$

or

$$V_2(s) = \frac{V_0}{s} + \frac{I_2(s)}{sC}$$

$$i_2 = C\frac{dv_2}{dt}, \quad v_2(0) = V_0 \tag{5.36b}$$

or

$$I_2(s) = CsV_2(s) - CV_0$$

Note that the terminal equation for the capacitor is available in two forms. From the system graph, we write one vertex and one circuit equation:

$$i_1 + i_2 = 0 \tag{5.37a}$$

$$-v_1 + v_2 = 0 \tag{5.37b}$$

Let us substitute Equations 5.35 and 5.36b into 5.37a using Laplace formulation. This yields

$$\frac{V_1}{R} + CsV_2 - CV_0 = 0$$

where $V_1 = V_1(s)$, $V_2 = V_2(s)$, but V_0 is a constant. Upon use of Equation 5.37b, the last equation now reads

$$V_2\left(\frac{1}{R} + Cs\right) = CV_0 \tag{5.38}$$

Equation 5.38 represents the Laplace transform of a first-order homogeneous linear differential equation. Its solution is the desired voltage, v_2, subject to the initial condition $v_2(0) = V_0$.

If we substitute Equations 5.35 and 5.36a into 5.37b it results in

$$-RI_1(s) + \frac{V_0}{s} + \frac{1}{Cs}I_2 = 0$$

$$I_1\left(R + \frac{1}{sC}\right) = \frac{V_0}{s} \tag{5.39}$$

The solution of Equation 5.39 will give the current through the resistor as a function of time. This current, of course, is the same throughout the entire circuit. Equation 5.39 may be solved by first solving for I_1 followed by finding the inverse Laplace transform.

$$I_1 = \frac{V_0}{R}\frac{1}{s + 1/RC} \tag{5.40}$$

The solution of Equations 5.38 and 5.40 using Table B.2, Equation (3) where $a = 1/RC$ is

$$v_2 = V_0 e^{-t/RC} \tag{5.41}$$

and

$$i_1 = \frac{V_0}{R}e^{-t/RC} \tag{5.42}$$

By use of Equations 5.37b and 5.35, we may show that Equation 5.41 is consistent with Equation 5.42.

When both solutions are plotted as functions of time, the familiar exponential decay curve is revealed, as shown in Figure 5.12.

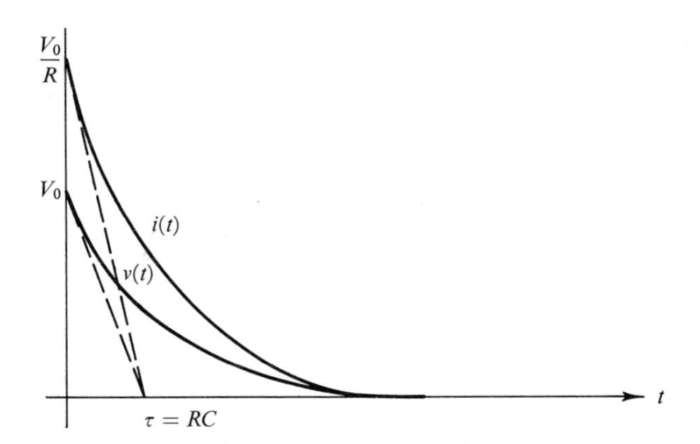

Fig. 5.12. *Resistor voltage and current.*

It is significant to note that the solutions are proportional to one another: the natures of the solutions are identical; they differ only in their initial values.

As another example, consider a fluid storage tank. It is initially filled up to a certain level and then allowed to drain through a pipe, as shown in Figure 5.13.

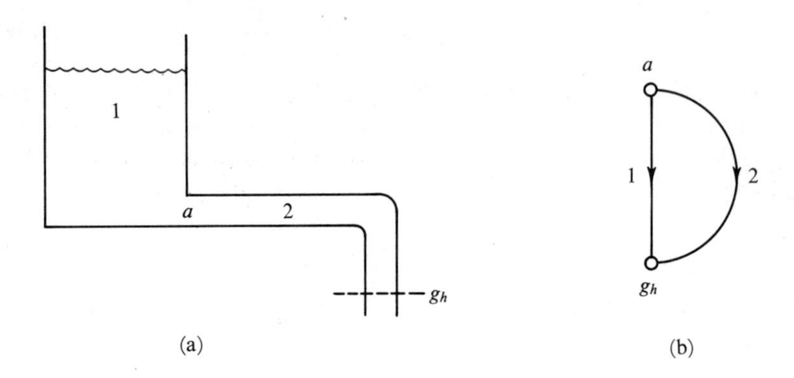

Fig. 5.13. *Storage tank with drainage:* (a) *schematic;* (b) *system graph.*

We will view this system as consisting of two components whose terminal representations are given as

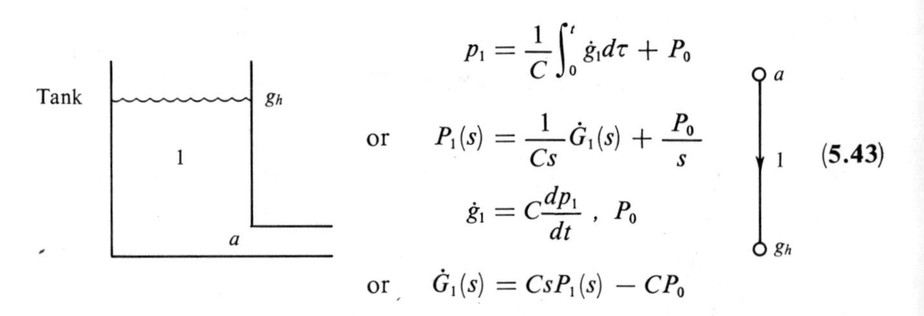

$$p_1 = \frac{1}{C}\int_0^t \dot{g}_1 d\tau + P_0$$

$$\text{or} \quad P_1(s) = \frac{1}{Cs}\dot{G}_1(s) + \frac{P_0}{s} \tag{5.43}$$

$$\dot{g}_1 = C\frac{dp_1}{dt}\,, \quad P_0$$

$$\text{or} \quad \dot{G}_1(s) = CsP_1(s) - CP_0$$

Pipe

a g_h

2

$$p_2 = R\dot{g}_2 \tag{5.44}$$

a

2

g_h

The system graph provides the information regarding the interconnection of the components

$$-p_1 + p_2 = 0 \tag{5.45}$$

$$\dot{g}_1 + \dot{g}_2 = 0 \tag{5.46}$$

As in the electrical system above, two equations may be constructed as a mathematical model of the system behavior, depending on whether one starts with Equation 5.45 or with Equation 5.46. Using Equation 5.45, it is found that where $\dot{G}_1 = \dot{G}_1(s)$, etc., $P_0 =$ constant,

$$-\frac{1}{Cs}\dot{G}_1 - \frac{P_0}{s} + R\dot{G}_2 = 0$$

but

$$\dot{g}_1 = -\dot{g}_2$$

$$\left(\frac{1}{Cs} + R\right)\dot{G}_2 = \frac{P_0}{s} \tag{5.47}$$

On the other hand, starting with Equation 5.46, the following sequence develops:

$$CsP_1 + \frac{P_2}{R} - CP_0 = 0$$

but

$$p_1 = p_2$$

so that

$$P_1\left(\frac{1}{R} + Cs\right) = CP_0 \tag{5.48}$$

The two equations obtained are of the same type as Equations 5.41 and 5.42. Again, an exponential solution is obtained. This behavior is characteristic of all systems composed of exactly one storage component with an initial condition and one dissipative component. Thus, if we had systems composed of a dashpot and a spring, a dashpot and a mass, or a resistor and an inductor, we would find the same characteristic exponential response.

In reviewing the steps that were taken in reaching an equation describing a particular system, an orderly pattern is observed. This is illustrated in the flow diagram of Figure 5.14. Two patterns of possible development are evident, one leading to an equation explicit in a through variable, the other leading to an equation explicit in an across variable. It is important to realize the existence of an orderly process in the formulation of a mathematical model of a system at this early stage of development. The formulation pattern as revealed by Figure 5.14 is basic to the entire procedure of system analysis and will be preserved essentially during more advanced system studies. On occasion, it may have to be modified to accommodate special circumstances.

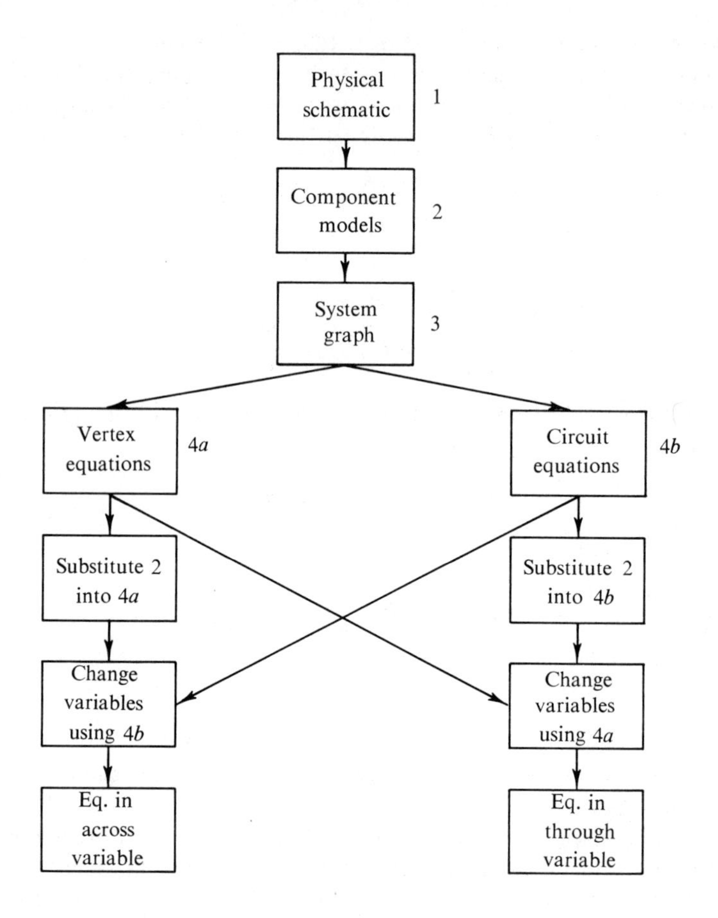

Fig. 5.14. *Flow diagram of formulation process.*

Systems of Two Storage Components

When two components capable of storing energy in two different modes are connected together, the resulting system will exhibit a free oscillatory response. Consider, for instance, the mechanical system shown in Figure 5.15.

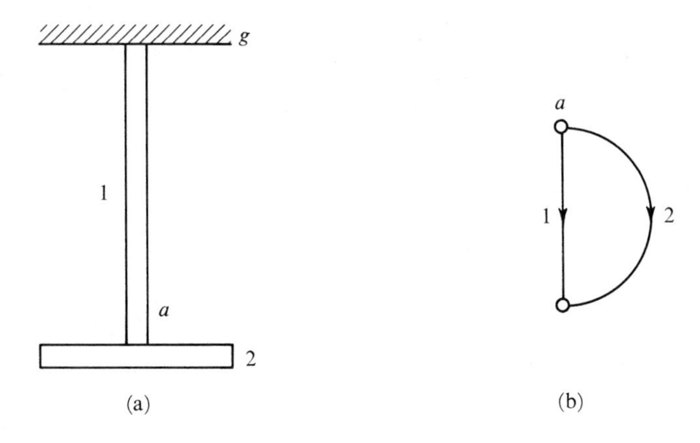

Fig. 5.15. *Oscillatory mechanical system:* (a) *schematic;* (b) *system graph.*

It consists of a flywheel suspended by a torsion bar. The component models are:

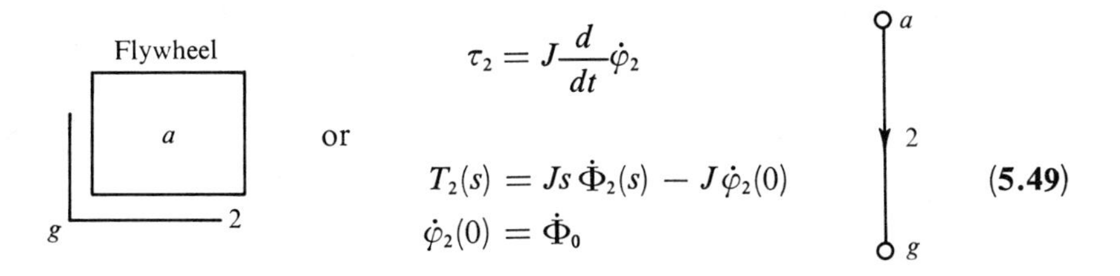

$$\tau_2 = J\frac{d}{dt}\dot{\varphi}_2$$

$$T_2(s) = Js\,\dot{\Phi}_2(s) - J\dot{\varphi}_2(0)$$
$$\dot{\varphi}_2(0) = \dot{\Phi}_0 \qquad \textbf{(5.49)}$$

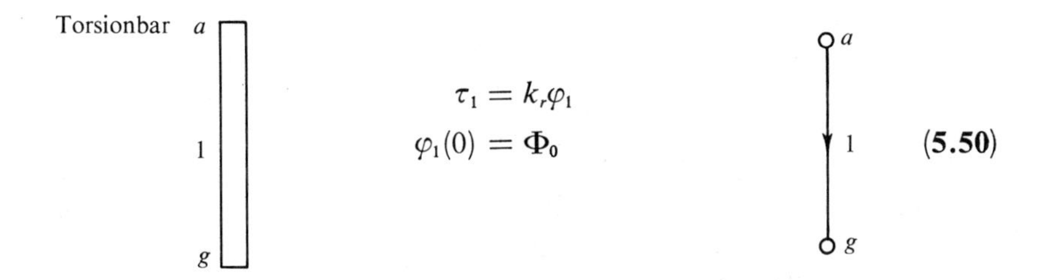

$$\tau_1 = k_r\varphi_1$$
$$\varphi_1(0) = \Phi_0 \qquad \textbf{(5.50)}$$

The initial energy states of the two storage components are most easily expressed in terms of across variables. Therefore, it is desirable to derive a mathematical model for the system in terms of a differential equation involving an across variable so that the specified initial conditions may be applied. Hence, according to the flow diagram of Figure 5.14, we will start with the vertex equation

$$\tau_1 + \tau_2 = 0$$

from which

$$k_r\varphi_1 + J\ddot{\varphi}_2 = 0$$

or

$$k_r\,\Phi_1(s) + Js^2\,\Phi_2(s) - Js\,\varphi_2(0) - J\,\dot{\varphi}_2(0) = 0$$

so that

$$k_r\,\Phi_1(s) + Js^2\,\Phi_1(s) = J[s\,\varphi_1(0) + \dot{\varphi}_1(0)] \qquad \textbf{(5.51)}$$

with initial conditions

$$\varphi_1(0) = \Phi_0\,, \qquad \dot{\varphi}_1(0) = \dot{\Phi}_0$$

Equation 5.51 represents an equation corresponding to a second-order differential equation. Solving by the use of Laplace transforms,

$$\Phi_1(s) = \frac{J(s\Phi_0 + \dot{\Phi}_0)}{k_r + Js^2} = \frac{s\Phi_0}{s^2 + k_r/J} + \sqrt{\frac{J}{k_r}}\frac{\sqrt{(k_r/J)}\dot{\Phi}_0}{s^2 + k_r/J} \qquad \textbf{(5.52)}$$

Using Equations (8) and (9) of Table B.2 where $\zeta = 0$, $\omega_n^2 = k_r/J$

$$\varphi_1(t) = \Phi_0 \cos \omega_n t + \frac{\dot{\Phi}_0}{\omega_n} \sin \omega_n t \qquad \textbf{(5.53)}$$

or using Equation (13)

$$\varphi_1(t) = \Phi_1 \sin(\omega_n t + \phi)$$

$$\Phi_1 = \sqrt{\Phi_0^2 + \left(\frac{\dot{\Phi}_0}{\omega_n}\right)^2}$$

$$\phi = \tan^{-1}\frac{\Phi_0\omega_n}{\dot{\Phi}_0} \qquad \textbf{(5.54)}$$

Equation 5.54 represents a convenient form with which to study the behavior of the system. This equation is identified as a periodic function whose amplitude is constant and dependent on the specified initial conditions. The frequency, $f = \omega_n/2\pi$, is determined by the parameters of the components involved.

Since the equations resulting in the formulation of a mathematical model involve either an across variable or a through variable, it is necessary to specify initial conditions in terms of the resulting variable. This requirement may not always be easily satisfied. Consider, for instance, the electrical system involving a capacitor and an inductor.

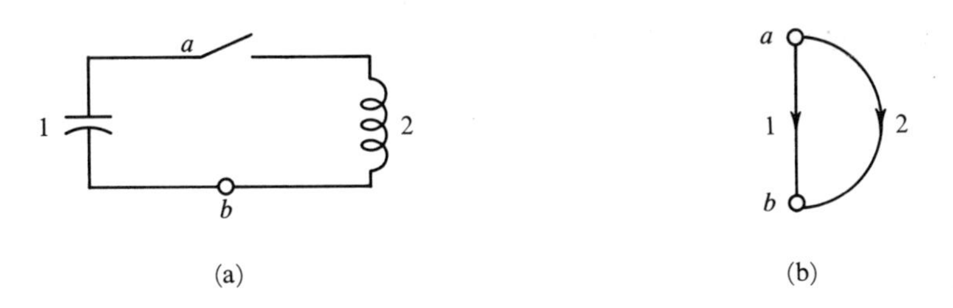

Fig. 5.16. *L-C circuit:* (a) *schematic;* (b) *system graph.*

The components are

Capacitor (a, 1, b) or (a, 1, b)

$$v_1 = V_0 + \frac{1}{C}\int_0^t i_1 d\tau \tag{5.55}$$

or

$$V_1(s) = \frac{V_0}{s} + \frac{I_1(s)}{Cs}$$

Inductor (a, 2, b) or (a, 2, b)

$$v_2 = L\frac{di_2}{dt} = L\frac{d^2q_2}{dt^2} \tag{5.56}$$

or

$$V_2(s) = Ls^2Q_2(s) - Lsq_2(0) - L\dot{q}_2(0)$$

$$i_2(0) = I_0 = \dot{q}_2(0)$$

The initial energy states of the components are most conveniently defined in terms of a voltage on the capacitor and a current in the inductor. Although the formulation of a mathematical model for the circuit may be straightforward, the solution of the resulting equation is complicated by the fact that the initial conditions are specified as one across variable and one through variable. This difficulty is overcome by recalling that the terminal equations of a capacitor may also be given in terms of charge and voltage,

$$v_1 = \frac{1}{C}q_1 \tag{5.57}$$

so that the initial energy state of the capacitor may be expressed by a through variable using Equation 5.57. We have

$$q_1(0) = CV_0$$

By starting with

$$-v_1 + v_2 = 0$$

we obtain

$$-\frac{1}{C}Q_1 + Ls^2Q_2 - Lsq_2(0) - L\dot{q}_2(0) = 0$$

or

$$\left(s^2 + \frac{1}{LC}\right)Q_2 = sq_2(0) + \dot{q}_2(0) \tag{5.58}$$

with initial conditions

$$q_2(0) = -CV_0$$
$$\dot{q}_2(0) = I_0$$

The solution to Equation 5.58 is

$$q_2(t) = Q \sin(\omega t + \phi) \tag{5.59}$$

where

$$Q = \sqrt{(I_0/\omega)^2 + (CV_0)^2}$$
$$\phi = \tan^{-1}\frac{I_0}{-\omega C V_0}$$

and

$$\omega = \frac{1}{\sqrt{LC}}$$

Again, the system is established as oscillatory, the frequency being determined entirely by the characteristics of the components. The voltage across the capacitor is given by

$$v_1 = v_2 = \frac{1}{C}q_2$$

and the current for the inductor by

$$i_2 = \frac{dq_2}{dt}$$

Systems of Two Storage and One Dissipative Component

Consider the *R-L-C* circuit shown in Figure 5.17. As in all other cases discussed so far, this is a system consisting of passive components with no external drivers. The excitation of this system is entirely due to the initial energy states of the components.

From the previous example, we have learned that initial conditions for capacitors and inductors are most conveniently expressed in terms of through variables (if one is restricted to a formulation in either a through variable or an across variable, a restriction evident from the formulation flow diagram in Figure 5.14).*

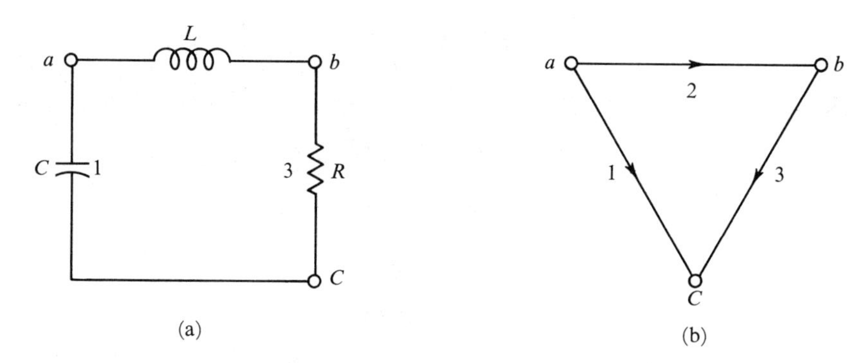

Fig. 5.17. *R-L-C circuit:* (a) *schematic;* (b) *system graph.*

The circuit the equation is

$$-v_1 + v_2 + v_3 = 0$$

Using the component equations in the s-domain,

$$-\frac{1}{Cs}I_1 - \frac{V_0}{s} + LsI_2 - Li_2(0) + RI_3 = 0$$

Since

$$I_2 = -I_1$$
$$I_3 = -I_1$$

we substitute and obtain

$$\frac{1}{Cs}I_1 + LsI_1 + RI_1 = Li_1(0) - \frac{V_0}{s} \tag{5.60}$$

with $i_1(0) = I_0$. Solving for $I_1 = I_1(s)$,

$$I_1 = \frac{sI_0 - V_0/L}{s_2 + (R/L)s + 1/LC} = \frac{I_0(s + \zeta\omega_n) - (V_0/L\omega_n + \zeta I_0)\omega_n}{s^2 + (R/L)s + 1/LC} \tag{5.61}$$

Using Equations (8) and (9) from Table B.2,

$$i_1 = I_0 e^{-\zeta\omega_n t} \cos \omega_n\sqrt{1 - \zeta^2}\, t - \frac{(V_0/L\omega_n) + \zeta I_0}{\sqrt{1 - \zeta^2}} e^{-\zeta\omega_n t} \sin \omega_n\sqrt{1 - \zeta^2}\, t \tag{5.62}$$

---

* In Chapter 6 a different method of formulating equations avoiding this restriction will be introduced.

where

$$\omega_n = \frac{1}{\sqrt{LC}}$$
$$\zeta\omega_n = \frac{R}{2L}$$
$$\zeta = \frac{R}{2}\sqrt{\frac{C}{L}}$$

Since

$$A\cos x - B\sin x = \sqrt{A^2 + B^2}\cos(x + \phi)$$

where

$$\phi = \tan^{-1}\frac{B}{A}$$

we may combine the cosine and sine terms into

$$i_1 = I_m e^{-\zeta\omega_n t}\cos(\omega_n\sqrt{1-\zeta^2}\,t + \phi) \tag{5.63}$$

where

$$I_m = \sqrt{\frac{I_0^2 + 2\zeta(V_0 I_0/L\omega_n) + (V_0/L\omega_n)^2}{1-\zeta^2}}$$

and

$$\phi = \tan^{-1}\frac{\zeta I_0 + V_0/L\omega_n}{I_0\sqrt{1-\zeta^2}}$$

The nature of the solution depends on the damping factor ζ. It is assumed for this circuit that the three component parameters are selected such that $0 < \zeta < 1$. For positive values of R, L, and C, $\zeta > 0$; however, for values of R, L, and C such that $\zeta = R/2\sqrt{C/L} > 1$, the solution takes a different form. The denominator of the expression for I_1 in Equation 5.61 may then be factored into two parts, $(s + a)(s + b)$. Using the quadratic formula to find the roots a and b, we have

$$s = -\zeta\omega_n + \sqrt{\zeta^2\omega_n^2 - \omega_n^2}$$

therefore

$$-a = \omega_n(-\zeta + \sqrt{\zeta^2 - 1})$$
$$-b = \omega_n(-\zeta - \sqrt{\zeta^2 - 1})$$

Then

$$I_1 = \frac{sI_0 - V_0/L}{(s+a)(s+b)} \tag{5.64}$$

Using Equation (6) in Table B.2,

$$i_1 = \frac{(I_0 b - V_0/L)e^{-bt} + (-I_0 a + V_0/L)e^{-at}}{b - a} \tag{5.65}$$

where

$$b = \omega_n(\zeta + \sqrt{\zeta^2 - 1}$$
$$a = \omega_n(\zeta - \sqrt{\zeta^2 - 1}$$
$$b - a = 2\omega_n\sqrt{\zeta^2 - 1}$$

If $a = b$, the solution is again of a different nature. If $\zeta = 1$,

$$I_1 = \frac{sI_0 - V_0/L}{(s + a)^2} \tag{5.66}$$

where $a = \zeta\omega_n$. Expanding, using partial fraction expansions,

$$I_1 = \frac{I_0}{s + a} - \frac{V_0/L + I_0 a}{(s + a)^2}$$

Then, using Equations (3) and (7) of Table B.1,

$$i_1 = I_0 e^{-at} - \left(\frac{V_0}{L} + I_0 a\right)te^{-at} \tag{5.67}$$

The solution for $\zeta > 1$ consists of two decaying exponential functions of time. This is modified if $\zeta = 1$ to a decaying exponential plus the same exponential multiplied by t. If $\zeta < 1$, the solution is an exponentially damped sinusoidal function typically characteristic of the free response of a system made up of two storage component and a dissipative component. As in the case of the system of two storage components, energy transfer takes place between the two storage components. However, in contrast to the conservative system, in this system energy is slowly being dissipated by the resistor, thus reducing the amplitude of oscillation as brought out by Equation 5.63.

Other variables of the electrical circuit may now be easily computed through use of the component equations.

$$q_1 = \int_0^t i_1 dt$$
$$v_1 = \frac{1}{C} q_1$$

where q_1 is the capacitor charge.

$$v_2 = L\frac{di_2}{dt} = -L\frac{di_1}{di}$$

$$v_3 = -Ri_1$$

As a second example, consider the torsional system shown in Figure 5.18. Consisting of a flywheel, torsion bar and rotational damper, it is also classified as a system of two storage components and one dissipative component.

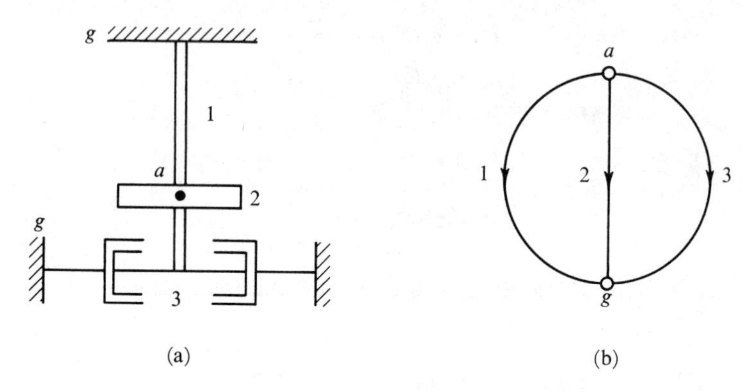

Fig. 5.18. *Torsional system:* (a) *schematic;* (b) *system graph.*

The system graph, as shown in Figure 5.18, is constructed by realizing that each of the three components of the system is characterized by a terminal graph with terminals corresponding to points a and g. If we assume that initial conditions are specified in terms of an initial displacement on the torsion rod and an initial velocity on the flywheel, we realize that a differential equation involving an across variable offers the most direct way to study the system. We start with a vertex equation at vertex a,

$$\tau_1 + \tau_2 + \tau_3 = 0$$

with the component equations substituted,

$$k_t\Phi_1 + Js^2\Phi_2 + Bs\Phi_3 = Js\varphi_2(0) + J\dot{\varphi}_2(0) + B\varphi_3(0)$$

Since, however,

$$\varphi_1 = \varphi_2 = \varphi_3$$

we write

$$(k_r + Js^2 + Bs)\Phi_1 = (Js + B)\varphi_1(0) + J\dot{\varphi}_1(0) \qquad \textbf{(5.68)}$$

Equation 5.68 is recognized to be of the form

$$(s^2 + 2\zeta\omega_n s + \omega_n^2)\Phi_1 = \left(s\frac{B}{J}\right)\varphi_1(0) + \dot{\varphi}_1(0)$$

And again we may obtain the solution directly from Equation (13) of Appendix B as being of the form

$$\varphi_1 = \Phi_m e^{-\zeta\omega_n t} \sin\left(\omega_n\sqrt{1-\zeta^2}\,t + \phi\right) \tag{5.69}$$

where Φ_m and ϕ are determined from the initial conditions $\varphi_1(0)$ and $\dot{\varphi}_1(0)$. This is left as an exercise.

Orientation of Elements in System Graph

A sequence of examples of simple systems has demonstrated how the system graph is constructed from the terminal graphs of the components simply by joining them in a one-to-one correspondence with the system schematic. In connection with the construction of the system graph, one question has not yet been discussed; it concerns the direction of the arrows on the individual elements in the system graph. Consider again the torsional system shown in Figure 5.18. Let us reverse the direction of element 3, as shown in Figure 5.19.

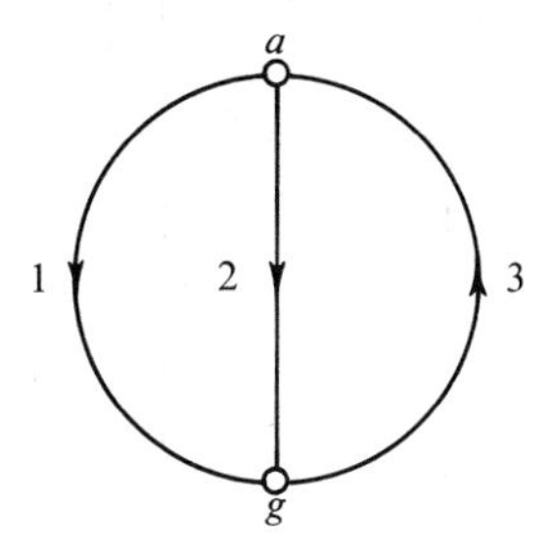

Fig. 5.19. *System graph of torsional system.*

Let us repeat the derivation of the differential equation using the second system graph as our source of component interconnection. The summation of torque at a is

$$\tau_1 + \tau_2 - \tau_3 = 0$$

This clearly is a different summation. Then, if initial conditions are zero,

$$k_r\Phi_1(s) + Js^2\Phi_2(s) - Bs\Phi_3(s) = 0$$

Since, however,

$$\varphi_1 = \varphi_2 = -\varphi_3$$

we obtain exactly the same equation

$$(k_r + Js^2 + Bs)\Phi_1(s) = 0 \tag{5.70}$$

It is therefore evident that the change of orientation of the element has no influence on the outcome. Indeed, in multiplying both the across variable and the through variable in the terminal equation by -1 the terminal representation of the dashpot was changed, resulting in a terminal representation no different from the first one. We may therefore conclude that terminal graphs of two-terminal components may be connected in system graphs with arbitrary orientation, as long as a change in orientation in a terminal graph does not change the terminal equation. This property is shared by *all* passive components. However, active components are different. The orientation of elements corresponding to drivers must be very carefully observed. This will be discussed subsequently.

Systems with Drivers

As an introductory example, consider the tank flow system shown in Figure 5.20. A pump of specified flow forces a fluid from a reservoir into the tank. The tank in turn discharges its contents through a pipe back into the reservoir.

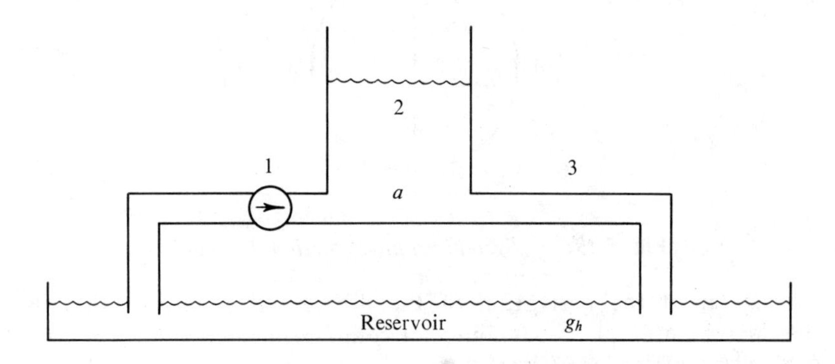

Fig. 5.20. *Tank system.*

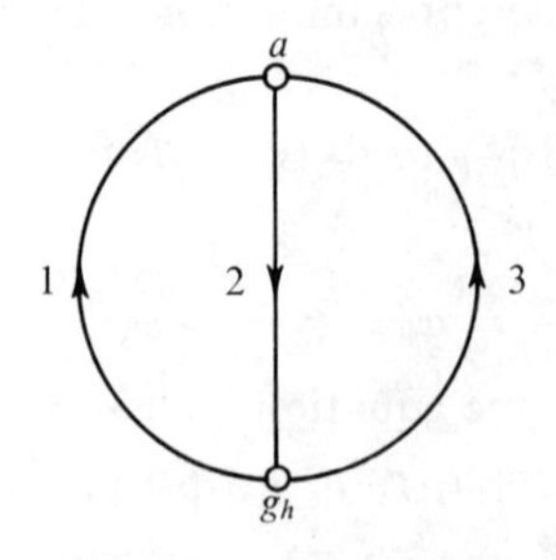

Fig. 5.21. *System graph.*

Then construct the system graph as shown in Figure 5.21. Only the orientation of element 1 is not arbitrary. The direction chosen is obvious.

Let us assume that the tank is initially empty (zero initial condition on the tank), and calculate the volume of the tank as a function of time. Since a flow variable is specified, we may state by the vertex equation

$$\dot{g}_1(t) = \dot{g}_2 - \dot{g}_3$$

Into this equation, substitute the component equations and note that $p_2 = -p_3$; we have

$$\frac{p_2}{R} + C\dot{p}_2 = \dot{g}_1(t) \tag{5.71}$$

In the s-domain,

$$\left(\frac{1}{R} + Cs\right)P_2(s) = \dot{G}_1 + Cp_2(0^+)$$

This is now a first-order non-homogeneous differential equation. When $\dot{g}_1(t) = G$, a constant, $\dot{G}_1(s) = G/s$, and if $p_2(0) = 0$ the solution is

$$P_2 = \frac{G}{sC(s + 1/RC)} = \frac{RG}{s} - \frac{RG}{s + 1/RC} \tag{5.72}$$

By taking the inverse Laplace transform,

$$p_2 = RG(1 - e^{-t/RC}) \tag{5.73}$$

To calculate the volume in the tank, use the tank component equation $g_2 = Cp_2$ to obtain

$$g_2 = RCG(1 - e^{-t/RC}) \tag{5.74}$$

The significance of this result may best be displayed by plotting Equation 5.74 as a function of time, as shown in Figure 5.22.

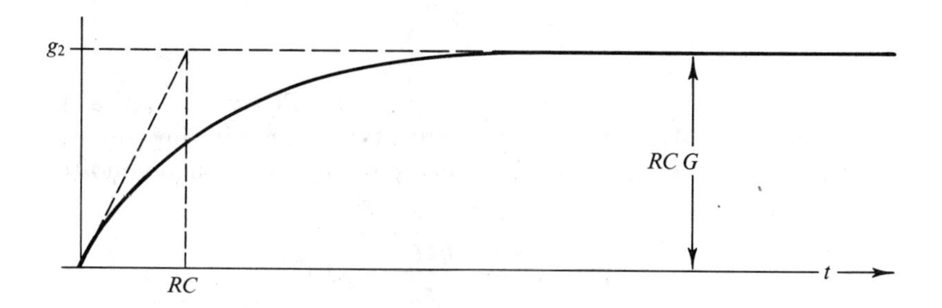

Fig. 5.22. *The volume in the tank as a function of time.*

We conclude, therefore, that the pressure at point a in the system rises from zero to the value RG in an exponential rise. Equation 5.73 is comprised of the free response *and* forced response. The free response enters into the solution despite the fact that the initial conditions are zero.

It is frequently convenient to separate a time solution like Equation 5.73 into a *transient* and a *steady state*. If we write Equation 5.73 as

$$p_2 = \underbrace{-RGe^{-t/RC}}_{\text{transient}} + \underbrace{RG}_{\text{steady state}} \tag{5.75}$$

we readily identify the first term as the transient and the second term as the steady state. The transient then corresponds to that part of the solution which changes according to some exponential law while the steady state is constant. We further note that the transient is influenced by the free *and* forced responses. The steady state, however, is entirely dependent on the forced response. It is therefore possible that the steady state is periodic, not simply constant, if the forcing function should happen to be periodic.

Consider now a modification of the flow problem just discussed. After the steady state is achieved, which can be considered the case after a five time-constant duration ($t = 5RC$), the flow rate of the pump is suddenly reduced to a fraction of its original value. Again, let us find the tank volume as a function of time. We recognize immediately that the physical interconnection of components remain intact; thus, Equation 5.71 is still valid. However the solution to Equation 5.76 is different. The problem may then be formulated in the s-domain as

$$P_2(1 + sRC) = R\dot{G}_1(s) + RCp_2(0) \tag{5.76}$$

$$\dot{g}_1(t) = G, \qquad \dot{G}_1(s) = \frac{G}{s}, \qquad p_2(0) = 0, \qquad 0 < t \leq 5RC$$

$$\dot{g}_1(t) = kG, \qquad \dot{G}_1(s) = \frac{Gk}{s}, \qquad p_2(0) = RG, \qquad 5RC < t,$$

$$0 < k \leq 1$$

Since the solution for the first part ($0 < t \leq 5RC$) is already available, we simply solve Equation 5.76 with the second driving function and specify a new initial condition corresponding to the final condition under the action of the first driving function:

$$P_2(1 + sRC) = \frac{RkG}{s} + R^2CG$$

or

$$P_2 = \frac{kRG}{s(1+RCs)} + \frac{R^2CG}{1+RCs} = \frac{kRG}{s} + \frac{-kRG+RG}{s+1/RC}$$

Taking the inverse Laplace transform, the solution then is

$$p_2 = kRG + (RG - kRG)e^{-t/RC}$$

or

$$p_2 = \underbrace{kRG}_{\text{steady state}} + \underbrace{RG(1-k)e^{-t/RC}}_{\text{transient}}$$

which, in terms of the volume, is

$$g_2 = k\,RCG + RCG(1-k)e^{-t/RC} \tag{5.77}$$

This result is added to the first plot as shown in Figure 5.23.

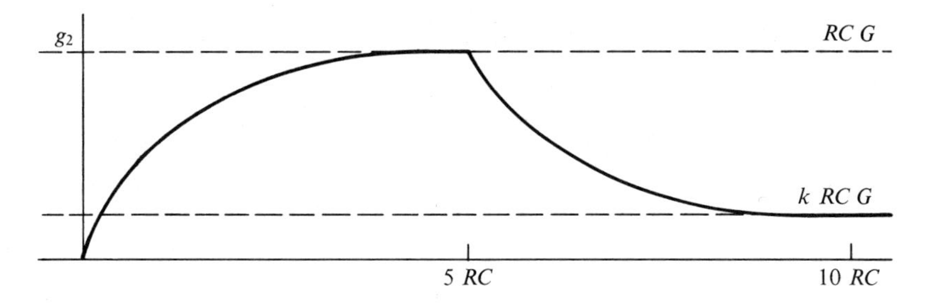

Fig. 5.23. *Complete response of tank flow system.*

Consider next the electrical circuit shown in Figure 5.24. It consists of two resistors and two batteries (constant across drivers).

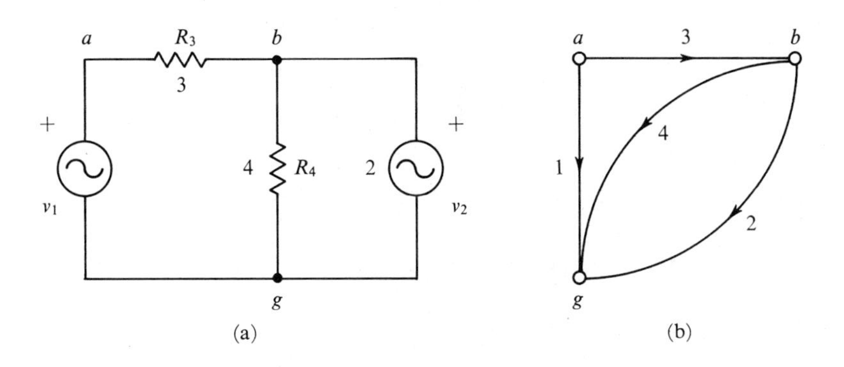

Fig. 5.24. *Electrical circuit:* (a) *schematic;* (b) *system graph.*

The power that each of the two batteries delivers is to be calculated. It is necessary, therefore, to determine the currents i_1 and i_2 since

$$P_1 = i_1 \cdot v_1$$

and

$$P_2 = i_2 \cdot v_2$$

Let us attempt a solution by writing the two circuit equations

$$v_1 = v_3 + v_4$$
$$v_2 = v_4$$

From this, the immediate result is

$$v_4 = v_2$$

and

$$v_3 = v_1 - v_2$$

Now, using the component equations we may compute the currents

$$i_4 = \frac{v_4}{R_4} = \frac{v_2}{R_4}$$

and

$$i_3 = \frac{v_3}{R_3} = \frac{v_1 - v_2}{R_3}$$

Since from the vertex equations for vertices a and b the currents are now related by

$$i_1 = -i_3$$

and

$$i_2 = i_3 - i_4$$

we obtain

$$i_1 = -\frac{v_1 - v_2}{R_3}$$

and

$$i_2 = -\frac{v_1}{R_3} - \left(\frac{1}{R_3} + \frac{1}{R_4}\right)v_2$$

Thus, the power functions for the two sources are

$$P_1 = -v_1\left(\frac{v_1 - v_2}{R_3}\right) \tag{5.78a}$$

$$P_2 = v_2\left[\frac{v_1}{R_3} - \left(\frac{1}{R_3} + \frac{1}{R_4}\right)v_2\right] \tag{5.78b}$$

The two power functions given by Equations 5.78a and 5.78b reveal some interesting properties relating to drivers. Consider the condition $v_1 > v_2$; then $P_1 < 0$. Hence, a negative power function corresponds to power being delivered *by* the source. When $v_2 > v_1$, then $P_1 > 0$; under this condition, power is being delivered *to* the source.

For the two power states, $P_1 > 0$ or $P_1 < 0$, consider the voltage-current relationship for the source, as shown in Figure 5.25. It is

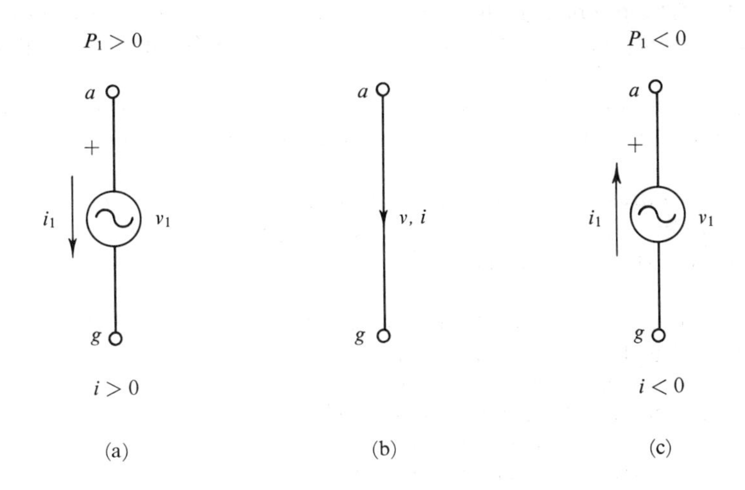

Fig. 5.25. *Voltage current relations for source:* (a) *power positive—current flows from from a to g;* (b) *orientation of voltage and current;* (c) *power negative—current flows from g to a.*

significant that the current flow changes direction with the sign of P_1 while the voltage orientation remains unchanged. The power function P_3 for the resistor R_3, on the other hand, is

$$P_3 = \frac{(v_1 - v_2)^2}{R_3} \geq 0 \tag{5.79}$$

In contrast to the drivers, the power function for a resistor (a dissipative component) is always non-negative, indicating that power can *never* be delivered by a dissipative component.

5.6 Transient Responses of Simple Systems

We have discussed two simple systems involving drivers, each of which emphasized a different aspect of systems involving drivers. The major results are summarized here in more general terms.

(a) A forcing function introduces terms on the right hand side of a differential equation, producing a non-homogeneous equation. The solution to this equation consists of a transient and a steady state. The transient should be looked upon as the transition of the system from an initial state to a new state specified by the forcing function. Thus, the transient is dependent upon both the initial conditions and the forcing function, involving both the free and forced response. The new state is the steady state.

(b) The product of the across variable and the through variable for a two-terminal component is negative when the component delivers power to the system.

(c) To interpret properly the mathematical results, it is always important to know the physical significance of the orientation of the drivers.

In order to illustrate more fully the transient response of simple systems with drivers, some further examples will be presented; all initial conditions are assumed to be zero.

Example 5.6 In the electrical circuit of Figure 5.26 the switch is closed at $t = 0$. Calculate and plot the following:

1. voltage across the capacitor C_2
2. current through the capacitor C_2
3. current through the resistor R_4
4. current through the resistor R_3
5. voltage across the resistor R_3

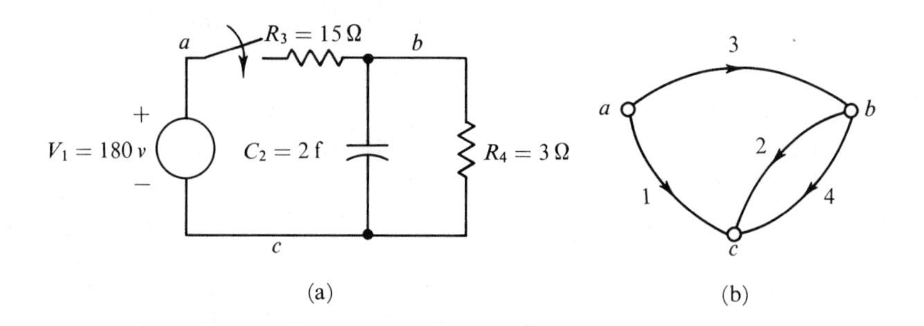

Fig. 5.26. (a) *Electrical circuit;* (b) *system graph.*

Use the loop and node equations,

$$i_3 = i_2 + i_4$$
$$v_1 = v_3 + v_2$$
$$v_2 = v_4$$

Since in the $s =$ domain

$$I_2 = 2sV_2$$
$$I_4 = \frac{V_4}{3} = \frac{V_2}{3}$$
$$I_3 = \frac{V_3}{15} = \frac{V_1 - V_2}{15}$$

then

$$I_3 = \frac{V_1 - V_2}{15} = I_2 + I_4 = 2sV_2 + \frac{V_2}{3}$$

Solving for V_2 produces

$$V_2 = \frac{V_1(s)}{30(s + 1/5)}$$

$V_1(t)$ is a step function input, therefore $V_1 = 180/s$, then

$$V_2 = \frac{6}{s(s + 1/5)} = \frac{30}{s} - \frac{30}{s + 1/5}$$

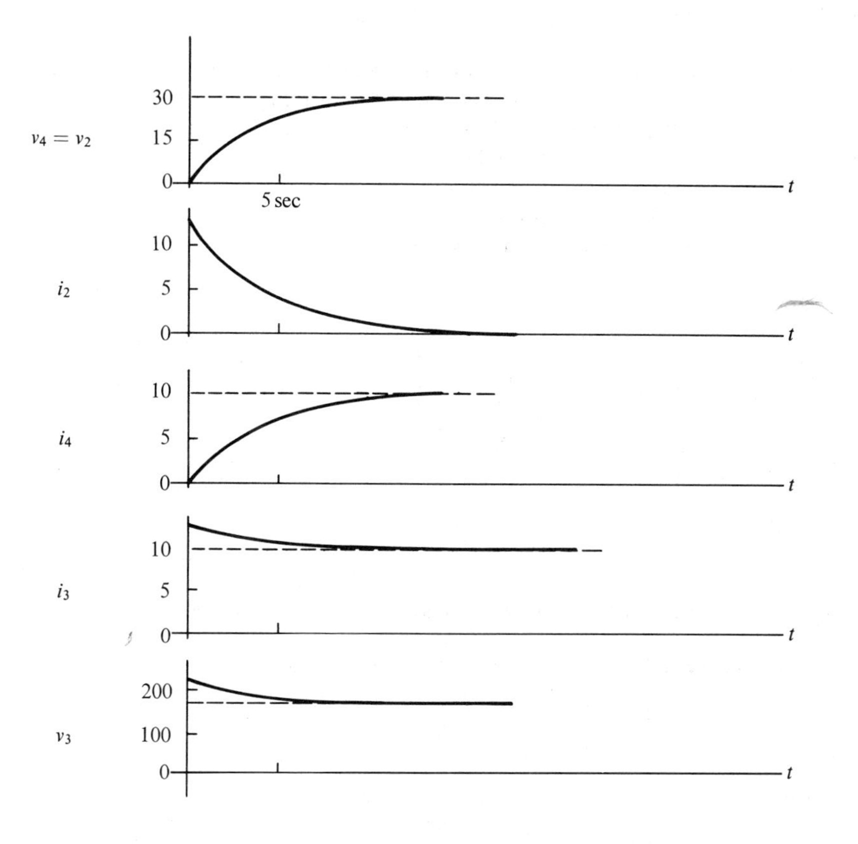

Fig. 5.27. *Time plots of electrical network variables.*

$$v_2 = 30(1 - e^{-t/5})$$
$$i_2 = 2\frac{dv_2}{dt} = 12e^{-t/5}$$
$$i_4 = \frac{v_2}{3} = 10(1 - e^{-t/5})$$
$$i_3 = i_2 + i_4 = 10 + 2e^{-t/5}$$
$$v_3(t) = 150 + 30e^{-t/5}$$

Figure 5.27 shows the time plots of the voltages and currents asked for. There are several interesting relationships between the currents and voltages. For example, the voltage v_4 across R_4 is directly proportional to the current i_4; the same is true for the voltage and current of R_3. Since the current through the capacitor is proportional to the rate of change of capacitor voltage, the current i_2 is maximum at $t = 0$ where the slope of v_2 is greatest. Note also that for all times

$$i_3 = i_2 + i_4$$
$$v_1 = v_3 + v_2$$

Example 5.7 If the capacitor in the network of example 5.6 is replaced by an inductance of 2 henrys, calculate and plot (See Figure 5.28):

1. voltage across the inductor L_2
2. current through the inductor L_2
3. current through the resistor R_4
4. current through the resistor R_3
5. voltage across the resistor R_3

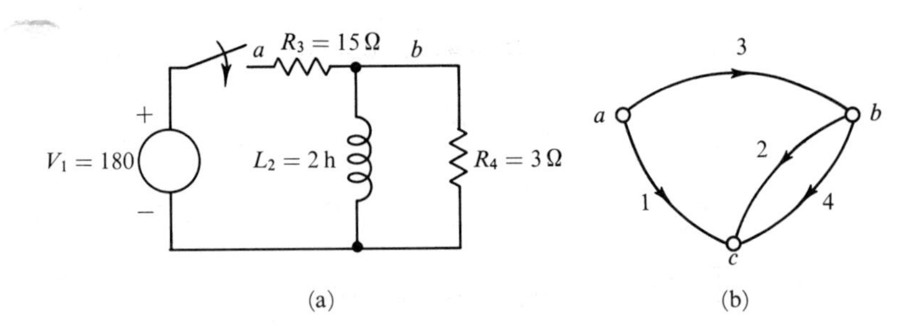

Fig. 5.28. (a) *Electrical circuit;* (b) *system graph.*

Using the same loop and node equations, we may write

$$V_1 = V_2 + V_3 = 2sI_2 + 15I_3 = 2sI_2 + 15(I_2 + I_4)$$
$$I_4 = \frac{V_4}{3} = \frac{V_2}{3} = \frac{2sI_2}{3}$$

then

$$V_1 = (2s + 15 + 10s)I_2$$

Letting $V_1 = 180/s$

$$I_2 = \frac{15}{s(s + 5/4)} = \frac{12}{s} - \frac{12}{s + 5/4}$$

$$i_2 = 12(1 - e^{-5t/4})$$

$$v_4 = v_2(t) = 2\frac{di_2(t)}{dt} = 30^{-5t/4}$$

$$v_3 = v_1 - v_2 = 180 - 30e^{-5t/4}$$

$$i_3 = 12 - 2e^{-5/4t}$$

$$i_4 = 10e^{-5t/4}$$

Figure 5.29 shows the time plots of the circuit variables. Note that the roles of voltages and currents in the capacitor circuit of Figure 5.26 are interchanged in the inductor circuit of Figure 5.28. In the latter the resistor voltages and currents are still proportional, but the inductor voltage is proportional to the time rate of change of the inductor current. Note also that the transient time is faster in Figure 5.29.

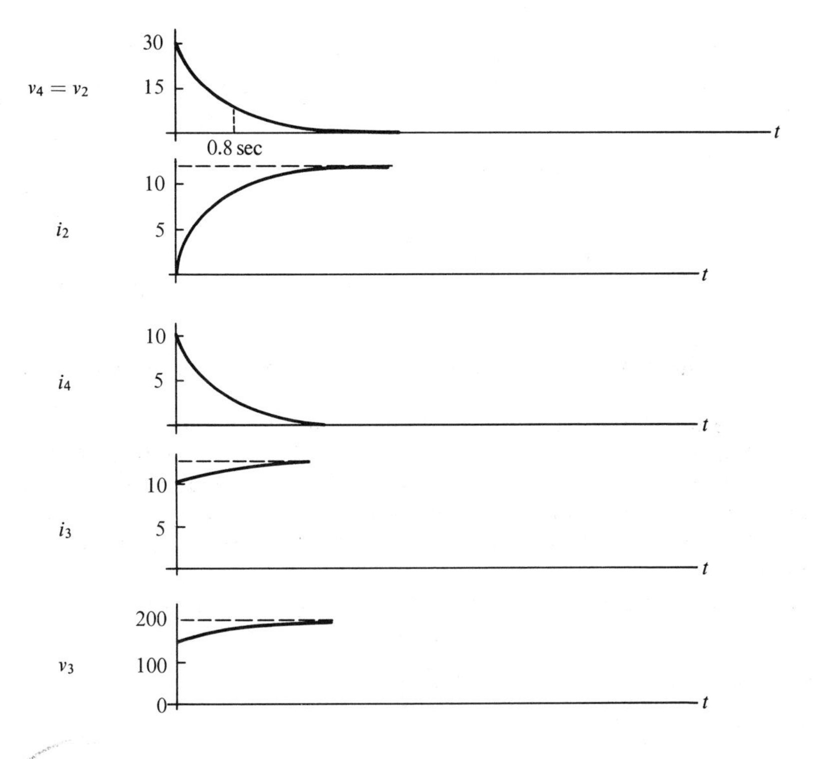

Fig. 5.29. *Time plots of inductive electrical network.*

The transient time is defined in terms of the system time constant. The time constant was defined in Chapter 3 as that time necessary for a transient decaying to zero to reach a value equal to $e^{-1} = 0.368$ of the starting value. In example 5.6, i_4 is decaying from 10 amperes to zero according to the formula

$$i_4 = 10e^{(-1/5)t}$$

When $t = 5$, $i_4 = 10e^{-1} = 3.68$ amperes. Therefore, the time constant is 5 seconds. In example 5.7, the time constant is 4/5 second. The time constant is always the reciprocal of the coefficient of t in the exponent of e.

Example 5.8 In the mechanical system of Figure 5.30, the input is a constant force applied at $t = 0$; find the following as a function of time:

1. displacement of dashpot δ_2
2. force in dashpot f_2
3. displacement of input δ_1
4. force in spring f_4

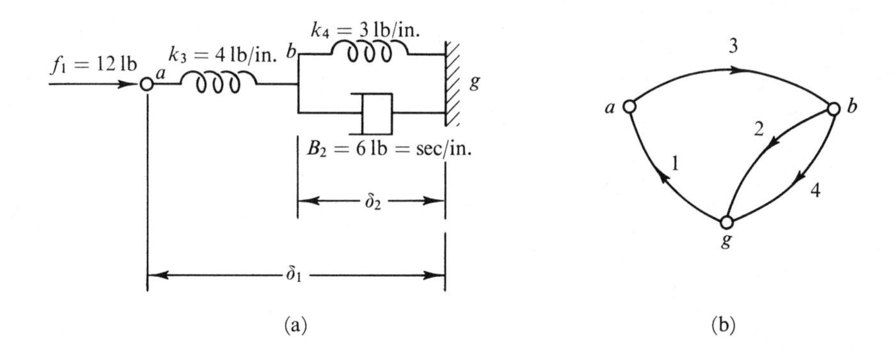

Fig. 5.30. (a) *A mechanical system;* (b) *system graph.*

If we define positive displacement as displacement to the right, then the input force is directed into node a in the system graph. The directions of arrows on elements 2, 3, and 4 are arbitrary—remember that the displacement at the tail end of the arrow is defined positive with respect to the arrow head. The solution obtained for $\delta_2(t)$ is in the defined positive direction of δ with respect to node g.

In the solution we will use the following node and loop equations:

$$f_3 = f_2 + f_4$$
$$f_3 = f_1$$
$$\delta_2 = \delta_4$$
$$\delta_1 = \delta_3 + \delta_2$$

The equations of the springs and dashpot are

$$f_3 = 4\delta_3$$
$$f_4 = 3\delta_4$$

$$f_2 = 6\frac{d\delta_2}{dt}$$

In the s-domain

$$F_3 = F_1 = 6s\Delta_2 + 3\Delta_4 = (6s + 3)\Delta_2$$

$$F_1(s) = \frac{12}{s}$$

since $f_1(t)$ is a step function

$$\Delta_2 = \frac{12}{s(6s + 3)} = \frac{4}{s} - \frac{4}{s + 1/2}$$

$$\delta_2 = 4(1 - e^{-t/2})$$

$$f_2 = 6\frac{d\delta_2}{dt} = 12e^{-t/2}$$

$$\delta_1 = \frac{12}{4} + 4(1 - e^{-t/2}) = 7 - 4e^{-t/2}$$

$$f_4 = 12(1 - e^{-t/2})$$

Figure 5.31 shows time plots of these variables. Note that the spring displacements are proportional to their forces and the dashpot force is proportional to the time derivative of its displacement.

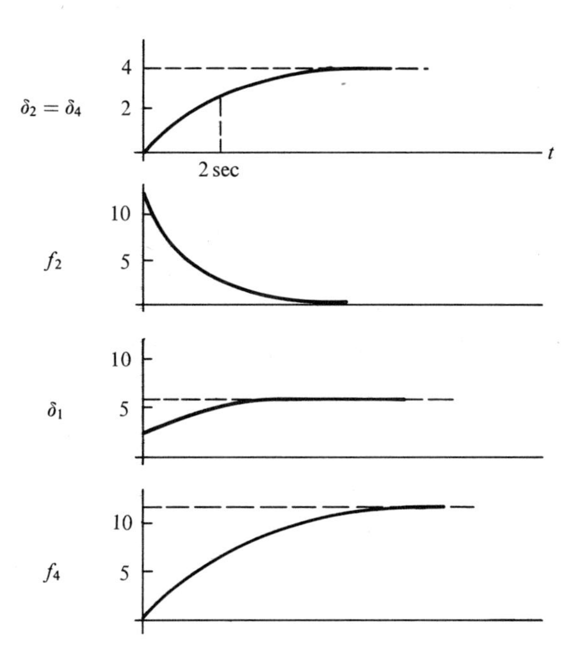

Fig. 5.31. *Time plots of mechanical system variables.*

Example 5.9 In the electrical system of Figure 5.32, calculate and plot versus time the following (the switch is closed at $t = 0$):

1. v_0
2. i
3. v_1
4. v_2
5. v_3

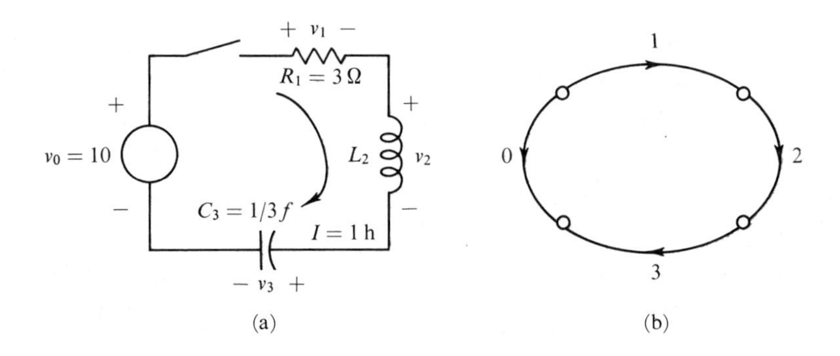

Fig. 5.32. (a) *Second-order electrical circuit;* (b) *system graph.*

From the system graph,

$$v_0 = v_1 + v_2 + v_3$$
$$i_1 = i_2 = i_3 = i$$

In the s-domain

$$V_0 = \frac{10}{s} = 3I + sI + \frac{2}{s}I$$

or

$$I = \frac{10}{s^2 + 3s + 2} = \frac{10}{s+1} - \frac{10}{s+2}$$
$$i = 10(e^{-t} - e^{-2t})$$
$$v_1 = 3i = 30(e^{-t} - e^{-2t})$$
$$v_2 = \frac{di}{dt} = 10(2e^{-2t} - e^{-t})$$
$$v_3 = 2\int_0^t i(\tau)d\tau = 10(e^{-2t} - 2e^{-t} + 1)$$

Figure 5.33 shows a time plot of the current which is composed of the sum of two transients.

Figure 5.34 shows time plots of the mesh current and the component voltages. Note that $v_0 = v_1 + v_2 + v_3$ at all times and v_2 is proportional to the derivative of v_1; v_3 is proportional to the time integral of v_1; conversely, v_1 is proportional to the derivative of v_3.

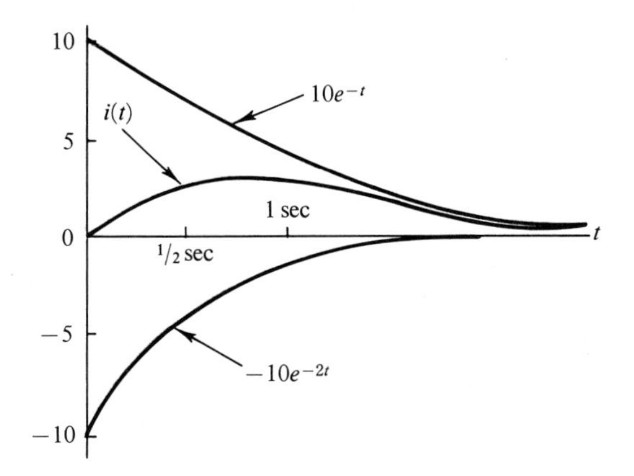

Fig. 5.33. *Time Plot of $i(t)$.*

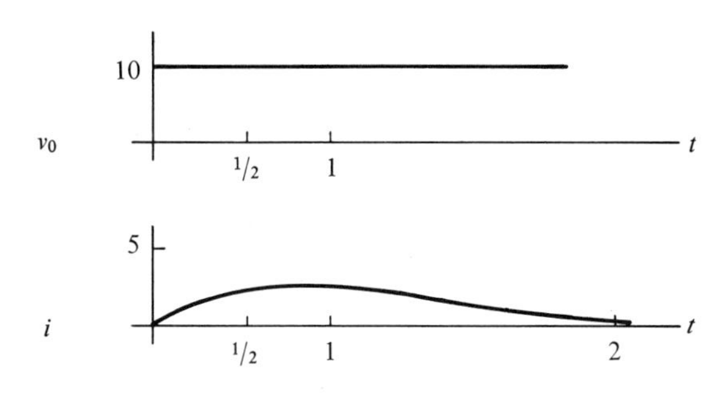

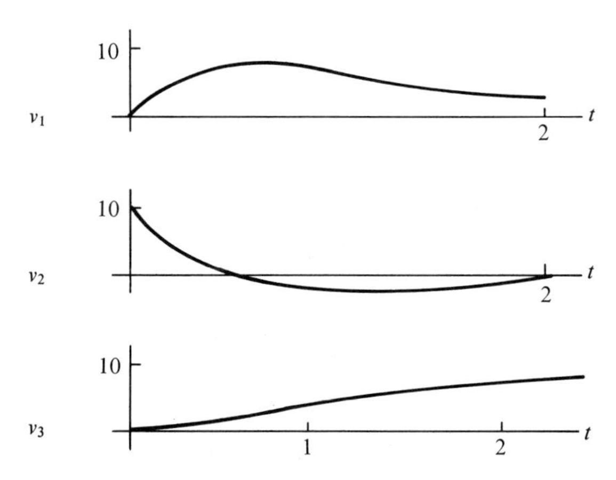

Fig. 5.34. *Time plots of electrical circuit variables.*

Example 5.10 As a final example consider the second order mechanical system of Figure 5.35.

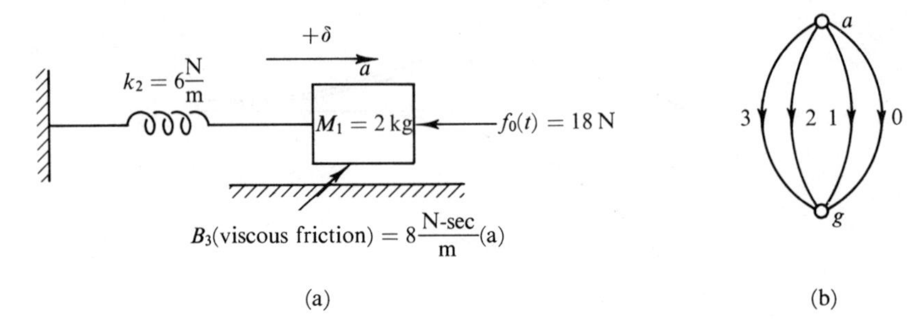

Fig. 5.35. (a) *A second order mechanical system;* (b) *system graph.*

$f_0(t)$ is a step force at $t = 0$ pushing on the mass. Since the force direction is negative relative to the defined positive direction of displacement, the system graph element representing the input force has its arrow directed away from node *a*.

The loop and node equations are

$$\delta_0 = \delta_1 = \delta_2 = \delta_3$$
$$f_0 + f_1 + f_2 + f_3 = 0$$

The equations of the components in the *s*-domain are

$$F_0 = \frac{18}{s}$$
$$F_1 = 2s^2\Delta_1$$
$$F_2 = 6\Delta_2$$
$$F_3 = 8s\Delta_3$$

Combining in the node equation, we have

$$(2s^2 + 8s + 6)\Delta = -\frac{18}{s}$$

$$\Delta = \frac{-9}{s(s+3)(s+1)} = \frac{-3}{s} + \frac{9/2}{s+1} - \frac{3/2}{s+3}$$

Taking the inverse Laplace transform of Δ

$$\delta = -3 + \frac{9}{2}e^{-t} - \frac{3}{2}e^{-3t}$$

$$f_1 = 2\frac{d^2\delta}{dt^2} = 9e^{-t} - 27e^{-3t}$$

$$f_2 = 6\delta = -18 + 27e^{-t} - 9^{-3t}$$

$$f_3 = 8\frac{d\delta}{dt} = -36e^{-t} + 36e^{-3t}$$

Figure 5.36 shows plots of the mass displacement and the forces in each component. The sum of the forces always equals −18 newtons, the friction force is the derivative of the displacement, and the mass force is the second derivative of the displacement.

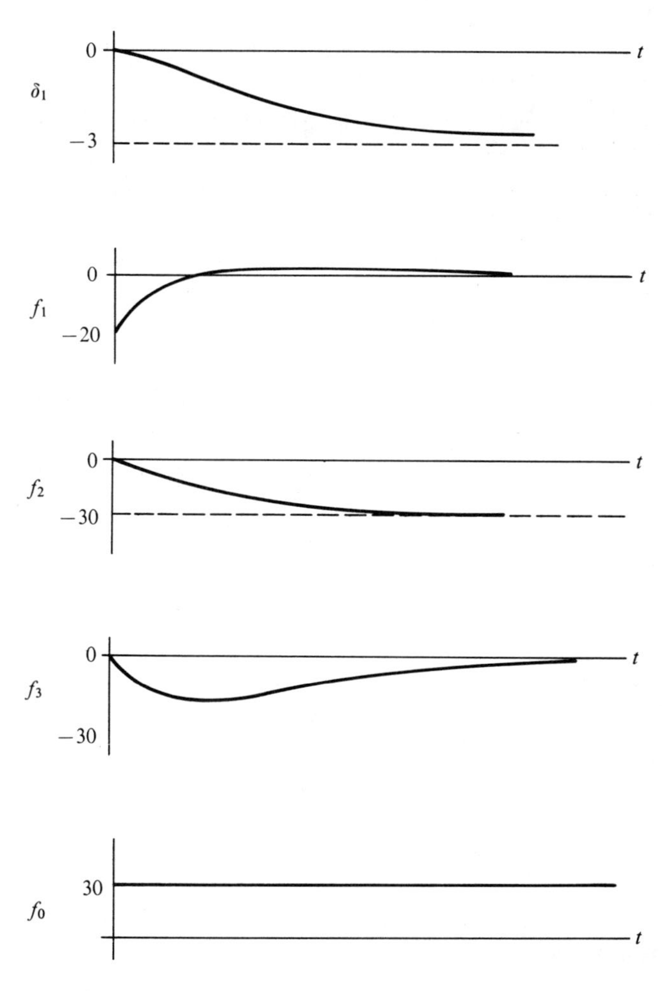

Fig. 5.36. *Time plots of mechanical circuit variables.*

ADDITIONAL READINGS

Aseltine, J.A., *Transform Method in Linear System Analysis,* New York: McGraw-Hill Book Co., 1958.

Bohn, E.V., *The Transform Analysis of Linear Systems,* Reading, Mass.: Addison-Wesley Publishing Co., Inc., 1963.

Churchill, R.V., *Modern Operational Methods in Engineering,* New York: McGraw-Hill Book Co., 1944.

Gardner, M.F., and J.L. Barnes, *Transients in Linear Systems,* New York: John Wiley & Sons, Inc., 1942.

Gupta, Someshwar C., *Transform and State Variable Methods in Linear Systems,* New York: John Wiley & Sons, Inc., 1966.

Kaplan, W., *Operational Methods for Linear Systems,* Reading, Mass.; Addison-Wesley Publishing Co., Inc., 1962.

Kuo, Benjamin C., *Linear Networks and Systems*, New York: McGraw-Hill Book Co., 1967.

Lepage, W.R., *Complex Variables and the Laplace Transform for Engineers,* New York: McGraw-Hill Book Co., 1961.

Lynch, W.A., and J.G. Truxal, *Introductory System Analysis,* New York: McGraw-Hill Book Co., 1961.

Pfeiffer, P.E., *Linear System Analysis*, New York: McGraw-Hill Book Co., 1961.

Sanford, Richard S., *Physical Networks,* Englewood Cliffs, New Jersey: Prentice-Hall, Inc., 1965.

Seely, S., *Dynamic Systems Analysis,* New York: Reinhold Publishing Corp., 1964.

Shearer, J. Lowen, Arthur T. Murphy, and Herbert H. Richardson, *Introduction to System Dynamics,* Reading, Mass.: Addison-Wesley Publishing Co., Inc., 1967.

Widder, P.V., *The Laplace Transform*, Princeton, New Jersey: Princeton University Press, 1941.

PROBLEMS

5.1. Determine schematic interconnection diagrams and systems graphs for the systems shown in Figure P 5.1.

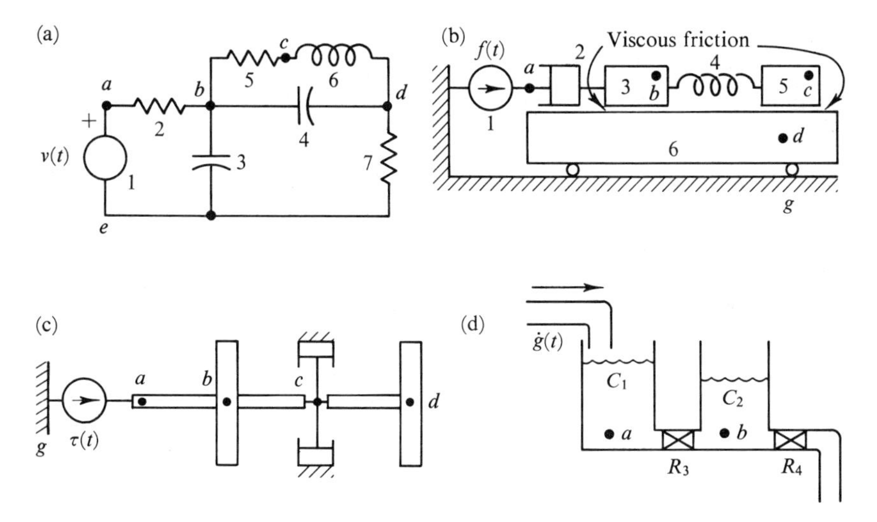

Fig. P 5.1.

Note: All components are to be viewed as two-terminal components.

5.2. Write the vertex and circuit equations for the systems of Problem 5.1.

5.3. Determine the natural frequency of oscillation of the systems shown in Figure P 5.3.

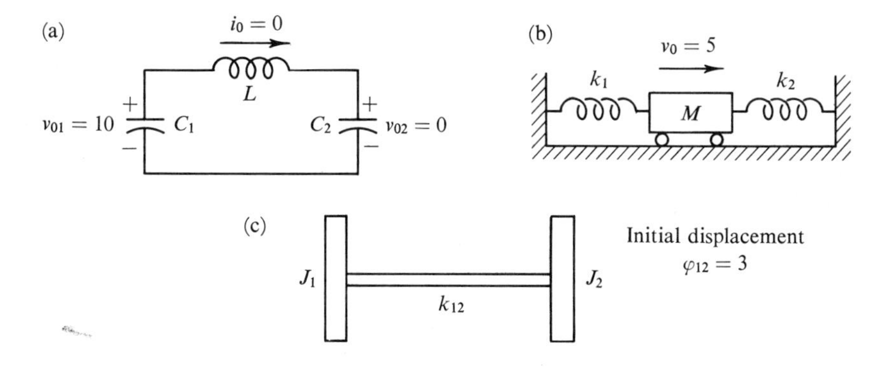

Fig. P 5.3.

5.4.

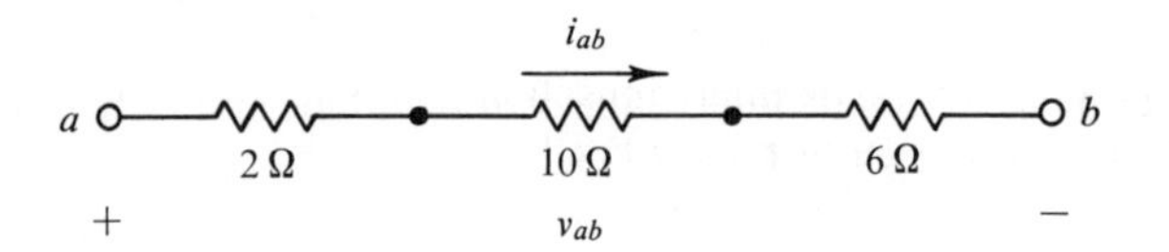

Fig. P 5.4.

a) Determine the current i_{ab} to produce a voltage difference $v_{ab} = 1$ volt.

b) Determine the voltage v_{ab} to produce a current $i_{ab} = 0.010$ amperes.

5.5.

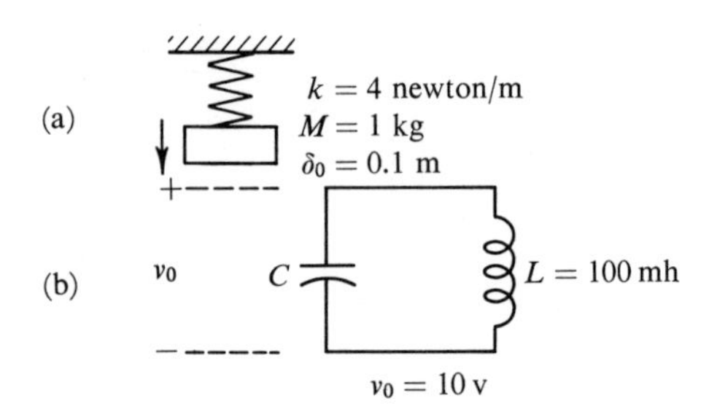

Fig. P 5.5.

a) Calculate the frequency at which the mechanical system of Figure P 5.5 oscillates.

b) Determine C in the electrical circuit such that the frequency of oscillation of the electrical circuit of Figure P 5.5 (b) is exactly 1000 times higher.

5.6.

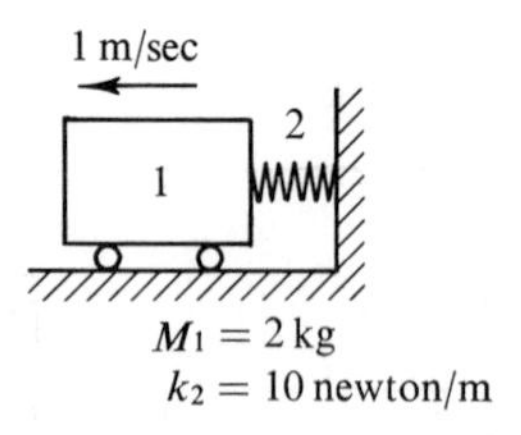

Fig. P 5.6.

Derive the mesh equation and the node equation for the system of Figure P 5.6. If the mass has an initial velocity of 1 meter/second, calculate the maximum deflection and force of spring.

5.7

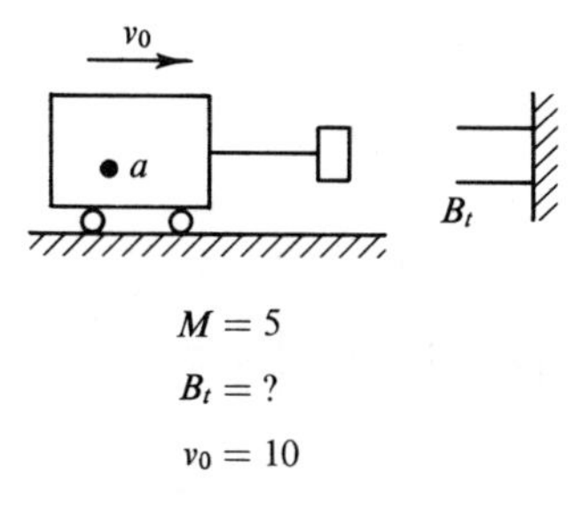

Fig. P 5.7.

A mass with velocity v_0 travels on frictionless rollers until a dashpot engages to decelerate it as shown in Figure P 5.7. Determine B_t such that the velocity of m is reduced to less than 0.05 v_0 in 5 seconds after engagement.

5.8

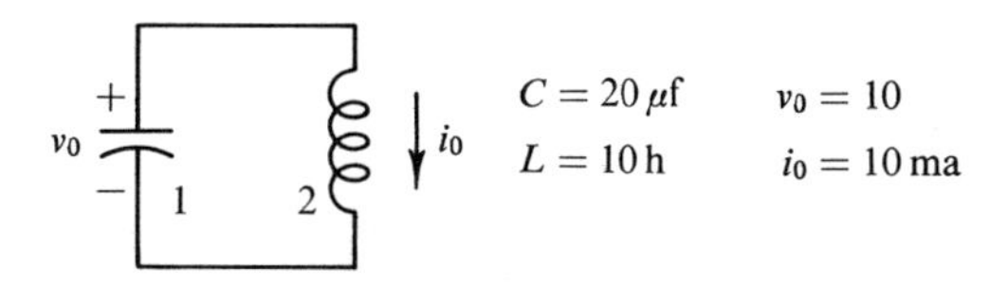

Fig. P 5.8.

Calculate the maximum voltage across the capacitor and maximum current in the inductor of the circuit shown in Figure P 5.8.

5.9. Show that the equations below constitute a proper mathematical model of the circuit in Problem 5.8.

$$\frac{d}{dt}i_2 = \frac{1}{L}v_1$$

$$\frac{d}{dt}v_2 = -\frac{1}{C}i_1$$

5.10. A cylinder of inertia, $J = 10$ kilogram meter^2 reaches a terminal velocity of 10 radians/second while rolling down an incline at an angle of 0.1 radians with the horizontal. It rolls out on a level section. Assuming only viscous friction, how many revolutions does it make on the level before it stops ?

5.11.

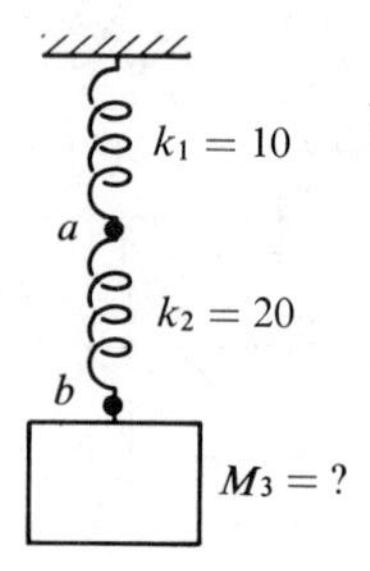

Fig. P 5.11.

Determine the mass m_3 to cause a total static deflection of 0.5 meter of the two springs of the system shown in Figure P 5.11. ($g = 9.81$ meter/second^2, acceleration of gravity.)

5.12.

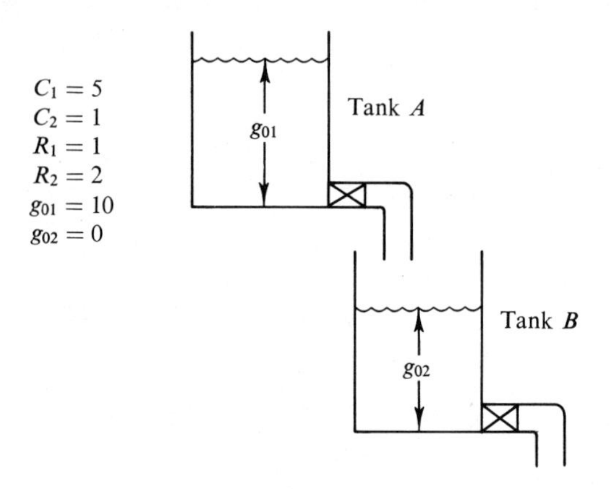

Fig. P 5.12.

Tank A discharges into Tank B as shown in Figure P 5.12. Calculate the pressures developed at the bottom of each tank as a function of time and make plots of $P_A(t)$ versus t and $P_B(t)$ versus t.

5.13.

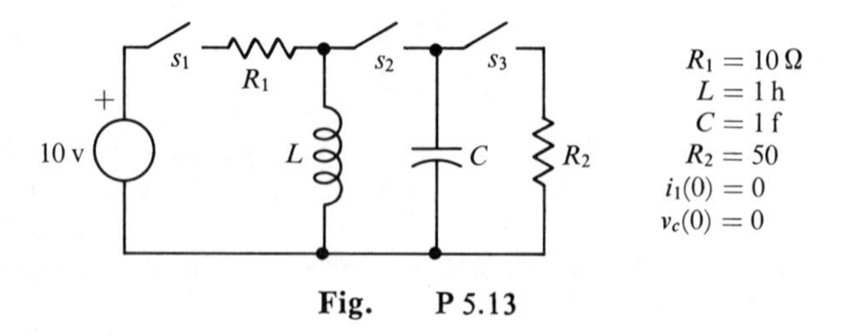

Fig. P 5.13

In the circuit shown in Figure P 5.13, determine the voltage across the capacitor when the switches are opened and closed according to Table P 5.13.

TABLE P 5.13.

t	s_1	s_2	s_3
0	close	open	open
0.5	open	close	open
$.5 + \pi/4$	open	open	close
$10.5 + \pi/4$	open	open	open

5.14. Determine the mesh and node equations for the systems in Problem 5.1.

5.15.

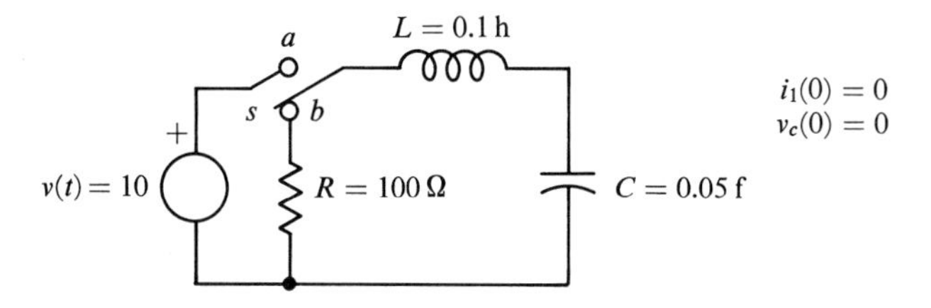

Fig. P 5.15.

At $t = 0$, switch s of the circuit shown in Figure P 5.15 is connected to a and held closed until $t = t_1$. Time t_1 is defined as the time at which the capacitor reaches maximum energy state for the first time. At $t = t_1$, switch s is connected to b and held there until $t = \infty$. Calculate the following:

a) $v_{c\,\text{maximum}}$, t_1, $\omega_c(t_1)$
b) the complete solution during $0 \leq t < t_1$ for $v_c(t)$
c) the complete solution during $t_1 \leq t$ for $v_c(t)$
d) the total energy delivered by $v(t)$, dissipated by R, stored by C } during $0 \leq t < \infty$

Identify the forced and free solutions for parts b) and c).

5.16.

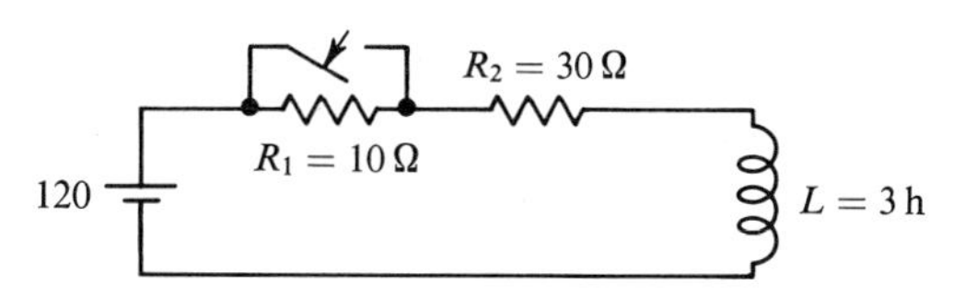

Fig. P 5.16.

In the problem sketched in Figure P 5.16, switch is opened at $t = 0$. Find $i(t)$.

5.17. Calculate the equivalent impedance (or admittance) of the systems shown in Figure P 5.17 (between vertices *a* and *b*).

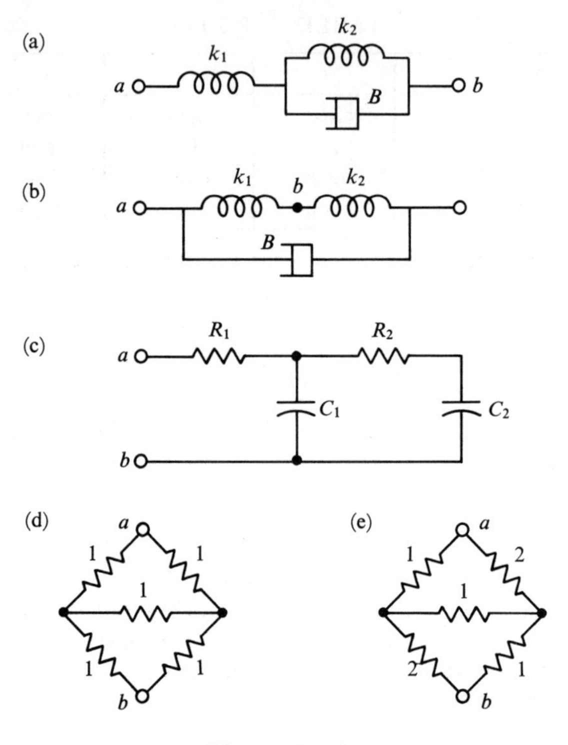

Fig. P 5.17.

5.18. The waveform shown in Figure P 5.18 is of the form $Ke^{-t/T} \sin \omega t$. What are approximate values of K, T, and ω ? What would be the undamped natural frequency ?

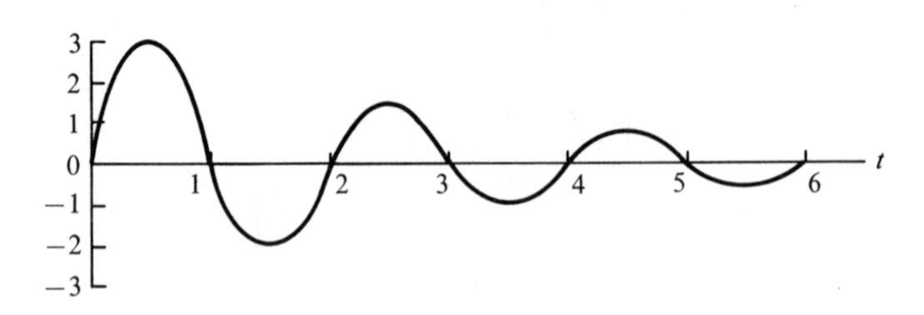

Fig. P 5.18.

5.19.

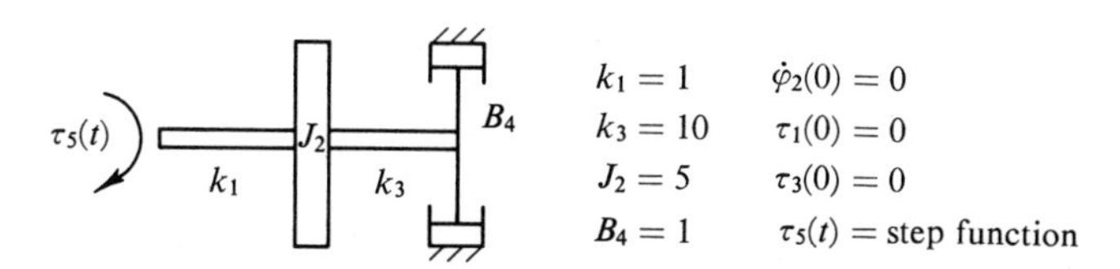

Fig. P 5.19.

For the rotational system shown in Figure P 5.19 calculate the velocity of the flywheel during the transient and in the steady state after the torque has been applied. Does the shaft connecting the applied torque driver to the flywheel experience a transient stress condition ? Evaluate the steady-state torque in shaft k_3 by use of the final value theorem of the Laplace-transform.

5.20.

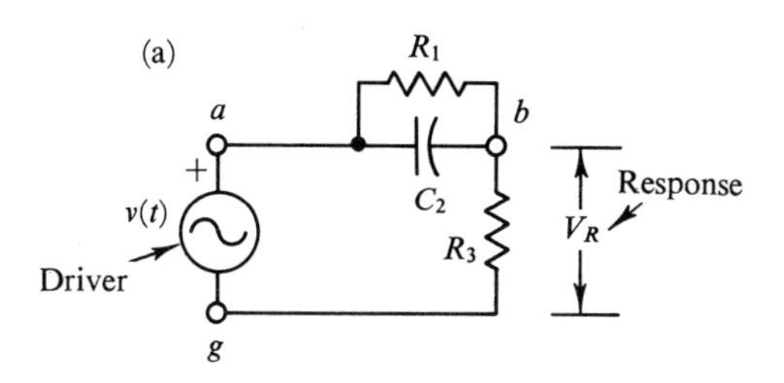

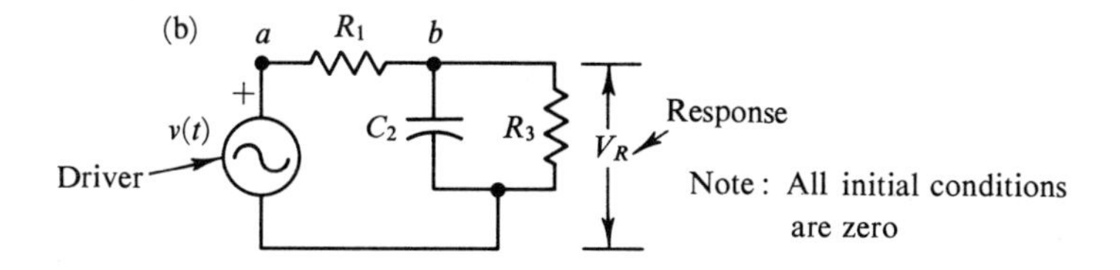

Fig. P 5.20.

Note: All initial conditions are zero.

Calculate the response to the drivers shown in Figure P 5.20 when the following conditions are specified:

$$v(t) = 10u(t)$$

$R_1 = 1$		$R_1 = 1$
$R_3 = 10$	and	$R_3 = 0.1$
$C_2 = 1$		$C_2 = 1$

Plot the response as a function of time in each case and compare the results. Make use of the initial and final value theorems.

General Methods of Formulation

6

6.1 Introduction

In the preceding chapter an introduction to the formulation and solution of simple systems—systems containing only two, three, or perhaps four components—was presented. In each case discussed, it was fairly obvious how to formulate a differential equation (or its Laplace transformed equivalent) to arrive at a system model. It was obvious because the mathematical model of the system consisted of only one equation. These systems, however, are unrealistically simple; they represent only a small sample of problems which in general are far more complex in structure. This chapter will develop techniques of formulation which will permit a systematic approach to the derivation of system models for systems of more complex structure.

A fundamental problem which arises in the formulation of more complex systems is the determination of a set of independent equations.

To bring this problem into focus, consider the following case. Figure 6.1 shows a circuit with five components. It is a system which is a bit more complex, but not overwhelmingly so. It has four vertices and three circuits. The vertices are obvious, the circuits perhaps not. But we can form circuits consisting of elements (1, 2, 3), (3, 4, 5), and (1, 2, 4, 5). For every one of these vertices and circuits we can write a vertex equation and a circuit equation respectively.

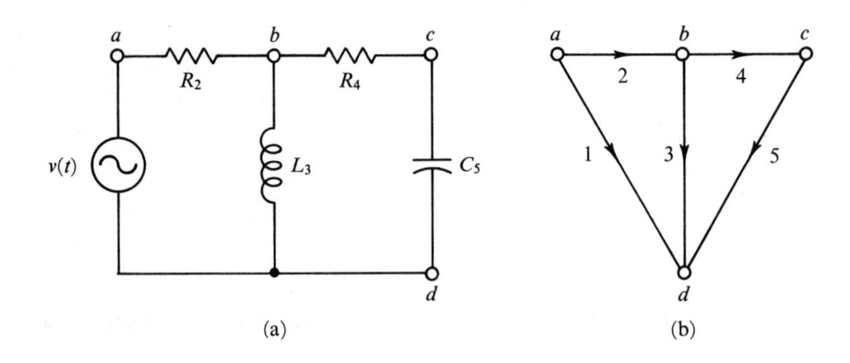

Fig. 6.1. *Electrical circuit:* (a) *schematic;* (b) *system graph.*

Vertex equations:

$$
\begin{array}{llllll}
a. & i_1 + i_2 & & & & = 0 \\
b. & & -i_2 + i_3 + i_4 & & & = 0 \\
c. & & & & -i_4 + i_5 & = 0 \\
d. & -i_1 & & -i_3 & - i_5 & = 0
\end{array}
\tag{6.1}
$$

Circuit equations:

$$
\begin{array}{lllll}
1. & -v_1 + v_2 + v_3 & & & = 0 \\
2. & & -v_3 + v_4 + v_5 & & = 0 \\
3. & -v_1 + v_2 & & + v_4 + v_5 & = 0
\end{array}
\tag{6.2}
$$

These equations form two sets of simultaneous algebraic equations. In matrix format they are

$$
\begin{bmatrix} 1 & 1 & 0 & 0 & 0 \\ 0 & -1 & 1 & 1 & 0 \\ 0 & 0 & 0 & -1 & 1 \\ -1 & 0 & -1 & 0 & -1 \end{bmatrix}
\begin{bmatrix} i_1 \\ i_2 \\ i_3 \\ i_4 \\ i_5 \end{bmatrix} = 0
\tag{6.3}
$$

$$\begin{bmatrix} -1 & 1 & 1 & 0 & 0 \\ 0 & 0 & -1 & 1 & 1 \\ -1 & 1 & 0 & 1 & 1 \end{bmatrix} \begin{bmatrix} v_1 \\ v_2 \\ v_3 \\ v_4 \\ v_5 \end{bmatrix} = 0 \tag{6.4}$$

These two sets of equations are mathematical statements of physical constraints that the variables $i_1, i_2, \cdots, i_5$, and $v_1, v_2, \cdots, v_5$ must obey in this particular system. They are representative of similar sets of equations in other system problems. The question that arises is whether all these equations are required as a complete statement of the physical constraints; are some of the equations saying the same thing? This question can be translated into the following mathematical statement: Are all the Equations 6.3 and 6.4 independent? It can be shown that only three of the Equations 6.3 are independent and only two of the Equations 6.4 are independent.

Consider the sum of the four rows of the matrix in 6.3. It yields a row of zeros. On the other hand, the sum of the first and second row minus the third row in 6.4 also yields a row of zeros. In other words, there exist linear combinations of the rows of the vertex and circuit matrix equations which yield zero. We must therefore conclude that not all the equations are independent, mathematically speaking. This conclusion indicates that not all vertex or circuit equations are necessary in the formulation of the system equations because some contain redundant information. The next section examines the question of independence in more detail.

6.2. Independence of Vertex and Circuit Equations

Let us begin with a definition of linear dependence. Given a set of m simultaneous algebraic equations in n variables, such as

$$\begin{bmatrix} c_{11} & c_{12} & \cdots & c_{1n} \\ c_{21} & c_{22} & \cdots & c_{2n} \\ \vdots & & & \\ c_{m1} & c_{m2} & \cdots & c_{mn} \end{bmatrix} \begin{bmatrix} x_1 \\ x_2 \\ \vdots \\ x_n \end{bmatrix} = \mathbf{0} \tag{6.5}$$

or

$$\mathbf{CX} = \mathbf{0}$$

and requested to determine whether all the equations are necessary for a complete statement of the interrelationship among the variables, it is sufficient to examine the matrix of coefficients $\mathbf{C}$. What the variables $x_1, x_2, \cdots, x_n$ represent is immaterial to this question.

Consider the $m \times n$ matrix $\mathbf{C}$. It has m rows, each containing n components. It is common to refer to these rows as vectors. Thus the m row vectors of $\mathbf{C}$ are

$$\begin{aligned} \mathbf{C}_1 &= [\, c_{11}\; c_{12} \cdots c_{1n} \,] \\ \mathbf{C}_2 &= [\, c_{21}\; c_{22} \cdots c_{2n} \,] \\ &\vdots \\ \mathbf{C}_m &= [c_{m1}\, c_{m2} \cdots c_{mn}] \end{aligned} \tag{6.6}$$

These m vectors are said to be linearly dependent if there exist m constants, $k_1, k_2, \cdots, k_m$, not all zero, such that

$$k_1\mathbf{C}_1 + k_2\mathbf{C}_2 + \cdots + k_m\mathbf{C}_m = 0 \tag{6.7}$$

Otherwise, the m vectors are said to be linearly independent.

As an illustration of the definition of linear dependence return to Equations 6.3. These are four vectors,

$$\begin{aligned} \mathbf{C}_1 &= [\;\;1 \quad\;\; 1 \quad 0 \quad\;\; 0 \quad\;\; 0] \\ \mathbf{C}_2 &= [\;\;0 \quad -1 \quad 1 \quad\;\; 1 \quad\;\; 0] \\ \mathbf{C}_3 &= [\;\;0 \quad\;\; 0 \quad 0 \quad -1 \quad\;\; 1] \\ \mathbf{C}_4 &= [-1 \quad\;\; 0 \quad -1 \quad\;\; 0 \quad -1] \end{aligned} \tag{6.8}$$

If we choose the four constants

$$k_1 = k_2 = k_3 = k_4 = 1$$

then we can easily verify that

$$k_1\mathbf{C}_1 + k_2\mathbf{C}_2 + k_3\mathbf{C}_3 + k_4\mathbf{C}_4 = 0$$

which shows that the four vectors are linearly dependent. On the other hand, if we choose the three constants

$$k_1 = k_2 = 1 \qquad \text{and} \qquad k_3 = -1$$

and apply them to the three rows of Equation 6.4, it is also established that they are linearly dependent.

An important consequence of linear dependence is that if a set of m vectors, such as 6.6, is linearly dependent, any one of the m vectors can be expressed as a linear combination of the remaining $m-1$ vectors. From 6.7 we can write

$$\mathbf{C}_i = -\frac{1}{k_1}[k_1\mathbf{C}_1 + k_2\mathbf{C}_2 + \cdots + k_{i-1}\mathbf{C}_{i-1} + k_{i+1}\mathbf{C}_{i+1} + \cdots + k_m\mathbf{C}_m]$$

$$i = 1, 2, \cdots, m \tag{6.9}$$

For instance, the second vector of 6.8 can be expressed as a linear combination of the other vectors; that is,

$$\mathbf{C}_2 = -\mathbf{C}_1 - \mathbf{C}_3 - \mathbf{C}_4$$

which can be readily verified by substituting the numerical values.

The physical significance of 6.9 is simply that one equation of the set of simultaneous Equations 6.5 is redundant.

It has been demonstrated that the question of linear dependence of a set of m simultaneous algebraic equations in n unknowns can be answered by an examination of the row vectors of the coefficient matrix. The definition of linear dependence provides a procedure for the testing of linear dependence. This test, however, is extremely impractical. A more tractable approach is provided by using the relation between the rank of a matrix and the dependence of the row vectors of the matrix. To establish this relationship we state here an important result from matrix algebra.

*Rank and Independence**

Given a matrix of m vectors of n components whose rank is $r < m$, there are exactly r vectors linearly independent. Futhermore, the remaining $m - r$ vectors can be expressed as a linear combination of these r vectors.

This important result will permit determination of exactly how many equations of a set of simultaneous equations are linearly independent.

Example 6.1. Determine the rank of the matrices of Equations 6.3 and 6.4. For the vertex equations we examine the rank of the matrix

$$\begin{bmatrix} 1 & 1 & 0 & 0 & 0 \\ 0 & -1 & 1 & 1 & 0 \\ 0 & 0 & 0 & -1 & 1 \\ -1 & 0 & -1 & 0 & -1 \end{bmatrix}$$

By a series of elementary matrix operations we can show this matrix to be equivalent to the matrix

$$\begin{bmatrix} 1 & 0 & 0 & 0 & 0 \\ 0 & 1 & 0 & 0 & 0 \\ 0 & 0 & 1 & 0 & 0 \\ 0 & 0 & 0 & 0 & 0 \end{bmatrix}$$

which clearly has rank 3.

Similarly, the matrix of the circuit equations can be shown to be equivalent to a matrix of rank 2; that is.

$$\begin{bmatrix} -1 & 1 & 1 & 0 & 0 \\ 0 & 0 & -1 & 1 & 1 \\ -1 & 1 & 0 & 1 & 1 \end{bmatrix} \sim \begin{bmatrix} 1 & 0 & 0 & 0 & 0 \\ 0 & 1 & 0 & 0 & 0 \\ 0 & 0 & 0 & 0 & 0 \end{bmatrix}$$

---

* For a proof of this result, see Chapter 9. See also Appendix A.

Now connect this result with our objective of investigating the linear independence of the vertex and circuit equations. It is clear that for this objective we need to know the rank of the coefficient matrices associated with the two sets of equations. Write the vertex equations and circuit equations symbolically.

Vertex equations:

$$\mathbf{AY} = 0 \tag{6.10}$$

where **Y** is a column matrix of through variables.

Circuit equations:

$$\mathbf{BX} = 0 \tag{6.11}$$

where **X** is a column matrix of across variables. We call **A** the vertex matrix and **B** the circuit matrix.

Regarding the order of the matrices, we know that the number of columns of **A** and **B** are the same and are equal to the number of elements in the system graph. This number is denoted

Number of elements in system graph: e

Thus the column matrices **Y** and **X** have e components. Furthermore, each row in the matrix **A** corresponds to one vertex, and each row in the matrix **B** corresponds to one circuit. The number of vertices is easily determined for a given graph. This number is denoted

Number of vertices in system graph: v

Thus the vertex has v rows. The number of circuits is not easily determined, a fact which is readily verified. However, we know it is finite. This number is denoted as n.

The vertex matrix and circuit matrix are of order

$$\mathbf{A}_{v \times e}$$

$$\mathbf{B}_{n \times e}$$

It was indicated earlier by means of an example that not all the row vectors in these matrices are independent. As will be shown in Chapter 9, there are exactly $v - 1$ independent rows in **A** and $e - v + 1$ independent rows in **B**. In other words, the ranks of these matrices are

Rank of vertex matrix: $v - 1$

Rank of circuit matrix: $e - v + 1$

Now that it is known *how many* independent equations can be written for the vertex and circuit equations, it remains to be shown *how* to *select* those vertices and circuits which correspond to independent equations. The selection of independent equations depends upon topological considerations which will also be studied in some detail in Chapter 9. In the meantime, it will suffice to concern ourselves with the study of procedures of writing independent vertex and circuit equations.

Two well-known techniques of writing these equations are the *node* formulation and the *mesh* formulation. As will be seen in the following sections, node formulation is based upon selecting $v-1$ vertices of a system graph. The $v-1$ vertex equations corresponding to these vertices are independent, since any $v-1$ vertex equations constitute an independent set. Mesh formulation, on the other hand, is based upon $e-v+1$ independent circuit equations which belong to those circuits made up by the "windows" or "meshes" of a graph.

6.3 Node Formulation

Node formulation is one of several practical procedures used to derive models of systems. Node formulation may be viewed as a modification of the formulation process used so far. It is based upon the introduction of a new set of across variables, called *node variables*. These node variables are defined as the variables which are associated with those across measurements made between each one of $v-1$ arbitrarily chosen vertices and the remaining v^{th} vertex of a system graph. The $v-1$ vertices thus chosen are called *nodes*, and the remaining vertex *reference* or *ground*. It was established in the last section that the $v-1$ vertex equations corresponding to these vertices are independent.

Node variables are measured positive from the nodes to ground, as illustrated by Figure 6.2.

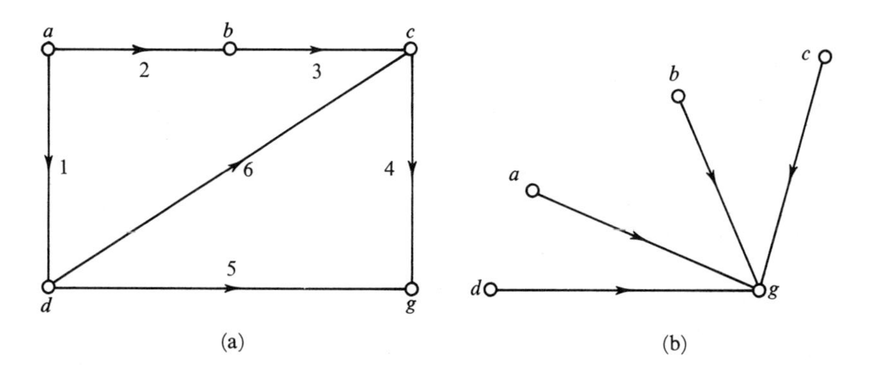

Fig. 6.2. *Relationship between nodes and ground nodes—a, b, c, d, ground—g:* (a) *system graph;* (b) *graph defining node variables.*

The use of the node variables is most effectively demonstrated by an example. Consider the electrical circuit shown in Figure 6.3. It is a resistor network, supplied by two constant voltage sources. We wish to calculate the voltage difference between vertices b and d. The system graph is shown in Figure 6.4.

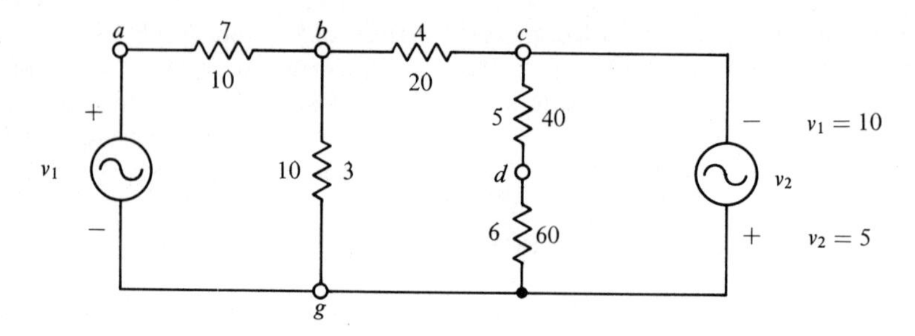

Fig. 6.3. *Resistor network.*

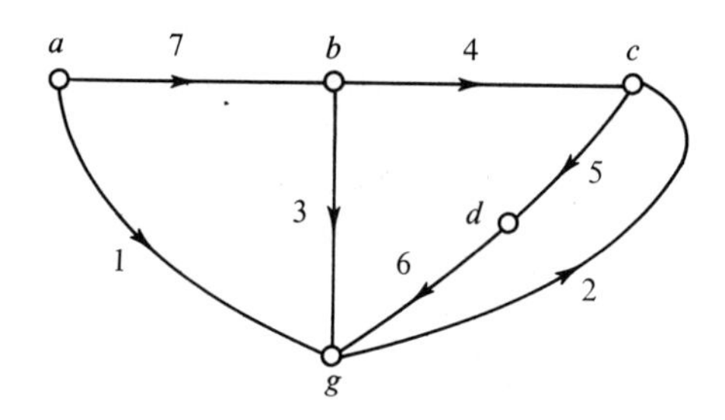

Fig. 6.4. *System graph.*

Since the desired information is in terms of voltages, it is advisable to attempt to derive equations in terms of across variables.

Vertices *a*, *b*, *c*, and *d* are defined as nodes. For each of the nodes, we will write a vertex equation and, where possible, make use of component equations.

$$\left.\begin{aligned} &a. && i_1 + \frac{v_7}{R_7} = 0 \\ &b. && -\frac{v_7}{R_7} + \frac{v_3}{R_3} + \frac{v_4}{R_4} = 0 \\ &c. && -\frac{v_4}{R_4} + \frac{v_5}{R_5} - i_2 = 0 \\ &d. && -\frac{v_5}{R_5} + \frac{v_6}{R_6} = 0 \end{aligned}\right] \tag{6.12}$$

If we attempted a solution of these equations at this time, we would be confronted with four equations and seven unknowns. We will now introduce the node variables as defined by the *node graph* of Figure 6.5. They are v_a, v_b, v_c, and v_d and express the system across variables in

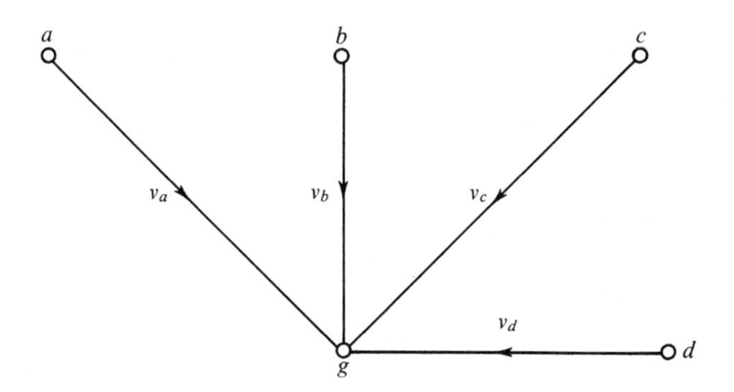

Fig. 6.5. *Node graph.*

terms of the node variables. To accomplish this, superimpose the node graph on the system graph, as shown in Figure 6.6.

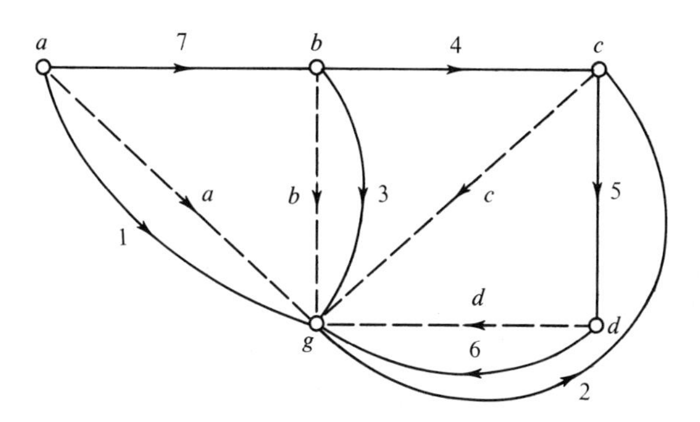

Fig. 6.6. *Combined system graph and node graph.*

From the combined graph we will write seven circuit equations from circuits formed by exactly one system element and whatever node elements it takes to complete a circuit.

$$\left.\begin{aligned} v_1 &= v_a \\ v_2 &= -v_c \\ v_3 &= v_b \\ v_4 &= v_b - v_c \\ v_5 &= v_c - v_d \\ v_6 &= v_d \\ v_7 &= v_a - v_b \end{aligned}\right] \tag{6.13}$$

Next, we substitute Equations 6.13 into Equations 6.12.

$$\left.\begin{aligned}
&a. \qquad & i_1 + \frac{v_a - v_b}{R_7} &= 0 \\
&b. \qquad & -\frac{v_a - v_b}{R_7} + \frac{v_b}{R_3} + \frac{v_b - v_c}{R_4} &= 0 \\
&c. \qquad & -\frac{v_b - v_c}{R_4} + \frac{v_c - v_d}{R_5} - i_2 &= 0 \\
&d. \qquad & -\frac{v_c - v_d}{R_5} + \frac{v_d}{R_6} &= 0
\end{aligned}\right] \qquad \textbf{(6.14)}$$

A count reveals that there are four equations and six unknowns. However, since $v_a = v_1$ and $v_c = -v_2$, which are the specified drivers, we can write Equation 6.14 as

$$\left.\begin{aligned}
i_i + \frac{v_1 - v_b}{R_7} &= 0 \\
\frac{v_b - v_1}{R_7} + \frac{v_b}{R_3} + \frac{v_b + v_2}{R_4} &= 0 \\
-\frac{v_b + v_2}{R_4} - \frac{v_2 + v_d}{R_5} i_2 &= 0 \\
\frac{v_2 + v_d}{R_5} + \frac{v_d}{R_6} &= 0
\end{aligned}\right] \qquad \textbf{(6.15)}$$

The last equations are four equations in four unknowns. In fact, they may be solved in a sequential manner, starting with the second equation. Using the numerical values, the results are

$$\begin{aligned}
v_b &= +3 \qquad & i_1 &= -0.7 \\
v_d &= -3 \qquad & i_2 &= -0.35
\end{aligned}$$

The desired result is $v_b - v_d = 6$.

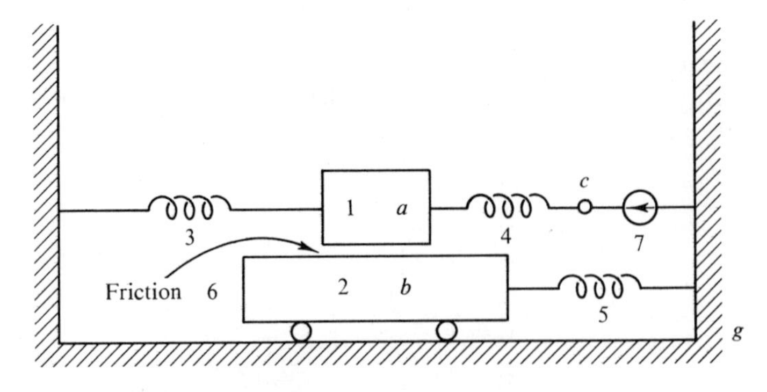

Fig. 6.7. *Mechanical vibration system.*

Consider next the mechanical system shown in Figure 6.7. The two masses are allowed to slide relative to one another with viscous friction. We will assume that the initial energy states of the components are zero, that is, the system is at rest when the force driver is applied. The node equations for this system are to be derived. The system graph is drawn by carefully investigating the component interconnections. Recall that masses, when viewed as two-terminal components, require a reference as the secend terminal. In this case, the foundation serves as the inertial reference; it will also serve conveniently as the nodal reference. As nodes, we then naturally select the vertices *a*, *b*, and *c*. Thus, as nodal variables we may choose either the displacements from the nodes to ground or the velocities. We will choose δ_a, δ_b, and δ_c. There will be three equations,one for each node.

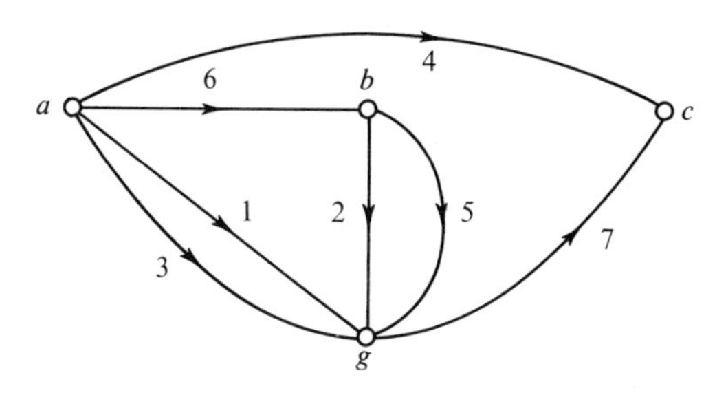

Fig. 6.8. *System graph.*

$$\left.\begin{aligned} a. \quad & k_3\delta_3 + M_1\ddot{\delta}_1 + B_6\dot{\delta}_6 + k_4\delta_4 = 0 \\ b. \quad & -B_6\dot{\delta}_6 + M_2\ddot{\delta}_2 + k_5\delta_5 = 0 \\ c. \quad & -k_4\delta_4 - f_7 = 0 \end{aligned}\right] \tag{6.16}$$

Note that each term in these equations represents a force.

The relationships between the nodal variables and the system variables are

$$\left.\begin{aligned} \delta_1 &= \delta_a \\ \delta_2 &= \delta_b \\ \delta_3 &= \delta_a \\ \delta_4 &= \delta_a - \delta_c \\ \delta_5 &= \delta_b \\ \delta_6 &= \delta_a - \delta_b \end{aligned}\right] \tag{6.17}$$

Notice that Equations 6.17 were written directly from the system graph without the addition of the node graph; it is not difficult to imagine the node graph superimposed. Equations 6.17 are now substituted into Equations 6.16, yielding the three node equations

$$k_3\delta_a + M_1\ddot{\delta}_a + B_6(\dot{\delta}_a - \dot{\delta}_b) + k_4(\delta_a - \delta_c) = 0$$
$$-B_6(\dot{\delta}_a - \dot{\delta}_b) + M_2\ddot{\delta}_b + k_5\delta_b = 0$$
$$-k_4(\delta_a - \delta_c) - f_7 = 0$$

Equations 6.18 represent three simultaneous equations. They are differential equations and non-homogeneous. For the present, we will not concern ourselves with the solution of these equations; instead attention is focused on the process of formulating node equations and the properties of node equations.

Properties of Node Equations

1. *Number of equations.* For a system graph with v vertices, there are exactly $v - 1$ node equations. The $v - 1$ equations are derived from $v - 1$ independent vertex equations of the graph. The number of unknowns is equal to the number of equations.
2. *Node variables.* The node variables are across variables, and may be defined by a node graph in their definition and orientation.
3. *Relation between node variables and system across variables.* The system across variables can be expressed as linear combinations of the node variables. This relationship is established through circuit equations resulting from the formation of circuits involving exactly *one* system element and whatever node elements it takes to complete a circuit in the combined node and system graph.
4. *Sign of node variable in an equation.* The node variable, x_i, and its related derivatives will appear with identical signs in the node equation corresponding to vertex i. This property is a consequence of the manner in which node variables are defined and the fact that the orientation of elements corresponding to passive components is arbitrary. This property is extremely useful in checking the signs of an equation.
5. *Drivers.* The through variables of drivers will appear in those node equations corresponding to vertices where driver elements are incident. These variables are known if they correspond to through drivers; they are unknown if they correspond to across drivers.

6.4 Mesh Formulation

If the formulation process is started with a set of $e-v+1$ independent circuit equations, we are led to mesh formulation. It is based upon the use of *mesh variables*. These are $e - v + 1$ through variables which are assumed to exist " flowing " in those $e - v + 1$ circuits which form

" windows " in a system graph. Considcr the system graph in Figure 6.9. It has $v = 5$ vertices and $e = 7$ elements.

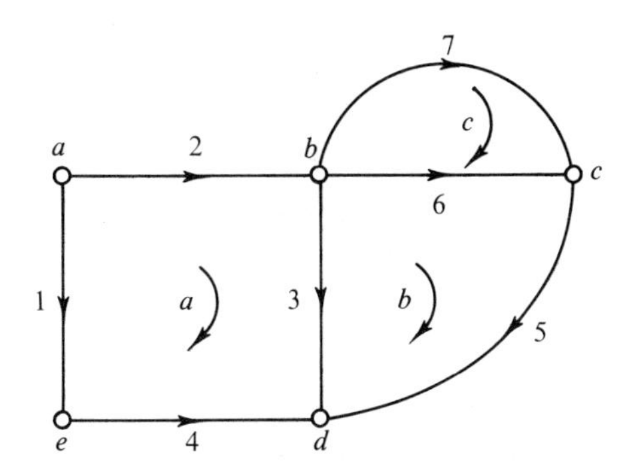

Fig. 6.9. *System graph and mesh circuits.*

There are $e - v + 1 = 3$ windows, as marked by letters a, b, and c. This number coincides with the number of independent circuit equations that can be written for this graph. These circuits are called *mesh circuits*. The mesh variables are positive when oriented clockwise. They are related to the system by the three circuit equations that can be written for the mesh circuit by appropriately expressing the system through variables as linear conbinations of the corresponding mesh variables.

We will consider a number of examples to demonstrate the use of the mesh variables in the formulation of a mathematical model for a system. Consider first the electrical network shown in Figure 6.10. Let the system be initially at rest. The system graph is constructed first.

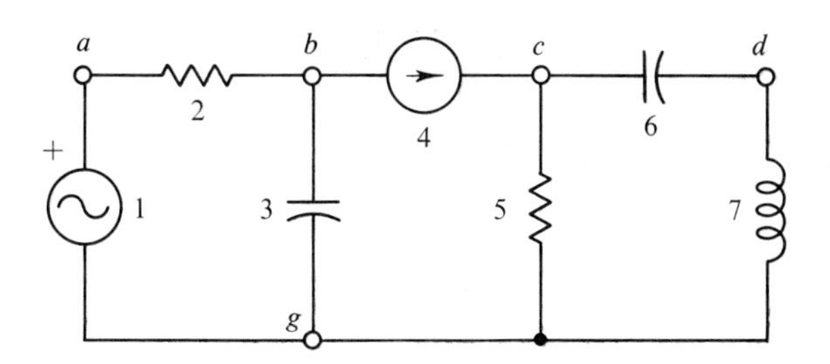

Fig. 6.10. *Electrical network.*

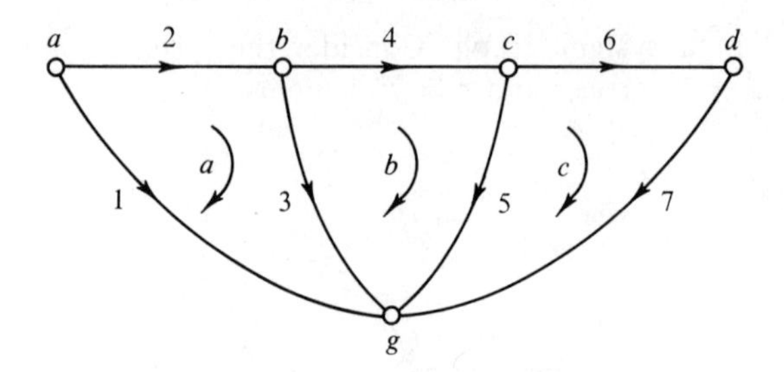

Fig. 6.11. *System graph.*

For the three mesh circuits we have

$$\left.\begin{array}{ll} a. & -v_1 + v_2 + v_3 = 0 \\ b. & -v_3 + v_4 + v_5 = 0 \\ c. & -v_5 + v_6 + v_7 = 0 \end{array}\right] \quad (6.18)$$

Now substitute the component equations into Equations 6.18. Using the Laplace transformation we obtain

$$\left.\begin{array}{ll} a. & R_2 I_2 + \dfrac{1}{C_3 s} I_3 = V_1 \\ b. & -\dfrac{1}{C_3 s} I_3 + V_4 + R_5 I_5 = 0 \\ c. & -R_5 I_5 + \dfrac{1}{C_6 s} I_6 + L_7 s I_7 = 0 \end{array}\right] \quad (6.19)$$

The system through variables (currents) are related to the mesh variables by

$$\left.\begin{array}{l} I_2 = I_a \\ I_3 = I_a - I_b \\ I_4 = I_b \\ I_5 = I_b - I_c \\ I_6 = I_c \\ I_7 = I_c \end{array}\right] \quad (6.20)$$

If Equations 6.20 are now substituted into Equations 6.19, we obtain the *mesh equations* of the system.

$$\left.\begin{array}{r} R_2 I_a + \dfrac{1}{C_3 s}(I_a - I_b) = V_1 \\ -\dfrac{1}{C_3 s}(I_a - I_b) + V_4 + R_5(I_b - I_c) = 0 \\ -R_5(I_b - I_c) + \dfrac{1}{C_6 s} I_c + L_7 s I_c = 0 \end{array}\right] \quad (6.21)$$

Equations 6.21 are three simultaneous equations. A solution of these equations is possible by Laplace transform procedures provided there are only three unknowns. Counting the unknowns, we have

$$V_4, I_a, I_b, I_c$$

but $I_b = I_4$, which is specified. So in fact there are exactly three unknowns and three equations. In this case, the first and third equations of Equations 6.21 may be solved independently of the second.

The next example concerns a rotational drive system, shown in Figure 6.12. Again, our object is to derive the mesh equations.

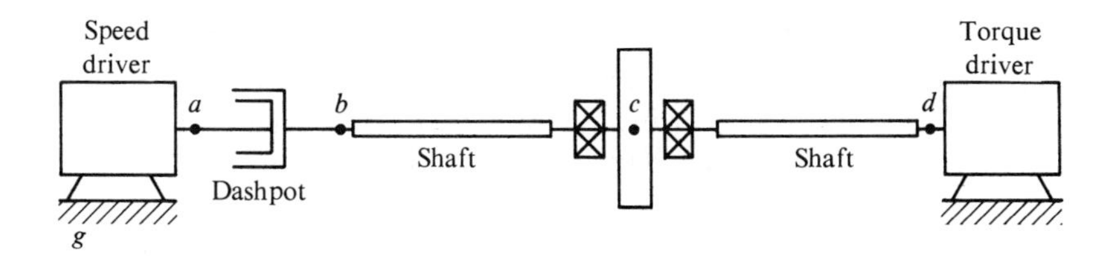

Fig. 6.12. *Rotational drive system.*

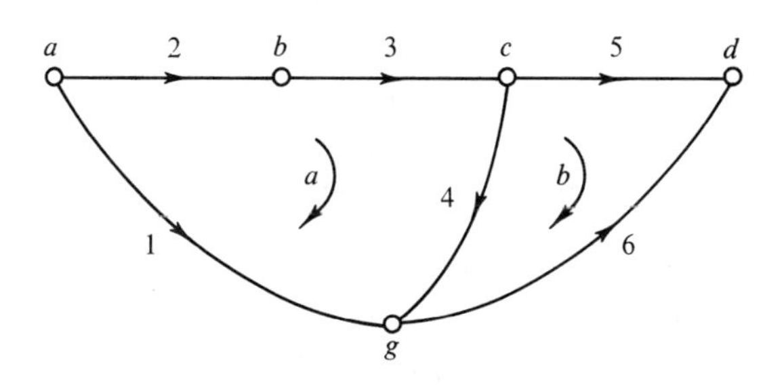

Fig. 6.13. *System graph.*

The system graph reveals two mesh circuits; this agrees with the equation count for independent circuits: $e - v + 1 = 6 - 5 + 1 = 2$. The equations corresponding to the two circuits are

$$-\dot{\varphi}_1 + \dot{\varphi}_2 + \dot{\varphi}_3 + \dot{\varphi}_4 = 0$$
$$-\dot{\varphi}_4 + \dot{\varphi}_5 - \dot{\varphi}_6 = 0$$

We are using rotational velocities in this example, since this is obviously a more appropriate variable in a rotational drive system.

The component equations are

$$\left.\begin{aligned}
&\dot{\varphi}_1 - \text{specified} \\
&\dot{\varphi}_2 = \frac{1}{B_2}\tau_2 \\
&\dot{\varphi}_3 = \frac{1}{k_3}\dot{\tau}_3 \qquad \text{or} \qquad \frac{1}{k_3}sT_3 = \dot{\Phi}_3 \\
&\dot{\varphi}_4 = \frac{1}{J_4}\int_0^t \tau_4 dx \qquad \text{or} \qquad \frac{1}{J_4 s}T_4 = \dot{\Phi}_4 \\
&\dot{\varphi}_5 = \frac{1}{k_5}\dot{\tau}_5 \qquad \text{or} \qquad \frac{1}{k_5}sT_5 = \dot{\Phi}_5 \\
&T_6 - \text{specified}
\end{aligned}\right] \tag{6.23}$$

Note that all component terminal equations are expressed explicitly in terms of the rotational velocities so that they may be readily substituted into the circuit equations. The mesh variable substitutions are

$$\left.\begin{aligned}
&T_1 = -T_a \\
&T_2 = T_a \\
&T_3 = T_a \\
&T_4 = T_a - T_b = T_a + T_6(s) \\
&T_5 = T_b = -T_6(s) \\
&T_6 = -T_b
\end{aligned}\right] \tag{6.24}$$

Equations 6.24 are first substituted into Equations 6.23; the result is then substituted into Equations 6.22, yielding

$$\left.\begin{aligned}
&\frac{1}{B_2}T_a + \frac{1}{k_3}sT_a + \frac{1}{J_4 s}[T_a + T_6(s)] = \dot{\Phi}_1(s) \\
&-\frac{1}{J_4}s[T_a + T_6(s)] - \frac{1}{k_5}sT_6(s) - \dot{\Phi}_6 = 0
\end{aligned}\right] \tag{6.25}$$

These are the mesh equations for the system. They contain exactly two unknowns, T_a and $\dot{\varphi}_6$.

Mesh formulation is characterized by a number of general properties which now may be listed.

1. *Number of equations*. For a system graph with v vertices and e elements, there are exactly $e - v + 1$ mesh equations. The equations are derived from the $e - v + 1$ independent circuit equations that exist for the windows of the system graph.

2. *Mesh variables*. The mesh variables are through variables which are assumed to exist flowing in the mesh circuits with a positive clockwise orientation.

6.5 Mesh Formulation Versus Node Formulation

In formulating a mathematical model of a physical system of two-terminal components, several criteria may have to be considered in determining the most suitable formulation process. The most important are: (1) the complexity of the resulting mathematical model; (2) utilization of information about the system's initial state; and (3) the consistency of the resulting model with stated objectives.

We will present several examples and consider these criteria in choosing the formulation process.

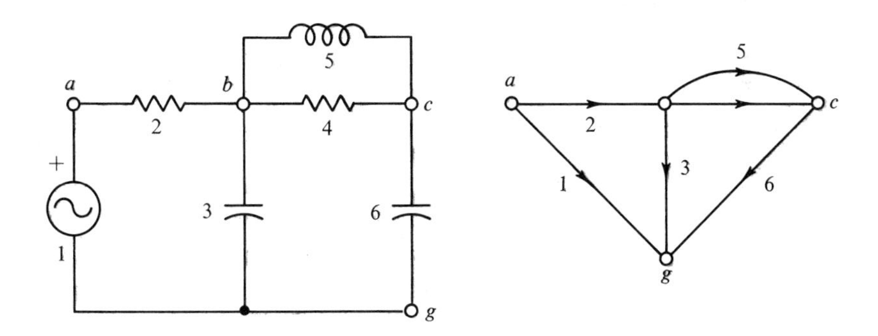

Fig. 6.14. *Electrical network and system graph.*

Example 6.1. For the network shown in Figure 6.14 there are $e = 6$ elements and $v = 4$ vertices. Hence, both mesh and node formulation will yield three equations to be solved. These are

Mesh equations:

$$\left.\begin{aligned} R_2 I_a + \frac{1}{C_3 s}(I_a - I_b) &= V_1 \\ \frac{1}{C_3 s}(I_b - I_a) + R_4(I_b - I_c) + \frac{1}{C_6 s} I_b &= 0 \\ R_4(I_c - I_b) + L_5 s I_c &= 0 \end{aligned}\right] \qquad (6.26)$$

Node equations:

$$\left.\begin{aligned} I_1 + \frac{V_1(s) - V_b}{R_2} &= 0 \\ \frac{V_b - V_1(s)}{R_2} + C_3 s V_b + \frac{V_b - V_c}{R_4} + \frac{1}{L_5 s}(V_b - V_c) &= 0 \\ \frac{V_c - V_b}{R_4} + \frac{1}{L_5 s}(V_c - V_b) + C_6 s V_6 &= 0 \end{aligned}\right] \qquad (6.27)$$

Both Equations 6.26 and 6.27 are sets of three simultaneous equations in three unknowns. The unknown variables are, for Equations 6.26, I_a, I_b, and I_c; and for Equations 6.27, I_1, V_b, and V_c.
It appears that an equal amount of effort will be required to solve each set of equations. However, a closer inspection of Equations 6.27 reveals that only the second and third equations will have to be solved simultaneously. This significant reduction in the complexity of the solution is due to the fact that one of the node variables, V_a, was specified from the beginning. In fact, this information was available before the equations were written. Thus, in this case, a decision in favor of node formulation could have been reached immediately.

Example 6.2. This example treats another electrical network which has $e = 8$ elements and $v = 5$ vertices. From an equation count, we determine that there are four node equations and four mesh equations.

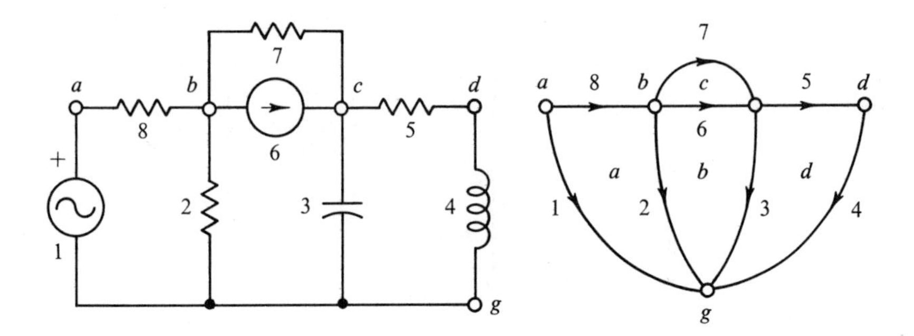

Fig. 6.15. *Electrical network and system graph.*

Node equations:

$$
\left.\begin{aligned}
I_1 + \frac{V_1(s) - V_b}{R_8} &= 0 \\
\frac{V_b - V_1(s)}{R_8} + \frac{V_b}{R_2} + I_6(s) + \frac{V_b - V_c}{R_7} &= 0 \\
\frac{V_c - V_b}{R^7} - I_6(s) + C_3 s V_c + \frac{V_c - V_d}{R_5} &= 0 \\
\frac{V_d - V_c}{R_5} + \frac{1}{L_4 s} V_d &= 0
\end{aligned}\right] \qquad (6.28)
$$

Initial condition are assumed to be zero.

Mesh equations:

$$
\left.\begin{aligned}
R_7 I_a + R_2(I_a - I_b) &= V_1(s) \\
R_2(I_b - I_a) + V_6(s) + \frac{1}{C_3 s}(I_b - I_d) &= 0 \\
\frac{1}{C_3}(I_d - I_b) + R_5 I_d + L_4 s I_d &= 0 \\
- V_6(s) + R_8 I_c &= 0
\end{aligned}\right] \qquad (6.29)
$$

In Equations 4.28, the node equations, there are four unknowns:

$$I_1, V_b, V_b, V_d$$

These may be determined by first solving the last three equations for V_b, V_c, and V_d and then solving the first equation for I_1. Thus, in node formulation, three simultaneous equations have to be solved.

The mesh equations, Equations 6.29, in their present form have five unknowns;

$$I_a, I_b, I_c, I_d, V_6$$

This number, however, is reduced to four when the so-far unused mesh substitution $I_6 = I_b - I_c$ is introduced into Equations 6.29. The four equations, however, must be solved simultaneously. As in the previous case, node formulation is preferred.

Example 6.3. For this mechanical system, we have to write three node equations and two mesh equations.

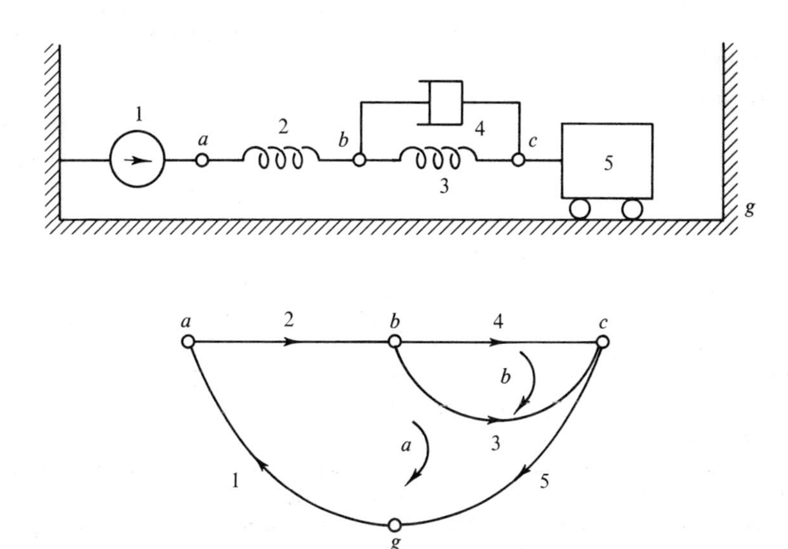

Fig. 6.16. *Mechanical system and system graph.*

Node equations:

$$\left.\begin{aligned} F_1(s) &= k_2(\Delta_a - \Delta_b) \\ k_2(\Delta_b - \Delta_a) + k_3(\Delta_b - \Delta_c) + B_4(\dot{\Delta}_b - \dot{\Delta}_c) &= 0 \\ k_3(\Delta_c - \Delta_b) + B_4(\dot{\Delta}_c - \dot{\Delta}_b) + M_5\ddot{\Delta}_c &= 0 \end{aligned}\right] \quad (6.30)$$

Mesh equations:

$$\left.\begin{aligned} \Delta_1 + \frac{F_1(s)}{k_2} + \frac{F_1(s) - F_b}{k_3} + \frac{1}{M_5 s^2} F_1(s) &= 0 \\ \frac{F_b - F_1(s)}{k_3} + \frac{F_b}{k_4} &= 0 \end{aligned}\right] \quad (6.31)$$

An inspection of the resulting equations immediately reveals that Equations 6.30 constitute three equations in three unknowns and all have to be solved simultaneously. On the other hand, Equations 6.31 contain two unknowns, and the second equation may be solved independently of the first. In this example, mesh formulation definitely is to be favored.

The decision to select mesh formulation or node formulation for solving a particular problem is influenced primarily by the number of simultaneous equations that have to be solved. We have seen from the above examples that the following equation count applies: mesh formulation, $e - v + 1$; node formulation, $v - 1$. In any case, these counts indicate the maximum number of simultaneous equations. In a great number of cases (however not as a general rule), the total number of equations is reduced by the number of drivers present. Let n_x be the number of across drivers and n_y be the number of through drivers present in a system. Then the minimum and maximum number of equations that may have to be solved for the two methods of formulation are

Mesh formulation:

$$\text{maximum,} \quad e - v + 1 \quad (6.32a)$$
$$\text{minimum,} \quad e - v + 1 - n_y \quad (6.32b)$$

Node formulation:

$$\text{maximum,} \quad v - 1 \quad (6.33a)$$
$$\text{minimum,} \quad v - 1 - n_x \quad (6.33b)$$

In analyzing the equation count for the three examples, we find that Example 6.1 required three node equations. However, one of the node variables was specified and the equation count was reduced by one, corresponding to the minimum as indicated by Equation 6.33b. For the same example, the equation count for mesh formulation was maintained at the maximum since there were no specified through drivers.

In Example 6.2, the number of simultaneous node equations was three, corresponding to the minimum. Again, a specified across driver reduced the number of unknown node variables. The number of simultaneous mesh equations was four, corresponding to the maximum. Despite the fact that one through driver was specified for the system, it could not be utilized to reduce the number of unknown mesh variables.

In Example 6.3, the number of simultaneous mesh equations was one, corresponding to the minimum. This was due to the fact that one mesh variable could be directly related to the specified through driver. The number of simultaneous node equations was three, which corresponds to the maximum since no across variables were specified.

The flow diagram of Figure 6.17 outlines the mesh and node formulation process. The basic formulation pattern as first indicated in Figure 5.14 is maintained.

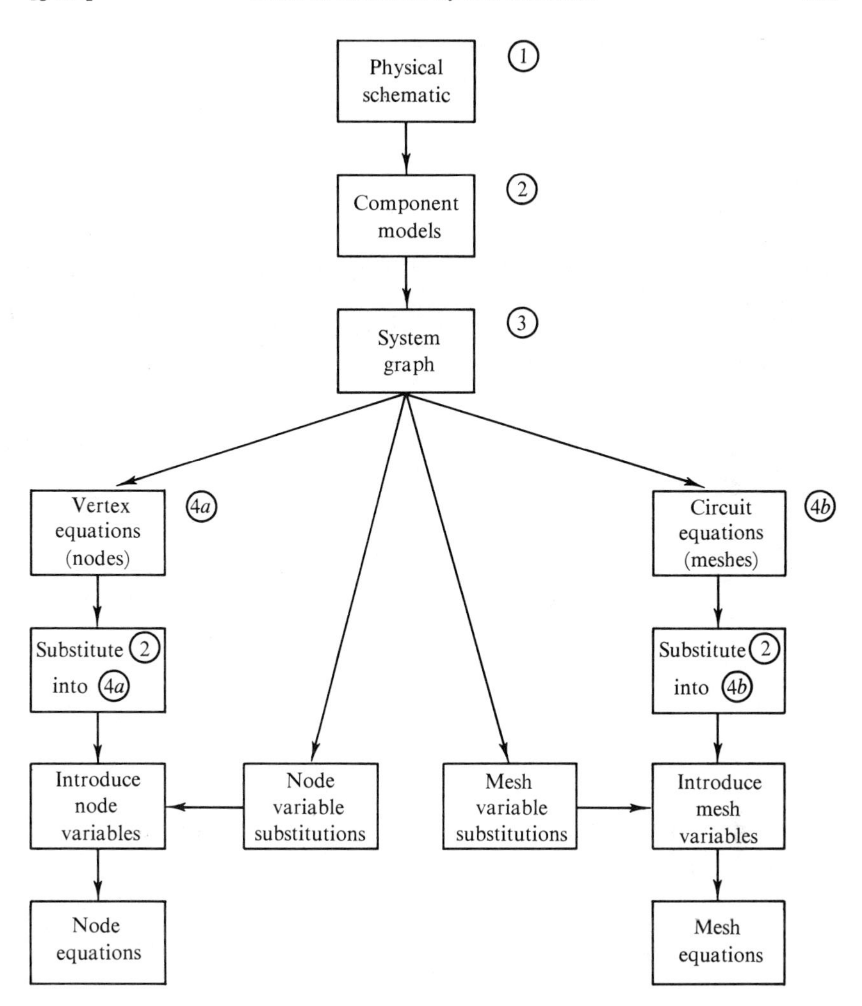

Fig. 6.17. *Flow chart of mesh and node formulation.*

6.6 Matrix Notation

As evidenced in the last three sections, the use of mesh and node techniques leads to the generation of several simultaneous linear equations as the mathematical model. These equations, in general, are first order or second order differential equations; upon application of the Laplace transform, they are simple algebraic equations. The solution of these equations is most easily accomplished by the use of Laplace transforms. Thus even if one desires to formulate the system equations as a time domain model, operational calculus is required to solve them. For this reason it is more practical to formulate mesh and node equations directly in the s-domain.

It is of considerable advantage to write the mesh and mode equation resulting in a formulation as a set of matrix equations. The value of matrix algebra in the solution of simultaneus equations is well established. Furthermore, the use of matrices will reveal a number of symmetry properties which will aid directly in the reduction of formulation errors. Consider the circuit shown in Figure 6.18 as an illustration of these advantages. We propose to calculate the voltage across the capacitor C_4 in response to the voltage source.

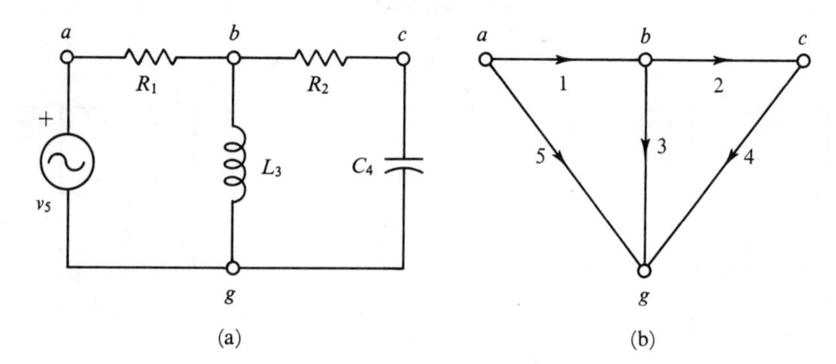

Fig. 6.18. *Electrical network and system graph.*

First consider the choice of formulation process. The equation count is

Mesh formulation:

$$e - v + 1 - n_y = 5 - 4 + 1 - 0 = 2$$

Node formulation:

$$v - 1 - n_x = 4 - 1 - 1 = 2$$

In this case, n_x is equal to 1 since the specified across driver can be used as a node variable. In view of the desired objective, choose node formulation.

The node equations are

$$\left.\begin{aligned} I_1 + (V_1(s) - V_b)/R_1 &= 0 \\ (V_b - V_1(s))/R_1 + I_{03}/s + V_b/sL_3 + (V_b - V_c)/R_2 &= 0 \\ (V_c - V_b)/R_2 + C_4(sV_c - V_{04}) &= 0 \end{aligned}\right] \quad \textbf{(6.34)}$$

where I_{03} is the initial condition for the inductor and V_{04} is the initial condition for the capacitor.

As predicted, Equations 6.34 involve the solution of two simultaneous equations in V_b and V_c, the last two equations. The top equation may be solved later for I_1. Since our objective is to determine v_4, we need to solve for V_c, hence the solution of the two simultaneous equations is necessary. In matrix format these two equations are written

$$\begin{bmatrix} 1/R_1 + 1/sL_3 + 1/R_2 & -1/R_2 \\ -1/R_2 & 1/R_2 + C_4 s \end{bmatrix} \begin{bmatrix} V_b \\ V_c \end{bmatrix} = \begin{bmatrix} V_1(s)/R_1 - I_{03}/s \\ C_4 V_{04} \end{bmatrix}$$

Since only the forced response is required, we may disregard the initial conditions and thus have

$$\begin{bmatrix} 1/R_1 + 1/sL_3 + 1/R_2 & -1/R_2 \\ -1/R_2 & 1/R_2 + C_4 s \end{bmatrix} \begin{bmatrix} V_b \\ V_c \end{bmatrix} \begin{bmatrix} V_1(s)/R_1 \\ 0 \end{bmatrix} \quad (6.35)$$

Equations 6.35 may be solved by calculating the inverse of the coefficient matrix on the left hand side and multiplying both sides through by it.

$$\begin{bmatrix} V_b \\ V_c \end{bmatrix} = \frac{1}{D(s)} \begin{bmatrix} 1/R_2 + C_4 s & +1/R_2 \\ +1/R_2 & 1/R_1 + 1/sL_3 + 1/R_2 \end{bmatrix} \begin{bmatrix} V_1(s)/R_1 \\ 0 \end{bmatrix}$$

where

$$D(s) = \frac{L_3 C_4 (R_1 + R_2) s^2 + (R_1 R_2 C_4 + L_3) s + R_1}{R_1 R_2 L_3 s}$$

so that

$$V_c = \frac{L_3 s V_1(s)}{L_3 C_4 (R_1 + R_2) s^2 + (R_1 R_2 C_4 + L_3) s + R_1} \quad (6.36)$$

If now $v_1(t)$ is given so that $V_1(s)$ may be calculated, then the inverse Laplace transform of Equation 6.36 will yield the desired t-domain result. This aspect of the solution will be deferred. Presently, we will concentrate on the formulation process using matrix notation. For convenience, it will be assumed that the energy states of all storage components involved in the systems are zero. Although this condition is

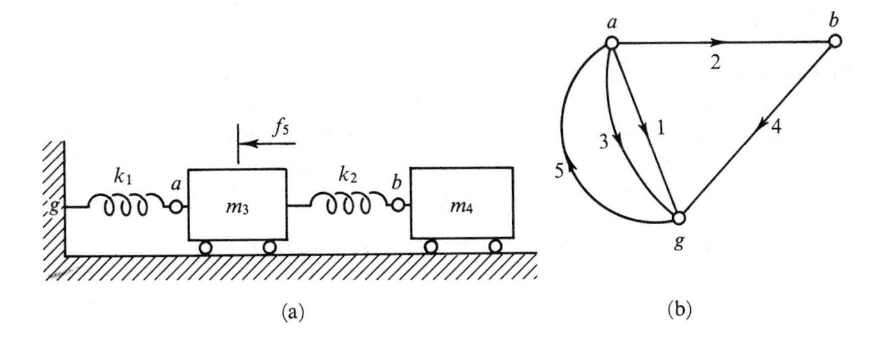

Fig. 6.19. *Mechanical system.*

not generally met, in most practical problems the interest is in the response of a system to external drivers.

Example 6.4. Suppose we have the mechanical system shown in Figure 6.19. An equation count reveals that for mesh formulation, $e-v+1-n_y=3-1=2$ (three equations, two simultaneous); for node formulation, $v-1=2$ (two equations, two simultaneous). A preference for node formulation is indicated. As usual, in mechanical systems vertex g is the reference node, leaving two node equations to be written. These are

$$M_3s^2\Delta_a + k_1\Delta_a + k_2(\Delta_a - \Delta_b) = F_5(s)$$
$$k_2(\Delta_b - \Delta_a) + M_4s^2\Delta_b = 0$$

In matrix format, this becomes

$$\begin{bmatrix} M_3s^2 + k_1 + k_2 & -k_2 \\ -k_2 & M_4s^2 + k_2 \end{bmatrix} \begin{bmatrix} \Delta_a \\ \Delta_b \end{bmatrix} = \begin{bmatrix} F_5(s) \\ 0 \end{bmatrix} \tag{6.37}$$

The coefficient matrix of Equation 6.37 is identified as a symmetric matrix. It may be written in the following symbolic form:

$$\begin{bmatrix} W_{11} & W_{12} \\ W_{21} & W_{22} \end{bmatrix}$$

It is called the *node-admittance matrix* of the system. Note the following relations between the coefficients of the matrix and the topology of the system.

1. The diagonal coefficients, W_{ii}, are composed of the sum of displacement admittances connected to the ith node ($i = a, b, c \cdots$). The sign is positive.

2. The off-diagonal coefficients, W_{ij}, are composed of the sum of the displacement admittances connected between nodes i and j ($i = a, b, c \cdots, j = a, b, c \cdots$). The sign is negative.

These two properties are valid in general for all node-admittance matrices. With a little practice the student will find them to be very useful in deriving the matrix equations directly.

Example 6.5. In this example, we will follow mesh formulation. An equation count reveals that there will be three simultaneous equations to be solved for mesh formulation as compared with four equations for node formulation. We immediately write the following mesh equations:

$$\left.\begin{aligned} -V_1(s) + R_2I_a + R_3(I_a - I_b) &= 0 \\ R_3(I_b - I_a) + \frac{1}{C_7s}(I_b - I_d) + L_4s(I_b - I_c) &= 0 \\ L_4s(I_c - I_b) + R_6(I_c - I_d) + \frac{1}{C_5s}I_c + R_9I_c &= 0 \\ V_8 + R_6(I_d - I_c) + \frac{1}{C_7s}(I_d - I_b) &= 0 \\ I_d &= I_8(s) \end{aligned}\right] \tag{6.38}$$

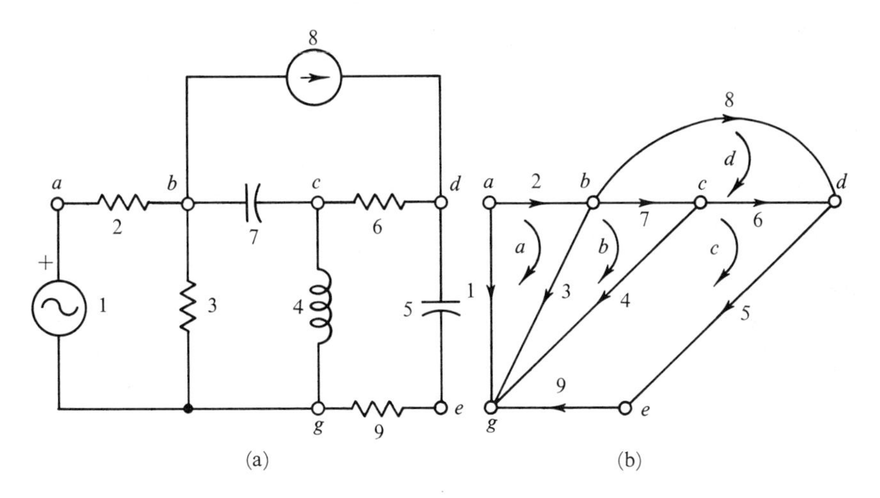

Fig. 6.20. *Electrical circuit:* (a) *schematic;* (b) *system graph.*

Equations 6.38 have four unknowns, the three mesh currents I_a, I_b, I_c, and the voltage V_8 associated with the current driver. In presenting Equations 6.38 in matrix format, we separate the current variables from the voltage variables by transferring them to the right hand side. We then have

$$\begin{bmatrix} R_2 + R_3 & -R_3 & 0 & 0 \\ -R_3 & R_3 + \dfrac{1}{C_7 s} + L_4 s & -L_4 s & -\dfrac{1}{C_7 s} \\ 0 & -L_4 s & L_4 s + R_6 + R_9 + \dfrac{1}{C_5 s} & -R_6 \\ 0 & -\dfrac{1}{C_7 s} & -R_6 & R_6 + \dfrac{1}{C_7 s} \end{bmatrix} \begin{bmatrix} I_a \\ I_b \\ I_c \\ I_d \end{bmatrix} = \begin{bmatrix} V_1(s) \\ 0 \\ 0 \\ -V_8 \end{bmatrix} \tag{6.39}$$

$$I_d = I_8(s)$$

The coefficient matrix of Equations 6.39, like that of Equations 6.37, is symmetric. It may be written in the following symbolic form:

$$\begin{bmatrix} Z_{11} & Z_{12} & Z_{13} & Z_{14} \\ Z_{21} & Z_{22} & Z_{23} & Z_{24} \\ Z_{31} & Z_{32} & Z_{33} & Z_{34} \\ Z_{41} & Z_{42} & Z_{43} & Z_{44} \end{bmatrix}$$

It is called the *mesh impedance matrix* of the system.

Note the following relations between the coefficients of the mesh impedance matrix and the topology of the system.

1. The diagonal coefficients, Z_{ii}, are composed of the sum of the impedances contained in mesh $i (i = a, b, \cdots)$. These coefficients are all positive.

2. The off-diagonal coefficients, Z_{ij}, are composed of the sum of the impedances corresponding to elements incident to both meshes i and $j(i = a, b, c \cdots, j = a, b, c \cdots)$. These coefficients are negative.

It should be pointed out that this relation is valid only as long as all mesh currents are assumed to be positive clockwise and the signs of the coefficients are determined with respect to the mesh current variables. An inspection of Equations 6.39 further reveals that the top three equations may be solved independently of the fourth equation, thus requiring the simultaneous solution of only three equations, as predicted by the equation count.

One further example will be discussed to characterize completely the structure of the resulting matrix equations.

Example 6.6. Our objective shall be to write the node equations for the previous example. We have

$$I_1 + \frac{V_a - V_b}{R_2} = 0$$
$$(V_b - V_a)/R_2 + C_7 s(V_b - V_c) + V_b/R_3 + I_8(s) = 0$$
$$C_7 s(V_c - V_b) + \frac{1}{L_4 s} V_c + (V_c - V_d)/R_6 = 0$$
$$(V_d - V_c)/R_6 + C_5 s(V_d - V_6) - I_8 = 0$$
$$C_5 s(V_e - V_d) + V_e/R_9 = 0$$
$$V_a = V_1$$

In matrix form,

$$\begin{bmatrix} G_2 & -G_2 & 0 & 0 & 0 \\ -G_2 & G_2 + G_3 + C_7 s & -C_7 s & 0 & 0 \\ 0 & -C_7 s & C_7 s + \dfrac{\Gamma_4}{s} + G_6 & -G_6 & 0 \\ 0 & 0 & -G_6 & G_6 + C_5 s & -C_5 s \\ 0 & 0 & 0 & -C_5 s & G_9 \end{bmatrix} \begin{bmatrix} V_a \\ V_b \\ V_c \\ V_d \\ V_e \end{bmatrix} = \begin{bmatrix} -I_1 \\ -I_8(s) \\ 0 \\ I_8 \\ 0 \end{bmatrix} \quad \textbf{(6.40)}$$

$$V_a = V_1(s)$$
$$\Gamma_4 = 1/L_4$$

The coefficient matrix of Equation 6.40 constitutes the node-admittance matrix of the circuit. Note that the bottom four equations can be solved independently from the top equation since the right hand matrix contains specified variables only for those rows.

In order to establish the general structure of the resulting matrix equation of the last two examples, we write Equation 6.39 symbolically as

$$\mathbf{Z}_m \cdot \mathbf{Y}_m = \mathbf{X}_d \quad \textbf{(6.41)}$$

where $\mathbf{Z}_m$ is the mesh-impedance matrix, $\mathbf{Y}_m$ is the column matrix representing *all* mesh variables, and $\mathbf{X}_d$ is a column matrix which is constructed as follows:

1. It contains only across variables.
2. Non-zero entries appear in rows corresponding to those mesh circuits containing a driver.
3. The sign is positive when the orientation of the driver element is opposite to the orientation of the mesh circuit.

Similarly, we write Equation 6.40 symbolically as

$$\mathbf{W}_n \cdot \mathbf{X}_n = \mathbf{Y}_d \tag{6.42}$$

where $\mathbf{W}_n$ is the node-admittance matrix, $\mathbf{X}_n$ is the column matrix representing all node variables, and $\mathbf{Y}_d$ is a column matrix which is constructed as follows:

1. It contains only through variables.
2. Non-zero entries appear in rows corresponding to those nodes at which a driver element is incident.
3. The sign is positive when the orientation of the driver element is toward the node.

The examples presented above demonstrate the order and precision by which matrix equations in either mesh or node form may be formulated in the s-domain. Although the orderly pattern which the resulting mathematical system models exhibit is most helpful in the formulation process, it should not be looked upon as the main source for writing s-domain equations. All too frequently, algorithms of the type developed above may backfire when used blindly. One must always remember that the origin of all equations, the mathematical models of systems, are always the vertex and circuit laws. This fact will become particularly significant when multiterminal components are introduced in the general study of physical systems.

6.7 A Time-Domain Solution

Having developed to some lengths the systematic procedures of mesh and node formulation, it is appropriate to present an example of a fully worked-out problem. As a medium for discussion, consider the mechanical system shown in Figure 6.21. A platform is moving with a constant velocity. It is carrying a mass, which is connected through

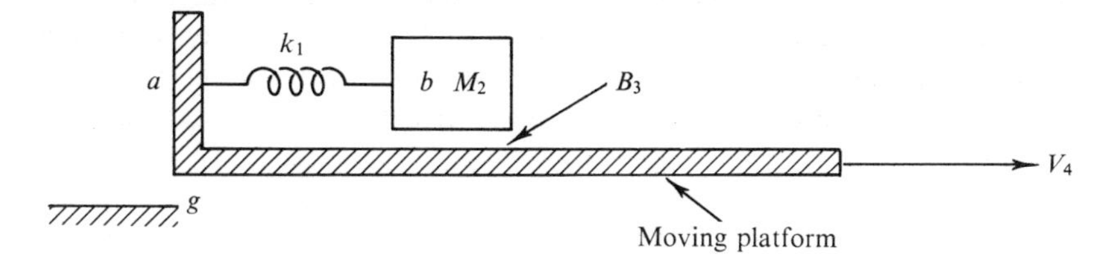

Fig. 6.21. *Moving platform.*

a viscous friction contact to point g. Suddenly the platform reverses its direction of motion, maintaining the same magnitude of velocity. We wish to calculate the motion of the mass after the change is applied. The system graph is shown in Figure 6.22.

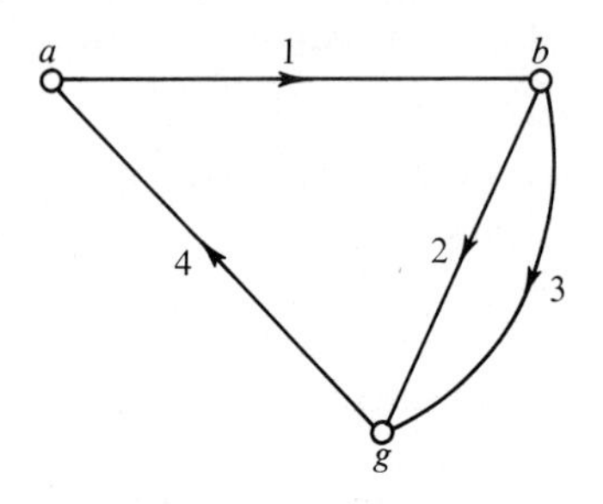

Fig. 6.22. *System graph.*

The node equations are written in terms of the velocity admittance matrix.

$$\begin{bmatrix} \dfrac{k_1}{s} & -\dfrac{k_1}{s} \\ -\dfrac{k_1}{s} & \dfrac{k_1}{s} + B_3 + M_2 s \end{bmatrix} \begin{bmatrix} \dot{\Delta}_a \\ \dot{\Delta}_b \end{bmatrix} = \begin{bmatrix} F_4 \\ M_2 V_0 \end{bmatrix} \qquad \textbf{(6.43)}$$

Equations 6.43 contain two equations in two unknowns, consistent with the node equation count. Since one of the node variables is specified, the two equations may be solved independently, starting with the bottom one. Thus we may write

$$\dot{\Delta}_b = \frac{s}{M_2 s^2 + B_3 s + k_1} \left[\frac{k_1}{s} \dot{\Delta}_a + M_2 V_0 \right] \qquad \textbf{(6.44)}$$

and

$$F_4 = \frac{k_1}{s} (\dot{\Delta}_b - \dot{\Delta}_a) \qquad \textbf{(6.45)}$$

Equation 6.44 expresses a relation between the two sources of excitation for the system, the velocity driver and the initial condition of the mass, and the velocity of the mass. The t-domain solution obtained from this equation is the total response of the system. To clarify this, separate Equation 6.44 into two parts corresponding to (a) response due to driver

$$\dot{\Delta}_b = \frac{k_1}{M_2 s^2 + B_3 s + k_1} \dot{\Delta}_a(s) \qquad \textbf{(6.46)}$$

and (b) response due to initial condition,

$$\dot{\Delta}_b = \frac{M_2 s}{M_2 s^2 + B_3 s + k_1} V_0 \tag{6.47}$$

The functions relating the respective responses to the drivers are called *transfer functions*. Symbolically, we may write

$$\underbrace{\dot{\Delta}_b}_{\text{response}} = \underbrace{G_1(s)}_{\text{transfer function}} \cdot \underbrace{\dot{\Delta}_a(s)}_{\text{excitation}} \tag{6.48}$$

and

$$\underbrace{\dot{\Delta}_b}_{\text{response}} = \underbrace{G_2(s)}_{\text{transfer function}} \cdot \underbrace{V_0}_{\text{excitation}} \tag{6.49}$$

where the transfer functions are

$$G_1(s) = \frac{k_1}{M_2 s^2 + B_3 s + k_1}$$

$$G_2(s) = \frac{M_2 s}{M_2 s^2 + B_3 s + k_1}$$

Equation 6.44 and Equations 6.48 and 6.49 taken separately correspond to the following conditions:

Equation 6.48 will give the solution to: system initially at rest; velocity driver applied at time $t = 0$.

Equation 6.49 will give the solution to: system initially at equilibrium with velocity V_0. At $t = 0$ the platform is stopped dead.

Equation 6.44 will give the solution to: system initially at equilibrium with velocity V_0. Velocity driver, $-V_0$, applied at time $t = 0$.

Now determine the time function corresponding to Equation 6.44. Let

$$\dot{\Delta}_a(s) = -\frac{V_0}{s}$$

then

$$\dot{\Delta}_b = \frac{-\omega_n^2}{s(s^2 + 2\zeta\omega_n s + \omega_n^2)} V_0 + \frac{s}{(s^2 + 2\zeta\omega_n s + \omega_n^2)} V_0 \tag{6.50}$$

where

$$\omega_n = \sqrt{\frac{k_1}{M_2}}$$

$$\zeta = \frac{B_3}{2\sqrt{k_1 M_2}}$$

Even though Equation 6.50 can be simplified, it will be advantageous to evaluate the inverse transform directly from its present form. We obtain

$$\dot{\delta}_b(t) = -V_0\left[1 - \frac{1}{\sqrt{1-\zeta^2}}e^{-\zeta\omega_n t}\sin(\omega_n\sqrt{1-\zeta^2}t + \phi_1)\right]$$

$$+ V_0\frac{1}{\sqrt{1-\zeta^2}}e^{-\zeta\omega_n t}\sin(\omega_n\sqrt{1-\zeta^2}t + \phi_1)$$

$$\phi_1 = \tan^{-1}\frac{\sqrt{1-\zeta^2}}{-\zeta} \quad \textbf{(6.51)}$$

The solution is interpreted as follows. The first part is response due to the velocity driver

$$\underbrace{\dot{\delta}_b(t)\Big]}_{\text{driver}} = \underbrace{-V_0\Big[1}_{\text{ss}} \underbrace{- \frac{1}{\sqrt{1-\zeta^2}}e^{-\zeta\omega_n t}\sin(\omega_n\sqrt{1-\zeta^2}t + \phi_1)\Big]}_{\text{transient}} \quad \textbf{(6.52)}$$

It consists of a transient and a steady state. The second part is the response due to the the initial condition,

$$\underbrace{\dot{\delta}_b(t)\Big]}_{\text{initial condition}} = \underbrace{V_0\frac{1}{\sqrt{1-\zeta^2}}e^{-\zeta\omega_n t}\sin(\omega_n\sqrt{1-\zeta^2}t + \phi_1)}_{\text{transient}} \quad \textbf{(6.53)}$$

It consists only of a transient.

The transient in both parts of the solution consists of an identical function. It is a characteristic of the system. It is related to the transfer function in that the time function is determined exclusively by the roots of the characteristic equation of the system,

$$s^2 + 2\zeta\omega_n s + \omega_n^2 = 0 \quad \textbf{(6.54)}$$

It is seen that the two transfer functions have an identical denominator.

Example 6.7. Determine the time response for the system described by Figure 6.21 when the following numerical values are specified:

$k_1 = 10$ newtons/meter
$M_2 = 1$ kilogram
$B_3 = 2$ newton-second/meter
$V_0 = 0.1$ meter/second

The characteristic equation is

$$s^2 + 2s + 10 = 0 \quad \textbf{(6.55)}$$

and

$$\omega_n = \sqrt{\frac{10}{1}} = 3.16 \text{ radians/second}$$

$$\zeta = \frac{2}{2\sqrt{10}} = \frac{1}{3.16} = 0.316$$

Since $\zeta < 1$ we conclude that the response will be underdamped. The response due to the driver is calculated from Equation 6.52.

$$\dot{\delta}_b(t)]_{\text{driver}} = 0.1[1 - 1.05e^{-t} \sin (3t + 108.4°)]$$

The response due to the initial conditions is obtained from Equation 6.53.

$$\dot{\delta}_b(t)]_{\substack{\text{initial}\\\text{condition}}} = 0.105e^{-t} \sin (3t + 108.4°)$$

To assist in plotting these responses, the initial and final values are calculated by letting $t = 0$ and $t = \infty$.
Initial value:

$$\dot{\delta}_b(0)]_{\text{driver}} = -0.1[1 - 1.05 \sin 108.4°] = 0$$

$$\dot{\delta}_b(0)]_{\substack{\text{initial}\\\text{condition}}} = 0.105 \sin 108.4° = 0.1$$

Final value:

$$\dot{\delta}_b(\infty)]_{\text{driver}} = -0.1[1 - 0] = -0.1$$

$$\dot{\delta}_b(\infty)]_{\substack{\text{initial}\\\text{condition}}} = 0$$

These four values can also be readily obtained directly from Equations 6.46 and 6.47 by use of the initial and final value theorems of Laplace transform theory.
Initial value:

$$\dot{\delta}_b(0)]_{\text{driver}} = \lim_{s \to \infty} s \frac{k_1}{M_2 s^2 + B_3 s + k_1}\left(-\frac{V_0}{s}\right) = 0$$

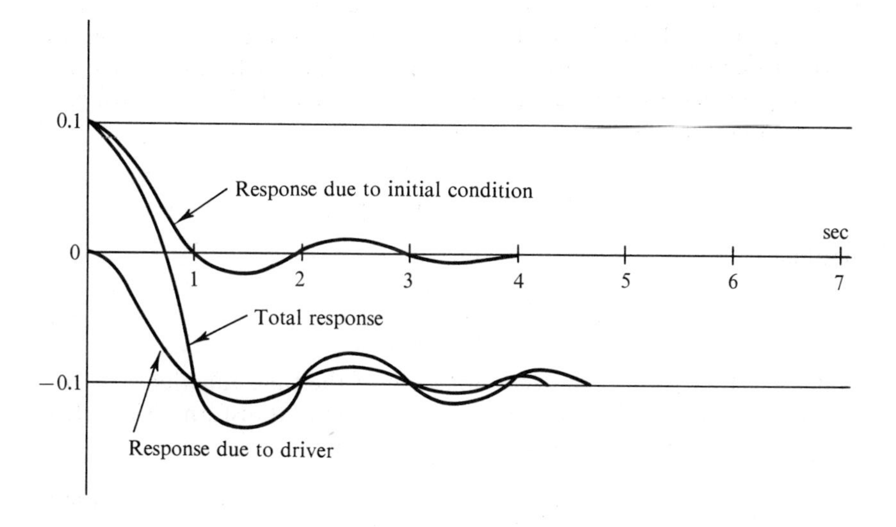

Fig. 6.23. *Response of moving mass.*

$$\dot{\delta}_b(0)]_{\substack{\text{initial}\\ \text{condition}}} = \lim_{s \to \infty} s \frac{M_2 s}{M_2 s^2 + B_3 s + k_1} V_0 = V_0$$

Final value:

$$\dot{\delta}_b(\infty)]_{\text{driver}} = \lim_{s \to \infty} s \frac{k_1}{M_2 s^2 + B_3 s + k_1} \left(- \frac{V_0}{s} \right) = -V_0$$

$$\dot{\delta}_b(\infty)_{\substack{\text{initial}\\ \text{condition}}} = \lim_{s \to 0} \frac{M_2 s^2}{M_2 s^2 + B_3 s + k_1} V_0 = 0$$

The responses are plotted in Figure 6.23.

6.8 The Transfer Function

In the last section the transfer function was introduced. It appeared in connection with relating two variables in the s-domain, the excitation and the response. This relationship is expressed as

$$\underbrace{X_2(s)}_{\text{response}} = \underbrace{G_{21}(s)}_{\text{transfer function}} \cdot \underbrace{X_1(s)}_{\text{excitation}}$$

In a more general setting, we will often find the transfer function being used to relate a system output to a system input. This is expressed as

$$\underbrace{X_{\text{out}}(s)}_{\text{output}} = G_{oi(s)} \cdot \underbrace{X_{\text{in}}(s)}_{\text{input}} \tag{6.56}$$

Due to the important role that the transfer function will assume in later work, particularly in the study of control systems, it is advantageous to investigate now some of the important properties of a transfer function.

Suppose that for a system the transfer function relating two variables has been derived as

$$G_{21}(s) = \frac{1}{(s+1)(s+5)}$$

so that

$$X_2(s) = \frac{5}{(s+1)(s+5)} X_1(s) \tag{6.57}$$

Equation 6.57 permits the determination of the time function $x_2(t)$ for any excitation function $x_1(t)$ for which a Laplace transform exists. Let $x_1(t)$ be a step function. Then $X_1(s) = 1/s$, and

$$X_2 = \frac{5}{s(s+1)(s+5)} \tag{6.57}$$

Or let $x_1(t)$ be a sine wave. Then

$$X_1(s) = \frac{\omega}{s^2 + \omega^2} \tag{6.58}$$

and

$$X_2 = \frac{5\omega}{(s^2 + \omega^2)(s + 1)(s + 5)} \tag{6.59}$$

Similar expressions may be set up for other excitations. For the excitation function leading to Equation 6.58, for instance, the time function $x_2(t)$ is calculated by first finding the partial fraction expansion

$$X_2(s) = \frac{A}{s} + \frac{B}{s+1} = \frac{C}{s+5}$$

where the expansion coefficients are calculated as

$$A = sX_2(s)\Big|_{s=0} = 1$$

$$B = (s+1)X_2(s)\Big|_{s=-1} = -\frac{5}{4}$$

$$C = (s+5)X_2(s)\Big|_{s=-5} = \frac{1}{4}$$

Hence,

$$X_2(t) = 1 - \frac{5}{4}e^{-t} + \frac{1}{4}e^{-5t}$$

As a general rule, a transfer function may be written in the form of a proper rational function, that is,

$$G(s) = \frac{P(s)}{Q(s)} = \frac{k(a_m s^m + a_{m-1}s^{m-1} + \cdots + a_1 s + a_0)}{s^n + b_{n-1}s^{n-1} + \cdots + b_1 s + b_0} \tag{6.60}$$

$P(s)$ and $Q(s)$ are polynomials in s such that $n > m$ and $b_n = 1$. Also, the Laplace transform of an input function may generally be written as

$$X_1(s) = \frac{P_1(s)}{Q_1(s)} \tag{6.61}$$

where $P_1(s)$ and $Q_1(s)$ are also polynomials.

In terms of the expressions specified by Equations 6.60 and 6.61, we now have for the response function

$$X_2(s) = \frac{P(s) \cdot P_1(s)}{Q(s) \cdot Q_1(s)} \tag{6.62}$$

In order to obtain the time function $x_2(t)$ it will be necessary to determine those values of s which are roots of the polynomials $Q(s)$ and $Q_1(s)$

so that the appropriate partial fraction expansion can be generated. These values are called the *zeros* of $Q(s)$ and $Q_1(s)$ and are of extreme significance inasmuch as the nature of the resulting time function is exclusively determined by them. The zeros of $Q(s) \cdot Q_1(s)$ are called the *poles* of the response function $X_2(s)$· In particular, the zeros of $Q(s)$ are the poles of $G(s)$ and the zeros of $Q_1(s)$ are the poles of $X_1(s)$. Also, the zeros of $Q(s)$ are the roots of the *characteristic equation* of the system,

$$Q(s) = 0$$

Let the poles all be simple. And let the poles of $G(s)$ be $p_1, p_2, \cdots, p_n$, and the poles of $X_1(s)$ be $p_a, p_b, \cdots$. Then the partial fraction expansion will take on the form

$$X_2(s) = \frac{k_1}{s - p_1} + \frac{k_2}{s - p_2} + \cdots + \frac{k_n}{s - p_n} + \frac{C_a}{s - p_a} + \frac{C_b}{s - p_b} + \cdots \tag{6.63}$$

and t-domain solution will be

$$X_2(t) = k_1 e^{p_1 t} + k_2 e^{p_2 t} + \cdots + k_n e^{p_n t} + C_a e^{p_a t} + C_b e^{p_a t} + \cdots \tag{6.64}$$

A comparison of Equation 6.64 with Equation 6.63 emphasizes the significance of the poles: each pole is the source of an exponential time function.

For the special case where the excitation is an impulse function

$$x_1(t) = \delta(t) \qquad \text{(impulse function)} \tag{6.65}$$

a simple relation for $X_2(s)$ results. The transform of the excitation is

$$X_1(s) = 1 \tag{6.66}$$

so that

$$X_2(s) = G(s)$$

and the response function is determined entirely by the poles of the system transfer function. This excitation function is particularly useful in demonstrating the relation between the poles and the corresponding time response. This is illustrated in Figure 6.24, where the following cases are presented:

Single pole
- p_1, p_2 in the left-half plane—decaying exponential
- p_3 in the right-half plane—increasing exponential
- p_4 at the origin—constant

Complex conjugate poles
- on the $j\omega$-axis—undamped sinusoid
- in the right-half plane—exponentially increasing sinusoid
- in the left-half plane—exponentially decreasing sinusoid

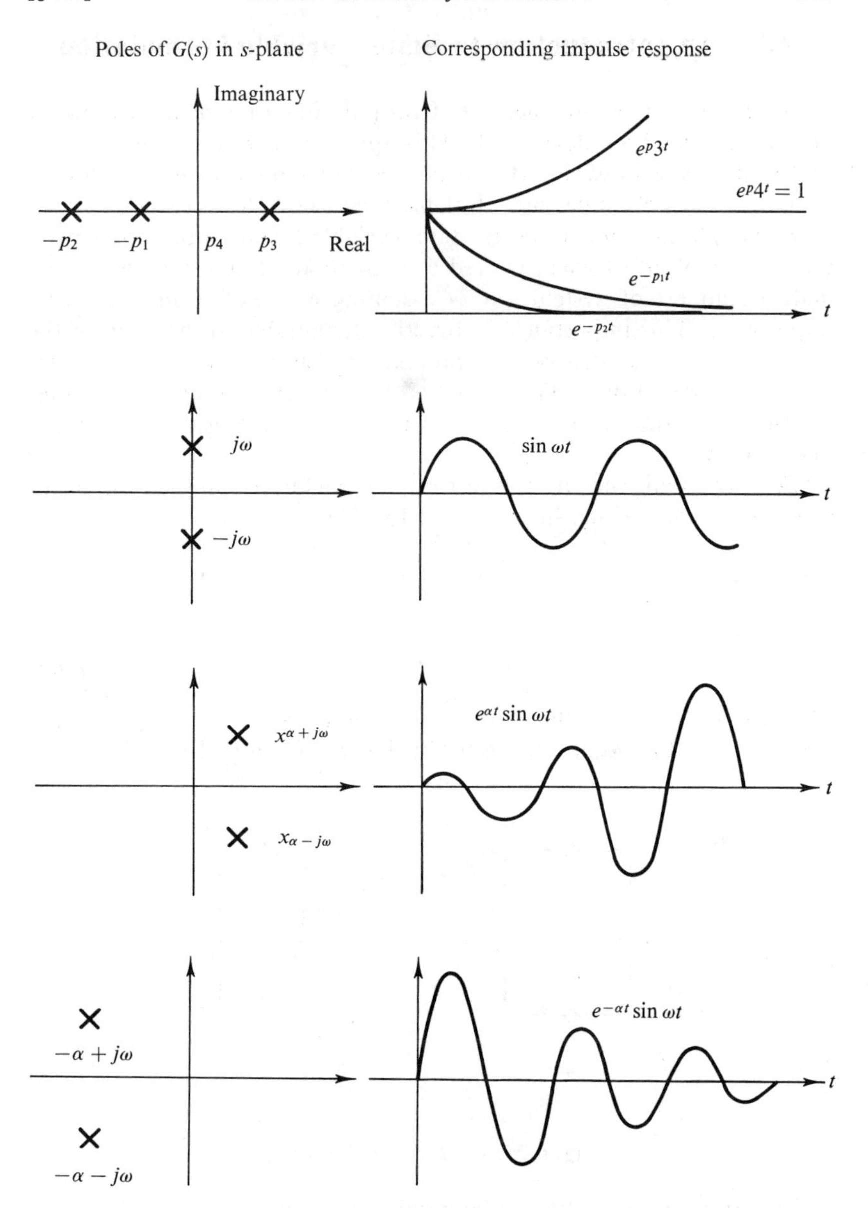

Fig. 6.24. *Relationship between pole configurations and impulse responses.*

A knowledge of the poles of the transfer function of a system completely reveals the nature of the transient response.

6.9 An Introduction to State Variable Formulation

In recent years a new method of formulating a mathematical model of a system has been developed. This approach is based upon the concept of a *state variable* briefly introduced in Chapter 4. It provides for techniques entirely independent of mesh and node techniques.

Although in some respects state variable formulation represents a duplication of effort when viewed as a method of developing mathematical models of systems, it is assuming a role of steadily growing importance. This importance is directly attributable to the form of the system model generated by this process, which is a set of first-order differential equations. This form is particularly useful in computer solutions of system equations. As an introduction, consider the following problem.

For the circuit shown in Figure 6.25(a) we know that the component equations when written in derivative form can be given as

$$\frac{d}{dt}v_1 = \frac{1}{C}i_1$$

$$\frac{d}{dt}i_2 = \frac{1}{L}v_2 \tag{6.67}$$

The subscripts refer to the capacitor and inductor, respectively, and the variables are defined according to the graph of Figure 6.25(b).

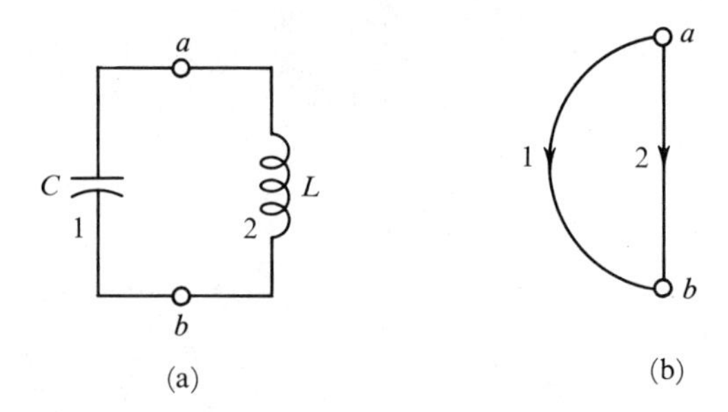

Fig. 6.25. *Electrical circuit.*

Equations 6.67 are two differential equations containing four unknowns. However, there are additional relations between these unknowns as given by the circuit equation

$$v_1 = v_2 \tag{6.68a}$$

and the vertex equation

$$i_1 = -i_2 \tag{6.68b}$$

Upon substitution of Equations 6.68 into Equations 6.67 one obtains

$$\frac{d}{dt} v_1 = -\frac{1}{C} i_2$$

$$\frac{d}{dt} i_2 = \frac{1}{L} v_1$$

The result may be written in matrix form as

$$\frac{d}{dt}\begin{bmatrix} v_1 \\ i_2 \end{bmatrix} = \begin{bmatrix} 0 & -\frac{1}{C} \\ \frac{1}{L} & 0 \end{bmatrix} \begin{bmatrix} v_1 \\ i_2 \end{bmatrix} \tag{6.69}$$

Equation 6.69 is a set of two simultaneous first-order differential equations. Their solution may be carried out utilizing the Laplace transform. Proceeding, we obtain

$$s\begin{bmatrix} V_1 \\ I_2 \end{bmatrix} = \begin{bmatrix} 0 & -\frac{1}{C} \\ \frac{1}{L} & 0 \end{bmatrix} \begin{bmatrix} V_1 \\ I_2 \end{bmatrix} + \begin{bmatrix} v_1(0) \\ i_2(0) \end{bmatrix} \tag{6.70}$$

where the initial conditions of the capacitor and the inductor are introduced as $v_1(0)$ and $i_2(0)$, respectively.

Solving Equations 6.70 for the unknowns,

$$\begin{bmatrix} s & \frac{1}{C} \\ -\frac{1}{L} & s \end{bmatrix} \begin{bmatrix} V_1 \\ I_2 \end{bmatrix} = \begin{bmatrix} v_1(0) \\ i_2(0) \end{bmatrix}$$

or

$$\begin{bmatrix} V_1 \\ I_2 \end{bmatrix} = \begin{bmatrix} s & \frac{1}{C} \\ -\frac{1}{L} & s \end{bmatrix}^{-1} \begin{bmatrix} v_1(0) \\ i_2(0) \end{bmatrix} = \frac{1}{s_2 + \frac{1}{LC}} \begin{bmatrix} s & -\frac{1}{C} \\ \frac{1}{L} & s \end{bmatrix} \begin{bmatrix} v_1(0) \\ i_2(0) \end{bmatrix}$$

In the t-domain,

$$\begin{bmatrix} v_1(t) \\ i_2(t) \end{bmatrix} = \begin{bmatrix} \cos \omega t & -\sqrt{\frac{L}{C}} \sin \omega t \\ \sqrt{\frac{C}{L}} \sin \omega t & \cos \omega t \end{bmatrix} \begin{bmatrix} v_1(0) \\ i_2(0) \end{bmatrix} \tag{6.71}$$

where

$$\omega = \sqrt{\frac{1}{LC}}$$

The manner in which this problem was formulated and solved is characteristic of the state-variable approach. Its solution is interpreted in the following way. The voltage $v_1(t)$ and the current $i_2(t)$ completely define the instantaneous relationship of the variables of the circuit; they completely define the " state " of the circuit for the range $0 < t$. The initial conditions define the state of the circuit at $t = 0$; they constitute the " memory " of the system for the interval $\infty < t < 0$. The memory of the circuit corresponds directly to the state of the system. For any given time t_1, $0 \leq t_1 \leq t$, one could terminate the solution of Equations 6.71 and define $v_1(t_1)$ and $i_2(t_1)$. These values constitute the memory of the state of the circuit at t_1. They would also represent the initial conditions for a continuation of the solution for the time interval $t_1 \leq t$.

The variables $v_1(t)$ and $i_2(t)$ are appropriately called the state variables of the circuit, and Equations 6.69 are called the state equations of the circuit.* It is shown in this example that the state variables correspond to the terminal variables of a capacitor and an inductor. Both these components are energy storage components: they are components with a memory. In mathematical terms these components are identified by the form of their terminal equation; it is expressed in terms of a first order derivative. It is indicated, therefore, that energy storage components such as capacitors, inductors, masses, springs, etc., will play a major role in the formulation of a set of state equations.

The example just discussed is an initial condition problem. The introduction to the state variable approach is continued by considering a system that has an external driver and resistive components (zero memory) in addition to energy storage components.

The circuit of Figure 6.26a contains two energy-storage components, L_1 and C_2. Their terminal equations are written in derivative form.

$$\frac{d}{dt}i_1 = \frac{1}{L_1}v_1$$
$$\frac{d}{dt}v_2 = \frac{1}{C_2}i_2 \tag{6.72}$$

Since there are two storage elements in the circuit, we expect that the final set of state equations will consist of two equations. These equations should be expressed in terms of the two state variables i_1 and v_2 and involve, of course, the driver $v_{in}(t)$. It is therefore necessary to

* As we will see later, state variables are not unique. There are usually a number of useful choices for a given system.

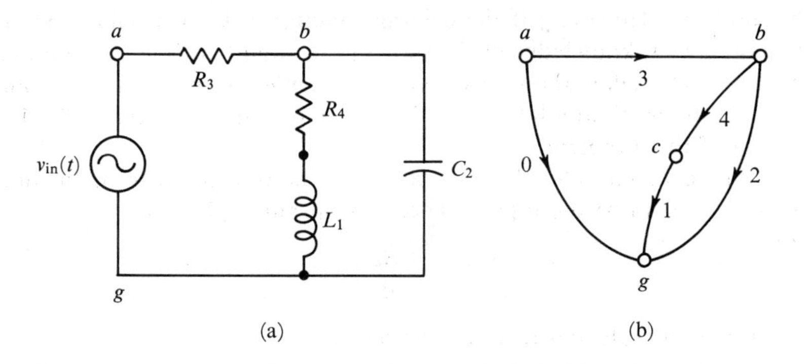

Fig. 6.26. *Circuit and system graph.*

eliminate v_1 and i_2 through the use of circuit and vertex equations as determined from the graph of Figure 6.26(b). Thus, we find

$$v_1 = v_2 - v_4$$
$$i_2 = i_3 - i_1{}^*$$

Since

$$v_4 = R_4 i_4 = R_4 i_1 \quad \text{and} \quad i_3 = \frac{1}{R_3} v_3 = \frac{1}{R_3}(v_{\text{in}} - v_2)$$

we have

$$v_1 = v_2 - R_4 i_1 \quad \text{and} \quad i_2 = \frac{1}{R_3}(v_{\text{in}} - v_2) - i_1 \tag{6.73}$$

Notice that the set of variables on the right side of Equation 6.73 contains only the state variables i_1, v_2, and the driver $v_{\text{in}}(t)$. We now substitute Equations 6.73 into the right-hand side of Equation 6.72 and, after rearrangement into matrix form, obtain

$$\frac{d}{dt}\begin{bmatrix} i_1 \\ v_2 \end{bmatrix} = \begin{bmatrix} \dfrac{-R_4}{L_1} & \dfrac{1}{L_1} \\ \dfrac{-1}{C_2} & \dfrac{-1}{R_3C_3} \end{bmatrix} \begin{bmatrix} i_1 \\ v_2 \end{bmatrix} + \begin{bmatrix} 1 \\ \dfrac{1}{R_3C_3} \end{bmatrix} v_{\text{in}}(t) \tag{6.74}$$

These are the state equations for the circuit. They may be solved as in the previous example by the Laplace transform. Knowledge of the driving function over the interval $-\infty$ to t is sufficient to determine

* This is a modified vertex equation. See Section 6.10.

the solution. However, if the driving function is known only over the interval t_0 to t, knowledge of the state of the circuit at time t_0 is required to completely define the solution for $t_0 \leq t$. We will return to the solution of this circuit at a later time. For the moment let us explore further aspects of this problem.

Suppose we consider the voltage across the resistor R_4 to be the output and $v_{\text{in}}(t)$ to be the input. Then the output is given as

$$\begin{aligned} v_{\text{out}}(t) &= R_4 i_4 \\ &= R_4 i_1 \end{aligned}$$

where i_1 is the solution to Equation 6.74.

The complete input-output relation for the circuit may then be obtained by combining the last equation with Equation 6.74.

$$\frac{d}{dt}\begin{bmatrix} i_1 \\ v_2 \end{bmatrix} = \begin{bmatrix} -\dfrac{R_4}{L_1} & \dfrac{1}{L_1} \\ -\dfrac{1}{C_2} & -\dfrac{1}{R_3 C_2} \end{bmatrix} \begin{bmatrix} i_1 \\ v_2 \end{bmatrix} \begin{bmatrix} 0 \\ \dfrac{1}{R_3 C_3} \end{bmatrix} v_{\text{in}}(t) \quad \textbf{(6.75a)}$$

The equation

$$v_{\text{out}}(t) = R_4 i_1 \quad \textbf{(6.75b)}$$

is the output equation. Finally, if we choose the voltage difference between vertices a and c as the output, we obtain for the output equation

$$v_{\text{out}}(t) = v_{ac} = v_{\text{in}}(t) - v_2 + v_4$$

or

$$v_{\text{out}}(t) = [R_4 \quad -1]\begin{bmatrix} i_1 \\ v_2 \end{bmatrix} + v_{\text{in}}(t) \quad \textbf{(6.76)}$$

Equation 6.76 shows the output to be a linear combination of the state variables and the input. A solution for the state variables must accompany Equation 6.76.

An interesting result is obtained when we remove the capacitor and the inductor from the circuit—when in fact the memory elements are removed. This is shown in Figure 6.27. The mathematical equivalent corresponds to letting both L_1 and C_2 approach zero. By multiplying the Equations 6.75a by L_1 and C_2, respectively, we can set L_1 and C_2 to zero, obtaining

$$\mathbf{0} = \begin{bmatrix} -R_4 & 1 \\ -1 & -\dfrac{1}{R_3} \end{bmatrix} \begin{bmatrix} i_1 \\ v_2 \end{bmatrix} + \begin{bmatrix} 0 \\ \dfrac{1}{R_3} \end{bmatrix} v_{\text{in}}(t)$$

from which

$$\begin{bmatrix} i_1 \\ v_2 \end{bmatrix} = \frac{R_3}{R_3 + R_4} \begin{bmatrix} \frac{1}{R_3} & 1 \\ -1 & R_4 \end{bmatrix} \begin{bmatrix} 1 \\ R_3 \end{bmatrix} v_{in}(t) = \frac{1}{R_3 + R_4} \begin{bmatrix} 1 \\ R_4 \end{bmatrix} v_{in}(t)$$

Substituting this result into Equation 6.75b yields

$$v_{out}(t) = \frac{R_4}{R_3 + R_4} v_{in}(t) \tag{6.77}$$

This result clearly shows that the circuit has been made a zero memory circuit; no state variables are required. The output is a direct function of the input. Equation 6.77, of course, is obvious if we consider Figure 6.27.

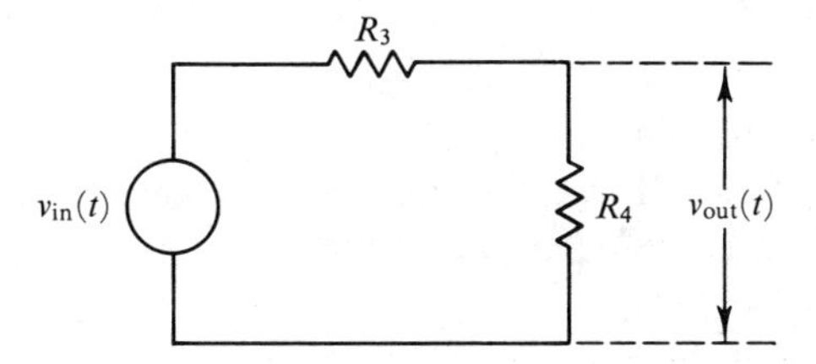

Fig. 6.27. *Reduced circuit corresponding to Equation 6.77.*

State Variable Formulation

The foregoing examples serve to illustrate the state variable approach to the solution of circuit problems. This approach requires the formulation of a set of state equations which in general are of the form

$$\frac{d}{dt} \begin{bmatrix} x_1 \\ x_2 \\ \cdot \\ \cdot \\ \cdot \\ x_n \end{bmatrix} = \begin{bmatrix} a_{11} & a_{12} & \cdots & a_{1n} \\ a_{21} & \cdot\cdot & & \cdot \\ \cdot & & & \cdot \\ \cdot & & & \cdot \\ \cdot & & & \cdot \\ a_{n1} & \cdot & \cdot & a_{nn} \end{bmatrix} \begin{bmatrix} x_1 \\ x_2 \\ \cdot \\ \cdot \\ \cdot \\ x_n \end{bmatrix} + \begin{bmatrix} b_1 \\ b_2 \\ \cdot \\ \cdot \\ \cdot \\ b_n \end{bmatrix} x_{in} \tag{6.78}$$

where $x_1, x_2, \cdots, x_n$ are the state variables of the circuit and x_{in} is the input. Coupled to the state equations is an output equation of the form

$$x_{out} = [c_1 c_2 \cdots c_n] \begin{bmatrix} x_1 \\ x_2 \\ \cdot \\ \cdot \\ \cdot \\ x_n \end{bmatrix} + d x_{in} \tag{6.79}$$

where x_{out} is the output variable.

It is usually expedient to use matrix notation for Equations 6.78 and 6.79. Then we write

$$\dot{\mathbf{x}} = \mathbf{A}\mathbf{x} + \mathbf{B}x_{in}(t)$$
$$x_{out}(t) = \mathbf{C}\mathbf{x} + dx_{in}(t) \tag{6.80}$$

where **A** is an $n \times n$ matrix, the system matrix; **B** is an $n \times 1$ matrix, the input matrix; **C** is a $1 \times n$ matrix, the output matrix; and

$$\mathbf{x} = \begin{bmatrix} x_1 \\ x_2 \\ \cdot \\ \cdot \\ \cdot \\ x_n \end{bmatrix}$$

We refer to **x** as the state vector.

The development of state variable techniques as a useful tool in systems analysis requires attention in the formulation of state equations and their solution.

As in the case of mesh and node equations, it will be necessary to consider the independence of those circuit and vertex equations used in the formulation of state equations. State equations must satisfy the form of Equations 6.78, which requires that the right hand side contains only state variables or specified variables. To fulfill this requirement, intelligent use must be made of the circuit and vertex equations. It may have been obvious that the circuit and vertex equations used in the last example did not correspond to a node equation or a mesh equation. Indeed, in attempting to use state variable formulation in more complicated problems it would rapidly become evident that we would be hopelessly lost without more knowledge on the subject of writing independent vertex and circuit equations. Therefore, the next section presents a more general method than that provided by nodes and meshes.

6.10 Fundamental Cutset and Circuit Equations

We have learned of the importance of writing independent vertex and circuit equations. In connection with mesh and node formulation we studied the technique of determining $v-1$ independent vertex equations for the nodes of a graph and $e - v + 1$ independent circuit equations for the meshes of a graph. Although these relationships are extremely useful, in fact essential, to the success of mesh and node formulation, their application and usefulness is limited to the above techniques. For the state variable formulation we need a more flexible way of defining independent equations. For this purpose we introduce the following definitions.

Definition 6.1: Tree.
A tree is a subset of elements of a graph satisfying any three of the following four conditions:

1. The elements of a tree are connected; that is, each element of a tree has at least one other element of a tree connected to it.
2. The elements of a tree do not form a circuit.
3. There are $v - 1$ elements in a tree.
4. A tree contains v vertices.

These conditions are easily satisfied, and it is a simple matter to determine a tree in any given graph. Trees are not unique; a graph can have many trees. For instance, for the graph shown in Figure 6.28, three trees are shown. It is left as an exercise to determine other possible trees. Usually, additional criteria are available through the nature of a given problem which greatly reduces the number of possible trees. More will be said about this later.

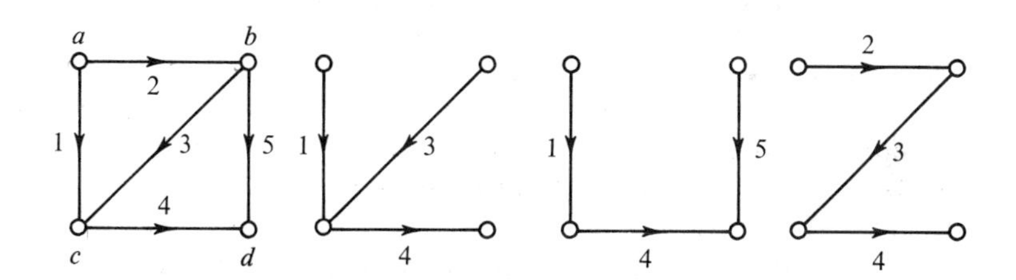

Fig. 6.28. *Graph and three trees.*

Definition 6.2: Branch.
The elements of a tree are called branches.

Definition 6.3: Chord.
The elements of a graph not belonging to a tree are called chords.

There are $v-1$ elements which are branches and $e - v + 1$ elements which are chords, once a tree has been selected. For a given graph it is helpful to mark the tree elements by drawing the branches heavier than the chords.

Associated with a tree are several important topological properties which will be investigated in detail in Chapter 9. The two most important properties are presented now in connection with the following two definitions.

Definition 6.4: Fundamental circuit.
A fundamental circuit consists of exactly one chord and those branches necessary to form a circuit. A fundamental circuit is unique, and there exist exactly $e - v + 1$ fundamental circuits. The orientation of a fundamental circuit is determined by the orientation of the chord.

Consider the graph shown in Figure 6.29. A tree consisting of elements 1, 2, and 3 is selected arbitrarily. Associated with this tree are two fundamental circuits consisting of elements (4, 2, 1) and (5, 3, 4). The orientation of both circuits is clockwise.

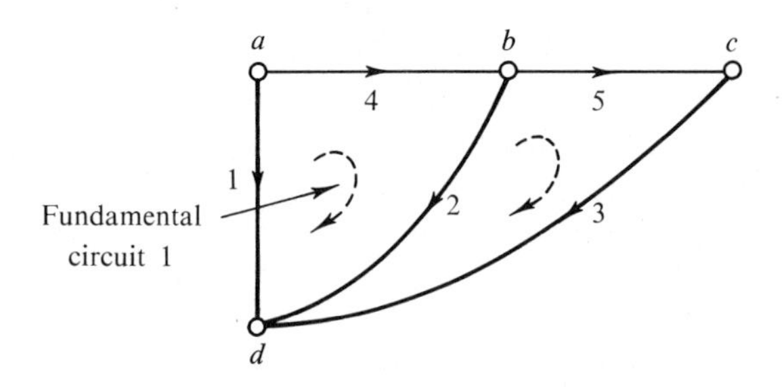

Fig. 6.29. *Graph showing a fundamental circuit.*

Definition 6.5: Fundamental cutset.
A fundamental cutset consists of exactly one branch and those chords which connect between the vertices of the two parts of the tree linked by the branch. A fundamental cutset is unique and there are exactly $v - 1$ cutsets for a given tree.

As an illustration, consider the graph of Figure 6.30. The tree is

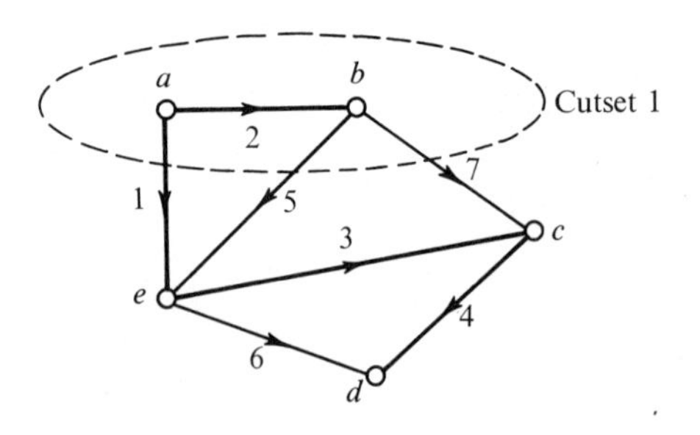

Fig. 6.30. *Graph showing a cutset.*

selected as shown. The four cutsets are determined as follows. Consider branch 1; it defines one cutset. Draw a line through the graph which intersects branch 1 and chords 5 and 7 as shown in Figure 6.30. This line separates the tree into two parts, consisting of vertices (a, b) and (e, c, d). Chords 3 and 4 are the only chords that provide connections between these two parts. Thus, this cutset consists of elements (1, 5, 7). The other cutsets belonging to this tree are branch 2, (2, 5, 7); branch 3, (3, 6, 7); branch 4, (4, 6).

Now consider the circuit equations that are associated with the fundamental circuits. For the graph of Figure 6.29, these equations are

$$-x_1 + x_2 + x_4 = 0$$
$$-x_2 + x_5 + x_3 = 0$$

or in matrix format

$$\begin{bmatrix} -1 & 1 & 0 & 1 & 0 \\ 0 & -1 & 1 & 0 & 1 \end{bmatrix} \begin{bmatrix} x_1 \\ x_2 \\ x_3 \\ x_4 \\ x_5 \end{bmatrix} = \mathbf{0} \tag{6.81}$$

In the same manner, we obtain these equations for the graph of Figure 30:

$$\begin{bmatrix} -1 & 1 & 0 & 0 & 1 & 0 & 0 \\ 0 & 0 & -1 & -1 & 0 & 1 & 0 \\ -1 & 1 & -1 & 0 & 0 & 0 & 1 \end{bmatrix} \begin{bmatrix} x_1 \\ x_2 \\ x_3 \\ x_4 \\ x_5 \\ x_6 \\ x_7 \end{bmatrix} = \mathbf{0} \tag{6.82}$$

Note that the fundamental circuits given by Equations 6.81 and 6.82 possess a very interesting and useful property. The matrices of both sets of equations contain a unit matrix in the trailing position. This is a general property of fundamental circuit equations. Thus the general form of fundamental circuit equations is

$$[\mathbf{B} \mid \mathbf{U}] \begin{bmatrix} \mathbf{X}_b \\ \hline \mathbf{X}_c \end{bmatrix} = \mathbf{0} \tag{6.83}$$

where $\mathbf{B}$ is an $(e - v + 1) \times (v - 1)$ submatrix, $\mathbf{U}$ is a unit matrix of order $e - v + 1$, $\mathbf{X}_b$ is the column matrix of branch across variables, and $\mathbf{X}_c$ is the column matrix of chord across variables.

In order to obtain the fundamental circuit equations in the form of Equations 6.83, it is necessary to arrange the numbering of the elements of the graph so that the branches are numbered first, starting with 1, and the chords are numbered second. This, however, is a requirement easily satisfied.

The fundamental circuit equations constitute a set of independent circuit equations, a fact which is easily proven by the presence of the unit matrix of order $e - v + 1$ in the circuit matrix of Equation 6.83. The unit matrix shows that the rank of the matrix is $e - v + 1$.

As in the fundamental circuit equations, we write equations that correspond to summations of through variables according to the elements of the cutsets of a graph. Consider the following equation belonging to the graph of Figure 6.30:

$$\begin{aligned} y_1 + y_5 + y_7 &= 0 \\ y_2 - y_5 - y_7 &= 0 \\ y_3 + y_6 + y_7 &= 0 \\ y_4 + y_6 \qquad &= 0 \end{aligned}$$

which in matrix format are

$$\begin{bmatrix} 1 & 0 & 0 & 0 & 1 & 0 & 1 \\ 0 & 1 & 0 & 0 & -1 & 0 & -1 \\ 0 & 0 & 1 & 0 & 0 & 1 & 1 \\ 0 & 0 & 0 & 1 & 0 & 1 & 0 \end{bmatrix} \begin{bmatrix} y_1 \\ y_2 \\ y_3 \\ y_4 \\ y_5 \\ y_6 \\ y_7 \end{bmatrix} = \mathbf{0} \qquad \textbf{(6.84a)}$$

Similarly, for the graph of Figure 6.29, one has

$$\begin{bmatrix} 1 & 0 & 0 & 1 & 0 \\ 0 & 1 & 0 & -1 & 1 \\ 0 & 0 & 1 & 0 & -1 \end{bmatrix} \begin{bmatrix} y_1 \\ y_2 \\ y_3 \\ y_4 \\ y_5 \end{bmatrix} = \mathbf{0} \qquad \textbf{(6.84b)}$$

Equations 6.84a and 6.84b can be symbolically represented as

$$[\mathbf{U} \,\vdots\, \mathbf{A}] \begin{bmatrix} \mathbf{Y}_b \\ \hline \mathbf{Y}_c \end{bmatrix} = \mathbf{0} \qquad \textbf{(6.85)}$$

where $\mathbf{U}$ is a unit matrix of order $v - 1$, $\mathbf{A}$ is a $(v - 1) \times (e - v + 1)$ submatrix, $\mathbf{Y}_b$ is the column matrix of branch through variables, and $\mathbf{Y}_c$ is the column matrix of chord through variables.

Equation 6.85 defines the general form of the so-called fundamental cutset equations. The presence of the unit matrix of order $v - 1$ shows that these equations are independent and that the matrix of Equations 6.84 is of maximum rank. We conclude that the fundamental cutset equations represent a set of $v-1$ linearly independent statements of the continuity constraints. Hence, they are totally equivalent to the $v-1$ vertex equations in serving as a basis for expressing the interrelation between the through variables of a system.

Both the fundamental cutset and circuit equations prove to be useful in several formulation techniques. Among them is the state variable formulation. Other formulation techniques will be presented in Chapter 10. Because of the distinction that exists between the node-vertex and mesh-circuit equations, and the fundamental cutset and circuit equations, it will be sufficient to refer to the latter simply as the cutset and circuit equations.

The presence of the unit matrices in the cutset and circuit equations permits these equations to be expressed in a different form. We rewrite Equations 6.83 and 6.85 respectively as

$$\mathbf{X}_c = -\mathbf{B}\mathbf{X}_b \tag{6.86}$$

and

$$\mathbf{Y}_b = -\mathbf{A}\mathbf{Y}_c \tag{6.87}$$

The forms of these equations signifies that all chord across variables may be expressed as linear combinations of the set of branch across variables, while the branch through variables may be expressed as linear combinations of the set of chord through variables. The branch across variables assume a role which corresponds to that of the node variables; a similar correspondence exists between the chord through variables and mesh variables. State variable formulations make extensive use of the relations expressed by Equations 6.86 and 6.87.

6.11 State Variable Equations

General Guidelines

A more systematic method for deriving state equations for a system is now considered. It involves a direct approach whereby the state variables are defined in correspondence with the energy storage components contained in a given system. State variables may be chosen to represent voltages across capacitors, currents through inductors, velocities of masses, pressures in hydraulic capacitors, and the like. The formulation of state equations may be systematically approached by consideration of the topological configuration of a system as expressed by the circuit and cutset equations.

The basic procedure to be used in formulating state equations of systems of two-terminal components was referred to briefly in Section 6.9. It will be reinforced by another example.

Example 6.8. Formulate a set of state equations for the twin-tee network shown in Figure 6.31 (a). The network contains three storage components, C_1, C_2, and C_3. In derivative form their component equations are

$$\frac{d}{dt}\begin{bmatrix} v_1 \\ v_2 \\ v_3 \end{bmatrix} = \begin{bmatrix} 1/C_1 & i_1 \\ 1/C_2 & i_2 \\ 1/C_3 & i_3 \end{bmatrix}$$

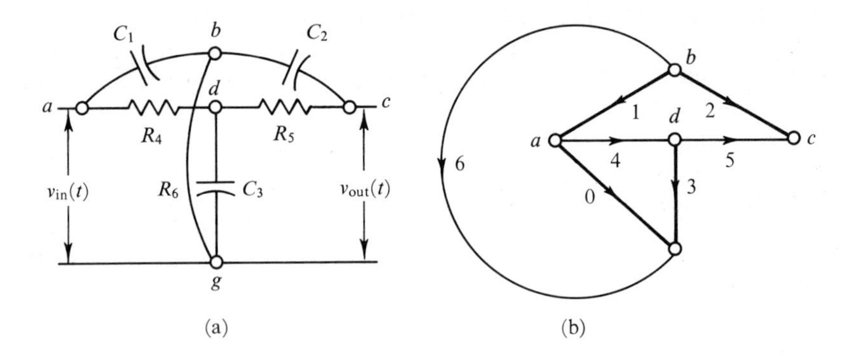

Fig. 6.31. (a) *Twin-tee network;* (b) *system graph.*

We select the voltages v_1, v_2, and v_3 as state variables. Therefore, the state equations should be expressed in terms of these variables. In addition, the input variable, v_{in}, should be included in the state equations. For this purpose we select a tree for the graph in Figure 6.31 (b) that will contain the elements 1, 2, 3, and 0. The choice of such a tree will permit the writing of convenient relations involving all across variables in terms of those variables desired for the state equations. We proceed toward this end in writing the following cutset equations:

$$\begin{aligned} i_1 &= -i_6 + i_5 \\ i_2 &= -i_5 \\ i_3 &= i_4 - i_5 \end{aligned}$$

Furthermore, we have the terminal equations for the resistors:

$$\begin{aligned} v_4 &= R_4 i_4 \quad &\text{or}\quad i_4 &= G_4 v_4 \\ v_5 &= R_5 i_5 \quad &\text{or}\quad i_5 &= G_5 v_5 \\ v_6 &= R_6 i_6 \quad &\text{or}\quad i_6 &= G_6 v_6 \end{aligned}$$

We will substitute these equations into the cutset equations, but before that, it is expedient to express v_4, v_5, and v_6 in terms of the tree voltages by the circuit equations

$$\begin{aligned} v_4 &= v_{in} - v_3 \\ v_5 &= -v_1 + v_2 + v_3 - v_{in} \\ v_6 &= v_1 + v_{in} \end{aligned}$$

Now performing the proposed substitutions, we obtain

$$i_1 = -G_6(v_{in} + v_1) + G_5(-v_1 + v_2 + v_3 - v_{in})$$
$$i_2 = -G_5(-v_1 + v_2 + v_3 + v_{in})$$
$$i_3 = G_4(v_{in} - v_3) - G_5(-v_1 + v_2 + v_3 - v_{in})$$

Rearranging into matrix format,

$$\begin{bmatrix} i_1 \\ i_2 \\ i_3 \end{bmatrix} = \begin{bmatrix} -(G_6 + G_5) & +G_5 & G_5 \\ +G_5 & -G_5 & -G_5 \\ +G_5 & -G_5 & -(G_5 + G_4) \end{bmatrix} \begin{bmatrix} v_1 \\ v_2 \\ v_3 \end{bmatrix} = \begin{bmatrix} -(G_5 + G_6) \\ +G_5 \\ G_4 + G_5 \end{bmatrix} v_{in}$$

and finally substituting into the capacitor component equations,

$$\frac{d}{dt}\begin{bmatrix} v_1 \\ v_2 \\ v_3 \end{bmatrix} = \begin{bmatrix} \frac{-(G_5 + G_6)}{C_1} & \frac{+G_5}{C_1} & \frac{G_5}{C_1} \\ \frac{+G_5}{C_2} & \frac{-G_5}{C_2} & \frac{-G_5}{C_2} \\ \frac{+G_5}{C_3} & \frac{G_5}{C_3} & \frac{-(G_5 + G_4)}{C_3} \end{bmatrix} \begin{bmatrix} v_1 \\ v_2 \\ v_3 \end{bmatrix} + \begin{bmatrix} \frac{(-G_5 + G_6)}{C_1} \\ \frac{G_5}{C_2} \\ \frac{(G_4 + G_5)}{C_3} \end{bmatrix} v_{in}(t) \tag{6.88}$$

These equations constitute the first part of the state equations. As anticipated, the state variables are the voltages across the capacitors, the storage components of the circuit.

We complete the state equations for the twin-tee network by introducing the output equation

$$v_{out}(t) = v_{in}(t) + v_1 - v_2$$

or in matrix form,

$$v_{out}(t) = [1\ -1\ 0]\begin{bmatrix} v_1 \\ v_2 \\ v_3 \end{bmatrix} + v_{in}(t)$$

Note the direct transfer term in the equations.

The above example suggests a systematic procedure for the formulation of state equations for systems of two-terminal components. Basically, three steps are involved:

1. Selection of state variables. In most cases, this may be accomplished by determining the storage components present in the system and selecting those variables in their component equation which are in derivative form.

2. Selection of a tree in the system graph. The tree should be selected such that it contains

   (a) all across drivers;

   (b) all those elements whose components have equations with an across variable as the derivative, such as capacitors and masses;

   (c) none of the elements whose components have equations with a through variable as the derivative, such as inductors and springs;

(d) no through drivers;
(e) finally, as many elements as are required to complete the tree corresponding to nonmemory components, such as resistors and dashpots.

3. Use of as many circuit and cutset equations as are necessary in combination with the component equations of non-memory components to eliminate all but the state variables.

Two-terminal components which are energy storage components (in other words, memory-type components) are listed in Table 6.1 for convenient reference. The variables which are expressed as derivatives can be used as state variables. Notice that the variables belonging in this category are made up of those system variables whose product of an across and a through variable represents power. The selection of state variables according to Table 6.1 is satisfactory for electrical and hydraulic system components. However, for systems with mechanical components, it is sometimes desirable or necessary to have the displacement available as a state variable. Usually, a simple modification in the state equations will result in the introduction of the displacement as a state variable.

A simple example will serve to demonstrate this point.

Example 6.9. Derive a state model for the mechanical system shown in Figure 6.32.

TABLE 6.1. *Energy storage components*

Component	Terminal equation	Initial condition
Capacitor	$\frac{d}{dt}v = \frac{1}{C}i$	$v(0)$
Inductor	$\frac{d}{dt}i = \frac{1}{L}v$	$i(0)$
Spring (translational)	$\frac{d}{dt}f = k_t\dot{\delta}$	$f(0)$
(rotational)	$\frac{d}{dt}\tau = k_r\dot{\varphi}$	$t(0)$
Mass (translational)	$\frac{d}{dt}\dot{\delta} = \frac{1}{M}f$	$\dot{\delta}(0)$
(rotational)	$\frac{d}{dt}\dot{\varphi} = \frac{1}{J}t$	$\dot{\varphi}(0)$
Hydraulic capacitor	$\frac{d}{dt}p = \frac{1}{C}\dot{g}$	$p(0)$
Hydraulic inertance	$\frac{d}{dt}\dot{g} = \frac{1}{I}p$	$\dot{g}(0)$

The input is $\delta_{in}(t)$, the output is $\delta_{out}(t)$, which represents the displacement of the mass. There are three memory-type components, the two springs and the mass. The derivative component equations are

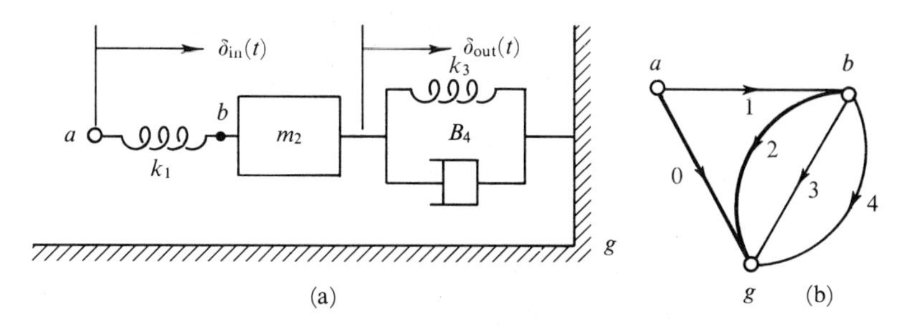

Fig. 6.32. (a) *Mechanical system;* (b) *system graph.*

$$\frac{d}{dt}f_1 = k_1\dot{\delta}_1$$
$$\frac{d}{dt}\dot{\delta}_2 = \frac{1}{M_2}f_2$$
$$\frac{d}{dt}f_3 = k_3\dot{\delta}_3$$

Thus f_1, $\dot{\delta}_2$, and f_3 appear to be an appropriate choice of state variables.

The tree is selected to consist of elements 0 and 2. Therefore,

$$\dot{\delta}_1 = \dot{\delta}_0 - \dot{\delta}_2 = \dot{\delta}_{in}(t) - \dot{\delta}_2$$
$$f_2 = f_1 - f_3 - f_4$$
$$\dot{\delta}_3 = \dot{\delta}_2$$

Also

$$f_4 = B_4\dot{\delta}_4 = B_4\dot{\delta}_3$$

Thus the state equations are obtained as

$$\frac{d}{dt}\begin{bmatrix} f_1 \\ \dot{\delta}_2 \\ f_3 \end{bmatrix} = \begin{bmatrix} 0 & -k_1 & 0 \\ \frac{1}{M_2} & \frac{-B_4}{M_2} & \frac{-1}{M_2} \\ 0 & k_3 & 0 \end{bmatrix} \begin{bmatrix} f_1 \\ \dot{\delta}_2 \\ f_3 \end{bmatrix} + \begin{bmatrix} k_1 \\ 0 \\ 0 \end{bmatrix} \dot{\delta}_{in}(t) \tag{6.89}$$

and

$$\dot{\delta}_{out}(t) = [0\ 1\ 0]\begin{bmatrix} f_1 \\ \dot{\delta}_2 \\ f_3 \end{bmatrix} = \dot{\delta}_2$$

Although this state model has been derived according to outlined procedure, it is unacceptable, because the input and output variables are velocities and not displacements, as required.

An alternate approach, selecting the state variables such that $\dot{\delta}_2$ and δ_2 are used, is available. Starting again with the terminal equation for the mass,

$$\frac{d}{dt}\dot{\delta}_2 = \frac{1}{M_2}f_2$$

and by simple integration

$$\frac{d}{dt}\delta_2 = \dot{\delta}_2$$

In order to avoid differentiation of the input, disregard the fact that springs are memory-type components and treat them as non-memory components. Then we can substitute into the equation

$$f_2 = f_1 - f_3 - f_4$$

the following relations:

$$\begin{aligned} f_1 &= k_1\delta_1 = k_1(\delta_0 - \delta_2) = k_1[\delta_{in}(t) - \delta_2] \\ f_3 &= k_3\delta_3 = k_3\delta_2 \\ f_4 &= B_4\dot{\delta}_4 = B_4\dot{\delta}_2 \end{aligned}$$

so that

$$f_2 = -(k_1 + k_3)\delta_2 - B_4\dot{\delta}_2 + k_1\delta_{in}(t)$$

Substituting this result into the terminal equation for the mass yields the state equations

$$\begin{aligned} \frac{d}{dt}\begin{bmatrix} \dot{\delta}_2 \\ \delta_2 \end{bmatrix} &= \begin{bmatrix} \dfrac{-B_4}{M_2} & \dfrac{-(k_1 + k_3)}{M_2} \\ 1 & 0 \end{bmatrix}\begin{bmatrix} \dot{\delta}_2 \\ \delta_2 \end{bmatrix} + \begin{bmatrix} \dfrac{k_1}{M_2} \\ 0 \end{bmatrix}\delta_{in}(t) \\ \delta_{out}(t) &= [0 \quad 1]\begin{bmatrix} \dot{\delta}_2 \\ \delta_2 \end{bmatrix} = \delta_2 \end{aligned} \tag{6.90}$$

These equations are acceptable since the proper input and output variables are used. One might wonder why the first result contains three state equations and the second only two. It is left as an exercise to show that the two results are equivalent. (Hint: Use the Laplace transform.)

In general, the rather simple procedure demonstrated in the above examples can always be used to formulate state equations for linear systems of two-terminal components provided, of course, that all across variables and all through variables appearing in the state vector can be classified, respectively, as branches and chords of a formulation tree. For the majority of systems such a classification is possible. However, systems can be constructed in which the across variables in the state vector in themselves form a circuit, or in which the through variables in the state vector in themselves form a cutset. Then such a formulation tree cannot be formed and the state variables are selected according to the tree that is possible*.

On occasion, it may be useful to derive the state equations for electrical circuits in a different manner. While it has been suggested to use the terminal equations of Table 6.1 to initiate the formulation process, it is also possible to use different terminal equations, as presented in Chapter 4. That is,

$$\left.\begin{aligned} q &= Cv \\ \lambda &= Li \end{aligned}\right] \tag{6.91}$$

for the component equation for a capacitor and inductor, respectively. The derivative form is then introduced by use of the additional equalities

* See Chapter 10.

$$\left.\begin{aligned} \frac{d}{dt}q &= i \\ \frac{d}{dt}\lambda &= v \end{aligned}\right] \tag{6.92}$$

The following example illustrates application of these equations.

Example 6.10. Using flux and charge as state variables, derive the state equations for the circuit shown in Figure 6.33. The tree is selected such that the voltage source and the two capacitors are included. This represents a complete tree. The formulation process is started by writing the four equations

$$\frac{d}{dt}\begin{bmatrix} q_2 \\ q_3 \\ \lambda_3 \\ \lambda_5 \end{bmatrix} = \begin{bmatrix} i_2 \\ i_3 \\ v_4 \\ v_5 \end{bmatrix} \tag{6.93}$$

Then express the variables on the right hand side to relate to the four state variables through the use of component equations and cutset and circuit equations. This is a simple matter. Following are the substitutions for i_2 and v_4 in detail.

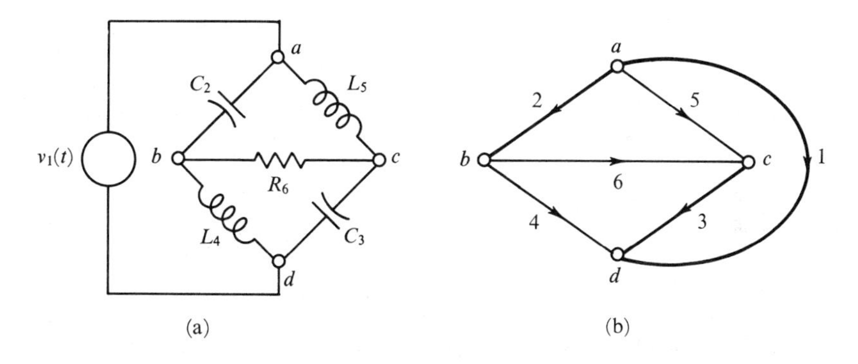

Fig. 6.33. (a) *Electrical circuit;* (b) *system graph.*

$$i_2 = i_6 + i_4 \qquad \text{(cutset equation)}$$

but

$$i_6 = G_6 v_6$$

and

$$v_6 = v_1 - v_2 - v_3 \qquad \text{(circuit equation)}$$

Now

$$i_4 = \frac{1}{L_4}\lambda_4$$

$$v_2 = \frac{1}{C_2}q_2$$

$$v_3 = \frac{1}{C_3} q_3$$

and

$$v_1 = \text{specified}$$

Combining,

$$i_2 = G_6 v_1 - \frac{G_6}{C_2} q_2 - \frac{G_6}{C_3} q_3 + \frac{1}{L_4} \lambda_4 \tag{6.94}$$

Similarly,

$$i_3 = G_6 v_1 - \frac{G_6}{C_2} q_2 - \frac{G_6}{C_3} q_3 + \frac{1}{L_5} \lambda_5 \tag{6.95}$$

Also

$$\begin{aligned} v_4 &= v_1 - v_2 \\ &= v_1 - \frac{1}{C_2} q_2 \end{aligned} \tag{6.96}$$

Similarly,

$$\begin{aligned} v_5 &= v_1 - v_3 \\ &= v_1 - \frac{1}{C_3} q_3 \end{aligned} \tag{6.97}$$

Combining Equations 6.94 through 6.97 with Equation 6.93 yields the desired state equations

$$\frac{d}{dt}\begin{bmatrix} q_2 \\ q_3 \\ \lambda_4 \\ \lambda_5 \end{bmatrix} = \begin{bmatrix} -G_6/C_2 & -G_6/C_3 & 1/L_4 & 0 \\ -G_6/C_2 & -G_6/C_3 & 0 & 1/L_5 \\ -1/C_2 & 0 & 0 & 0 \\ 0 & -1/C_3 & 0 & 0 \end{bmatrix} \begin{bmatrix} q_2 \\ q_3 \\ \lambda_4 \\ \lambda_5 \end{bmatrix} + \begin{bmatrix} G_6 \\ G_6 \\ 1 \\ 1 \end{bmatrix} v_1 \tag{6.98}$$

The above example illustrates the simple application of the previously developed formulation rules to the case in which flux and charge are used as state variables. The flux-charge approach will later be shown to be applicable in transformer circuits or in time-varying circuits.

Simultaneous Elimination of Several Variables

Quite frequently it will be necessary to eliminate several system variables simultaneously in the process of reducing the number of variables to just those corresponding to the state variables. The following example will illustrate such a case and demonstrate an appropriate procedure.

Example 6.11. Formulate the state equations for the circuit shown in Figure 6.34.

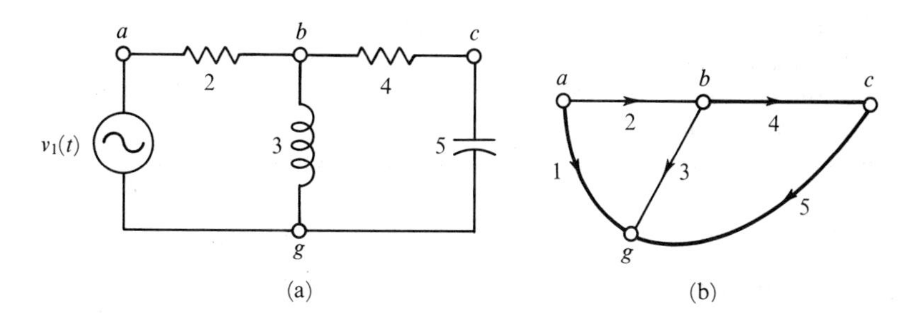

Fig. 6.34. *Electrical circuit and system graph.*

The derivative terminal equations are

$$\frac{d}{dt}i_3 = \frac{1}{L}v_3$$

$$\frac{d}{dt}v_5 = \frac{1}{C}i_5$$

Thus i_3 and v_5 are the state variables. The tree is selected in this order: element 1, 5 and either 2 or 4; 4 has been arbitrarily chosen. The terminal equations require substitutions for v_3 and i_5. One has from the system graph

$$v_3 = v_4 + v_5$$

and

$$i_5 = i_2 - i_3$$

Further substitutions for i_2 and v_4 are required in terms of the driver v_1 and the state variables i_3 and v_5. But it can readily be seen that an attempt to determine these substitutions for each variable individually keeps one going in circles. The two variables must be solved simultaneously. For this purpose we rewrite the last equations in matrix form.

$$\frac{d}{dt}\begin{bmatrix} i_3 \\ v_5 \end{bmatrix} = \begin{bmatrix} 0 & \frac{1}{L} \\ -\frac{1}{C} & 0 \end{bmatrix}\begin{bmatrix} i_3 \\ v_5 \end{bmatrix} + \begin{bmatrix} 0 & \frac{1}{L} \\ \frac{1}{C} & 0 \end{bmatrix}\begin{bmatrix} i_2 \\ v_4 \end{bmatrix}$$

From the remaining components, R_2 and R_4, we have

$$\begin{bmatrix} i_2 \\ v_4 \end{bmatrix} = \begin{bmatrix} G_2 & 0 \\ 0 & R_4 \end{bmatrix}\begin{bmatrix} v_2 \\ i_4 \end{bmatrix}$$

and by use of the circuit equation and cutset equation for elements 2 and 4, respectively, we set up the following equations:

$$\begin{bmatrix} v_2 \\ i_4 \end{bmatrix} = \begin{bmatrix} 1 \\ 0 \end{bmatrix} v_1 + \begin{bmatrix} 0 & -1 \\ -1 & 0 \end{bmatrix}\begin{bmatrix} i_3 \\ v_5 \end{bmatrix} + \begin{bmatrix} 0 & -1 \\ 1 & 0 \end{bmatrix}\begin{bmatrix} i_2 \\ v_4 \end{bmatrix}$$

We note that the right hand side of the last equation is divided according to this classification:

(1) the driver,
(2) the state variables,
(3) the branch across variable and the chord through variables of the non-memory components.

Substituting these equations into the previous one and multiplying,

$$\begin{bmatrix} i_2 \\ v_4 \end{bmatrix} = \begin{bmatrix} G_2 \\ 0 \end{bmatrix} v_1 + \begin{bmatrix} 0 & -G_2 \\ -R_4 & 0 \end{bmatrix} \begin{bmatrix} i_3 \\ v_5 \end{bmatrix} + \begin{bmatrix} 0 & -G_2 \\ R_4 & 0 \end{bmatrix} \begin{bmatrix} i_2 \\ v_4 \end{bmatrix}$$

upon collecting terms

$$\begin{bmatrix} 1 & G_2 \\ -R_4 & 1 \end{bmatrix} \begin{bmatrix} i_2 \\ v_4 \end{bmatrix} = \begin{bmatrix} G_2 \\ 0 \end{bmatrix} v_1 + \begin{bmatrix} 0 & -G_2 \\ -R_4 & 0 \end{bmatrix} \begin{bmatrix} i_3 \\ v_5 \end{bmatrix}$$

An inverse of a two $\times$ two matrix is required. This yields

$$\begin{aligned} \begin{bmatrix} i_2 \\ v_4 \end{bmatrix} &= \frac{1}{1 + R_4G_2} \begin{bmatrix} 1 & -G_2 \\ R_4 & 1 \end{bmatrix} \left\{ \begin{bmatrix} G_2 \\ 0 \end{bmatrix} v_1 + \begin{bmatrix} 0 & -G_2 \\ -R_4 & 0 \end{bmatrix} \begin{bmatrix} i_3 \\ v_5 \end{bmatrix} \right\} \\ &= \frac{1}{1 + R_4G_2} \left\{ \begin{bmatrix} G_2 \\ R_4G_2 \end{bmatrix} v_1 + \begin{bmatrix} R_4G_2 & -G_2 \\ -R_4 & -G_2R_4 \end{bmatrix} \begin{bmatrix} i_3 \\ v_5 \end{bmatrix} \right\} \end{aligned}$$

This expression represents the desired substitution. Using it, one obtains the final state equations

$$\frac{d}{dt} \begin{bmatrix} i_3 \\ v_5 \end{bmatrix} = \begin{bmatrix} \dfrac{-R_4}{L(1 + R_4G_2)} & \dfrac{1}{L(1 + R_4G_2)} \\ \dfrac{-1}{C(1 + R_4G_2)} & \dfrac{-G_2}{C(1 + R_4G_2)} \end{bmatrix} \begin{bmatrix} i_3 \\ v_5 \end{bmatrix} + \begin{bmatrix} \dfrac{R_4G_2}{L(1 + R_4G_2)} \\ \dfrac{G_2}{C(1 + R_4G_2)} \end{bmatrix} v_2 \tag{6.99}$$

An output equation may be selected as required.

The preceding example demonstrates the general procedure of formulating state equations for systems of two-terminal equations. Although it is only shown for a case of limited complexity, it can readily be extended to larger problems.

6.12 Problems in Formulation and Solution

The preceding sections of this chapter present three formulation techniques: mesh formulation, node formulation, and state variable formulation. Systematic procedures were developed for the application of these formulation techniques. It is now appropriate to discuss the formulation and solution of a number of problems to explore more fully the ramifications of the above techniques. It is particularly important to establish some correlation and comparison among the techniques and demonstrate means of solving the resulting equations. It will be shown, for instance, that the Laplace transformation may be quite conveniently employed to solve the first order differential equations resulting from a state variable formulation.

Example 6.12. Derive the transfer function relating the output to the input for the circuit shown in Figure 6.35. Employ either mesh or node formulation and state variable formulation.

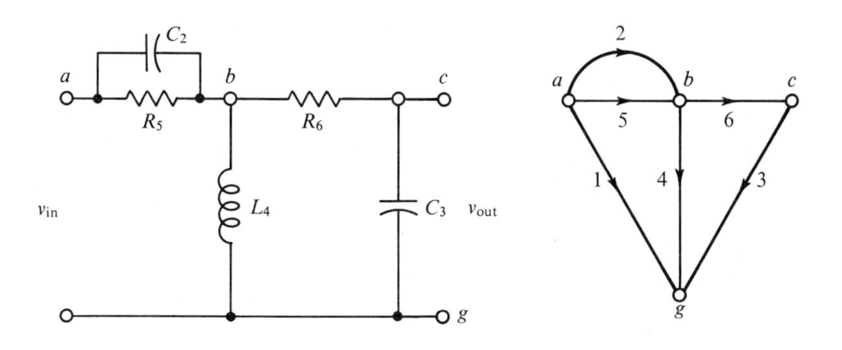

Fig. 6.35. *Electrical circuit and graph.*

A. *State variable formulation.* The tree is selected to include elements 1, 2, and 3, representing the input voltage driver and the two capacitors. We begin the formulation with the energy storage components. Thus

$$\frac{d}{dt}v_2 = \frac{1}{C_2}i_2$$

$$\frac{d}{dt}v_3 = \frac{1}{C_3}i_3$$

$$\frac{d}{dt}i_4 = \frac{1}{L_4}v_4$$

The following cutset and circuit equations are needed:

$$i_2 = i_4 - i_5 + i_6$$

$$i_3 = i_6$$

$$v_4 = v_1 - v_2$$

Furthermore,

$$i_5 = \frac{v_5}{R_5} = \frac{v_2}{R_5}$$

$$i_6 = \frac{v_6}{R_6} = \frac{v_1 - v_2 - v_3}{R_6}$$

so that

$$i_2 = i_4 = \frac{v_2}{R_5} + \frac{v_1 - v_2 - v_3}{R_6}$$

$$i_3 = \frac{v_1 - v_2 - v_3}{R_6}$$

$$v_4 = v_1 - v_2$$

and finally

$$\frac{d}{dt}\begin{bmatrix} v_2 \\ v_3 \\ i_4 \end{bmatrix} = \begin{bmatrix} -\frac{1}{C_2}\left[\frac{1}{R_5}+\frac{1}{R_6}\right] & -\frac{1}{C_2R_6} & \frac{1}{C_2} \\ -\frac{1}{C_3R_6} & -\frac{1}{C_3R_6} & 0 \\ -\frac{1}{L_4} & 0 & 0 \end{bmatrix}\begin{bmatrix} v_2 \\ v_3 \\ i_4 \end{bmatrix} + \begin{bmatrix} \frac{1}{C_2R_6} \\ \frac{1}{C_3R_6} \\ \frac{1}{L_4} \end{bmatrix} v_{in}(t) \tag{6.100}$$

The output equation is simply

$$v_{out} = v_3 \tag{6.101}$$

To obtain the desired transfer function we take the Laplace transform of Equation 6.100. This yields

$$s\begin{bmatrix} V_2 \\ V_3 \\ I_4 \end{bmatrix} = \begin{bmatrix} -\frac{1}{C_2}\left[\frac{1}{R_5}+\frac{1}{R_6}\right] & -\frac{1}{C_2R_6} & \frac{1}{C_2} \\ -\frac{1}{C_3R_6} & -\frac{1}{C_3R_6} & 0 \\ -\frac{1}{L_4} & 0 & 0 \end{bmatrix}\begin{bmatrix} V_2 \\ V_3 \\ I_4 \end{bmatrix} + \begin{bmatrix} v_2(0) \\ v_3(0) \\ i_4(0) \end{bmatrix} + \begin{bmatrix} \frac{1}{C_2R_6} \\ \frac{1}{C_3R_6} \\ \frac{1}{L_4} \end{bmatrix} V_{in}$$

In view of the output equation the last equations need only be solved for V_3/V_{in}. In the calculation of a transfer function it is not necessary to consider initial conditions; hence we take

$$v_2(0) = v_3(0) = i_4(0) = 0$$

Collecting the state variables yields

$$\begin{bmatrix} C_2s + \frac{1}{R_5} + \frac{1}{R_6} & \frac{1}{R_6} & -1 \\ \frac{1}{R_6} & C_3s + \frac{1}{R_6} & 0 \\ 1 & 0 & sL_4 \end{bmatrix}\begin{bmatrix} V_2 \\ V_3 \\ I_4 \end{bmatrix} = \begin{bmatrix} \frac{1}{R_6} \\ \frac{1}{R_6} \\ 1 \end{bmatrix} V_{in}$$

or upon clearing the denominators,

$$\begin{bmatrix} R_5R_6C_2s + R_5 + R_6 & R_5 & -R_5R_6 \\ 1 & R_6C_3s + 1 & 0 \\ 1 & 0 & sL_4 \end{bmatrix}\begin{bmatrix} V_2 \\ V_3 \\ I_4 \end{bmatrix} = \begin{bmatrix} R_5 \\ 1 \\ 1 \end{bmatrix} V_{in} \tag{6.102}$$

To solve for the state variables we have to find the inverse of the matrix of Equation 6.102, which premultiplies the state variables. This inverse is

$$\frac{1}{D(s)}\begin{bmatrix} (R_6C_3s + 1)L_4s & -R_5L_4s & -R_5R_6(1 + R_6C_3s) \\ -sL_4 & sL_4(R_5R_6C_2s + R_5 + R_6) + R_5R_6 & -R_5R_6 \\ R_6C_3s + 1 & -R_5 & \begin{matrix} R_5R_6^2C_2C_3s^2 \\ +R_6(R_5C_2+R_5C_3+R_6C_3)s \\ + R_6 \end{matrix} \end{bmatrix}$$

where

$$D(s) = R_5R_6^2C_2C_3L_4s^3 + [(R_5 + R_6)C_3 + R_5C_2]R_6L_4s^2 + [R_6L_4 + R_5R_6^2C_3]s + 1$$

To determine the desired transfer function we need to solve for V_3 as a function of V_{in}. Thus,

$$V_{out}(s) = V_3 = \frac{L_4R_5R_6L_2s^2 + R_6L_4s}{D(s)} \quad V_{in}(s) \tag{6.103}$$

B. *Node formulation.* As the second approach to this problem we choose node formulation. Although both mesh and node equations result in the same number of unknowns to be determined (two), it is of advantage to use node formulation because the result will be in terms of voltage, which is closer to the objective.

Writing the node equations, then, yields

$$\begin{bmatrix} \frac{1 + R_5C_2s}{R_5} & -\frac{1 + R_5C_2s}{R^5} & 0 \\ -\frac{1 + R_5C_2s}{R_5} & \frac{1 + R_5C_2s}{R_5} + 1/L_4s + 1/R_6 & -\frac{1}{R_6} \\ 0 & -\frac{1}{R_6} & \frac{1 + R_6C_3s}{R_6} \end{bmatrix} \begin{bmatrix} V_a \\ V_b \\ V_c \end{bmatrix} = \begin{bmatrix} -I_1 \\ 0 \\ 0 \end{bmatrix} \tag{6.104}$$

Upon clearing the denominators we obtain

$$\begin{bmatrix} 1 + R_5C_2s & -(1 + R_5C_2s) & 0 \\ -(1 + R_5C_2s)R_6L_4s & (1 + R_5C_2s)R_6L_4s + R_5R_6 + R_5L_4s & -R_5L_4s \\ 0 & -1 & 1 + R_6C_3s \end{bmatrix} \begin{bmatrix} V_a \\ V_b \\ V_c \end{bmatrix} = \begin{bmatrix} -I_1R_5 \\ 0 \\ 0 \end{bmatrix} \tag{6.105}$$

We extract the last two equations from Equation 6.105 to solve for the unknown node voltages V_b and V_c. Thus

$$\begin{bmatrix} (1 + R_5C_2s)R_6L_4s + R_5L_4s + R_5R_6 & -R_5L_4s \\ -1 & 1 + R_6C_3s \end{bmatrix} \begin{bmatrix} V_b \\ V_c \end{bmatrix} = \begin{bmatrix} (1 + R_5C_2s)R_6L_4s \\ 0 \end{bmatrix} V_a$$

And upon taking the inverse,

$$\begin{bmatrix} V_b \\ V_c \end{bmatrix} = \frac{1}{D(s)} \begin{bmatrix} 1 + R_6C_3s & R_5L_4s \\ 1 & [(1 + R_5C_2s)R_6 + R_5]L_4s + R_5R_6 \end{bmatrix} \begin{bmatrix} (1 + R_5C_2s)R_6L_4s \\ 0 \end{bmatrix} V_a$$

where $D(s)$ is defined as before. Finally, the desired transfer function is

$$V_{out}(s) = V_c(s) = \frac{R_5R_6C_2L_4s^2 + R_6L_4s}{D(s)} V_{in}(s) \tag{6.106}$$

We see that the two formulations yield the same result.

Both formulation procedures require the calculation of an inverse. As was seen, a two $\times$ two matrix had to be inverted for the node formulation, while the state variable formulation required a three × three inverse. In view of the complexity of the matrices involved, the difference in the order was significant.

Example 6.13. For the system shown in Figure 6.36, derive a mathematical model by node formulation and by state variable formulation and calculate the position of the mass in response to a step input.

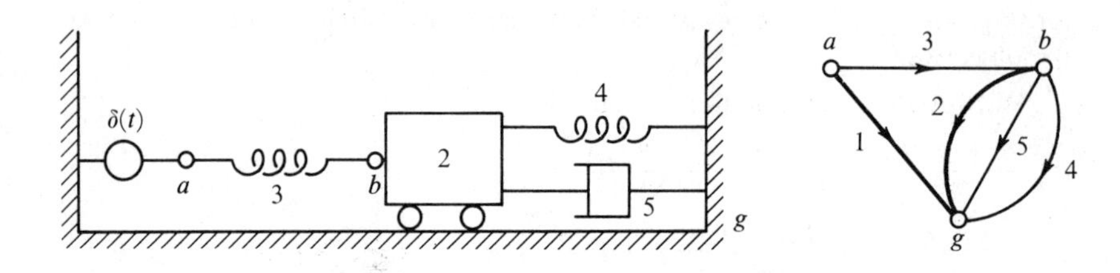

Fig. 6.36. *Mechanical system and graph.*

The initial objective will be determination of the transfer function relating $\Delta_3(s)$ to $\Delta_1(s)$, the output to the input.

A. *Node formulation.* The node equations are

$$\begin{bmatrix} k_3 & -k_3 \\ -k_3 & k_3 + k_4 B_5 s + M_2^2 s \end{bmatrix} \begin{bmatrix} \Delta_a(s) \\ \Delta_b(s) \end{bmatrix} = \begin{bmatrix} -F_1(s) \\ 0 \end{bmatrix} \tag{6.107}$$

The node variable $\Delta_a(s)$ is equal to the displacement driver

$$\Delta_a(s) = \Delta_1(s)$$

Solving for the displacement of the mass, we obtain

$$\Delta_b(s) = \frac{k_3}{k_3 + k_4 + B_5 s + M_2 s^2} \Delta_1(s) \tag{6.108}$$

B. *State variable formulation.* The state variables are selected as the velocity and displacement of the mass. Thus

$$\frac{d}{dt}\begin{bmatrix} \dot{\delta}_2 \\ \delta_2 \end{bmatrix} = \begin{bmatrix} \dfrac{1}{M_2} f_2 \\ \dot{\delta}_2 \end{bmatrix}$$

But

$$\begin{aligned} f_2 &= f_3 - f_4 - f_5 \\ &= k_3(\delta_1 - \delta_2) - k_4\delta_2 - B_5\dot{\delta}_2 \end{aligned}$$

so that

$$\frac{d}{dt}\begin{bmatrix} \dot{\delta}_2 \\ \delta_2 \end{bmatrix} = \begin{bmatrix} -B_5/M_2 & -\dfrac{k_3 + k_4}{M_2} \\ 0 & 0 \end{bmatrix} \begin{bmatrix} \dot{\delta}_2 \\ \delta_2 \end{bmatrix} + \begin{bmatrix} k_3/M_2 \\ 0 \end{bmatrix} \delta_1 \tag{6.109}$$

Taking the Laplace transform of Equation 6.109 and collecting terms,

$$\begin{bmatrix} \dot{\Delta}_2(s) \\ \Delta_2(s) \end{bmatrix} = \begin{bmatrix} s + B_5/M_2 & \dfrac{k_3 + k_4}{M_2} \\ -1 & s \end{bmatrix}^{-1} \left\{ \begin{bmatrix} \dot{\delta}_2(0) \\ \delta_2(0) \end{bmatrix} + \begin{bmatrix} k_3/M_2 \\ 0 \end{bmatrix} \Delta_1(s) \right\} \quad \textbf{(6.110)}$$

Since the system is initially at rest we can set $\dot{\delta}_2(0) = \delta_2(0) = 0$. Then the desired transfer function may be easily obtained by the inverse matrix.

$$\Delta_2(s) = \frac{k_3/M_2}{s(s + B_5/M_2) + \dfrac{k_3 + k_4}{M_2}} \Delta_1(s)$$

or

$$\Delta_2(s) = \frac{k_3}{k_3 + k_4 + B_5 s + M_2 s^2} \Delta_1(s) \quad \textbf{(6.111)}$$

Equation 6.111 is identical to Equation 6.108.

The transfer function which related the input displacement to the output displacement has been derived. Now consider the response of the mass to a step input. Set

$$\Delta_1(s) = \frac{1}{s}$$

Equation 6.111 becomes then

$$\Delta_2(s) = \frac{k_3}{k_3 + k_4 + B_5 s + M_2 s^2} \frac{1}{s}$$

If now

$$k_3 = k_4 = 1, \qquad M_2 = 0.5 \qquad \text{and} \qquad B_5 = 2.5$$

then

$$\Delta_2(s) = \frac{1}{2 + 2.5s + 0.5s^2} \quad \frac{1}{s} = \frac{1}{s(s + 5s + 4)}$$

By a partial fraction expansion we find that

$$\Delta_2(s) = \frac{A}{s} + \frac{B}{s+1} + \frac{C}{s+4}$$

where

$$A = \frac{2}{(s+1)(s+4)} \Bigg|_{s=0} = 0.5$$

$$B = \frac{2}{s(s+4)} \Bigg|_{s=-1} = -\frac{2}{3}$$

$$C = \frac{2}{s(s+1)} \Bigg|_{s=-4} = \frac{1}{6}$$

so that

$$\Delta_2(s) = \frac{0.5}{s} - \frac{2/3}{s+1} + \frac{1/6}{s+4}$$

and

$$\delta_2(t) = 0.5 - 2/3e^{-t} + 1/6e^{-4t}, \qquad t \geq 0$$

This response is shown as a time function plot in Figure 6.37. For the particular choice of numerical constants for mass, dashpot and springs, the response is purely exponential, with a predominant time constant of 1 second. In the steady state, the mass will be in a position corresponding to one-half of the input. This latter result can be easily verified by applying the final value theorem of the Laplace transform to the transfer function, i.e.,

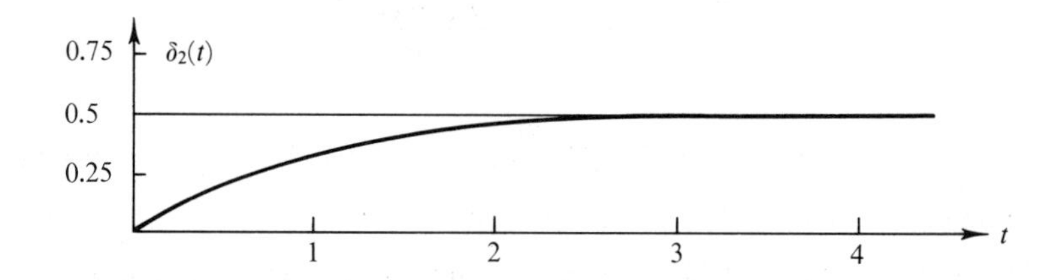

Fig. 6.37. *Response of mass to a step input.*

$$\lim_{t\to 0} \delta_2(t) = \lim_{s\to 0} s\Delta_2(s) = \lim_{s\to 0} s\frac{k_3}{k_3 + k_4 + B_5 s + M_2 s^2}\frac{1}{s}$$
$$= \frac{k_3}{k_3 + k_4}$$
$$= \frac{1}{1+1} = \frac{1}{2}$$

This last result may also be readily obtained by using the state equations directly. The left hand side of Equation 6.109 will go to zero when steady state has been reached since all change with respect to time must have vanished. Thus, for $t \to \infty$,

$$0 = \begin{bmatrix} -B_5/M_2 & -\dfrac{k_3 + k_4}{M_2} \\ 1 & 0 \end{bmatrix} \begin{bmatrix} \dot{\delta}_2 \\ \delta_2 \end{bmatrix} + \begin{bmatrix} k_3/M_2 \\ 0 \end{bmatrix} \delta_1$$

But $\dot{\delta}_2 = 0$, therefore,

$$\frac{-(k_3 + k_4)}{M_2}\delta_2 + \frac{k_3}{M_2}\delta_1 = 0$$

or

$$\delta_2 = \frac{k_3}{k_3 + k_4}$$

Example 6.14. Suppose for the circuit shown in Figure 6.38 it is important that the current through R never changes direction during the transient which results when the switch is closed. Given L, C, and E, find R such that the above condition will be satisfied.

To investigate the feasibility of this condition, we derive the state equations for this circuit. These are easily shown to be

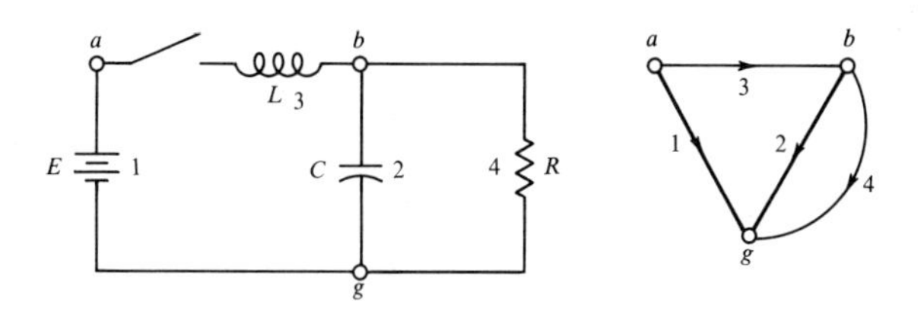

Fig. 6.38. *Electric circuit.*

$$\frac{d}{dt}\begin{bmatrix} v_2 \\ i_3 \end{bmatrix} = \begin{bmatrix} -\dfrac{1}{RC} & \dfrac{1}{C} \\ -\dfrac{1}{L} & 0 \end{bmatrix}\begin{bmatrix} v_2 \\ i_3 \end{bmatrix} = \begin{bmatrix} 0 \\ \dfrac{1}{L} \end{bmatrix} E \tag{6.112}$$

The current through R obviously will not change direction so long as the voltage of the capacitor does not change polarity. To solve this problem we therefore have to investigate the time behavior of this voltage.

Taking the Laplace transform of Equation 6.112 yields

$$\begin{bmatrix} V_2 \\ I_3 \end{bmatrix} = \begin{bmatrix} s + \dfrac{1}{RC} & -\dfrac{1}{C} \\ \dfrac{1}{L} & s \end{bmatrix}^{-1} \left\{ \begin{bmatrix} v_2(0) \\ i_3(0) \end{bmatrix} + \begin{bmatrix} 0 \\ \dfrac{E}{sL} \end{bmatrix} \right\}$$

$$= \frac{1}{s^2 + \dfrac{s}{RC} + \dfrac{1}{LC}} \begin{bmatrix} s & \dfrac{1}{C} \\ -\dfrac{1}{L} & s + \dfrac{1}{RC} \end{bmatrix} \left\{ \begin{bmatrix} v_2(0) \\ i_3(0) \end{bmatrix} + \begin{bmatrix} 0 \\ \dfrac{E}{sL} \end{bmatrix} \right\} \tag{6.113}$$

Equation 6.113 clearly shows how the solution is separated into two parts: one part due to the initial conditions and the other due to the voltage source. We will consider these separately and then superimpose the individual results.

Response due to initial conditions. From Equation 6.113 we have

$$V_2 = \frac{s v_2(0) + \dfrac{1}{C} i_3(0)}{s^2 + \dfrac{s}{RC} + \dfrac{1}{LC}} \tag{6.114}$$

Although we could determine $v(t)$ from this last expression in a straightforward manner by finding the inverse Laplace transform, our approch will be to use an approximation, appropriate for this problem.

Consider the solution of Equation 6.114 when $R = \infty$. Letting R assume that value corresponds to the removal of R from the circuit, which leaves the circuit without a dissipative component.

$$V_2 = \frac{s v_2(0)}{s^2 + \dfrac{1}{LC}} + \frac{\sqrt{\dfrac{1}{LC}}\dfrac{L}{C} i_3(0)}{s^2 + \dfrac{1}{LC}}$$

from which

$$v_2(t) = v_2(0) \cos \omega t + \sqrt{\frac{L}{C}} i_3(0) \sin \omega t \tag{6.115}$$

where

$$\omega = \sqrt{\frac{1}{LC}}$$

A plot of Equation 6.115 shown in Figure 6.39 shows that when $R = \infty$ the response consists of two sinusoidal waveforms of constant amplitude.

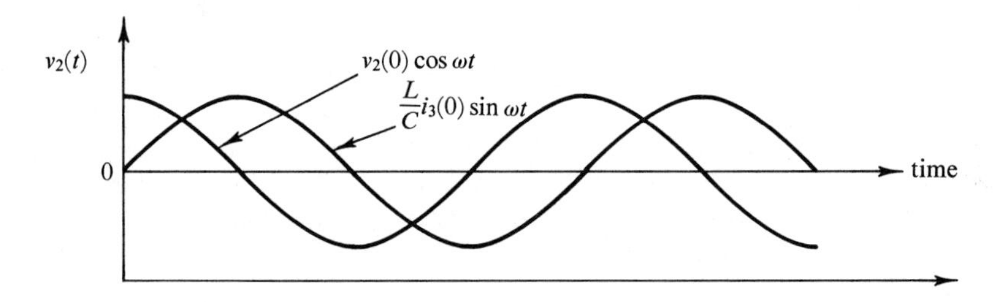

Fig. 6.39. *Response due to initial conditions* ($R = \infty$).

If we now add the effect of $R \neq \infty$ to this response, we can immediately conclude that the presence of the resistor will have a damping influence on the response as shown in Figure 6.40.

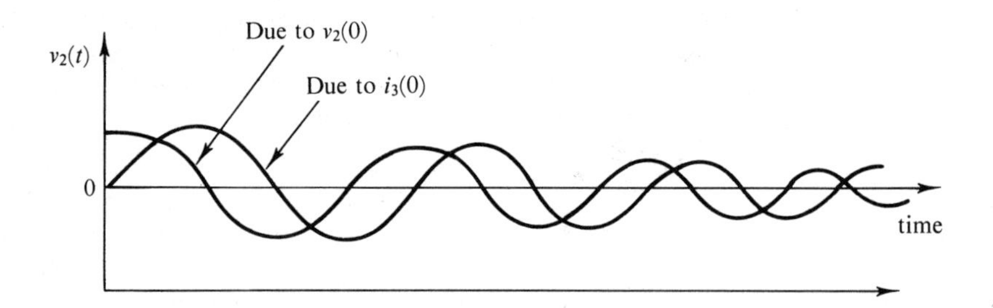

Fig. 6.40. *Response due to initial conditions* ($R < \infty$).

The damping will become more pronounced as R decreases.

Responses due to voltage source. By letting $R = \infty$ as before, we find from Equation 6.113 that

$$V_2 = \frac{1/LC}{s\left(s^2 + \frac{1}{LC}\right)} E$$

and

$$v_2(t) = (1 - \cos \omega t)E \tag{6.116}$$

This is plotted in Figure 6.41. Also shown in this plot is the effect of adding

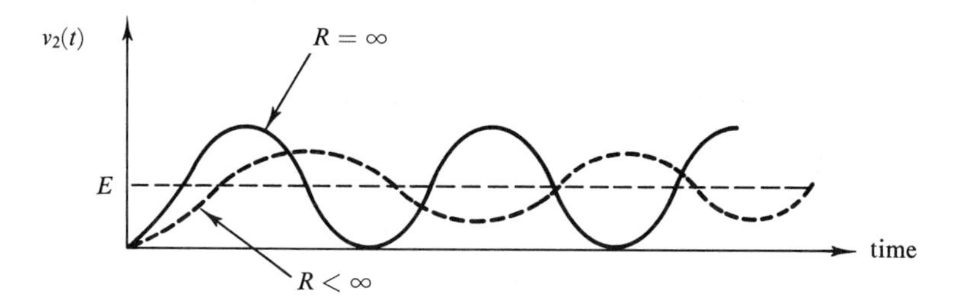

Fig. 6.41. *Response due to driver.*

the resistor into the circuit. As does the initial condition response, the response becomes increasingly damped as R decreases.

With the preparation of this information we are now in a position to establish an answer to the problem.

a. With all initial conditions equal to zero, $v_2(t)$ will always be positive according to Figure 6.41. The current will never change direction.

b. With initial conditions not equal to zero, it is very easily possible to produce a negative voltage $v_2(t)$ and hence a change in the direction of the current. One possible combination is simply to set

$$v_2(0) = -E \quad \text{and} \quad i_3(0) = 0$$

Many other combination may be established.

Example 6.15. Consider the hydraulic pumping system shown in Figure 6.42. A reciprocating pump forces fluid through a check-valve into a tank. The fluid in the tank is drained through a constant restriction. Determine the pressure in the tank as a function of time.

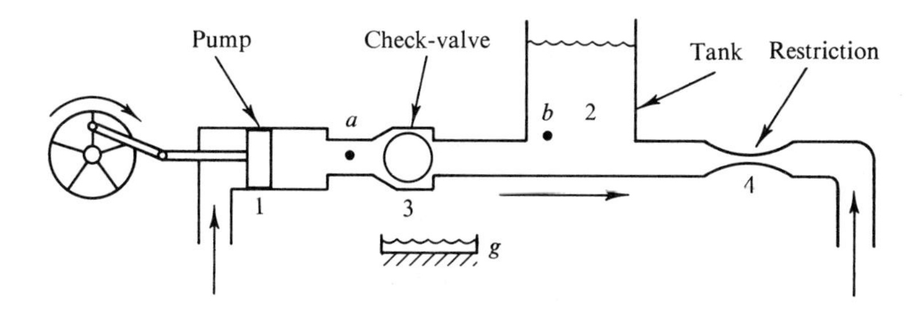

Fig. 6.42. *Hydraulic pumping system.*

For safety reasons, the piston pump is fitted with a relief valve. We may therefore consider the pump essentially as a pressure driver with a periodic waveform approximated by a pulse train as indicated in Figure 6.43. The relief valve is set at P_0.

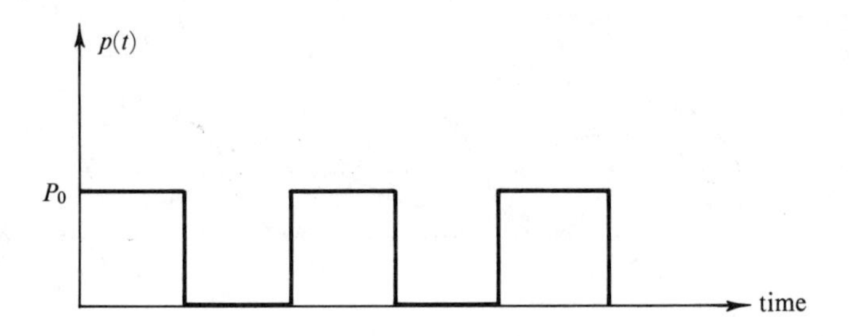

Fig. 6.43. *Waveform of pump.*

The check-valve is a system component which has not been introduced. It will permit flow in one direction only; it is naturally oriented to permit flow in the direction in which the pump delivers the fluid. It may be characterized as a two-valued resistor, that is,

$$R = R_3 \qquad p_a > p_2$$

$$R = \infty \qquad p_a \leq p_b$$

We are now in a position to draw a system graph, which is shown in Figure 6.44.

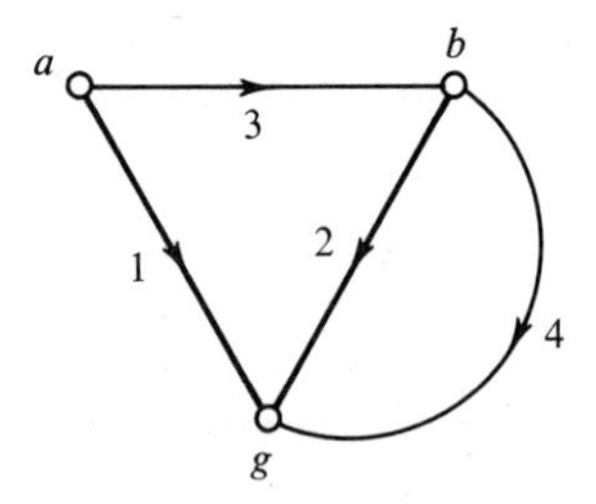

Fig. 6.44. *System graph of pump system.*

The system thus consists of the following components:

1. pump, across driver

2. tank
3. nonlinear resistor
4. linear resistor

To develop a mathematical model, we start with the component equation of the tank,

$$\frac{d}{dt}p_2 = \frac{1}{C}\dot{g}_2$$

But

$$\dot{g} = \dot{g}_3 - \dot{g}_4$$
$$= \frac{p_1 - p_2}{R} - \frac{p_2}{R_4}$$

Therefore

$$\frac{d}{dt}p_2 = -\frac{1}{R_4C}p_2 - \frac{1}{RC}p_2 + \frac{1}{RC}p_1, \qquad R = \begin{Bmatrix} R_3, & p_1 > p_2 \\ \infty, & p_1 \leq p_2 \end{Bmatrix} \tag{6.117}$$

Equation 6.117 completely describes the dynamics of the system. It may be broken up into two parts, corresponding to the two modes of operation of the check valve.

1. $p_1 > p_2$,

$$\frac{d}{dt}p_2 = -\frac{R_3 + R_4}{CR_3R_4}p_2 + \frac{1}{R_3C}p_1 \tag{6.118a}$$

2. $p_2 \leq p_1$,

$$\frac{d}{dt}p_2 = -\frac{1}{R_4C}p_2 \tag{6.118b}$$

The solution to Equation 6.118b is

$$p_2(t) = p_2(0)e^{-t/R_4C}$$

where $p_2(0)$ is the condition of the tank at the beginning of the period at which Equation 6.118b applies. To determine the solution to Equation 6.118a, one has to consider $p_1(t)$. It was shown to be a square wave. Since $p_2(t)$ will always be positive, it can be seen that $p_1 > p_2$ during the pump stroke and $p_1 \leq p_2$ during the back stroke of the pump. Therefore, Equation 6.118a will apply during the first half of the cycle, while Equation 6.118b applies during the second. The pressure source $p_1(t)$ is then a step function. Hence the solution to Equation 6.118a is found to be

$$p_2(t) = p_2(0)e^{-\frac{R_3+R_4}{CR_3R_4}t} + \frac{R_4}{R_3 + R_4}\left(1 - e^{-\frac{R_3+R_4}{CR_3R_4}t}\right)$$

where $p_2(0)$ is the pressure in the tank at the beginning of each pump stroke. Figure 6.45 shows the response of this system over several cycles. It is assumed here that the tank is initially empty. Notice that the solution is simply exponential and depends upon the numerical value of two time constants. During the pump stroke the time constant is

$$t_p = \frac{R_3R_4C}{R_3 + R_4}$$

and during the back-up stroke it is

$$t_b = R_4C$$

Clearly,

$$t_p < t_b$$

Therefore the level of the tank will rise when the piecewise linear solutions are combined until a steady state is reached.

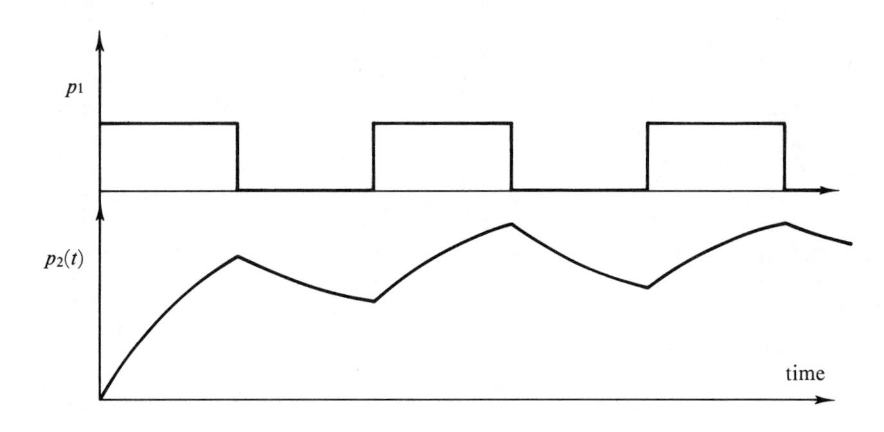

Fig. 6.45. *Response of pump system.*

6.13 Solution of State Variable Equations

In some of the preceding sections we have shown the use of state variables to be a formulation technique equally as powerful and valuable as mesh and node formulation. While mathematical models arising from the latter approach normally require a Laplace transform solution, state variable models may be solved in a unique manner. The following paragraphs will demonstrate this by presenting techniques of solution for the system of equations

$$\frac{d}{dt}\mathbf{x} = \mathbf{A}\mathbf{x} + \mathbf{B}\mathbf{x}_{\text{in}} \tag{6.119}$$

$$\mathbf{x}_{\text{out}} = \mathbf{C}\mathbf{x} + \mathbf{D}\mathbf{x}_{\text{in}} \tag{6.120}$$

The solution to these equations is completed when Equation 6.119 is solved.

The one-dimensional homogeneous equivalent of Equation 6.119 is

$$\dot{x} = ax \tag{6.121}$$

Its solution is known to be

$$x(t) = e^{at}x(0) \tag{6.122}$$

where $x(0)$ is the value of $x(t)$ at $t = 0$.

Now consider the n-dimensional homogeneous part of Equation 6.119,

$$\frac{d}{dt}\mathbf{x} = \mathbf{A}\mathbf{x} \tag{6.123}$$

On the basis of Equation 6.122, we might formally indicate the solution as

$$\mathbf{x}(t) = e^{\mathbf{A}t}\mathbf{x}(0) \tag{6.124}$$

where $e^{\mathbf{A}t}$ denotes an $n \times n$ matrix, which is really a " function " of a matrix, $\mathbf{A}$.

We are naturally prompted to question the meaning of a function of a matrix. The following will help to answer this question. Consider the solution of Equation 6.123 by use of the Laplace transform

$$s\mathbf{X}(s) = \mathbf{A}\mathbf{X}(s) + \mathbf{x}(0)$$

Solving for $\mathbf{X}(s)$,

$$\mathbf{X}(s) = [s\mathbf{U} - \mathbf{A}]^{-1}\mathbf{x}(0)$$

where U is the identity matrix,

$$\begin{bmatrix} 1 & 0 & 0 & \cdots & 0 \\ 0 & 1 & 0 & \cdots & 0 \\ 0 & 0 & 1 & \cdots & 0 \\ \cdot & \cdot & \cdot & & \\ \cdot & \cdot & \cdot & & \\ 0 & 0 & 0 & \cdots & 1 \end{bmatrix}$$

Inverting,

$$\mathbf{x}(t) = \mathscr{L}^{-1}\{[s\mathbf{U} - \mathbf{A}]^{-1}\}\mathbf{x}(0) \tag{6.125}$$

Comparing Equations 6.124 and 6.125, the conclusion is that

$$e^{\mathbf{A}t} = \mathscr{L}^{-1}\{[s\mathbf{U} - \mathbf{A}]^{-1}\} \tag{6.126}$$

Thus the function $e^{\mathbf{A}t}$ is identified as a matrix of exponential functions. This matrix will be called the *transition matrix*. It will play an important role in the study of systems by state variable techniques. Therefore a special notation has been adopted for it.

$$e^{\mathbf{A}t} \triangleq \boldsymbol{\phi}(t)$$

Since the solution of state equations is effectively achieved once the transition matrix is known, the main emphasis is placed upon techniques of determining the transition matrix.

Example 6.16. Determine the transition matrix for the system shown in Figure 6.46 by use of the Laplace transform.

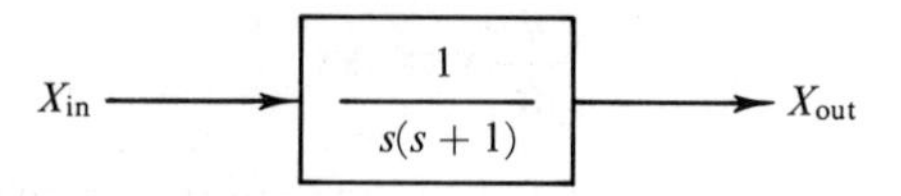

Fig. 6.46. *Linear transfer function.*

First, determine the state equations. By use of single-input programming* we obtain

$$\frac{d}{dt}\begin{bmatrix} x_1 \\ x_2 \end{bmatrix} = \begin{bmatrix} -1 & 0 \\ 1 & 0 \end{bmatrix}\begin{bmatrix} x_1 \\ x_2 \end{bmatrix} + \begin{bmatrix} 1 \\ 0 \end{bmatrix} x_{in}(t)$$

$$x_{out} = x_2$$

Thus

$$\mathbf{A} = \begin{bmatrix} -1 & 0 \\ 1 & 0 \end{bmatrix}$$

and

$$[s\mathbf{U} - \mathbf{A}] = \begin{bmatrix} s+1 & 0 \\ -1 & s \end{bmatrix}$$

Using Equation 6.126, we determine the inverse of the last matrix.

$$[s\mathbf{U} - \mathbf{A}]^{-1} = \frac{1}{s(s+1)}\begin{bmatrix} s & 0 \\ 1 & s+1 \end{bmatrix}$$

And finally, performing the inverse Laplace transform yields the transition matrix

$$\phi(t) = \begin{bmatrix} e^{-t} & 0 \\ 1 - e^{-t} & 1 \end{bmatrix}$$

Example 6.17. Determine the transition matrix for the circuit shown in Figure 6.47.

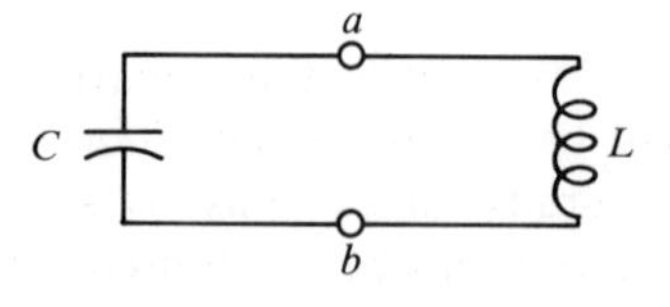

Fig. 6.47. *Simple circuit.*

The state equations for this circuit were derived in Section 6.9 as

* See Chapter 12.

$$\frac{d}{dt}\begin{bmatrix} v_1 \\ i_2 \end{bmatrix} = \begin{bmatrix} 0 & -\dfrac{1}{C} \\ \dfrac{1}{L} & 0 \end{bmatrix} \begin{bmatrix} v_1 \\ i_2 \end{bmatrix} \tag{6.127}$$

Hence

$$\mathbf{A} = \begin{bmatrix} 0 & -\dfrac{1}{C} \\ \dfrac{1}{L} & 0 \end{bmatrix}$$

and from Equations 6.71 we can identify the transition matrix as

$$\boldsymbol{\phi}(t) = \begin{bmatrix} \cos \omega t & -\sqrt{\dfrac{L}{C}} \sin \omega t \\ \sqrt{\dfrac{C}{L}} \sin \omega t & \cos \omega t \end{bmatrix}$$

where

$$\omega = \sqrt{\frac{1}{LC}}$$

Knowledge of the transition matrix is needed to obtain the solution of the homogeneous equation of the matrix differential Equation 6.119. As will be seen later, this knowledge is also sufficient to solve the non-homogeneous equation, the entire Equation 6.119. Useful techniques of evaluating the transition matrix, as well as a number of its important properties, are developed in Appendix C.

The complete solution of the first part of Equations 6.119 is now continued. Using a technique similar to that of solving an ordinary differential equation of the first order (assume an exponential function), we assume that the solution is of the form

$$\mathbf{x}(t) = e^{\mathbf{A}t}\mathbf{y}(t) \tag{6.128}$$

where $\mathbf{y}(t)$ is a vector of unknown functions. Substitute Equation 6.128 into Equation 6.119 by differentiating

$$\begin{aligned} \frac{d}{dt}\mathbf{x}(t) &= \frac{d}{dt}(e^{\mathbf{A}t})\mathbf{y}(t) + e^{\mathbf{A}t}\frac{d}{dt}\mathbf{y}(t) \\ &= \mathbf{A}e^{\mathbf{A}t}\mathbf{y}(t) + e^{\mathbf{A}t}\frac{d}{dt}\mathbf{y}(t) \\ &= \mathbf{A}\mathbf{x}(t) + e^{\mathbf{A}t}\frac{d}{dt}\mathbf{y}(t) \end{aligned}$$

so that

$$e^{\mathbf{A}t}\frac{d}{dt}\mathbf{y}(t) = \mathbf{B}\mathbf{x}_{\text{in}}(t)$$

or

$$\frac{d}{dt}\mathbf{y}(t) = e^{-\mathbf{A}t}\mathbf{B}\mathbf{x}_{\text{in}}(t)$$

This is a set of differential equations which can be integrated directly from t_0 to t. Thus

$$\mathbf{y}(t) = \int_{t_0}^{t} e^{-\mathbf{A}t_1}\mathbf{B}\mathbf{x}_{\text{in}}(t_1)\,dt_1 + \mathbf{y}(0) \tag{6.129}$$

where

$$\mathbf{y}(0) = \mathbf{y}(t_0)$$

This result is substituted into Equation 6.128

$$\mathbf{x}(t) = e^{\mathbf{A}t}\mathbf{y}(0) + \int_{t_0}^{t} e^{\mathbf{A}(t-t_1)}\mathbf{B}\mathbf{x}_{\text{in}}(t_1)\,dt_1$$

Since

$$\mathbf{y}(0) = e^{-\mathbf{A}t_0}\mathbf{x}(0)$$

the final form of the solution may be given as

$$\begin{aligned}\mathbf{x}(t) &= e^{\mathbf{A}(t-t_0)}\mathbf{x}(0) + \int_{t_0}^{t} e^{\mathbf{A}(t-t_1)}\mathbf{B}\mathbf{x}_{\text{in}}(t_1)\,dt_1 \\ &= \phi(t-t_0)\,\mathbf{x}(0) + \int_{t_0}^{t} \phi(t-t_1)\mathbf{B}\mathbf{x}_{\text{in}}(t_1)\,dt_1\end{aligned} \tag{6.130}$$

We may also obtain a solution to Equation 6.119 by the use of Laplace transforms. Transform Equation 6.119:

$$s\mathbf{X}(s) = \mathbf{A}\mathbf{X}(s) + \mathbf{x}(0) + \mathbf{B}\mathbf{X}_{\text{in}}(s) \tag{6.131}$$

Solvins for $\mathbf{X}(s)$

$$\mathbf{X}(s) = [s\mathbf{U} - \mathbf{A}]^{-1}\mathbf{x}(0) + [s\mathbf{U} - \mathbf{A}]^{-1}\mathbf{B}\mathbf{x}_{\text{in}}(s) \tag{6.132}$$

To invert Equation 6.132 into the time-domain we use

$$\phi(t) = \mathscr{L}^{-1}\{[s\mathbf{U} - \mathbf{A}]^{-1}\}, \qquad 0 \leq t$$
$$\phi(t-t_0) = \mathscr{L}^{-1}\{[s\mathbf{U} - \mathbf{A}]^{-1}\}, \qquad t_0 \leq t$$

and the convolution integral for $0 \leq t_0 \leq t$,

$$\mathscr{L}^{-1}\{F_1(s) \cdot F_2(s)\} = \int_{t_0}^{t} f_1(t-t_1)f_2(t_1)\,dt_1$$

and obtain

$$\mathbf{x}(t) = \phi(t-t_0)\,\mathbf{x}(0) + \int_{t_0}^{t} \phi(t-t_1)\mathbf{B}\mathbf{x}_{\text{in}}(t_1)\,dt_1 \tag{6.133}$$

This, of course, is identical to Equation 6.130.

Equations 6.130 and 6.133 represent the general solution to Equation 6.119. The solution has two parts, the complementary solution

$$\mathbf{x}(t) = \phi(t-t_0)\,\mathbf{x}(0) \tag{6.134}$$

and the particular solution

$$\mathbf{x}(t) = \int_{t_0}^{t} \phi(t-t_1)\mathbf{B}\mathbf{x}_{\text{in}}(t_1)\,dt_1 \tag{6.135}$$

These parts are interpreted physically as follows. The complementary solution applies when only initial conditions constitute the disturbance to the system represented by Equation 6.119. Equation 6.134 then describes the trajectory of the system state as it moves from $\mathbf{x}(0)$ to its equilibrium position (for a stable system).

The particular solution represents the forced solution, that is, the response of the system to the driving function $\mathbf{x}_{in}(t)$. It describes the trajectory of the system state as it moves from $\mathbf{x}(0) = 0$ to follow the driving function.

The following example illustrate these interpretations.

Example 6.18. Obtain the state variable solution for the system shown in Figure 6.48. The mass is initially displaced by one unit.

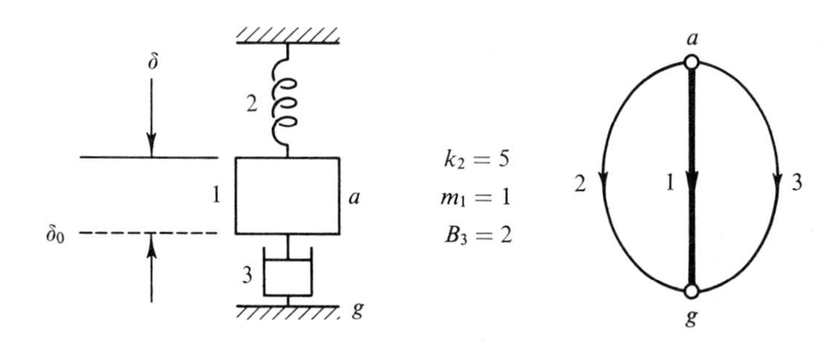

Fig. 6.48. (a) *Mechanical system;* (b) *system graph.*

Derive the state equations:

$$\frac{d}{dt}\dot{\delta}_1 = \frac{1}{M_1} f_1 = \frac{1}{M_1}(-f_2 - f_3)$$
$$= \frac{1}{M_1}(k_2\delta_2 - B_3\dot{\delta}_3)$$
$$= -\frac{1}{M_1}(k_2\delta_1 + B_3\dot{\delta}_1)$$

and

$$\frac{d}{dt}\delta_1 = \dot{\delta}_1$$

Hence

$$\frac{d}{dt}\begin{bmatrix} \dot{\delta}_1 \\ \delta_1 \end{bmatrix} = \begin{bmatrix} -\dfrac{B_3}{M_1} & -\dfrac{k_2}{M_1} \\ 1 & 0 \end{bmatrix} \begin{bmatrix} \dot{\delta}_1 \\ \delta_1 \end{bmatrix}$$

With the component values substituted,

$$\frac{d}{dt}\begin{bmatrix} \dot{\delta}_1 \\ \delta_1 \end{bmatrix} = \begin{bmatrix} -2 & -5 \\ 1 & 0 \end{bmatrix} \begin{bmatrix} \dot{\delta}_1 \\ \delta_1 \end{bmatrix}$$

The initial conditions are

$$\begin{bmatrix} \dot{\delta}_1(0) \\ \delta_1(0) \end{bmatrix} = \begin{bmatrix} 0 \\ 1 \end{bmatrix}$$

The system obviously has an equilibrium point,

$$\begin{bmatrix} \dot{\delta}_1(0) \\ \delta_1(0) \end{bmatrix} = 0$$

since the dashpot provides energy dissipation.

The transition matrix is calculated by use of the Sylvester Expansion* theorem.

The eigenvalues are

$$\det\begin{bmatrix} \lambda + 2 & 5 \\ -1 & \lambda \end{bmatrix} = \lambda^2 + 2\lambda + 5 = 0$$

$$\lambda_{1,2} = -1 + 2j$$

The constituent matrices are

$$\mathbf{A}_1 = \frac{\mathbf{A} - \lambda_2\mathbf{U}}{\lambda_1 - \lambda_2} = \frac{1}{4j}\begin{bmatrix} -1 + 2j & -5 \\ 1 & 1 + 2j \end{bmatrix}$$

$$\mathbf{A}_2 = \frac{\mathbf{A} - \lambda_1\mathbf{U}}{\lambda_2 - \lambda_1} = \frac{1}{4j}\begin{bmatrix} 1 + 2j & 5 \\ -1 & -1 + 2j \end{bmatrix}$$

Check:

$$\mathbf{A}_1 + \mathbf{A}_2 = \mathbf{U}$$

$$\boldsymbol{\phi}(t) = \mathbf{A}_1 e^{\lambda_1 t} + \mathbf{A}_2 e^{\lambda_2 t}$$

$$= \frac{1}{4j}\begin{bmatrix} -1 + 2j & -5 \\ 1 & 1 + 2j \end{bmatrix} e^{(-1+2j)t} + \frac{1}{4j}\begin{bmatrix} 1 + 2j & 5 \\ -1 & -1 + 2j \end{bmatrix} e^{(-1-2j)t}$$

Since the time functions are complex conjugates, it is expedient to combine them into functions of the form $e^{\alpha t}\sin\beta t$ and $e^{\alpha t}\cos\beta t$. For instance, the (1, 1) coefficients of the matrices may be changed into

$$\frac{1}{4j}[(-1 + 2j)e^{(-1+2j)t} + (1 + 2j)e^{(-1-2j)t}] = \frac{e^{-t}(e^{-2jt} - e^{2jt})}{4j} + \frac{e^{-t}(e^{2jt} + e^{-2jt})}{2j}$$

$$= -\frac{1}{2}e^{-t}\sin 2t + e^{-t}\cos 2t$$

The other coefficients are combined similarly. Therefore, the transition matrix may be written

$$\boldsymbol{\phi}(t) = \begin{bmatrix} e^{-t}(\cos 2t - \frac{1}{2}\sin 2t) & -\frac{5}{2}e^{-t}\sin 2t \\ \frac{1}{2}e^{-t}\sin 2t & e^{-t}(\cos 2t + \frac{1}{2}\sin 2t) \end{bmatrix}$$

The solution then becomes

$$\dot{\delta}_1(t) = -\frac{5}{2}e^{-t}\sin 2t$$

$$\delta_1(t) = e^{-t}\left(\cos 2t + \frac{1}{2}\sin 2t\right)$$

To determine the trajectory of the system state as it moves from the initial condition to the final state, we plot the solution on a two-dimensional plot,

* See Appendix C.

$\dot{\delta}_1(t)$ versus $\delta_1(t)$. This is shown in Figure 6.49 as an inward exponential spiral starting at the state (0, 1) going to (0, 0).

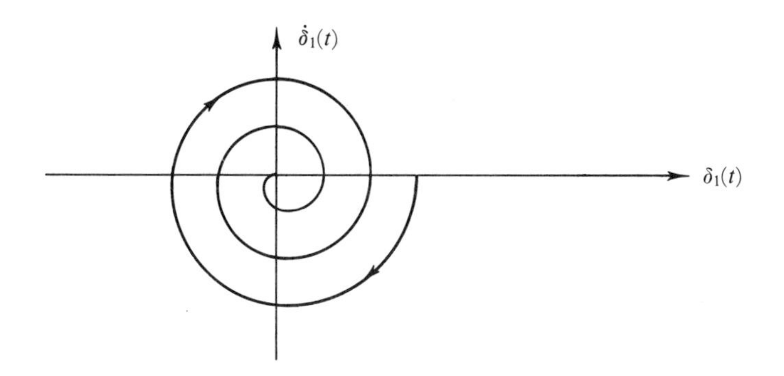

Fig. 6.49. *State space plot of mechanical system.*

Example 6.19. The network in Figure 6.50(a) contains two drivers. Obtain the state variable solution due to these drivers, assuming zero initial conditions. Consider the output to be the voltage across the capacitor.

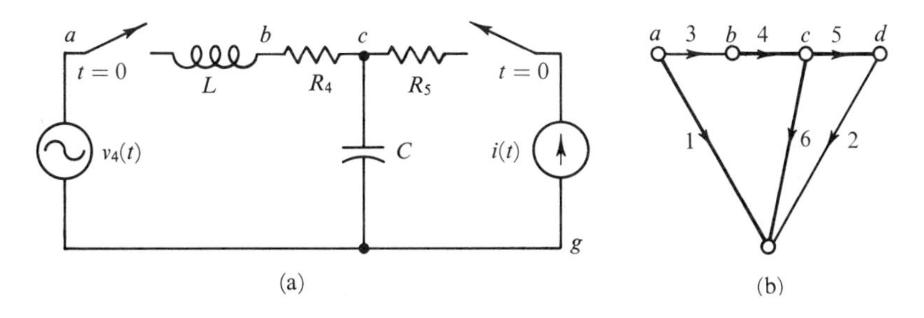

Fig. 6.50. (a) *Electric circuit;* (b) *system graph.*

To derive the state equations, select a tree consisting of elements 1, 4, 5, 6. Then the state equations are

$$\frac{d}{dt}v_6 = \frac{1}{C}(i_3 - i_2)$$

$$\frac{d}{dt}i_3 = \frac{1}{L}(v_1 - R_4 i_3 - v_6)$$

or

$$\frac{d}{dt}\begin{bmatrix} v_6 \\ i_3 \end{bmatrix} = \begin{bmatrix} 0 & \frac{1}{C} \\ -\frac{1}{L} & -\frac{R_4}{L} \end{bmatrix}\begin{bmatrix} v_6 \\ i_3 \end{bmatrix} + \begin{bmatrix} 0 & -\frac{1}{C} \\ \frac{1}{L} & 0 \end{bmatrix}\begin{bmatrix} v_1 \\ i_2 \end{bmatrix}$$

and the output is given

$$v_{out} = v_6$$

If, for convenience, we let

$$C = 0.5$$
$$L = 1$$
$$R_4 = 3$$

the state equations become

$$\frac{d}{dt}\begin{bmatrix} v_6 \\ i_3 \end{bmatrix} = \begin{bmatrix} 0 & 2 \\ -1 & -3 \end{bmatrix}\begin{bmatrix} v_6 \\ i_3 \end{bmatrix} + \begin{bmatrix} 0 & -2 \\ 1 & 0 \end{bmatrix}\begin{bmatrix} v_1 \\ i_2 \end{bmatrix}$$

or

$$\frac{d}{dt}\mathbf{x} = \mathbf{A}\mathbf{x} + \mathbf{B}\mathbf{x}_{in}(t)$$

The eigenvalues of **A** are

$$\begin{vmatrix} \lambda & -2 \\ 1 & \lambda + 3 \end{vmatrix} = \lambda^2 + 3\lambda + 2 = 0$$

$$\lambda_1 = -1$$
$$\lambda_2 = -2$$

By use of Appendix C we write

$$e^{\mathbf{A}t} = \alpha_0 \mathbf{U} + \alpha_1 \mathbf{A}$$

and

$$e^{\lambda_1 t} = \alpha_0 + \alpha_1 \lambda_1$$
$$e^{\lambda_2 t} = \alpha_0 + \alpha_1 \lambda_2$$

from which

$$\alpha_1 = \frac{e^{\lambda_1 t} - e^{\lambda_2 t}}{\lambda_1 - \lambda_2} = e^{-t} - e^{-2t}$$

$$\alpha_0 = \frac{\lambda_2 e^{\lambda_1 t} - \lambda_1 e^{\lambda_2 t}}{\lambda_2 - \lambda_1} = 2e^{-t} - e^{-2t}$$

therefore

$$\boldsymbol{\phi}(t) = \begin{bmatrix} 2e^{-t} - e^{-t} & 2e^{-t} - 2e^{-2t} \\ -e^{-t} + e^{-2t} & -e^{-t} + 2e^{-2t} \end{bmatrix}$$

For the solution we use Equation 6.135,

$$\mathbf{x}(t) = \int_0^t \boldsymbol{\phi}(t - t_1)\mathbf{B}\mathbf{x}_{in}(t_1)\,dt_1$$

or

$$\begin{bmatrix} v_6 \\ i_3 \end{bmatrix} = \int_0^t \begin{bmatrix} -2e^{-(t-t_1)} \\ 2e^{-(t-t_1)} \end{bmatrix} dt_1$$

since

$$\mathbf{x}_{in}(t) = \begin{bmatrix} v_1 \\ i_2 \end{bmatrix} = \mathbf{u}(t)$$

finally

$$\begin{bmatrix} v_6 \\ i_3 \end{bmatrix} = 2\begin{bmatrix} e^{-t} & -1 \\ 1 & -e^{-t} \end{bmatrix}$$

This result is portrayed in two-dimensional state space as shown in Figure 6.51.

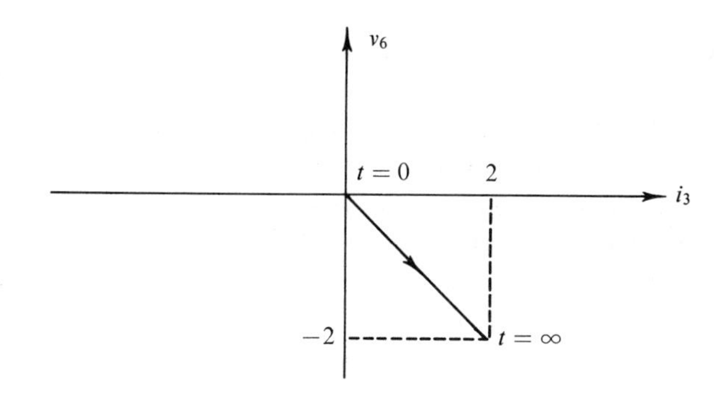

Fig. 6.51. *State space trajectory.*

Summary

Three formulation procedures are presented in this chapter, mesh formulation, node formulation, and state-variable formulation. The first two are most conveniently applied in connection with the Laplace transform; they are basically s-domain techniques. In contrast, the latter technique is most effective in the t-domain.

To employ a formulation technique systematically, elementary notions of graph theory are required in determining independent vertex (cutset) and circuit equations. Mesh and node equations, which in general are several simultaneous equations, are best solved by the Laplace transform. Resulting transfer functions are inverted into time-domain solutions by the use of a partial fraction expansion or tables of Laplace transforms.

State-variable equations, which are a set of first-order simultaneous differential equations, may be solved either by application of the Laplace transform (completely in the time domain), or by use of the state transition matrix. State-variable equations, furthermore, provide a unique mathematical form which is directly amenable to computer solution. This topic is treated in detail in Chapter 12.

ADDITIONAL READINGS

Bellman, R., *Introduction to Matrix Analysis*, New York: McGraw-Hill Book Co., 1960.

Bohn, E. V., *The Transform Analysis of Linear Systems*, Reading, Mass.: Addison-Wesley Publishing Co., Inc., 1963.

Churchill, R. V., *Modern Operational Methods in Engineering*, New York: McGraw-Hill Book Co., 1944.

Gupta, Someshwar C., *Transform State Variable Methods in Linear Systems*, New York: John Wiley & Sons, Inc., 1966.

Kaplan, W., *Operational Methods for Linear Systems*, Reading, Mass.: Addison-Wesley Publishing Co., Inc., 1962.

Koenig, Herman E., and William A. Blackwell, *Electromechanical System Theory*, New York: McGraw-Hill Book Co., 1961.

Koenig, Herman E., Y. Tokad, and H. K. Kesavan, *Discrete Physical Systems*, New York: McGraw-Hill Book Co., 1966.

Kuo, Benjamin C., *Linear Networks and Systems*, New York: McGraw-Hill Book Co., 1967.

Lueg, Russell E., and Erwin A. Reinhard, *Basic Electric Circuits for Engineers*, Scranton, Pa.: International Textbook Co., 1967.

Lynch, W. A., and J. G. Truxal, *Introductory System Analysis*, New York: McGraw-Hill Book Co., 1961.

Olson, H. F., *Dynamical Analogies*, New York: D. Van Nostrand Co., Inc., 1943.

Pfeiffer, P. E., *Linear System Analysis*, New York: McGraw-Hill Book Co., 1961.

Sanford, Richard S., *Physical Networks*, Englewood Cliffs, New Jersey: Prentice-Hall, Inc., 1965.

Seshu, S., and N. Balabanian, *Linear Network Analysis*, New York: John Wiley & Sons, Inc., 1959.

Shearer, J. Lowen, Arthur T. Murphy, and Herbert H. Richardson, *Introduction to System Dynamics*, Reading, Mass.: Addison-Wesley Publishing Co., Inc., 1967.

Timothy and Bona, *State Space Analysis—An Introduction*, New York: McGraw-Hill Book Co., 1967.

Tropper, A. M., *Matrix Theory for Electrical Engineers*, Reading, Mass.: Addison-Wesley Publishing Co., Inc., 1962.

Van Valkenburg, M. E., *Network Analysis*, Englewood Cliffs, New Jersey: Prentice-Hall, Inc., 1964.

PROBLEMS

6.1. Write the vertex equations for the graphs shown in Figure P 6.1. In each case verify the fact that the rank of the coefficient matrix is $v - 1$.

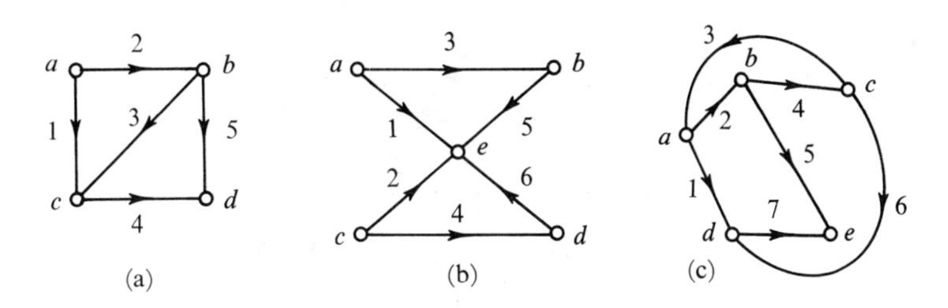

Fig. P 6.1.

6.2. Write mesh circuit equations for each of the graphs shown in Problem 6.1. In each case verify that the rank of the coefficient matrix is $e - v + 1$.

6.3. Determine system graphs for the systems shown in Figure P 6.3.

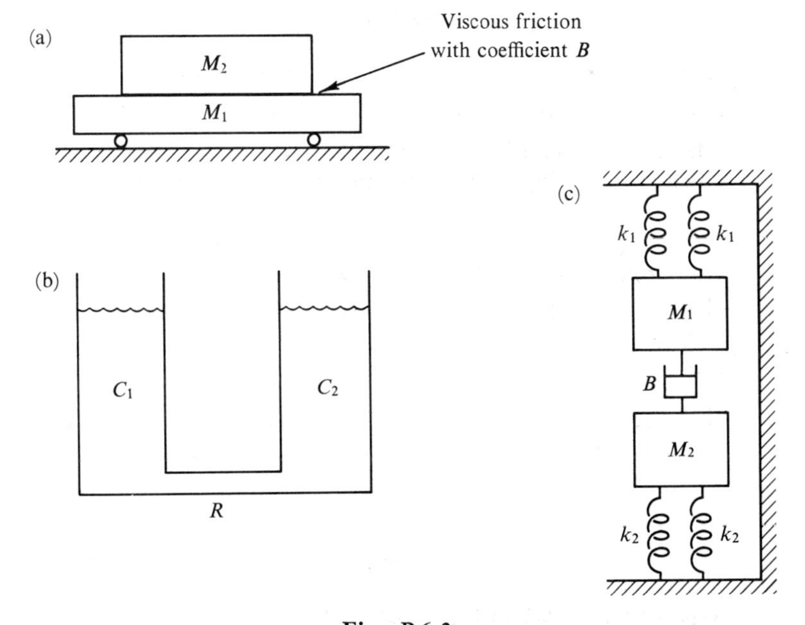

Fig. P 6.3.

6.4. Write mesh equations for the systems shown in Figure P 6.4.

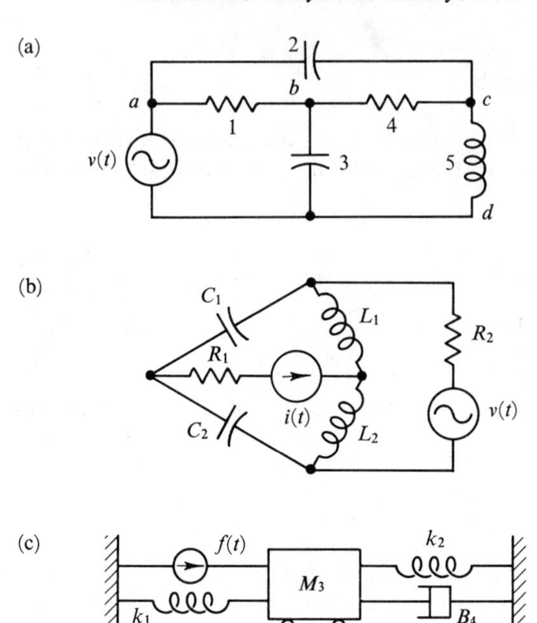

Fig. P 6.4.

6.5. Write node equations for the systems of Problem 6.4.

6.6. Derive the state equations for the systems of Problem 6.4.

6.7. The electric circuit of Figure 6.7 is driven by a pulse of the form shown. Calculate the voltage across the capacitor as a function of time.

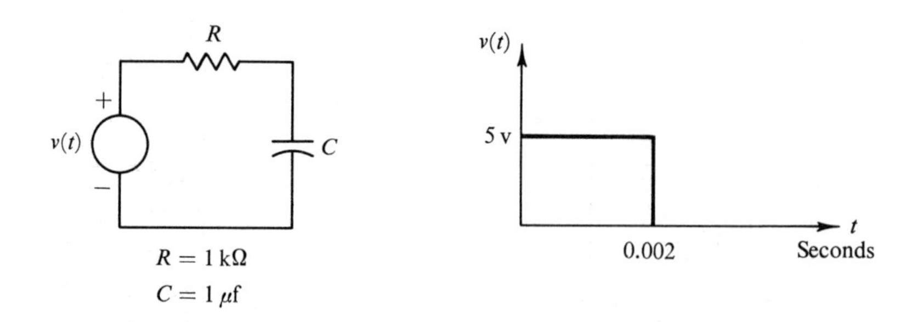

Fig. P 6.7.

6.8. Repeat Problem 6.7 with $R = 0.1$ kilohm and $C = 1$ microfarad.

6.9. Write fundamental cutset and circuit equations for the graphs of Problem 6.1.

6.10.

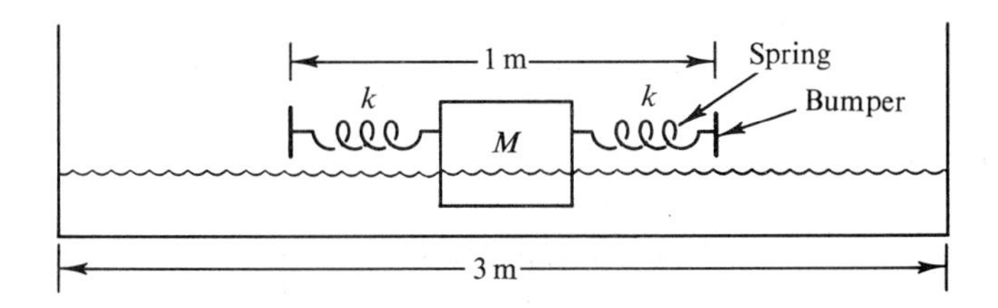

Fig. P 6.10.

The tank shown in Figure P 6.10 is partially filled with a viscous fluid supporting a float. This float is moving back and forth making contact with the walls of the tank through springs. If the float is initially located at the center and moves with a velocity of 0.5 meter/second, calculate the length of time required for the float to return to the same position making contact with each wall once. The following constants are given: $M = 1$ kilogram, $k = 5$ newton/meter, $B = 0.05$ newton-second/meter (B is the viscous drag coefficient).

6.11.

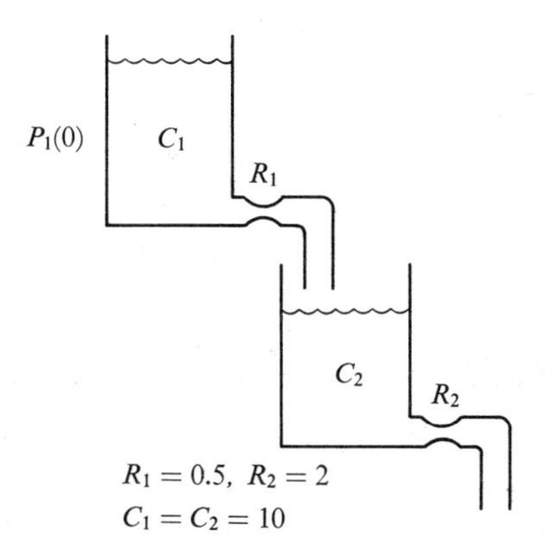

Fig. P 6.11.

A tank which is initially filled to a pressure of $p_1(0) = 10$ drains into a second tank. The second tank is also draining. Calculate the pressure in the second tank as a function of time. See Figure P 6.11.

6.12. Calculate the transfer function of the system shown in Figure P 6.12 using state variable techniques and check your result by use of either mesh or node formulation.

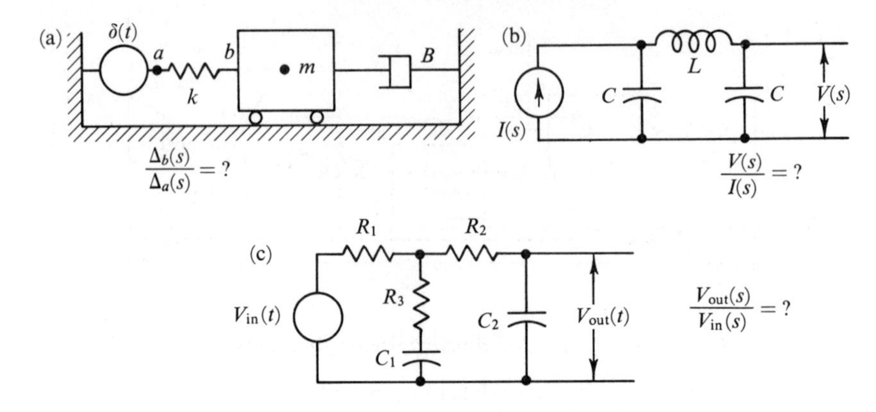

Fig. P 6.12.

6.13. Compute the inverse of the matrix $[s\mathbf{U} - \mathbf{A}]$ when

$$\mathbf{A} = \begin{bmatrix} -2 & -4 & -1 \\ 1 & 0 & 0 \\ 0 & 1 & 0 \end{bmatrix}$$

6.14. Show that the transfer function

$$X_{\text{out}}(s) = \frac{s+1}{s^2 + 3s + 1} X_{\text{in}}(s)$$

is equivalent to the state variable representation

$$\frac{d}{dt}\begin{bmatrix} x_{\text{out}} \\ x_2 \end{bmatrix} = \begin{bmatrix} -3 & 1 \\ -1 & 0 \end{bmatrix}\begin{bmatrix} x_{\text{out}} \\ x_2 \end{bmatrix} = \begin{bmatrix} 1 \\ 1 \end{bmatrix} x_{\text{in}}$$

6.15. Find the input impedance of the two networks shown in Figure P 6.15.

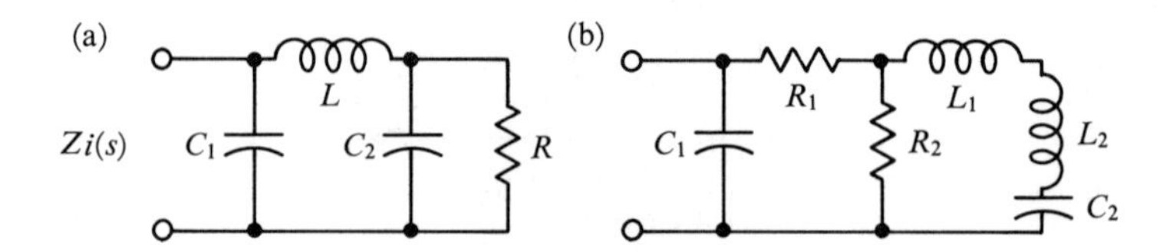

Fig. P 6.15.

6.16. Find the input admittance of the two mechanical systems shown in Figure P 6.16.

(a)

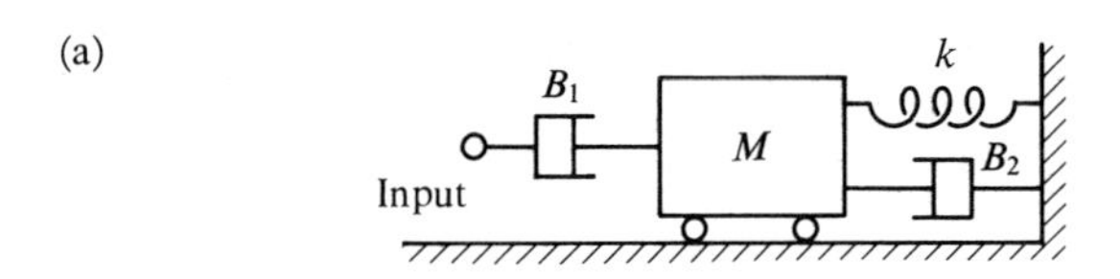

(b)

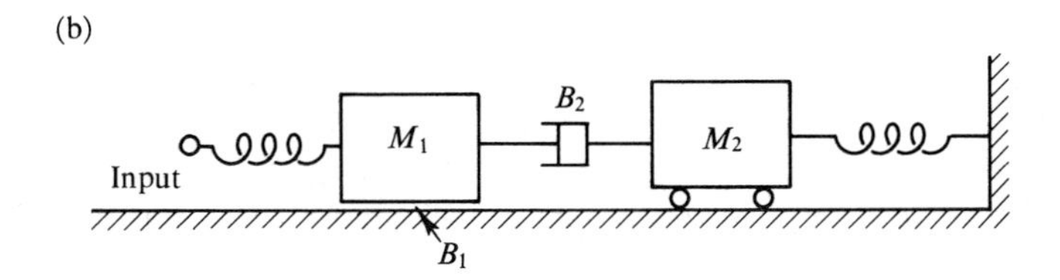

Fig. P 6.16.

6.17. Write the node equations for the system shown in Figure P 6.17.

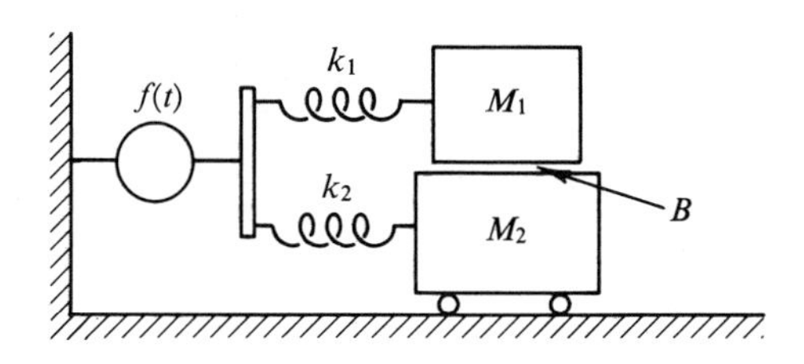

Fig. P 6.17.

6.18. Find the node admittance matrix for the system shown in Figure P 6.18.

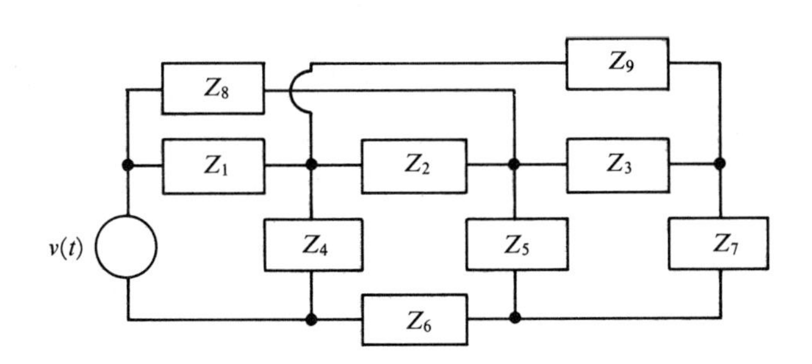

Fig. P 6.18.

6.19. Find the mesh-impedance matrix of the system in problem 6.18.

6.29. The circuit shown in Figure P 6.20 is called a twin-T circuit. Determine the transfer function E_2/E_1.

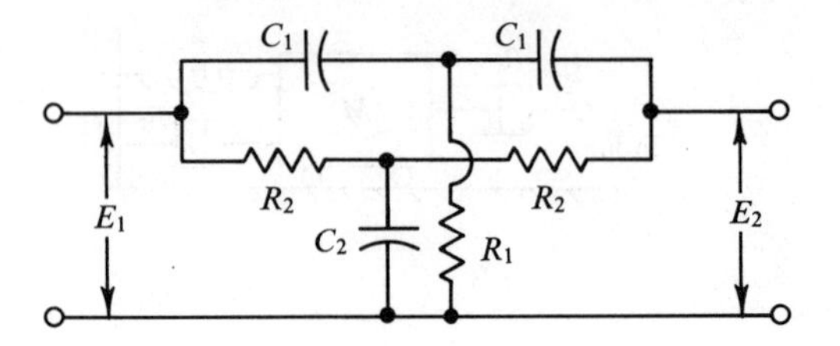

Fig. P 6.20.

6.21. What is the general form for state equations of a multi-input multi-output system ?

6.22. Compute $e^{\mathbf{A}t}$ when $\mathbf{A}$ is given by

a)

$$\mathbf{A} = \begin{bmatrix} -2 & -1 \\ 1 & 0 \end{bmatrix}$$

b)

$$\mathbf{A} = \begin{bmatrix} -1 & 0 & -3 \\ 1 & 1 & 0 \\ 1 & 0 & 1 \end{bmatrix}$$

6.23. Solve the following problem using state-variable techniques.

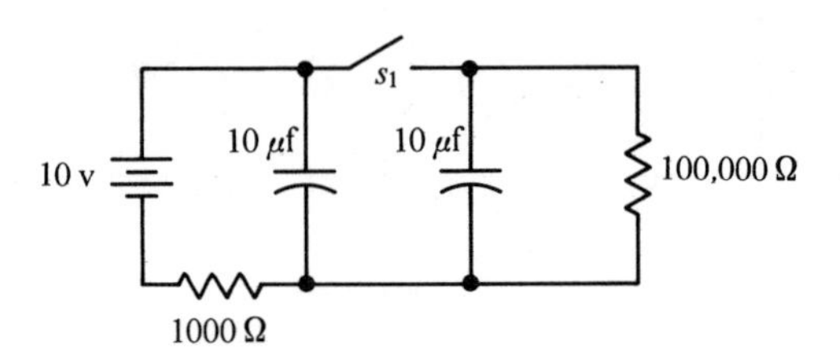

Fig. P 6.23.

A switch s_1 is closed and opened at 1 second intervals. Determine the voltage across the 100,000 ohm resistor as shown in Figure P 6.23.

6.24. Write state equations for the systems of Problems 6.17 and 6.4(a).

6.25. Formulate state-variable equations for each of the systems shown in Figure P 6.25.

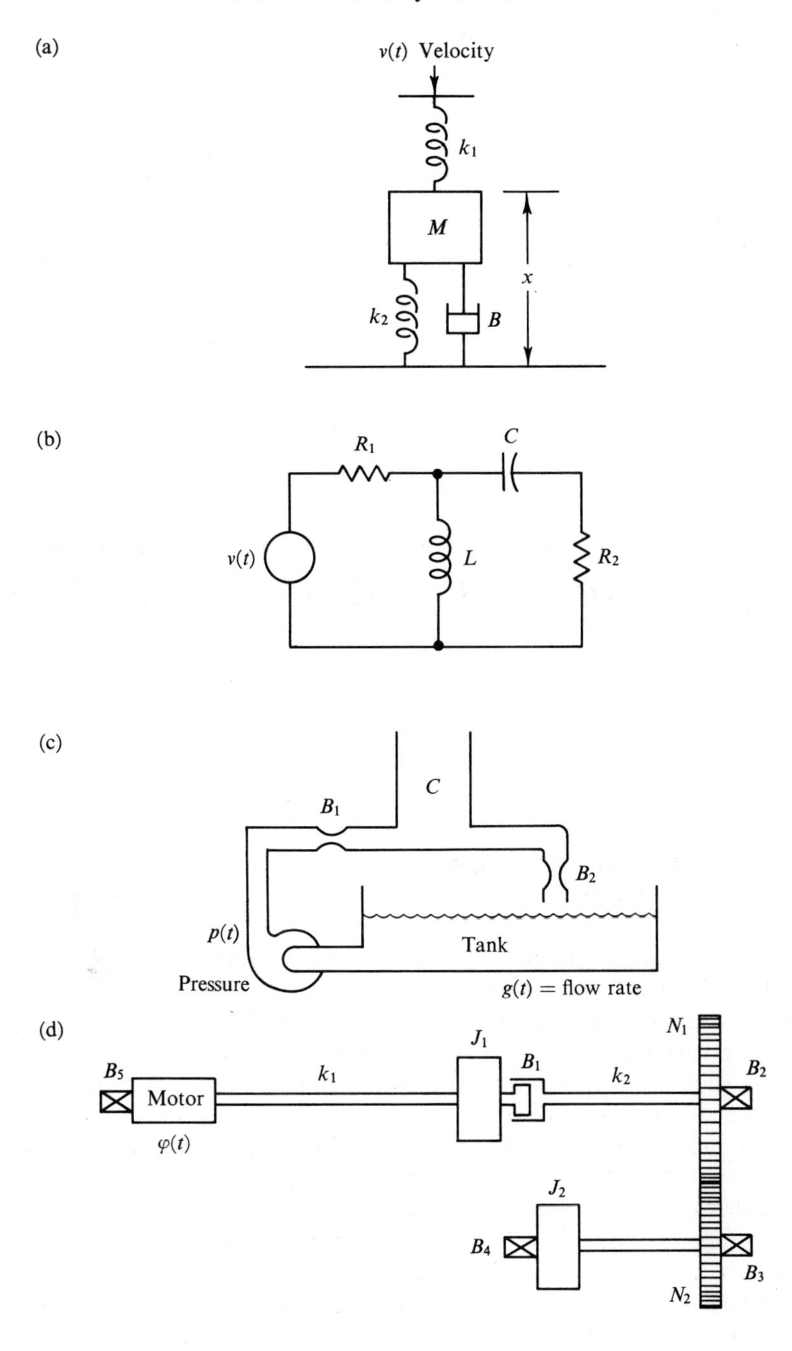
(a)
$v(t)$ Velocity
k_1
M
x
k_2
B
(b)
R_1
C
$v(t)$
L
R_2
(c)
C
B_1
B_2
$p(t)$
Tank
Pressure
$g(t)$ = flow rate
(d)
N_1
J_1
B_5
Motor
k_1
B_1
k_2
B_2
$\varphi(t)$
J_2
B_4
B_3
N_2

Fig. P 6.25.

Frequency Response, Resonance, and AC Circuit Power Analysis

7

7.1 Inputs and Outputs of General Systems

The preceding chapter presented three general methods for the formulation of system equations: the loop (or mesh) formulation, node formulation, and the state-variable formulation. All methods began with a system graph, and in each method a set of simultaneous equations was written for which a solution was required.

The most complete solution consists of a unique time response for each variable in the system. In an electrical system, for example, these variables are the voltages and currents of every element in the system. The responses arise either from a set of initial " states " (initial conditions) or from one or more inputs.

In any system there is a set of variables which are the desired outputs. Certain of the outputs are identical to certain variables found in the system, and others are linear combinations of these variables. In most cases the output requires a solution only for a limited number of the total variables in the system, but it is frequently necessary to find the simultaneous solutions for more variables than appear in the output.

Example 7.1. In the resistive electrical circuit shown in Figure 7.1 let the output be the voltage across R_6. Find $v_{out}(t)$ as a function of the input $I(t)$.

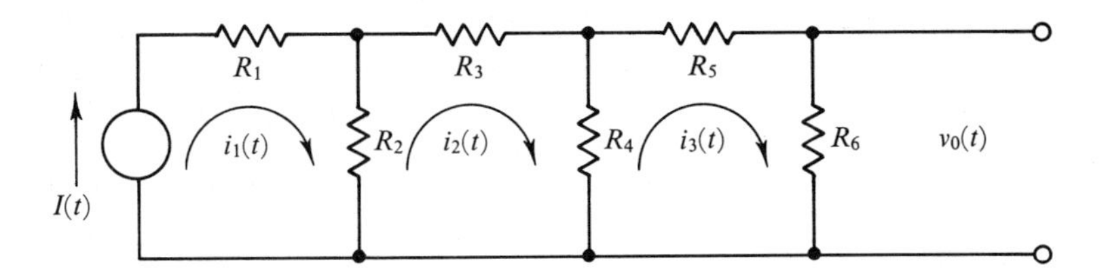

Fig. 7.1. *An electrical network.*

Since $i_1(t) = I(t)$ is known, a solution of the remaining two mesh equations gives $i_2(t)$ and $i_3(t)$. However, only $i_3(t)$ is needed for finding $v_0(t) = R_6 i_3(t)$. The two mesh equations are

$$(R_2 + R_3 + R_4) i_2(t) - R_4 i_3(t) = R_2 I(t)$$
$$-R_4 i_2(t) + (R_4 + R_5 + R_6) i_3(t) = 0$$

For a system with more than one output and more than one input, the outputs may be expressed in a general matrix equation:

$$\begin{bmatrix} X_{1\text{out}} \\ X_{2\text{out}} \\ \vdots \\ X_{p\text{out}} \end{bmatrix} = \begin{bmatrix} c_{11} & c_{12} \cdots c_{1n} \\ c_{21} & c_{22} \cdots c_{2n} \\ & \vdots \\ c_{p1} & c_{p2} \cdots c_{pn} \end{bmatrix} \begin{bmatrix} X_1 \\ X_2 \\ \vdots \\ X_n \end{bmatrix} + \begin{bmatrix} d_{11} & d_{12} \cdots d_{1m} \\ d_{21} & d_{22} \cdots d_{2m} \\ & \vdots \\ d_{p1} & d_{p2} \cdots d_{pm} \end{bmatrix} \begin{bmatrix} X_{1\text{in}} \\ X_{2\text{in}} \\ \vdots \\ X_{m\text{in}} \end{bmatrix} \quad (7.1)$$

where p = the total number of outputs, n = the number of variables in the solution equation, and m = the number of inputs. These equations may be written simply as

$$\mathbf{X}_{\text{out}} = \mathbf{CX} + \mathbf{DX}_{\text{in}} \quad (7.2)$$

where $\mathbf{X}_{\text{out}}$ = the output vector, $\mathbf{X}$ = the system variable vector, $\mathbf{X}_{\text{in}}$ = the input vector, $\mathbf{C} = [c_{ij}]$ is the matrix defining the contribution of each variable to each output, and $\mathbf{D} = [d_{ij}]$ is the matrix defining the contribution of the inputs to the outputs.

7.2 Importance of Steady State Frequency Response

This chapter is mainly concerned with systems which have one input and one output. An input, in general, can be any specified function of time, but the fundamental type of input which will be discussed is the sinusoidal input. The output steady-state response to a variable frequency sinusoidal input is a very important type of response for several reasons:

1. The electrical power industry requires the steady-state solution of electrical network systems to determine power requirements, transmission line design requirements, etc. The steady state solution of power systems is discussed later in this chapter.
2. Communication systems use high-frequency sinusoidal signals for transmitting radio, television, and general information from point to point.
3. Any periodic input can be broken down into a sum of sinusoidal frequencies by the Fourier Series Technique. Then the response of a system to any periodic input consists of the sum of the response to the component sinusoidal frequency inputs.
4. The design of mechanical or hydraulic systems may require information about the vibration modes of the system. The characteristics of the vibration modes can readily be found using sinusoidal inputs and finding the frequency response.

Example 7.2. It can be shown that the square wave shown in Figure 7.2 is equivalent to the infinite series

$$v(t) = \frac{4V}{\pi}\left[\sin t + \frac{1}{3}\sin 3t + \frac{1}{5}\sin 5t \cdots\right]$$

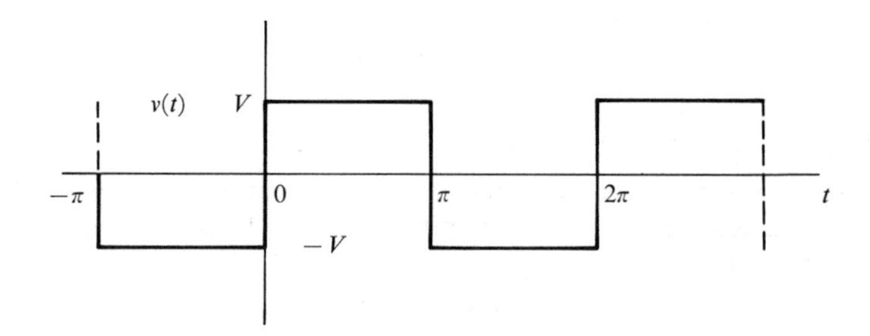

Fig. 7.2. *A square wave.*

In practice, the square wave may be adequately represented by using only a few of the terms of the series. The output response is the sum of the system responses to sin t, sin $3t$, etc.

Example 7.3. In the simple mechanical system in Figure 7.3, driving the mass with a force $f(t) = F \sin \omega t$ where ω is a variable, we find that the output motion "resonates" near the natural frequency defined as

$$\omega_n = \sqrt{\frac{k}{M}}$$

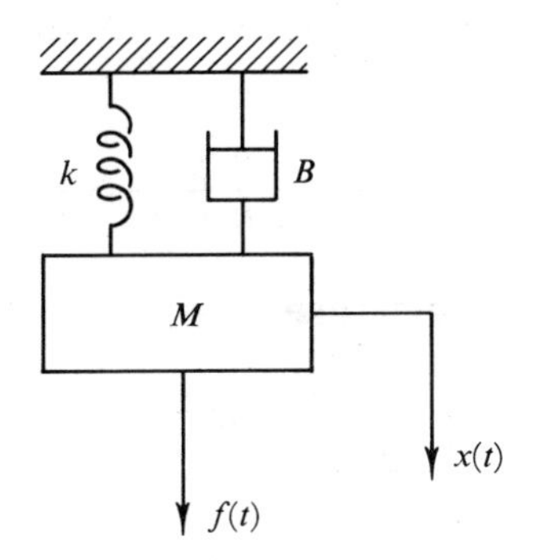

Fig. 7.3. *A mechanical system driven by a sinusoidal force.*

7.3 Transfer Functions of Systems

A single input-single output system may be presented as a simple block diagram shown in Figure 7.4. $G(s)$ is called the transfer function

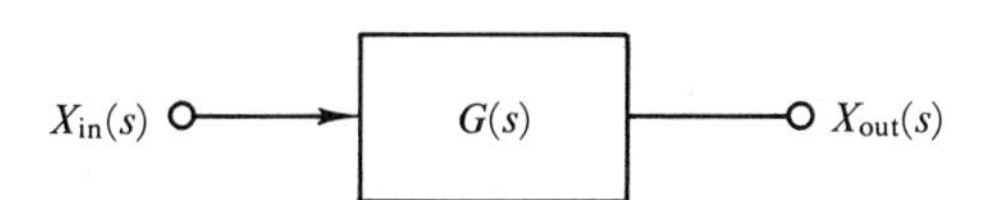

Fig. 7.4. *Block diagram of a system.*

of the system where s is the Laplace variable. The transfer function is simply the solution equation of the output as a function of the input written in the s-domain.

$$X_{\text{out}}(s) = G(s)\,X_{\text{in}}(s)$$

Initial " states " are always assumed to be zero when finding $G(s)$.

Example 7.4. In the RC circuit shown in Figure 7.5 find the transfer function, $G(s)$.

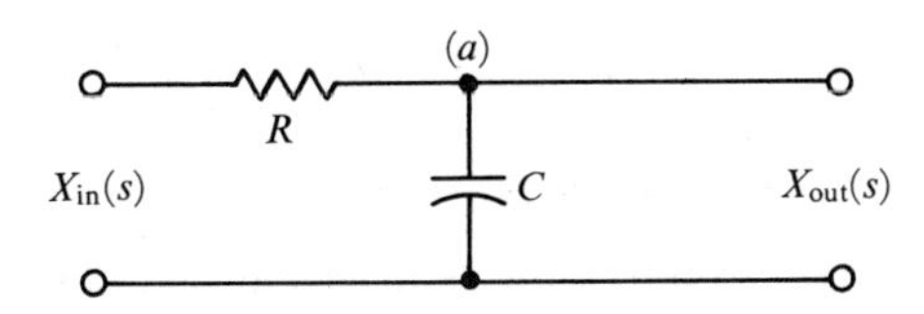

Fig. 7.5. *A one input-output system.*

The output is identical to the voltage at node (a), and a node equation written for node (a) in the s-domain is

$$\left(sC + \frac{1}{R}\right)X_{\text{out}}(s) = \frac{1}{R}X_{\text{in}}(s)$$

Therefore

$$G(s) = \frac{X_{\text{out}}(s)}{X_{\text{in}}(s)} = \frac{1/R}{1/R + sC} = \frac{1}{1 + sRC}$$

7.4 Frequency Response

The steady-state frequency response is found by driving the system with an input $x_{\text{in}}(t) = X_m \sin \omega t$ where ω is variable. In the Laplace domain,

$$X_{\text{in}}(s) = \frac{X_m\omega}{s^2 + \omega^2} \tag{7.3}$$

since

$$X_{\text{out}} = G(s)X_{\text{in}}(s) \tag{7.4}$$

then

$$X_{\text{out}}(s) = \frac{G(s)X_m(\omega)}{s^2 + \omega^2} \tag{7.5}$$

In general, $G(s)$ is the ratio of two polynominals in s, or $G(s) = P(s)/Q(s)$. Let

$$Q(s) = (s - s_1)(s - s_2) \cdots (s - s_n)$$

where s_1 through s_n are the roots of $Q(s) = 0$. Then, by expanding $X_{\text{out}}(s)$ in a partial fraction expansion, we have

$$\begin{aligned} X_{\text{out}}(s) &= \frac{X_m\omega P(s)}{(s - s_1) \cdots (s - s_n)(s + j\omega)(s - j\omega)} \\ &= \frac{K_1}{s - s_1} + \cdots + \frac{K_n}{s - s_n} + \frac{K_\omega}{s + j\omega} + \frac{K_\omega^*}{s - j\omega} \end{aligned} \tag{7.6}$$

Here K_1 through K_n are constants, some of which may be complex if certain roots of $Q(s) = 0$ are complex. The solution for $x_{\text{out}}(t)$ is found by taking the inverse Laplace transform of $X_{\text{out}}(s)$. $X_{\text{out}}(t)$ is written

$$X_{\text{out}}(t) = \underbrace{K_1e^{s_1t} + K_2e^{s_2t} + \cdots + K_ne^{s_nt}}_{\text{transient response}} + \underbrace{K_\omega e^{-j\omega t} + K_\omega^* e^{j\omega t}}_{\text{steady-state response}} \tag{7.7}$$

In a stable system, s_1 through s_n have negative real parts, therefore the total response consists of two parts: a transient response which decays to zero in time, and a steady-state response. We are only interested in the latter, and need to evaluate K_ω and K_ω^* where K_ω^* is the complex conjugate of K_ω. Since $s^2 + \omega^2 = 0$ has two simple imaginary poles,

$$K_\omega = (s + j\omega)\frac{X_m \omega G(s)}{s^2 + \omega^2}\bigg|_{s=-j\omega} = \frac{X_m G(-j\omega)}{-2j} \tag{7.8}$$

$$K_\omega^* = \frac{X_m G(j\omega)}{2j} \tag{7.9}$$

Let $K_\omega = a + jb$; then $K_\omega^* = a - jb$, and if we recombine the two steady-state terms,

$$X_{\text{out}}(s)\bigg|_{\text{steady state}} = \frac{a + jb}{s + j\omega} + \frac{a - jb}{s - j\omega} = \frac{2as + 2b\omega}{s^2 + \omega^2} \tag{7.10}$$

where

$$a + jb = \frac{jX_m G(-j\omega)}{2} \qquad \text{and} \qquad a - jb = \frac{-jX_m G(j\omega)}{2}$$

$$2a = X_m \operatorname{Im}[G(j\omega)] \qquad 2b = X_m \operatorname{Re}[G(j\omega)] \tag{7.11}$$

Im[ ] means the "imaginary part of" and Re[ ] means "real part of." Let $R(\omega) = \operatorname{Re}[G(j\omega)]$ and $I(\omega) = \operatorname{Im}[G(j\omega)]$; then

$$X_{\text{out}}(s)\bigg|_{\text{ss}} = \frac{X_m[I(\omega)s + R(\omega)\omega]}{s^2 + \omega^2} \tag{7.12}$$

$$x_{\text{out}}(t)\bigg|_{\text{ss}} = X_m[I(\omega)\cos\omega t + R(\omega)\sin\omega t] \tag{7.13}$$

From the trigonometric identity

$$\sin(x + y) = \sin x \cos y + \cos x \sin y$$

we can write the steady-state response in the form

$$X_{\text{out}}(t)\bigg|_{\text{ss}} = X_m\sqrt{R(\omega)^2 + I(\omega)^2}\sin(\omega t + \phi)$$

where

$$\phi = \tan^{-1}\frac{I(\omega)}{R(\omega)}$$

$$x_{\text{out}}(t)\bigg|_{\text{ss}} = X_m|G(j\omega)| \measuredangle \phi \tag{7.14}$$

where $|G(j\omega)|$ is the magnitude of $G(j\omega j)$, and $\phi = \tan^{-1} I(\omega)/R(\omega)$ is the "argument" of $G(j\omega)$.

Response to a Cosinusoidal Input

Suppose the input is $x_{\text{in}}(t) = X_m \cos\omega t$ (instead of $X_m \sin\omega t$); then

$$X_{\text{in}}(s) = \frac{X_m s}{s^2 + \omega^2} \tag{7.15}$$

$$X_{\text{out}}(s) = \frac{X_m s G(s)}{s^2 + \omega^2} = \frac{X_m s P(s)}{(s - s_1) \cdots (s - s_n)(s + j\omega)(s - j\omega)} \tag{7.16}$$

The steady-state part of $X_{\text{out}}(s)$ is

$$X_{\text{out}}(s)\Big|_{\text{ss}} = \frac{K_\omega}{s + j\omega} = \frac{K_\omega^*}{s - j\omega} \tag{7.17}$$

and

$$K_\omega = (s + j\omega)\frac{X_m s G(s)}{s^2 + \omega^2}\Big|_{s=-j\omega} = \frac{X_m G(-j\omega)}{2} = a + jb \tag{7.18}$$

$$K_\omega^* = \frac{X_m G(j\omega)}{2} = a - jb$$

$$2a = X_m \operatorname{Re}[G(j\omega)] = X_m R(\omega)$$

$$2b = -X_m \operatorname{Im}[G(j\omega)] = -X_m I(\omega) \tag{7.19}$$

$$X_{\text{out}}(s)\Big|_{\text{ss}} = X_m \frac{[R(\omega)s - I(\omega)\omega]}{s^2 + \omega^2} \tag{7.20}$$

$$x_{\text{out}}(t)\Big|_{\text{ss}} = X_m[R(\omega)\cos\omega t - I(\omega)\sin\omega t] \tag{7.21}$$

$$= X_m|G(j\omega)|\cos(\omega t + \phi) \tag{7.22}$$

where

$$\phi = \tan^{-1}\frac{I(\omega)}{R(\omega)}$$

Response to Exponential Function

The most general sinusoidal input may be represented by

$$x_{\text{in}}(t) = X_m e^{j\omega t} = X_m(\cos\omega t + j\sin\omega t) \tag{7.23}$$

The response to this input is

$$x_{\text{out}}(t)\Big|_{\text{ss}} = X_m|G(j\omega)|[\cos(\omega t + \phi) + j\sin(\omega t + \phi)]$$

$$= X_m|G(j\omega)|e^{j(\omega t + \phi)} \tag{7.24}$$

If

$$x_{\text{in}}(t) = X_m \sin(\omega t + \Psi) = X_m(\sin\omega t\cos\Psi + \cos\omega t\sin\Psi) \tag{7.25}$$

then

$$x_{out}(t)\Big|_{ss} = X_m|G(j\omega)|\,[\sin(\omega t + \phi)\cos\Psi + \cos(\omega t + \phi)\sin\Psi] \tag{7.26}$$

$$= X_m|G(j\omega)|\sin(\omega t + \Psi + \phi) \tag{7.27}$$

Frequency Response of First-Order Systems

A first-order system is one which contains only one energy storage element. Several examples of these were presented in previous chapters. A general description of a first-order linear system is the equation

$$\frac{dx_{out}}{dt} + ax_{out} = b_1\frac{dx_{in}}{dt} + b_0 x_{in} \tag{7.28}$$

where x_{out} is the output and x_{in} is the input; a, b_1, b_0 are constants in a time invariant system. Taking the Laplace transform of this equation with a zero initial value of x_{out},

$$(s + a)X_{out}(s) = (sb_1 + b_0)X_{in}(s) \tag{7.29}$$

Then

$$G(j\omega) = \frac{j\omega b_1 + b_0}{j\omega + a} \tag{7.30}$$

$R(\omega)$ and $I(\omega)$ can be found by multiplying the numerator and denominator by the conjugate of the denominator

$$G(j\omega) = \frac{j\omega b_1 + b_0}{j\omega + a} \times \frac{-j\omega + a}{-j\omega + a} = \frac{(b_0 a + \omega^2 b_1) - j\omega(b_0 - ab_1)}{a^2 + \omega^2}$$

$$= R(\omega) + jI(\omega) \tag{7.31}$$

Then

$$x_{out}(t)\Big|_{ss} = \frac{X_m}{a^2 + \omega^2}[(b_0 a + \omega^2 b_1)\sin\omega t - \omega(b_0 - ab_1)\cos\omega t]$$

$$= \sqrt{\frac{b_0^2 + \omega^2 b_1^2}{\omega^2 + a^2}}\sin(\omega t + \phi)$$

$$\phi = \tan^{-1}\frac{\omega(ab_1 - b_0)}{b_0 a + \omega^2 b_1} \tag{7.32}$$

Example 7.5. Find the steady-state response of the electrical network shown in Figure 7.5.

$$G(s) = \frac{1}{1 + sRC}$$

$$G(j\omega) = \frac{1}{1 + j\omega RC}\,\frac{1 - j\omega RC}{1 - j\omega RC} = \frac{1 - j\omega RC}{1 + \omega^2 R^2 C^2}$$

$$X_{out}(t)\Big|_{ss} = X_m[R(\omega)\sin\omega t + I(\omega)\cos\omega t]$$

$$= \frac{X_m}{1+\omega^2R^2C^2}[\sin\omega t - \omega RC\cos\omega t]$$

$$= \frac{X_m}{\sqrt{1+\omega^2R^2C^2}}\sin(\omega t+\phi) \qquad \phi = \tan^{-1}\frac{-\omega RC}{1}$$

Frequency Response of Second-Order Systems

A second-order system contains two energy storage elements. A general differential equation describing such a system is

$$\frac{d^2x_{out}}{dt^2} + a_1\frac{dx_{out}}{dt} + a_0x_{out} = b_2\frac{d^2x_{in}}{dt^2} + b_1\frac{dx_{in}}{dt} + b_0x_{in} \qquad \textbf{(7.33)}$$

Again taking the Laplace transform with zero initial conditions,

$$(s^2 + a_1s + a_0)X_{out}(s) = (b_2s^2 + b_1s + b_0)X_{in}(s) \qquad \textbf{(7.34)}$$

then

$$G(s) = \frac{b_2s^2 + b_1s + b_0}{s^2 + a_1s + a_0} \qquad \textbf{(7.35)}$$

$$G(j\omega) = \frac{b_0 - b_2\omega^2 + j\omega b_1}{a_0 - \omega^2 + j\omega a_1}$$

$$= \frac{(b_0-b_2\omega^2)(a_0-\omega^2) + \omega^2a_1b_1 - j\omega[a_1(b_0 - b_2\omega^2) - b_1(a_0-\omega^2)]}{(a_0-\omega)^2 + a_1^2\omega^2}$$

$R(\omega)$ = the real part of this expression and $I(\omega)$ is the imaginary part.

$$x_{out}(t)\Big|_{ss} = X_m[R(\omega)\sin\omega t + I(\omega)\cos\omega t]$$

$$= X_m\left[\frac{(b_0-b_2\omega^2)^2 + \omega^2b_1^2}{(a_0-\omega^2)^2 + \omega^2a_1^2}\right]^{1/2}\sin(\omega t+\phi) \qquad \textbf{(7.37)}$$

$$\phi = \tan^{-1}\frac{-\omega[a_1(b_0-b_2\omega^2) - b_1(a_0-\omega^2)]}{(b_0-b_2\omega^?)(a_0-\omega^2) + \omega^2a_1b_1}$$

Example 7.6. Find the steady-state sinusoidal response of the mechanical system shown in Figure 7.6.
The node equation for node (a) is

$$M\frac{d\dot{\delta}}{dt} + B\dot{\delta} + k\int\dot{\delta}\,dt = f(t) = F\sin\omega t$$

where $\dot{\delta}$ is the velocity of the mass. In the s-domain

$$\left(sM + B + \frac{k}{s}\right)\dot{\Delta}(s) = F(s)$$

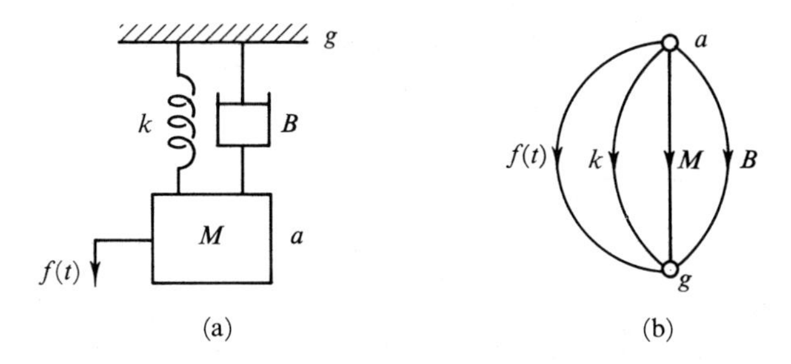

Fig. 7.6. *A second-order mechanical system:* (a) *system sketch;* (b) *system graph.*

or

$$\left(s^2 + \frac{B}{M}s + \frac{k}{M}\right)\dot{\Delta}(s) = \frac{s}{M}F(s)$$

$$G(j\omega) = \frac{\dot{\Delta}(j\omega)}{F(j\omega)} = \frac{j\omega/M}{(k/M - \omega^2) + j\omega(B/M)}$$

$$R(\omega) = \frac{\omega^2 B/M^2}{(k/M - \omega^2)^2 + (\omega B/M)^2}$$

$$I(\omega) = \frac{\omega/M(k/M - \omega^2)}{(k/M - \omega^2)^2 + (\omega B/M)^2}$$

$$|G(j\omega)| = \frac{\omega/M}{[(k/M - \omega^2)^2 + (\omega B/m)^2]^{1/2}}$$

$$\phi = \tan^{-1}\frac{(k/M - \omega^2)}{\omega B/M}$$

$$\dot{\delta}(t)|_{ss} = F[R(\omega)\sin\omega t + I(\omega)\cos\omega t]$$

If the positional frequency response instead of the velocity response is required, let $\delta(t)$ be the instantaneous position of the mass; then

$$\dot{\delta}(t) = \frac{d\delta(t)}{dt}$$

$$\dot{\Delta}(s) = s\Delta(s) \tag{7.38}$$

$$G_x(j\omega) = \frac{1/M}{(k/M - \omega^2) + j(\omega B/M)} = \frac{1/M(k/M - \omega^2) - j\omega(B/M^2)}{(k/M - \omega^2)^2 + (\omega B/M)^2} \tag{7.39}$$

$$|G_x(j\omega)| = \frac{1/M}{[(k/M - \omega^2)^2 + (\omega B/M)^2]^{1/2}} \qquad \phi = \tan^{-1}\frac{-\omega B/M}{k/M - \omega^2} \tag{7.40}$$

$$\delta(t)|_{ss} = R_x(\omega)\sin\omega t + I_x(\omega)\cos\omega t \tag{7.41}$$

This response could also have been found by integrating $\dot{\delta}(t)|_{ss}$; that is, if

$$\dot{\delta}(t)\Big|_{ss} = F[R(\omega)\sin\omega t + I(\omega)\cos\omega t] \tag{7.42}$$

Then

$$\delta(t)\Big|_{ss} = \int \dot{\delta}(t)\Big|_{ss} = F\left[-\frac{R(\omega)}{\omega}\cos\omega t + \frac{I(\omega)}{\omega}\sin\omega t\right] \quad (7.43)$$

Therefore

$$R_x(\omega) = \frac{I(\omega)}{\omega} \quad \text{and} \quad I_x(\omega) = \frac{-R(\omega)}{\omega} \quad (7.44)$$

These results can be used to find a new frequency response if the new variable is the time integral of the original variable. Similarly, the steady-state acceleration is the derivative of the velocity and

$$\ddot{\delta}(t)\,|_{ss} = F[\omega R(\omega)\cos\omega t - \omega I(\omega)\sin\omega t]$$

It is convenient to normalize the frequency response of a second-order system. This is done in the steps illustrated for the mechanical system of Example 7.6. Let

$$\omega_n^2 = \frac{k}{M}, \qquad 2\zeta\omega_n = \frac{B}{M}$$

then

$$G_x(j\omega) = \frac{1/M}{k/M - \omega^2 + j(\omega B/M)} = \frac{1/M}{\omega_n^2 - \omega^2 + j2\zeta\omega_n} \quad (7.46)$$

Dividing numerator and denominator by ω_n^2,

$$G_x(j\omega) = \frac{1/k}{1 - \omega^2/\omega_n^2 + j(2\zeta\omega/\omega_n)} \quad (7.47)$$

Let

$$u = \frac{\omega}{\omega_n}$$

then

$$G_x(ju) = \frac{1/k}{1 - u^2 + j2\zeta u} \quad (7.49)$$

and u is a dimensionless frequency variable. Finally,

$$\delta(t)\Big|_{ss} = \frac{F/k}{\sqrt{(1-u^2)^2 + 4\zeta u^2}}\sin(\omega t + \phi)$$

$$\phi = \tan^{-1}\frac{-2\zeta u}{1 - u^2} \quad (7.50)$$

7.5 Graphical Display of Sinusoidal Response

It is evident from Equations 7.14, 7.22, 7.24, and 7.27 that the basic characteristic of sinusoidal response is preserved under a variety of sinusoidal input functions; the amplitude of response is $|G(j\omega)|$ and the phase shift between the driving function and the response is Arg $\{G(j\omega)\}$. These characteristics are preserved whether the driving function is $\sin\omega t$, $\cos\omega t$, or $e^{j\omega t}$. In fact, if the amplitude and the phase shift are known, it matters little whether the driving function is sin ωt, cos ωt, or $e^{j\omega t}$. Therefore, we could use any one of the three as a basis to investigate the sinusoidal response of a linear system.

On many occasions, it is very effective to display the results of a sinusoidal response analysis graphically. We have several ways at our disposal.

A. *Sinusoidal waveform.* We assume the driving function to be $X_m \sin \omega t$, and display it by showing one cycle. The response is also shown on the same plot, shifted phase-wise and with a different amplitude. See Figure 7.7.

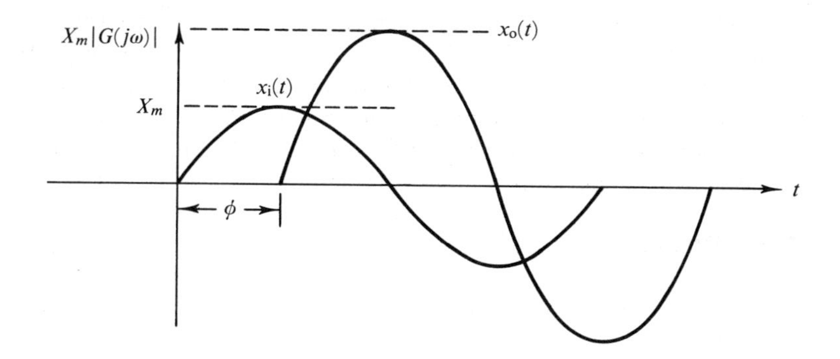

Fig. 7.7. *Waveform display of sinusoidal response.*

B. *Phasor diagram.* We assume the driving function to be $X_m e^{j\omega t}$ and display it as a complex number with magnitude X_m and argument ωt. The response is also shown as a complex number, with a different magnitude and rotated by the phase angle ϕ. See Figure 7.8.

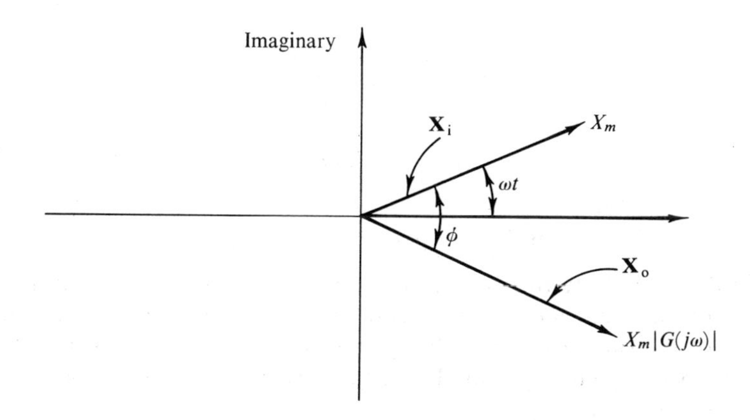

Fig. 7.8. *Phasor diagram displaying sinusoidal response.*

The result is a pair of vectors rotating counterclockwise with an angular frequency ω. They are permanently displaced from one another by the phase angle ϕ. These rotating vectors are called *phasors*.

In comparing the two methods of graphically displaying the sinusoidal response of a linear system, the phasor diagram offers several advantages over the waveform plot. The pertinent information is more effectively displayed. Furthermore, the waveform plot tends to be crowded when more than two or three functions are included, since they overlap; on the phasor diagram this is not the case. Perhaps most important of all, since the sinusoidal response is characterized by the complex number $G(j\omega)$, the vector operations of addition and subtraction may be performed graphically also. It is for this reason, namely the ease and effectiveness by which sinusoidal response information can be displayed on the phasor diagram, that in general it will be convenient to assume the sinusoidal input to be complex. In the next section, this concept will be developed more completely.

7.6 Phasors

A phasor is defined as a rotating vector, and is represented mathematically as

$$p(t) = \mathbf{P}e^{j\omega t} \tag{7.51}$$

where $\mathbf{P}$ is a complex function of ω expressible as

$$\mathbf{P} = |P|e^{j\,\mathrm{Arg}\,\{P\}} \tag{7.52}$$

A phasor is a means of graphically displaying the sinosuidal response of a linear system. As we saw in Section 7.3, if

$$x_{\mathrm{in}}(t) = e^{j\omega t}$$

and

$$X_{\mathrm{out}}(s) = G(s) \cdot X_{\mathrm{in}}(s)$$

then

$$x_{\mathrm{out}}(t) = \mathbf{G}(j\omega)e^{j\omega t} \tag{7.53}$$

where

$$\mathbf{G}(j\omega) = |G(j\omega)|e^{j\,\mathrm{Arg}\,\{G(j\omega)\}} \tag{7.54}$$

In displaying the functions $x_{\mathrm{in}}(t)$ and $x_{\mathrm{out}}(t)$ on a phasor diagram, it is usually sufficient merely to indicate the relative amplitudes and phase angles of the functions, even though the phasors are all rotating at ω radians per second. On this basis, the driving function is represented as the phasor in this special notation:

$$\mathbf{X}_{\mathrm{in}} = 1 \measuredangle 0^\circ \tag{7.55}$$

and the response as the phasor

$$\mathbf{X}_{\text{out}} = |G(j\omega)| \measuredangle \text{Arg}\{G(j\omega)\} \tag{7.56}$$

and the phasors remain stationary. Equations 7.55 and 7.56 retain only the essential information needed to prepare the phasor diagram shown in Figure 7.9.

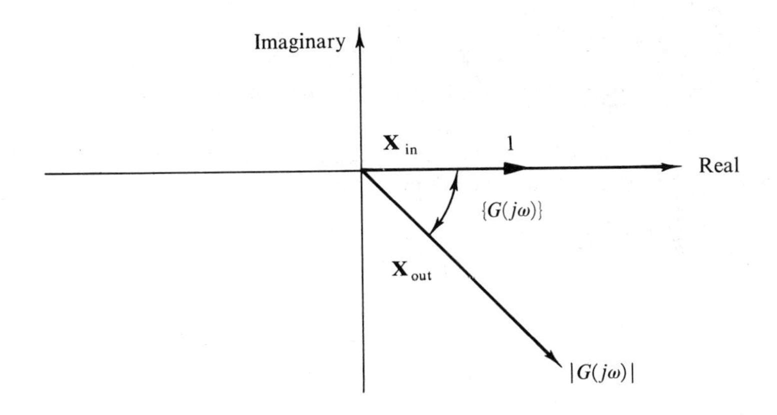

Fig. 7.9. *Phasor diagram, lagging phase angle.*

If the magnitude of the driving function is different from unity, it will appear simply as a multiplicative factor in the response.

Now consider several examples to illustrate the application of phasors in sinusoidal analysis.

Example 7.7. Determine the phasor relations for various two-terminal components.

a. *Capacitor.* Consider a sinusoidal current passing through a capacitor. We determine the voltage across the capacitor using the relation

$$V(s) = \frac{1}{Cs} I(s)$$

so that

$$v(t) = \frac{1}{C\omega} \sin(\omega t - 90°)$$

when

$$i(t) = \sin \omega t$$

This information is represented by the phasors

$$\mathbf{I} = 1 \measuredangle 0°$$

$$\mathbf{V} = \frac{1}{C\omega} \measuredangle -90°$$

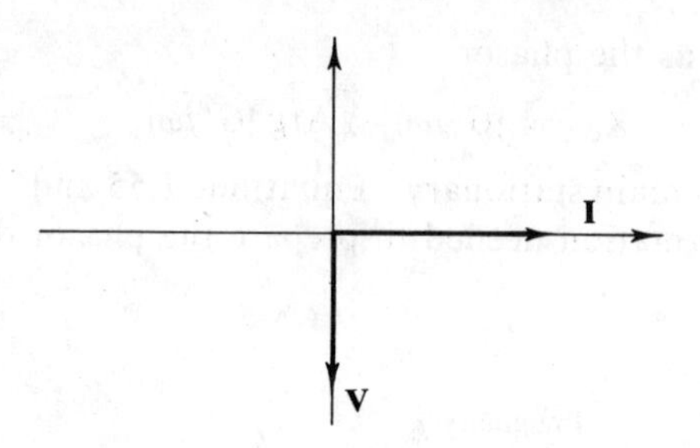

Fig. 7.10. *Phasor diagram for a capacitor.*

Note that the voltage across a capacitor lags the current through the capacitor by 90°. Capacitive reactance is defined as $X_c = 1/C\omega$.

b. *Inductor.*

$$V(s) = LsI(s)$$

Let

$$\mathbf{I} = 1 \measuredangle 0°$$

then

$$\mathbf{V} = L\omega \measuredangle +90°$$

We conclude that the voltage across an inductor leads the current through the inductor by 90°. Inductive reactance is defined as $X_L = L\omega$.

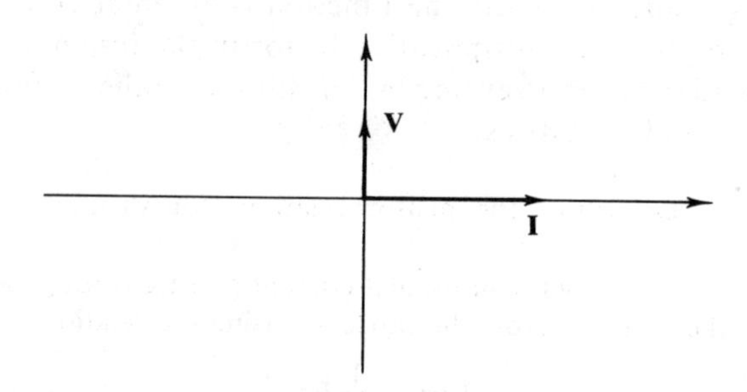

Fig. 7.11. *Phasor diagram for an inductor.*

Example 7.8. Calculate the displacement at point b in the spring-dashpot mechanism shown in Figure 7.12. The system graph of the mechanism is shown in Figure 7.13.

The node equations are (node admittance matrix)

$$\begin{bmatrix} k_2 & -k_2 \\ -k_2 & k_2 + k_3 + B_4 s \end{bmatrix} \begin{bmatrix} \Delta_a \\ \Delta_b \end{bmatrix} = 0 \tag{7.57}$$

Since Δ_a is specified,

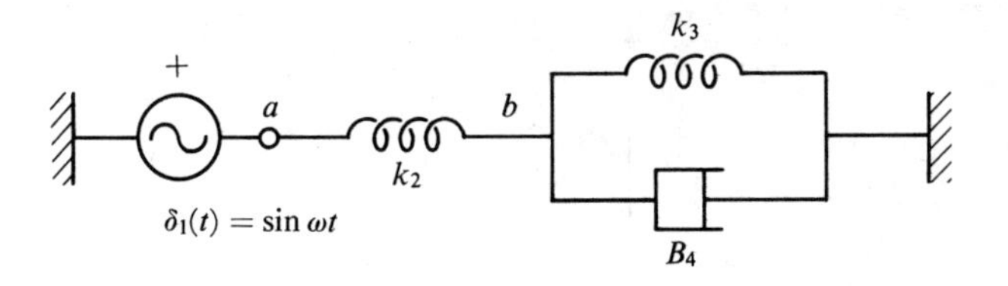

Fig. 7.12. *Spring-dashpot mechanism.*

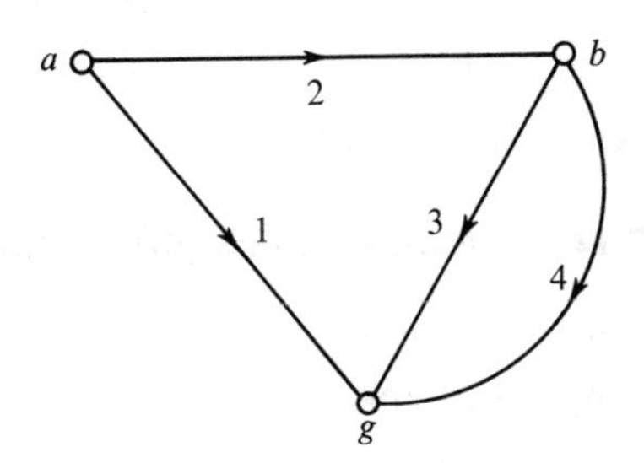

Fig. 7.13. *System graph of spring-dashpot mechanism.*

$$\mathbf{\Delta}_b = \frac{k_2}{k_2 + k_3 + B_4 s}\mathbf{\Delta}_a \tag{7.58}$$

Equation 7.58 contains the transfer function needed to establish the sinusoidal response. Let the driving function be represented by the phasor

$$\mathbf{\Delta}_a = 1 \measuredangle 0^\circ$$

Then we calculate the response as follows:

$$G(s) = \frac{k_2}{k_2 + k_3 + B_4 s}$$

$$|G(j\omega)| = \frac{k_2}{\sqrt{(k_2 + k_3)^2 + (B_4\omega)^2}}$$

$$\text{Arg }\{G(j\omega)\} = -\tan^{-1}\frac{B_4\omega}{k_2 + k_3}$$

Let the following numerical values be given for the parameters of this system: $k_2 = k_3 = 2$, $B_4 = 0.2$, and $\omega = 10$. Then

$$\mathbf{G}(j\omega) = 0.447 \measuredangle -26.6^\circ$$

and

$$\mathbf{\Delta}_b = 0.447 \measuredangle -26.6^\circ$$

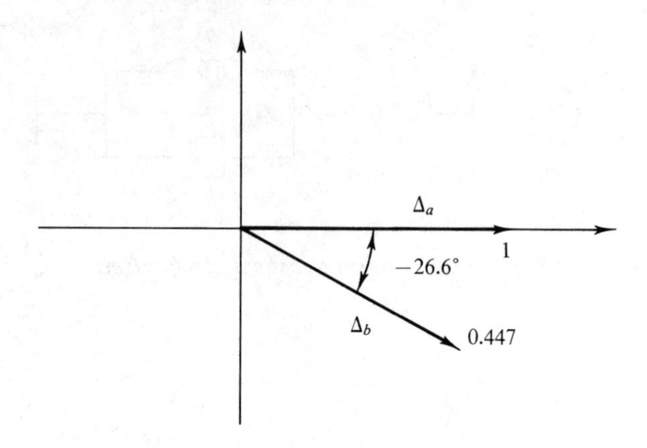

Fig. 7.14. *Phasor diagram for mechanism.*

We therefore have for

$$\delta_a(t) = \sin 10t$$

that

$$\delta_b(t) = 0.447 \sin (10t - 26.6°)$$

Example 7.9. Determine the phasors representing all unknown voltages and currents in the electrical circuit shown in Figure 7.15.

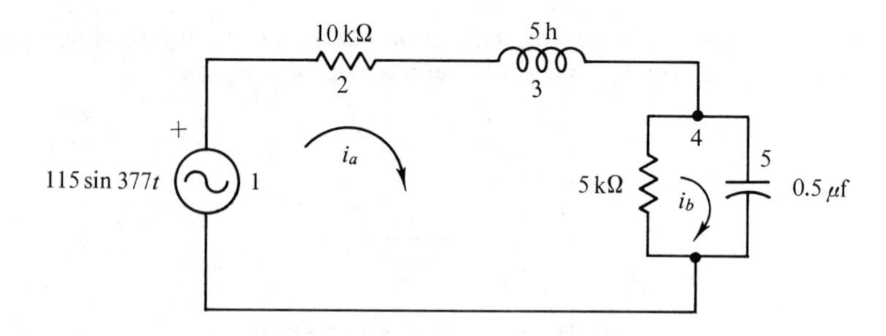

Fig. 7.15. *Electrical circuit.*

The mesh equations for the circuit are

$$\begin{bmatrix} R_2 + R_4 + L_3 s & -R_4 \\ -R_4 & R_4 + \dfrac{1}{C_5 s} \end{bmatrix} \begin{bmatrix} I_a \\ I_b \end{bmatrix} = \begin{bmatrix} V_1 \\ 0 \end{bmatrix}$$

$$\begin{bmatrix} I_a \\ I_b \end{bmatrix} = \frac{1}{D(s)} \begin{bmatrix} R_4 + \dfrac{1}{C_5 s} \\ R_4 \end{bmatrix} V_1$$

where

$$D(s) = \frac{R_4C_5L_3s^2 + (L_3 + R_4R_2C_5)s + R_4 + R_2}{C_5s}$$

so that

$$I_a = \frac{1 + R_4C_5s}{R_4C_5L_3s^2 + (L_3 + R_4R_2C_5)s + R_4 + R_2} V_1$$

and

$$I_b = \frac{R_4C_5s}{R_4C_5L_3s^2 + (L_3 + R_4R_2C_5)s + R_4 + R_2} V_1$$

Let

$$\mathbf{V}_1 = 115 \measuredangle 0^\circ$$

then

$$\begin{aligned}
\mathbf{I}_a &= \frac{1 + 0.943j}{13{,}200 + 11{,}000j} \cdot 115 \\
&= \frac{1.377 \measuredangle 43.3^\circ}{17.200 \measuredangle 39.8^\circ} \cdot 115 \\
&= 0.918 \cdot 10^{-2} \measuredangle 3.5^\circ
\end{aligned}$$

and similarly

$$\begin{aligned}
\mathbf{I}_b &= \frac{0.943j}{17{,}200 \measuredangle 39.8^\circ} = 0.631 \cdot 10^{-2} \measuredangle 50.2^\circ \\
\mathbf{V}_2 &= R_2\mathbf{I}_a = 91.8 \measuredangle 3.5^\circ \\
\mathbf{V}_3 &= j\omega L_3\mathbf{I}_a \\
&= 1885 \measuredangle 90^\circ \cdot \mathbf{I}_a \\
&= 17.3 \measuredangle 93.5^\circ \\
\mathbf{V}_4 = \mathbf{V}_5 &= \frac{1}{j\omega C_5}\mathbf{I}_b \\
&= 5310 \measuredangle -90^\circ \cdot \mathbf{I}_b \\
&= 33.5 \measuredangle -39.8^\circ
\end{aligned}$$

These phasors are shown on the phasor diagram of Figure 7.16.

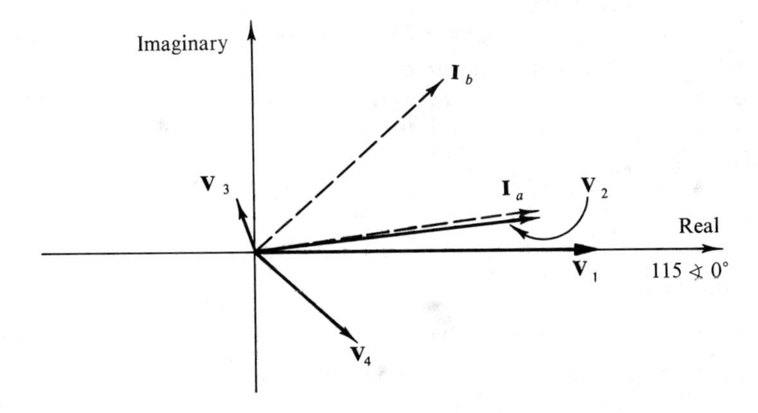

Fig. 7.16. *Phasor diagram.* (*Current phasors times* 10^4).

It is important to notice that the sum of the four phasors $\mathbf{V}_1$, $\mathbf{V}_2$, $\mathbf{V}_3$, $\mathbf{V}_4$ vanishes when they are added vectorially, as shown in Figure 7.17. This, of course, is a necessary consequence of the circuit law.

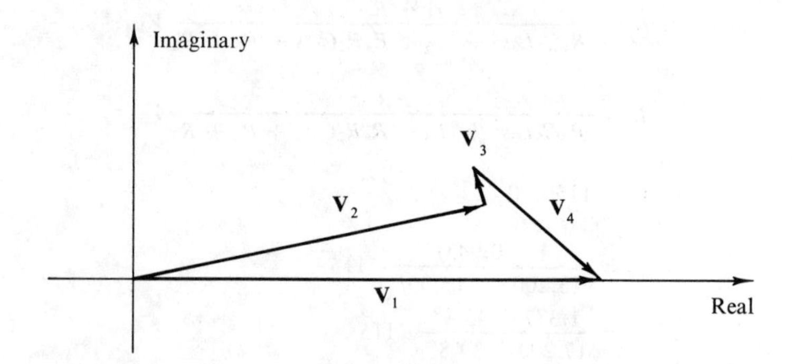

Fig. 7.17. *Vectorial sum check of voltage phasors.*

7.7 Impedances and Admittances as Phasors

In the previous section we saw the employment of the phasor in representing the magnitude and phase angle of sinusoidally varying system variables. When, for instance, the quantity

$$x_1(t) = X_m \sin(\omega t + \phi)$$

is represented as a phasor, we simply write

$$\mathbf{X}_1 = X_m \measuredangle \phi$$

Again, a phasor is merely a complex number totally obeying the rules of complex algebra.

Impedances and admittances can also be viewed as phasors when employed in sinusoidal system operation. In fact, we can readily establish that under sinusoidal excitation an impedance $Z(s)$ and an admittance $Y(s)$ will transform into complex numbers when s is replaced by $j\omega$. Thus,

$$\begin{aligned}\mathbf{Z}(j\omega) &= |Z(j\omega)|e^{j\,\mathrm{Arg}\,\{Z(j\omega)\}} \\ &= |Z| \measuredangle \phi_z \end{aligned} \tag{7.59}$$

and similarly,

$$\mathbf{Y}(j\omega) = |Y| \measuredangle \phi_y \tag{7.60}$$

In the form of Equations 7.59 and 7.60, we recognize that an impedance or admittance is simply a phasor. Consider the following example.

Example 7.10. Determine the impedances and the current of the circuit shown in Figure 7.18 by means of phasors.

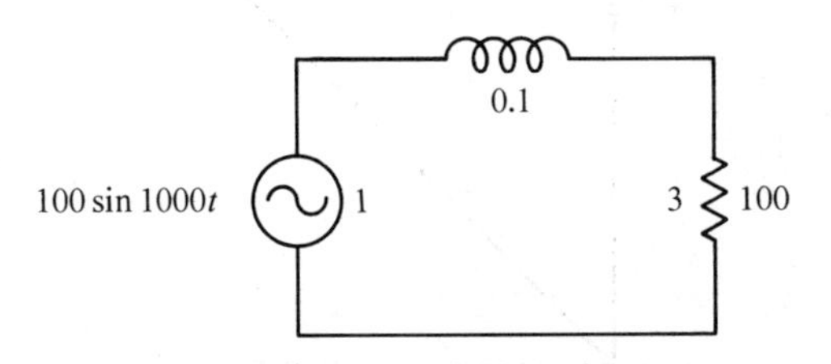

Fig. 7.18. *Electrical circuit.*

The impedances of the circuit are

$$\begin{aligned}\mathbf{Z}_L &= j\omega L \\ &= 100 \measuredangle +90^\circ\end{aligned}$$

Since the inductive reactance is defined as ωL, the impedance of an inductor is imaginary and

$$\begin{aligned}\mathbf{Z}_L &= jX_L \\ \mathbf{Z}_R &= R \\ &= 100 \measuredangle 0^\circ\end{aligned}$$

The mesh equation for the circuit is expressed in terms of phasors

$$\mathbf{V}_1 = (\mathbf{Z}_L + \mathbf{Z}_R)\mathbf{I}$$

When this equation is solved for **I**,

$$\begin{aligned}\mathbf{I} &= \frac{\mathbf{V}_1}{\mathbf{Z}_L + \mathbf{Z}_R} \\ &= \frac{100 \measuredangle 0^\circ}{100 \measuredangle 90^\circ + 100 \measuredangle 0^\circ} \\ &= \frac{100 \measuredangle 0^\circ}{142 \measuredangle 45^\circ} = 0.707 \measuredangle -45^\circ\end{aligned}$$

This information is illustrated in the phasor diagram of Figure 7.19. Although we can represent an impedance as a phasor, we cannot represent it by a time function. So in Example 7.10 only the variables of the system, the voltage and the current, can be expressed as

$$v_1(t) = 100 \sin 1000\, t$$

and

$$i(t) = 0.707 \sin (1000\, t - 45^\circ)$$

However, it is meaningless to talk of an impedance time function. It is therefore only in the "$j\omega$-domain," where all quantities are phasors, that impedances and admittances are mathematically equivalent to variables.

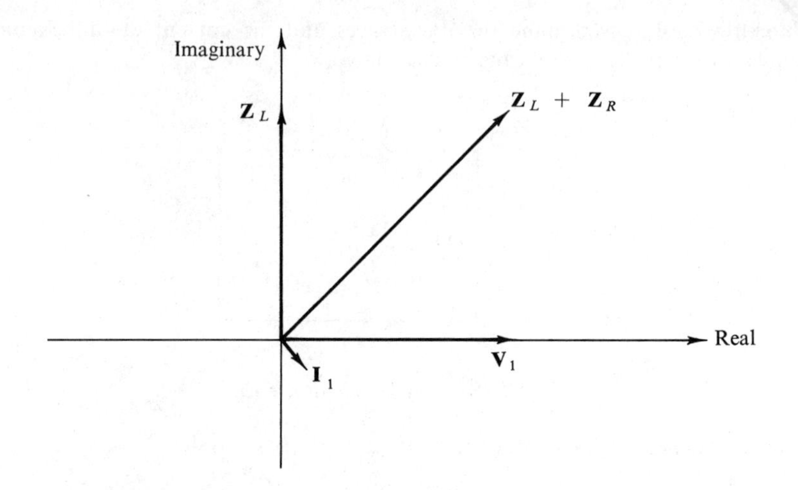

Fig. 7.19. *Phasor diagram (current 10 times).*

Example 7.11. Solve Example 7.8 by treating the individual impedances or admittances as phasors. We view the problem as shown in Figure 7.20.

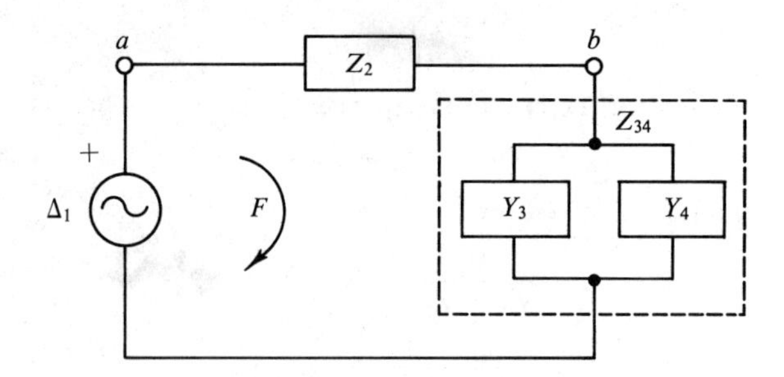

Fig. 7.20. *Another representation of spring-dashpot mechanism.*

From a mesh equation, we have

$$\Delta_1 = (\mathbf{Z}_2 + \mathbf{Z}_{34}) \cdot \mathbf{F}$$

or

$$\mathbf{F} = \frac{\Delta_1}{\mathbf{Z}_2 + \mathbf{Z}_{34}}$$

and

$$\Delta_b = \mathbf{Z}_{34} \cdot \mathbf{F} = \frac{\mathbf{Z}_{34}}{\mathbf{Z}_2 + \mathbf{Z}_{34}} \cdot \Delta_1$$

This can also be written as

$$\Delta_b = \frac{\mathbf{Y}_2}{\mathbf{Y}_2 + \mathbf{Y}_3 + \mathbf{Y}_4} \Delta_1$$

We calculate

$$\begin{aligned}
\mathbf{Y}_2 &= k_2 \measuredangle 0^\circ = 2 \measuredangle 0^\circ \\
\mathbf{Y}_2 + \mathbf{Y}_3 + \mathbf{Y}_4 &= k_2 \measuredangle 0^\circ + k_3 \measuredangle 0^\circ + B_4\omega \measuredangle 90^\circ \\
&= 4 + 2 \measuredangle 90^\circ \\
&= 4.47 \measuredangle 26.6^\circ \\
\frac{\mathbf{Y}_2}{\mathbf{Y}_2 + \mathbf{Y}_3 + \mathbf{Y}_4} &= \frac{2 \measuredangle 0^\circ}{4.47 \measuredangle 26.6^\circ} = 0.447 \measuredangle -26.6^\circ \\
\Delta_2 &= (0.447 \measuredangle -26.6^\circ)(1 \measuredangle 0^\circ) \\
&= 0.447 \measuredangle -26.6^\circ
\end{aligned}$$

This answer agrees with the one previously obtained.

It is easily seen that the systematic for formulation procedures of mesh and node formulation are completely extendable into the $j\omega$-domain. One simply has to recall that the formulation of equations is actually carried out in the s-domain, with s then being replaced by $j\omega$ for the sinusoidal steady state.

7.8 Graphical Representation of Frequency Response

We have described two methods for graphically displaying the sinusoidal response of a system at some particular frequency. Of these two methods, the phasor diagram is the more useful. However, if the frequency is variable, it is necessary to draw a new phasor diagram for each frequency, which may be highly impractical. In this section we consider methods of representing the frequency response of a system for all frequencies.

The sinusoidal response to the input $x_{\text{in}}(t) = X_m \sin \omega t$ is given as

$$\begin{aligned}
x_{\text{out}}(t)\Big|_{\text{ss}} &= X_m|G(j\omega)| \sin(\omega t + \phi) \\
&= X_m|G(j\omega)| \measuredangle \phi(\omega)
\end{aligned} \tag{7.61}$$

The ratio of output to input is

$$|G(j\omega)| \measuredangle \phi(\omega)$$

Suppose we were to plot two graphs, one of $|G(j\omega)|$ versus ω, the other of $\phi(\omega)$ versus ω. The effect of any change in frequency on the output to input response of a system is quite effectively displayed in these plots.

Frequency Response Plots of First-Order Systems

The following example illustrates the method of plotting $|G(j\omega)|$ and $\phi(\omega)$ for a representative first-order system.

Example 7.12. In the simple RL network shown in Figure 7.21, find and plot $|G(j\omega)|$ and $\phi(\omega)$ versus ω.

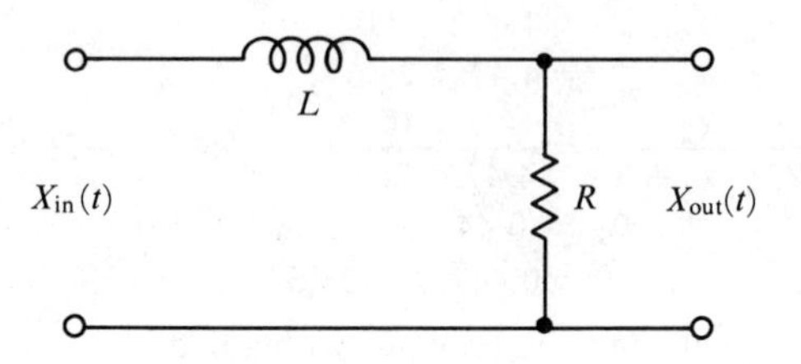

Fig. 7.21. *R-L network.*

$$\frac{X_{out}(s)}{X_{in}(s)} = \frac{R}{sL + R}$$

$$G(j\omega) = \frac{X_{out}(j\omega)}{X_{in}(j\omega)} = \frac{R}{j\omega L + R} = \frac{1}{1 + j\omega(L/R)}$$

Define $\omega_0 = R/L$ and let $u = \omega/\omega_0$.

$$|G(ju)| = \frac{1}{\sqrt{1 + u^2}} \qquad \phi(u) = \tan^{-1}(-u)$$

Figure 7.22 shows a plot of $|G(ju)|$ versus u.

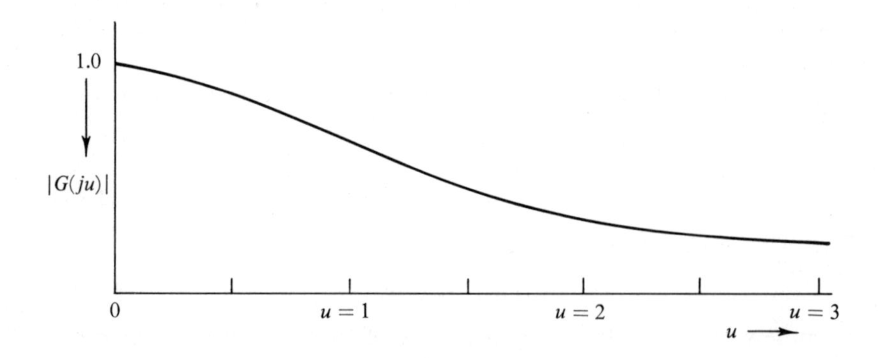

Fig. 7.22. *Plot of G(ju) versus u.*

For any value of $R/L = \omega_0$,

$$|G(j\omega)| = |G(ju\omega_0)|$$

It is evident that this one plot describes the amplitude response for similar first-order systems. Figure 7.23 shows a plot of $\phi(u)$ versus u. Again, this plot describes the phase response for similar first-order systems.

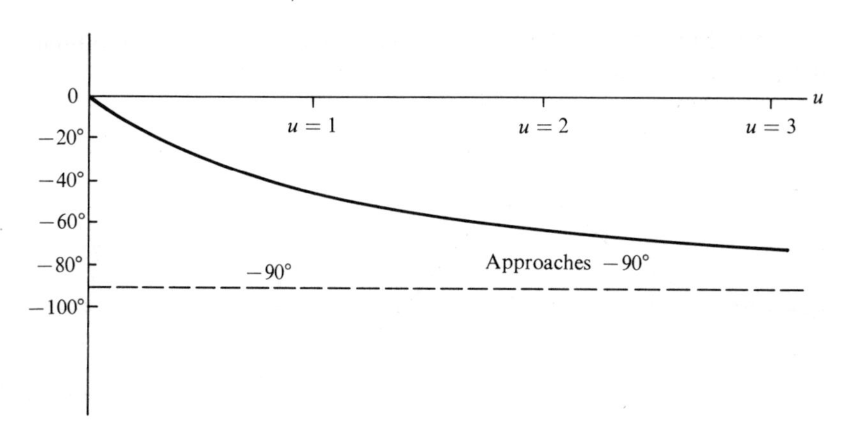

Fig. 7.23. $\phi(u)$ *versus u.*

Frequency Response Plots of Second-Order Systems

Consider the mechanical system of Figure 7.6. The frequency response of this system was analyzed in Section 7.4, Example 7.6. After normalizing, we have

$$|G(ju)| = \frac{F/k}{\sqrt{(1-u^2)^2 + 4\zeta^2u^2}} = A(u)$$

$$\phi(ju) = \tan^{-1}\frac{-2\zeta u}{1-u^2} \tag{7.62}$$

where $\omega = \omega_n u$ and ω_n is the natural resonant frequency. The constant, ζ, depends on the viscous damping in the system. In an undamped system, $\zeta = 0$, but ζ can assume any positive value. For most systems of interest, ζ will be restricted to the range $0 < \zeta < 1.0$.

Suppose $\zeta = 0.25$ for this example. Let us plot both $A(\omega)$ and $\phi(\omega)$ as a function of frequency. For the amplitude plot, we can quickly determine that

$$|G(0)| = A(0) = F/k$$

static spring displacement,

$$|G(j\omega_n)| = A(\omega_n) = \frac{F/k}{2\zeta} = \frac{2F}{k}$$

double static spring displacement,

$$A(\infty) = 0$$

These three values, in addition to the fact that $A(\omega)$ is a continuous and positive function of ω, now permit the construction of the amplitude plot shown in Figure 7.24.

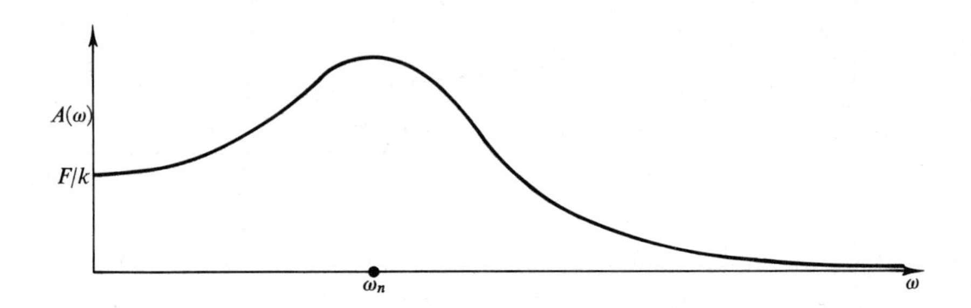

Fig. 7.24. *Amplitude plot of mass displacement.*

We see that the amplitude rises to exactly twice the zero-frequency magnitude at $\omega = \omega_n$. This, of course, is the well-known characteristic of *resonance*. This is the phenomenon that all potentially oscillatory systems will exhibit when excited by a periodic signal in the vicinity of the system's natural frequency.

For the same values of frequency, namely $\omega = 0$, ω_n, and ∞, we calculate

$$\phi(0) = 0$$

$$\phi(\omega_n) = -\tan^{-1}\frac{0.5}{0} = -90°$$

$$\phi(\infty) = -\tan^{-1}\frac{1}{\infty} = -180°$$

The phase shift when plotted as a function of frequency is shown in Figure 7.25.

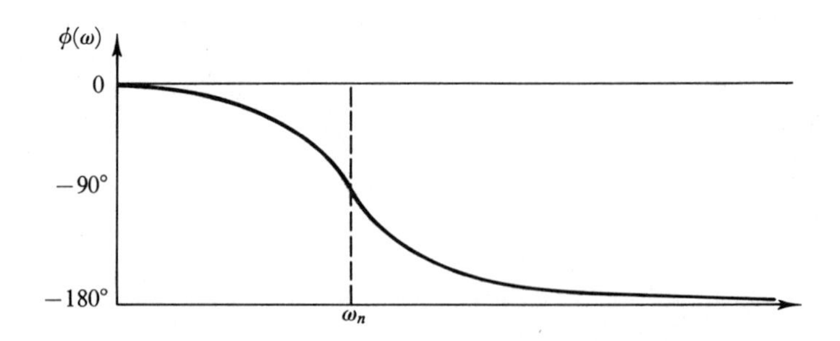

Fig. 7.25. *Phase shift of mechanical system.*

The example introduces a second method of displaying the frequency response information of a particular system. The two plots are called the *amplitude* and *phase shift plots*.

Both the polar plot and the amplitude and phase shift plot convey the same amount of information. But there is a difference in the effectiveness with which certain system response properties are brought into focus. One usually is well advised to be able to draw both types of plots in order to benefit from both of them.

Bode Plots

Bode amplitude and phase plots are a variation of the amplitude and phase plots. There are still two plots representing the frequency response of a system. In both, the abscissa or the frequency axis is made logarithmic to the base 10. The ordinate of the phase plot remains a linear function of phase angle, but the ordinate of the magnitude plot is also made logarithmic to the base 10. The phase plot is normally made on semi-log graph paper and the amplitude plot on log-log or semi-log graph paper.

Example 7.13. For the $R - L$ network of Figure 7.21, make Bode plots. These plots are shown in Figures 7.26 and 7.27.

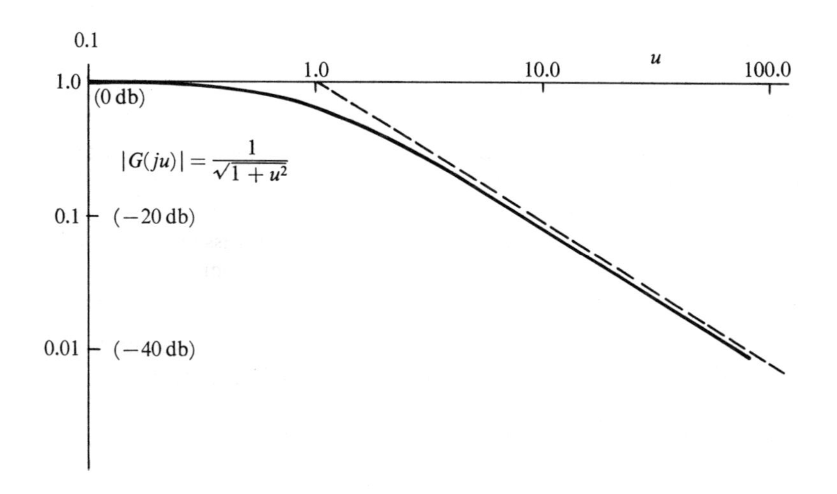

Fig. 7.26. *Bode amplitude plot of* $|G(ju)| = 1/\sqrt{1+u^2}$.

There are advantages in the use of Bode plots over linear scale frequency response plots. Note that the amplitude plot becomes asymptotic to straight

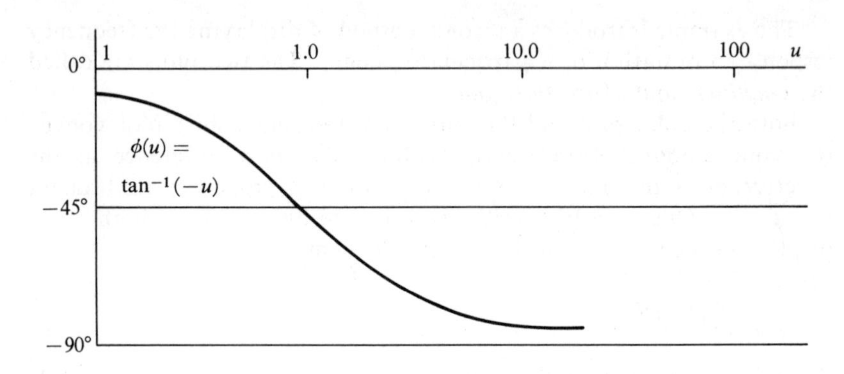

Fig. 7.27. *Bode phase plot of* $\phi(u) = \tan^{-1}(-u)$.

lines at frequencies below and above $u = 1.0$. The frequency $u = 1$ is known as a "break frequency," for this is the junction point of the two straight asymptotic lines. When $u \ll 1$, $|G(ju)| = 1$, and when $u \gg 1$, $|G(ju)| = 1/u$. The slope of the asymptote for $u > 1$ is -1 bel per decade. The bel is the name given to a decade change in amplitude. In engineering practice, the decibel is used and one bel = 20 decibels (db) amplitude change. Many times the ordinate of the Bode amplitude plot is made a linear scale and 20 × (log of the amplitude) is calculated before plotting. Since $\log_{10}(1.0) = 0$, $\log_{10}(10) = 1$, etc., then $|G(ju)| = 1.0$ (=) 0 db, $|G(ju)| = 0.1$ (=) −20 db, $|G(ju)| = 10$ (=) + 20 db, etc. There is, therefore, a 20 db change for every decade amplitude change.

The Bode phase plot is asymptotic to 0° for $u < 1$ and asymptotic to −90° for $u > 1$. There is a direct correlation between the asymptotic phase angle and the slope of the log amplitude plot. This correlation, stated simply, is: For an amplitude asymptotic slope of n bel/decade, the phase asymptote is $(90n°)$. In Example 7.13, $n = 0$ for $u < 1$, hence $\phi_{u<1} = 0°$; and $n = -1$ for $u > 0$, hence $\phi_{u>1} = -90°$. This correlation holds only for the class of systems known as "minimum phase," but a majority of all physical systems are "minimum phase."

The basic ideas just presented can be applied to a system transfer function of any complexity. Consider the following example.

Example 7.14. Draw the Bode plots of a system whose transfer function is given as

$$G(s) = \frac{10(s + 10)}{s(s^2 + \sqrt{2}s + 8)(s + 50)}$$

we need first to find

$$G(j\omega) = \frac{10(j\omega + 10)}{j\omega(-\omega^2 + j\sqrt{2}\,\omega + 8)(j\omega + 50)}$$

There is no advantage in normalizing this system equation since there is more than one denominator factor. The factors of the second-order term $s^2 + \sqrt{2}s + 8$ are

$$\left[s + \frac{1}{\sqrt{2}} + j\left(2\sqrt{2} - \frac{1}{2}\right)\right]$$

and

$$\left[s + \frac{1}{\sqrt{2}} - j\left(2\sqrt{2} - \frac{1}{2}\right)\right]$$

and are complex. There is a "double break" in the two asymptotic lines associated with this term. That is, for frequencies such that $\omega^2 < 8$, the asymptotic slope is 0 bel/decade. For $\omega^2 > 8$, the slope is -2 bel/decade. The break frequencies for all the factors of $G(s)$ are listed in Table 7.1.

TABLE 7.1.

Factor	*Break frequency*
$\frac{1}{s}$	0
$s + 10$	$\omega = 10$
$s^2 + \sqrt{2}s + 8$	$\omega = 2\sqrt{2}$
$s + 50$	$\omega = 50$

Table 7.2 lists the asymptotic slopes for various frequency ranges and the corresponding phase asymptotes.

TABLE 7.2.

Frequency range	*Asymptote slope*	*Phase asymptote*
$\omega < 2\sqrt{2}$	-1	$-90°$
$2\sqrt{2} < \omega < 10$	-3	$-270°$
$10 < \omega < 50$	-2	$-180°$
$\omega > 50$	-3	$-270°$

Figure 7.28 shows Bode plots of this system. The asymptotic lines are drawn first, followed by a more detailed calculation of the amplitude and phase in the region of the break frequencies. Note that $\omega = 1$ is less than any of the break frequencies. Therefore the magnitude of the asymptote $|G(j\omega)|$ when $\omega = 1$ can be easily found by the expression

$$|G(j1)| = \frac{10\ (10)}{1\ (8)\ (50)} = \frac{1}{4}$$

where only constant terms of each factor are included. Expressed in bels or decibels,

$$G(j1) = \log_{10}\left(\frac{1}{4}\right) = -\log_{10}(4) = -0.602 = -12.04 \text{ db}$$

A set of points which are easy to plot are the magnitudes at the break frequencies. For first-order terms,

$$|G(ju)| = |G(j1)| = \frac{1}{\sqrt{1+1}} = \frac{1}{\sqrt{2}}$$

$$\log_{10}\left(\frac{1}{\sqrt{2}}\right) = -\log_{10}\sqrt{2} = -0.15$$

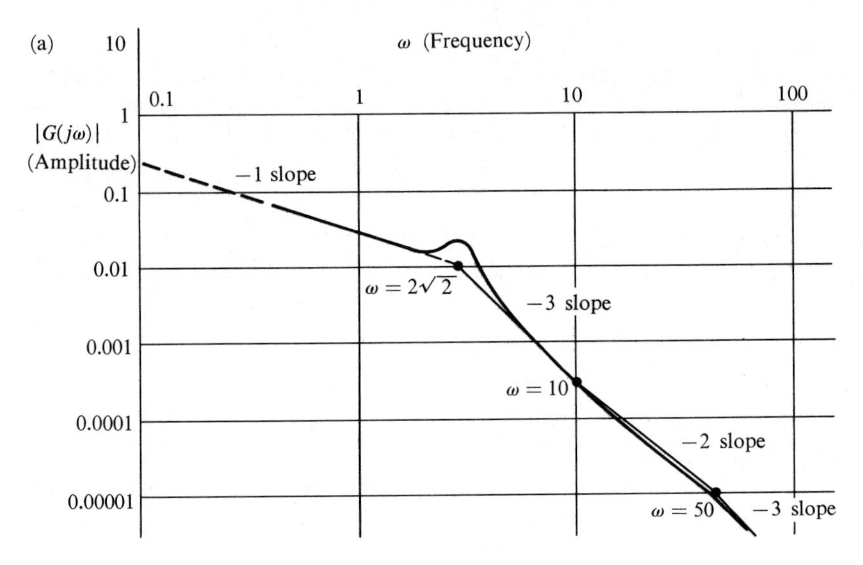

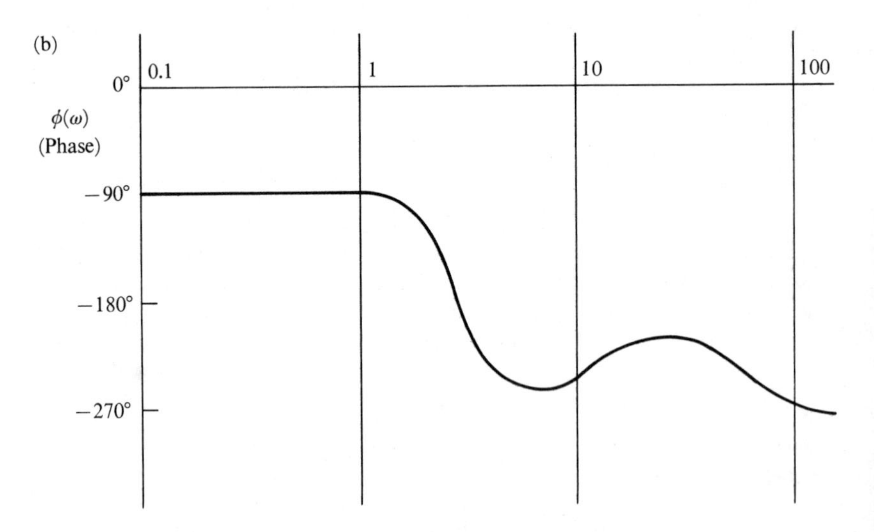

Fig. 7.28. (a) *Amplitude plot;* (b) *phase plot.*

Therefore, if the first-order term is in the denominator, the true plot lies -0.15 bel below the junction of the two asymptotic plots. If the first-order term is in the numerator, the true plot lies 0.15 bel above the asymptotic junction.

For second-order terms,

$$|G(ju)| = |G(j1)| = \frac{1}{2\zeta}$$

which is a function of ζ. For the second-order term in this example, $\zeta = 1/4$, $1/2\zeta = 2$, therefore, the plot is $\log_{10}(2) = 0.602$ bel above the break frequency junction. Other values of $|G(j\omega)|$ in the vicinity of the break frequencies can be found from standardized plots of $|G(ju)|$ for each first- and second-order factor of $G(j\omega)$ where $\omega = \omega_0 u$ for a first-order factor and $\omega = \omega_n u$ for a second-order factor. This is discussed in the next section.

7.9 Resonance in Simple System

In Chapter 5, we learned that a system must be made up of at least two components which are capable of storing different kinds of energy in order to have an oscillatory free response. A typical electrical system would be a resistor-inductor-capacitor series circuit. A mathematical criterion for an oscillatory system has been established: The roots of the characteristic equation of the system must include at least two complex conjugates for a system to exhibit an oscillatory transient. This condition requires that the order of a system be at least two. A system of order one can never oscillate in its free response.*

The examples treated in the first sections of this chapter involved second-order systems, which was clearly evidenced by the fact that the characteristic equation contained a second degree polynominal equation written in the standard form

$$s^2 + 2\zeta\omega_n s + \omega_n{}^2 = 0$$

In this section, we will investigate the frequency response of systems whose characteristic equation is of this standard form. Let the transfer function of a second-order system be given as

$$G(s) = \frac{\omega_n^2}{s^2 + 2\zeta\omega_n s + \omega_n^2} \tag{7.63}$$

The sinusoidal response of this system is now calculated.

$$x_0(t) = A(\omega)\sin[\omega t + \phi(\omega)] \tag{7.64}$$

$$\begin{aligned} A(\omega) &= |G(j\omega)| \\ &= \frac{\omega_n^2}{\sqrt{(\omega_n^2 - \omega^2)^2 + (2\zeta\omega_n\omega)^2}} \end{aligned}$$

* Except, of course, when a first-order system is excited by a sinusoidal driver.

$$= \frac{1}{\sqrt{(1-u^2)^2 + (2\zeta u)^2}} \tag{7.65}$$

$$\phi(\omega) = \operatorname{Arg}\{G(j\omega)\}$$

$$= -\tan^{-1}\frac{2\zeta\omega_n\omega}{\omega_n^2 - \omega}$$

$$= -\tan^{-1}\frac{2\zeta u}{1-u^2} \tag{7.66}$$

where, as before, the dimensionless ratio $u = \omega/\omega_n$ has been introduced.

Similar expressions had been encountered in Section 7.8. Compare, for instance, Equation 7.62. Of course, this agreement is in order since the examples treated earlier also were second-order systems.

Now consider Equations 7.65 and 7.66 in full detail, with both ζ and ω as variable parameters. Consider first the amplitude function. A few key quantities are calculated, as shown in Table 7.3.

TABLE 7.3. *Selected values of $A(\omega)$*

ω \ ζ	0	0.1	0.25	0.5	0.707	1	2
0	1		1	1	1	1	1
ω_n	∞	5	2	1	0.707	0.5	0.25
∞	0	0	0	0	0	0	0

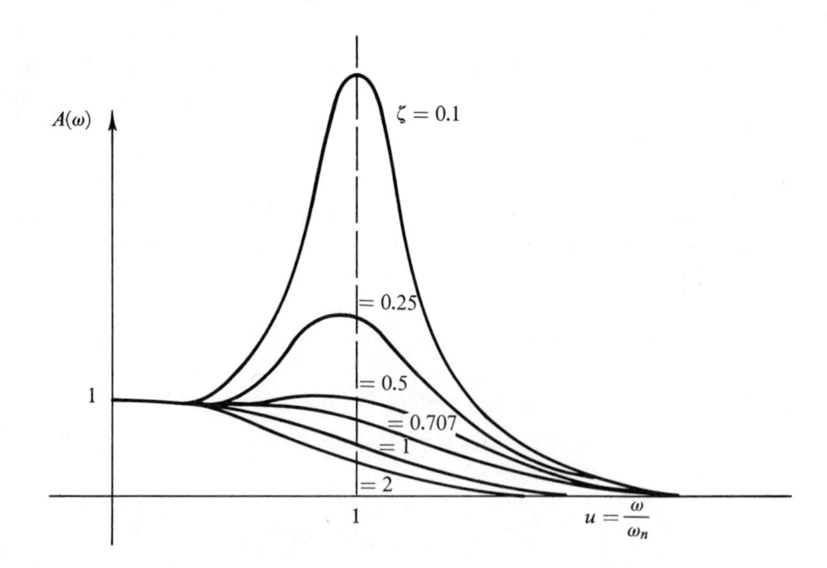

Fig. 7.29. *$A(\omega)$ versus u for second-order system.*

With the aid of the values of this table and several more calculations, we prepare the amplitude plot shown in Figure 7.29. One fact becomes immediately obvious on this plot. The amplitude function is very sensitive to changes in the damping factor in the vicinity of $\omega = \omega_n$. In fact, for $\omega = \omega_n$,

$$A(\omega_n) = \frac{1}{2\zeta}$$

The particular phenomenon of amplitude reinforcement under sinusoidal excitation is called *resonance*. Note that the amplitude of oscillation becomes infinite when $\zeta = 0$; the system is completely undamped. As ζ increases, the amplitude is reduced; however, the peak amplitude does not occur at $\omega = \omega_n$, but at $\omega < \omega_n$. We call ω_n the *undamped natural frequency* of the system. Assume that the peak frequency occurs at $\omega = \omega_p$. We can calculate this frequency by maximizing $A(\omega)$. The result is

$$\omega_p = \omega_n\sqrt{1 - 2\zeta^2} \tag{7.67}$$

and the peak amplitude

$$A_p(\omega) = A(\omega_p) = \frac{1}{2\zeta\sqrt{1 - \zeta^2}} \tag{7.68}$$

The derivation of Equations 7.67 and 7.68 is left as an exercise. We will call ω_p the *resonant frequency* of the system.

From Equation 7.67 it is evident that the peak amplitude is not associated with the undamped natural frequency, but is shifted to the left of it. In fact, $\omega_p = 0$ when $\zeta = 0.707$. This implies that resonance will occur only as long as $\zeta < 0.707$.

Let us turn now to the phase shift function $\phi(\omega)$, and investigate the shape of the plot of $\phi(\omega)$ versus ω for the various values of ζ. We establish immediately that for any value of $\phi(0) = 0$,

$$\phi(\omega_n) = -90°$$
$$\phi(\infty) = -180°$$

The effect of a variation in ζ is best demonstrated by the plot itself, shown in Figure 7.30. This plot calls attention to an interesting characteristic. The phase shift is negligible for low frequencies, and roughly $-180°$ for high frequencies relative to the natural frequency. The change in phase shift is gradual when the system has damping, and becomes more rapid as the damping factor decreases. It is most pronounced when $\zeta = 0$; the phase shift changes abruptly from 0 to $-180°$ as the undamped natural frequency is passed.

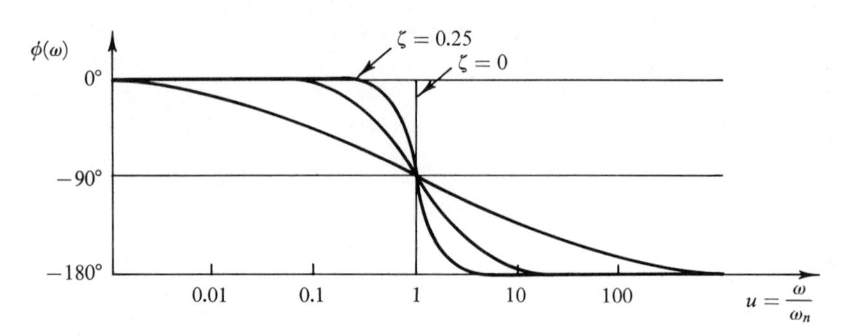

Fig. 7.30. *$\phi(\omega)$ versus u for second-order system.*

The frequency response characteristics portrayed by Figures 7.29 and 7.30 are of far-reaching importance in the physical world. A great variety of physical systems can be modeled as three components whose combination results in a mathematical model involving a second-order transfer function. In addition, a typical feedback control system can be modeled adequately by second-order transfer functions.

We have investigated resonance for a second-order system; it represents the minimum-order system to exhibit resonance, which is reinforcement of amplitude under the excitation of a sinusoidal driving function. It was shown in the case of the second-order system that resonance is a function of the amount of damping present in the system: the smaller the amount of damping, as measured by the damping factor ζ, the more accentuated the resonance effect becomes.

The extent to which resonance becomes important in a higher-order system also depends upon the amount of damping present in the system. For higher-order systems, however, one cannot relate the damping characteristics directly to the various dissipative components present in the system. In other words, it will not usually be possible to specify an association of the amplitude reinforcement at a particular frequency with the magnitude of a particular resistor or dashpot. A more quantitative discussion of this will be given in a later section on the basis of a pole-zero configuration of the transfer function.

The Q-Factor of a Resonance Circuit

Consider the series circuit shown in Figure 7.31. It consists of a resistor, inductor, and capacitor, with a sinusoidal voltage driver. Using phasor relations, we calculate

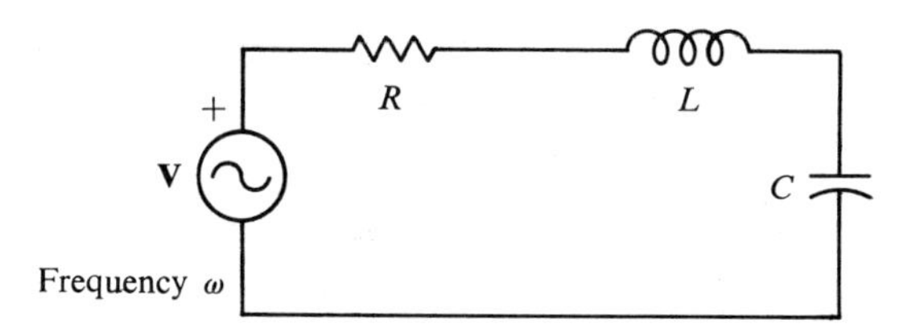

Fig. 7.31. *Series R-L-C circuit.*

$$\mathbf{I} = \frac{1}{R + j\left(\omega L - \dfrac{1}{\omega C}\right)} \cdot \mathbf{V}$$

$$= \frac{1}{1 + j\left(\omega \dfrac{L}{R} - \dfrac{1}{\omega RC}\right)} \frac{\mathbf{V}}{R}$$

$$= \frac{1}{1 + j\left(\omega_n \dfrac{L}{R} \dfrac{\omega}{\omega_n} - \dfrac{1}{\omega_n RC} \dfrac{\omega_n}{\omega}\right)} \frac{\mathbf{V}}{R} \quad (7.69)$$

Since we had established earlier that for a circuit of this topology $\omega_n = 1/\sqrt{LC}$, we can easily demonstrate that the quantities $\omega_n L/R$ and $1/\omega_n RC$ are dimensionless and equal. We introduce here the symbol

$$Q = \frac{\omega_n L}{R} = \frac{1}{\omega_n RC} \quad (7.70)$$

so that

$$\mathbf{I} = \frac{1}{1 + Qj\left(\dfrac{\omega}{\omega_n} - \dfrac{\omega_n}{\omega}\right)} \frac{\mathbf{V}}{R}$$

and the magnitude for the current is

$$|\mathbf{I}| = \frac{1}{\sqrt{1 + Q^2\left(\dfrac{u^2 - 1}{u}\right)^2}} \left|\frac{\mathbf{V}}{R}\right|$$

or

$$|\mathbf{I}| = \frac{1}{\sqrt{1 + Q^2\left(\dfrac{u^2 - 1}{u}\right)^2}} \frac{V}{R} \quad (7.71)$$

If we let I_n represent the magnitude of current when $\omega = \omega_n$, then from Equation 7.71 we have

$$|\mathbf{I}| = I_n = \frac{V}{R}$$

so that

$$\frac{|\mathbf{I}|}{I_n} = \frac{1}{\sqrt{1 + Q^2\left(\frac{u^2 - 1}{u}\right)^2}} \tag{7.72}$$

The plot of Equation 7.72 is shown in Figure 7.32.

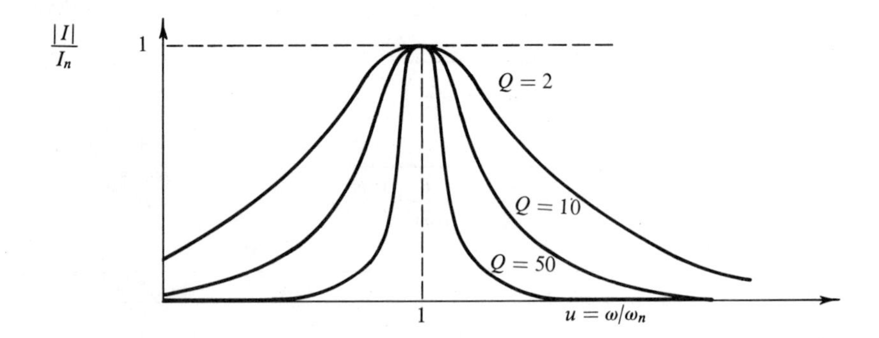

Fig. 7.32. *Normalized Q-curves.*

The frequency response of this circuit is characterized very neatly by the so-called Q-curves of Figure 7.32. Notice that an applied voltage produces a significant current flow when Q is high only when ω is approximately ω_n. Thus, this circuit acts like a frequency detector, responding only to the frequency equal to its own natural frequency. This principle is effectively exploited in tuning circuits in radios.

Q was found to be proportional to the ratio of L/R. Consider now a circuit consisting of an inductor and a capacitor, driven in series by a sinusoidal source. The inductor as a real component will have some internal resistance so that the actual model of this circuit is well approximated by the R-L-C circuit of Figure 7.31. The tuning qualities of this circuit, that is, the sharpness to which the circuit may select its own resonant frequency from the range of frequencies presented by the driver, is dependent upon Q. The higher Q, in other words, the purer the inductor and the better the tuning quality. It is for this reason that the quantity Q bears the name *quality factor* of an induction coil.

7.10 Resonant Frequencies

Quite frequently an engineering problem requires the determination of resonant frequencies of a system. These may readily be obtained from the characteristic equation of the system. It has been shown that all transfer functions relating any system variable to any excitation that might be applied were characterized by the same poles. These poles, of course, are the roots of the characteristic equation which is derived from the determinant corresponding to the minimum number of simultaneous equations, or from the determinant $|s\mathbf{I} - \mathbf{A}|$ if equations are in the state variable form. Let the transfer function relating a system variable to a sinusoidal driver be given

$$X_{\text{out}}(s) = G(s) \cdot X_{\text{in}}(s) \tag{7.73}$$

The transfer function is, in general, expressible as the rational function

$$G(s) = \frac{P(s)}{Q(s)} \tag{7.74}$$

We know that

$$Q(s) = 0$$

is the characteristic equation of the system, derived from the determinant of the simultaneous equations. To determine the frequency response, let $s = j\omega$ in $G(s)$, that is,

$$x_{\text{out}}(t) = |G(j\omega)| \sin \{\omega t + \text{Arg}[G(j\omega)]\} \tag{7.75}$$

At this time let us take a closer look at the function $G(j\omega)$. We assume that we can determine the poles and zeros of $G(s)$.* Let a pole be denoted by p_i and a zero by z_j. We can then express the transfer function in the factored form

$$G(s) = \frac{K(s - z_1)(s - z_2) \cdots (s - z_m)}{(s - p_1)(s - p_2) \cdots (s - p_n)} \tag{7.76}$$

where K is a constant. The poles and zeros may be either real or complex; if they are complex, they will occur in pairs of complex conjugates since $G(s)$ is a rational function of real coefficients.

If we now set $s = j\omega$ in Equation 7.76, we can calculate the frequency response. However, we propose an alternate way. It is a graphical method, based upon the pole-zero configuration of the transfer function.

As an introduction to the method, consider again the second-order system characterized by the transfer function

$$G(s) = \frac{1}{s^2 + 2\zeta\omega_n s + \omega_n^2} \tag{7.77}$$

* This, in general, is a difficult task. It is probably most effectively accomplished through the use of a digital computer.

In factored form, this is

$$G(s) = \frac{1}{(s + \zeta\omega_n - j\omega_n\sqrt{1 - \zeta^2})(s + \zeta\omega_n + j\omega_n\sqrt{1 - \zeta^2})} \tag{7.78}$$

Equation 7.78 shows that there are no zeros and 2 poles at

$$p_1 = -\zeta\omega_n + j\omega_n\sqrt{1 - \zeta^2}$$

and

$$p_2 = -\zeta\omega_n - j\omega_n\sqrt{1 - \zeta^2}$$

We locate these poles in the s-plane, as shown in Figure 7.33.

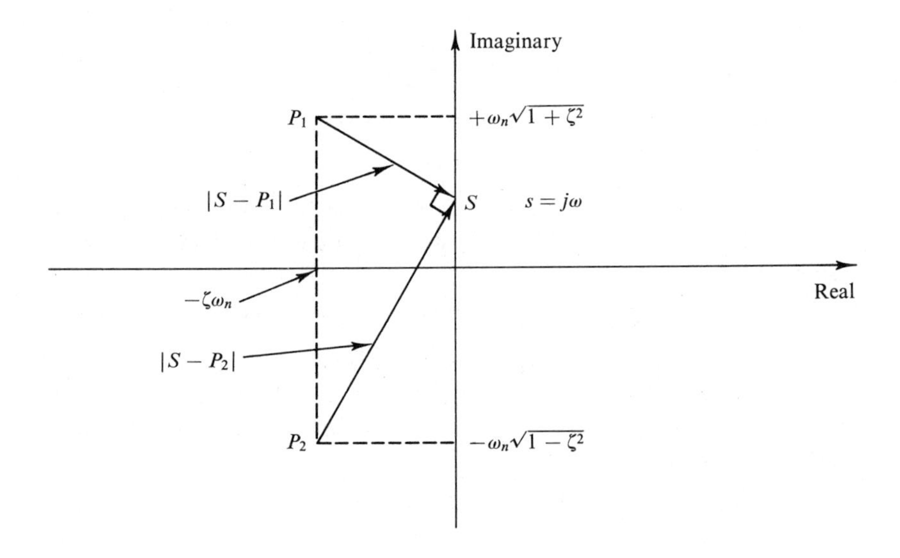

Fig. 7.33. *Pole-zero configuration of Equation* 7.78.

If we set $s = j\omega$ in Equation 7.78 and take the absolute value, we have the amplitude function

$$A(\omega) = \frac{1}{|j\omega + \zeta\omega_n - j\omega_n\sqrt{1 - \zeta^2}|\,|j\omega + \zeta\omega_n + j\omega_n\sqrt{1 - \zeta^2}|} \tag{7.79}$$

The denominator of $A(\omega)$ is composed of two factors. We recognize these factors to be phasors, which have an important geometric interpretation. Their absolute values represent the distance from a pole to the point $s = j\omega$ located on the imaginary axis. Hence, we may express the amplitude function of Equation 7.79 as

$$A(\omega) = \frac{1}{\overline{P_1S} \cdot \overline{P_2S}} \tag{7.80}$$

Through this simple geometric interpretation, the entire amplitude frequency response may be obtained by letting the points $(s = j\omega)$ move along the positive half of the imaginary axis. The value of frequency for which the product of two distances reaches a minimum, and thus for which $A(\omega)$ reaches a maximum, represents the resonant frequency. It is left as an exercise to show that this will occur when the triangle $\overline{P_1P_2S}$ is a right triangle with S forming the apex. By simple geometric relations, we can verify the previously obtained result that the resonance peak occurs at

$$\omega_p = \omega_n\sqrt{1 - 2\zeta^2} \tag{7.67}$$

On the basis of this graphical interpretation, it is obvious that the resonance peak, namely $A(\omega_p)$, will be a function of the location of the poles relative to the imaginary axis. We observe that if (1) the poles are moved horizontally closer to the imaginary axis, or (2) the poles are moved vertically out on the imaginary axis, but parallel to it, the resonance peak will increase. The peak resonance amplitude is given in Equation 7.68 as

$$A(\omega_p) = \frac{1}{2\zeta\sqrt{1 - \zeta^2}} \tag{7.68}$$

We conclude that it is only a function of ζ. Hence, if we can locate contours of constant ζ on the s-plane, we will be able to state precisely what effect a change in location of the roots will have on the resonance peak.

For the second-order system, the coordinates of pole p_1 are

$$p_1 = -\zeta\omega_n + \omega_n\sqrt{1 - \zeta^2}$$

If we consider the angle ψ as shown on Figure 7.34, we find

$$\tan\psi = \frac{\sqrt{1 - \zeta^2}}{\zeta}$$

from which we obtain

$$\cos\psi = \zeta \tag{7.81}$$

This simple result, interpreted geometrically, means that poles located on constant angle lines will rise to equal peak amplitudes in the frequency response. It was noted earlier that the peak resonance occurs when the triangle $\overline{P_1P_2S}$ is a right triangle. A right triangle can be formed as long as $2\Psi \geq 90°$ or, in terms of ζ, as long as $\Psi \geq 45°$ or $\zeta \leq \cos 45° = 0.707$.

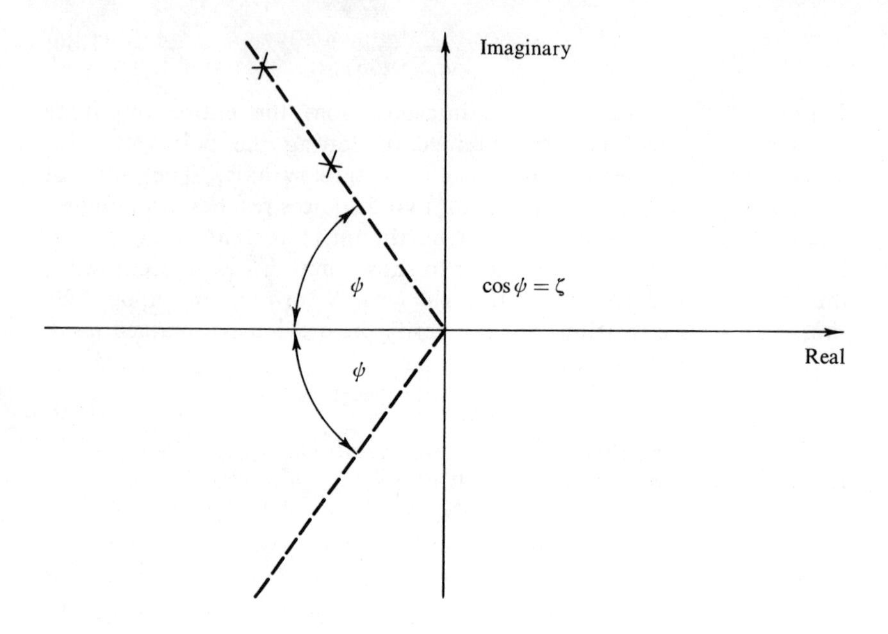

Fig. 7.34. *Lines of constant ζ and equal peak amplitude.*

Undamped resonance will occur when the poles of the second-order equation are located exactly on the imaginary axis. Since the distance $\overline{P_1S}$ (or $\overline{P_2S}$) is zero, then the amplitude is infinite.

Similar to the geometric relation that exists between amplitude function and the pole-zero configuration for the second-order system,

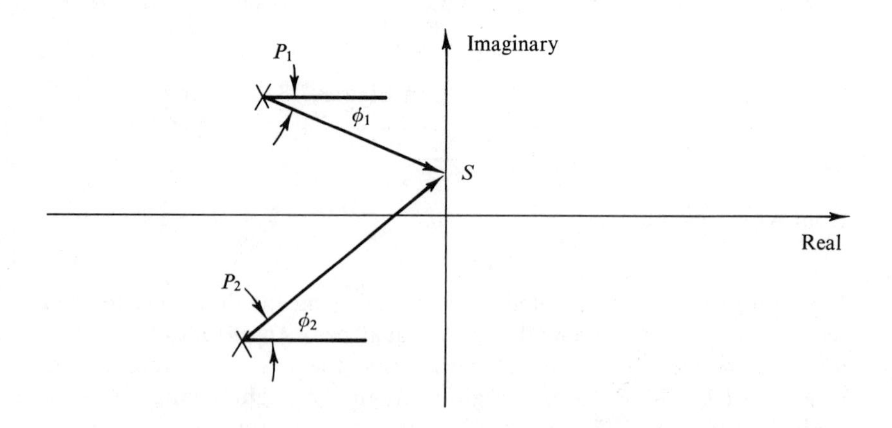

Fig. 7.35. *Argument function from pole-zero plot.*

one may determine a relation for the argument function. Consider the angles ϕ_1 and ϕ_2 in Figure 7.35. The argument is expressed in terms of these angles as

$$\text{Arg}\,\{G(j\omega)\} = -\phi_1 - \phi_2$$

For $\omega = 0$, the point S is at the origin of the s-plane, $\phi_1 = -\phi_2$ and $\text{Arg}\,\{G(j\omega)\} = 0$. As ω increases, the point S moves upward and $\phi_1 + \phi_2$ approaches 180°. We concluded earlier, on the basis of Figure 7.27, that the rate at which the argument function changes from 0° to 180° as ω passes through ω_n depends greatly upon the magnitude of ζ. Since $\zeta\omega_n$ represents the real part of the poles of the second-order system, we can see a very effective demonstration of this rapid change-over characteristic. The closer the poles are located to the imaginary axis, in other words the smaller ζ is, the more rapid the angle ϕ_1 changes from almost $-90°$ to $+90°$. Of course, the limit is reached when $\zeta = 0$ and the angle ϕ_1 changes abruptly from $-90°$ to $+90°$ while ϕ_2 remains at $+90°$.

We have presented here the resonance characteristics of a second-order system as viewed from the pole-zero configuration of the transfer function. This knowledge will now be extended to higher-order systems.

In general, it will be impossible to establish simple geometric relations between resonance peak and peak frequency and the pole-zero configuration of a higher-order system. We may, however, state that for a frequency response the amplitude function for a system having a transfer function as given by Equation 7.76 is geometrically related by

$$A(\omega) = \frac{K|s - z_1||s - z_2|\cdots|s - z_n|}{|s - p_1||s - p_2|\cdots|s - p_n|} \tag{7.82}$$

where $s = j\omega$ is a point on the imaginary axis moving from $\omega = 0$ to $\omega = \infty$. The amplitude is given as the ratio of the zero-distances to the pole-distances to a point on the imaginary axis as shown in Figure 7.36. Again, we recognize that these quantities are phasors. It is evident from the plot that a resonance frequency exists whenever one of the complex poles is close enough to the imaginary axis that the associated pole-distance will be small enough to produce a peaking in the amplitude. Of course, an undamped natural frequency will exist whenever a pair of poles lies directly on the axis. It is not meaningful to discuss the case where a pair of poles lies in the light half plane as part of the frequency response because the frequency response of that system does not exist.

The argument function of $G(s)$ is similarly expressed as

$$\begin{aligned}\phi(\omega) = &\measuredangle(s - z_1) + \measuredangle(s - z_2) + \cdots + \measuredangle(s - z_n)\\ &- \measuredangle(s - p_1) - \measuredangle(s - p_2) - \cdots - \measuredangle(s - p_n)\end{aligned} \tag{7.83}$$

where $\measuredangle$ means " angle of."

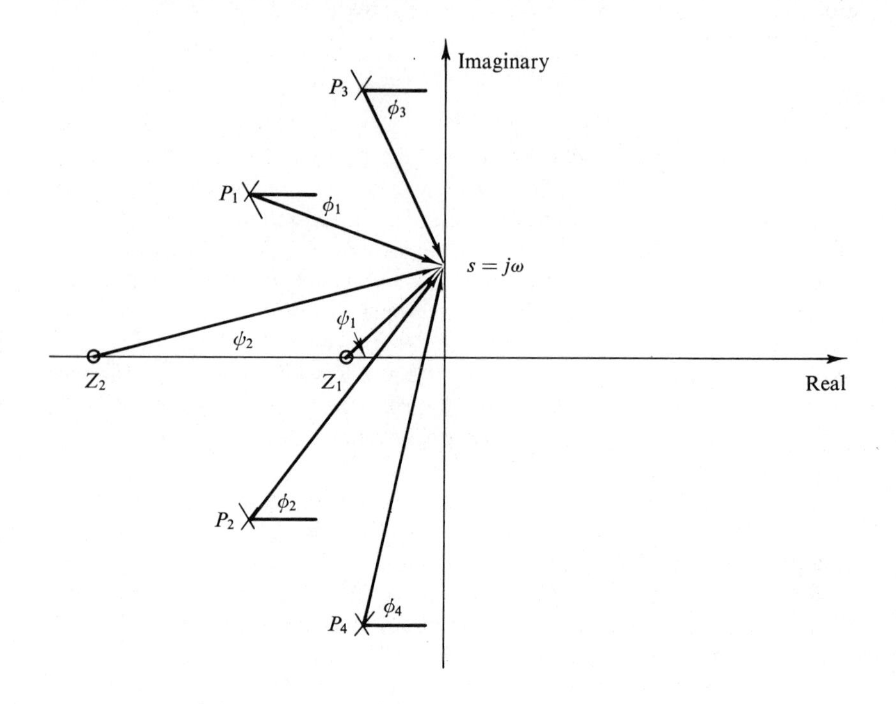

Fig. 7.36. *Frequency response on pole-zero plot.*

The definition of the angles of the various zero- and pole-phasors is illustrated by Figure 7.36.

Example 7.15. Determine the approximate resonant frequencies of the electrical circuit shown in Figure 7.37 (a). We obtain the equivalent "lossless" circuit, shown in figure 7.37 (b).

Frequently, it is necessary to determine the resonant frequencies of a system that is only slightly damped. In such a case, one may obtain a good ap-

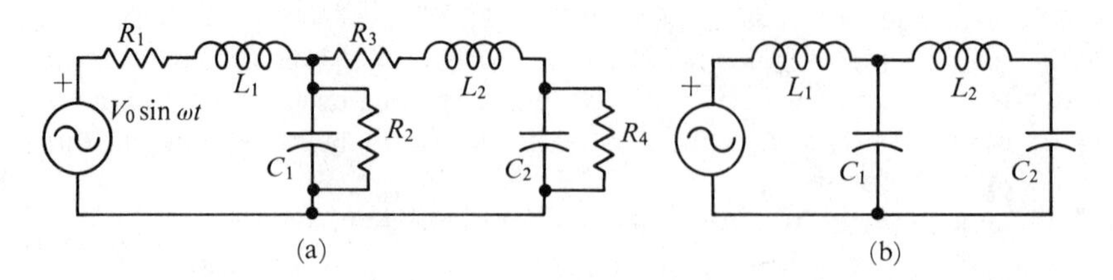

Fig. 7.37. (a) *Electrical circuit;* (b) *equivalent lossless circuit.*

proximation to the resonant frequencies by determining the undamped natural frequencies of the system.

We determine the mesh-impedance matrix of the equivalent circuit,

$$\begin{bmatrix} L_1 s + \dfrac{1}{C_1 s} & -\dfrac{1}{C_1 s} \\ -\dfrac{1}{C_1 s} & \dfrac{1}{C_1 s} + L_2 s + \dfrac{1}{C_2 s} \end{bmatrix} \begin{bmatrix} I_a \\ I_b \end{bmatrix} = \begin{bmatrix} V_0(s) \\ 0 \end{bmatrix}$$

The characteristic equation is the determinant of the coefficients of the two simultaneous equations that will have to be solved. We find

$$L_1 s\left(\frac{1}{C_1 s} + L_2 s + \frac{1}{C_2 s}\right) + \frac{1}{C_1 s}\left(L_2 s + \frac{1}{C_2 s}\right) = 0$$

Upon multiplying out and bringing all terms on a common denominator, the characteristic equation is

$$L_1 C_1 L_2 C_2 s^4 + (L_1 C_1 + L_1 C_2 + L_2 C_2) s^2 + 1 = 0$$

To determine the resonant frequencies of this equation, we set $s = j\omega$,

$$L_1 C_1 L_2 C_2 \omega^4 - (L_1 C_1 + L_1 C_2 + L_2 C_2) \omega^2 + 1 = 0$$

This equation is easily solved for two resonant frequencies, $\pm\omega_1$ and $\pm\omega_2$.

The reader may wish to verify, as an exercise, that the same characteristic equation could have been determined from the node-admittance matrix or from the determinant of $| s\mathbf{I} - \mathbf{A} |$ of the state variable formulation.

7.11 AC Circuit Power Analysis

An extensive area in which system excitation is sinusoidal is represented by alternating current systems. The excitation is a sinusoidal voltage expressible by the time function

$$v(t) = V_m \sin \omega t$$

Voltages generated for the specific purpose of distribution to industry and households will have these common characteristics.

For households:

$$V_m = 166 \text{ volts (117 volts effective)}$$

or

$$V_m = 332 \text{ volts (234 volts effective)}$$

and

$$\omega = 377 \text{ radians/second (60 Hertz)}$$

These are single phase voltages requiring two and three wires for transmission. A phasor representation of these single phase voltages in shown in Figure 7.38.

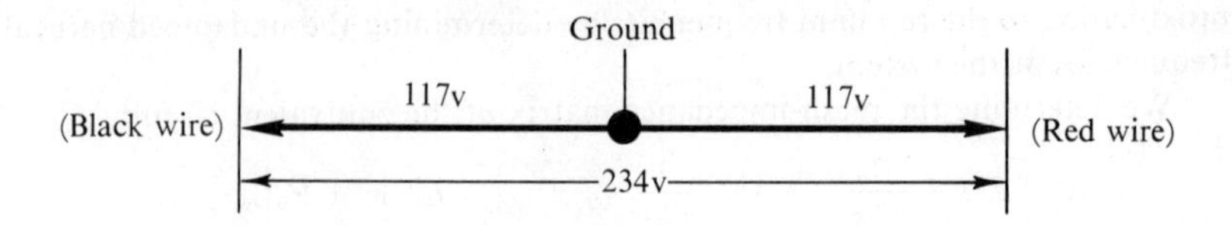

Fig. 7.38. *Phasor diagram of household voltages (three-wire).*

For industry:

$$v_1(t) = V_m \sin \omega t$$
$$v_2(t) = V_m \sin (\omega t + 120°)$$
$$v_3(t) = V_m \sin (\omega t - 120°)$$

These are three phase voltages of 220 or 440 volts effective and 60 Hertz, requiring three and four wires for transmission. A phasor diagram illustrates two possible voltage configurations in Figure 7.39.

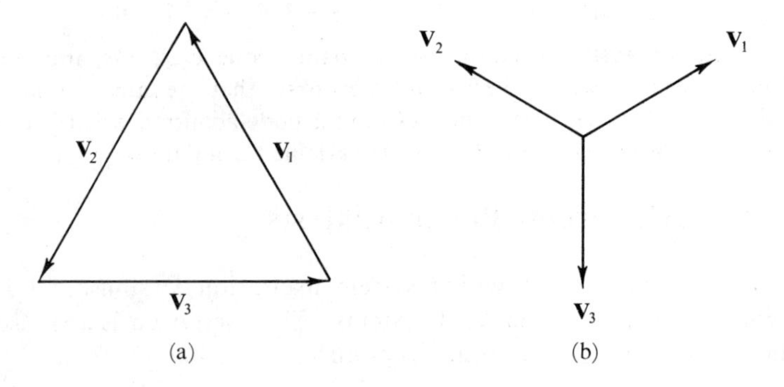

Fig. 7.39. *Phasor diagram of three phase voltages:* (a) *delta-phase relationship;* (b) *wye-phase relationship.*

Single-Phase Systems

Most alternating current problems are concerned with the determination of power consumption and its most economic distribution. This section will be devoted to a cursory introduction to this problem as it is encountered in single-phase systems. A later section will deal with three-phase systems. Let

$$v(t) = V_m \sin \omega t$$

and

$$i(t) = I_m \sin (\omega t + \phi)$$

be the voltage and current measured at points *a* and *b* system as shown in Figure 7.40.

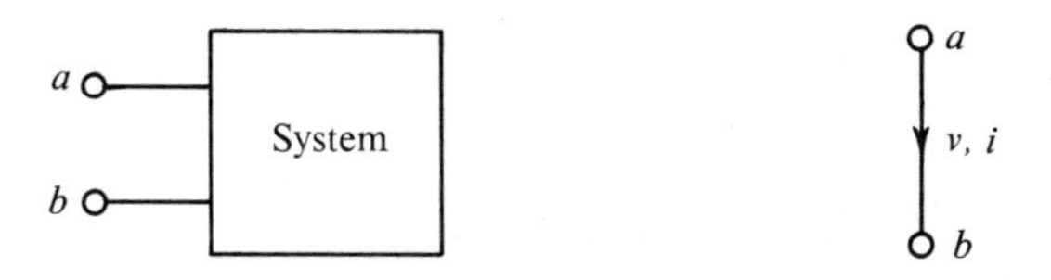

Fig. 7.40. *Single-phase system.*

The instantaneous power dissipated by the system is given as

$$\begin{aligned} p(t) &= v(t) \cdot i(t) \\ &= V_m I_m \sin \omega t \sin (\omega t + \phi) \end{aligned}$$

The average power is determined by

$$\begin{aligned} \text{Power}\Big|_{\text{ave}} &= \frac{\omega}{2\pi} \int_0^{2\pi/\omega} p(t)\,dt \\ &= \frac{1}{2\pi} \int_0^{2\pi} (V_m I_m)^{1/2} [\cos \phi - \cos (2\omega t + \phi)]\, d(\omega t) \\ &= \frac{V_m I_m}{\sqrt{2}\sqrt{2}} \cos \phi \\ \text{Power}\Big|_{\text{ave}} &= V_{\text{eff}} I_{\text{eff}} \cos \phi \end{aligned} \tag{7.84}$$

Equation 7.84 defines what is referred to as *true power*, identified by the symbol **P**. The quantity $\cos \phi$ is called the *power factor*.

Example 7.16

Power dissipated by a resistor;

$$\begin{aligned} \mathbf{P} &= V_{\text{eff}} \cdot I_{\text{eff}} \cos 0^\circ \\ &= I_{\text{eff}} R \cdot I_{\text{eff}} \\ &= I^2_{\text{eff}} R \end{aligned}$$

Power flow into an inductor:

$$\begin{aligned} \mathbf{P} &= V_{\text{eff}} \cdot I_{\text{eff}} \cos 90^\circ \\ &= 0 \end{aligned}$$

Power consumption serves frequently as a basis for specifying component ratings. As such, true power is not useful for a system where the power factor is small while the voltage and current may be large quantities. Another quantity is needed, then, to be useful. *Apparent power* is defined as the phasor

$$\mathbf{P}_{\text{app}} = V_{\text{eff}} \cdot I_{\text{eff}} \measuredangle \phi \tag{7.85}$$

where ϕ is the phase angle between voltage and currrent. It is convenient to consider a third quantity, *reactive power*, defined as

$$\mathbf{Q} = V_{\text{eff}} \cdot I_{\text{eff}} \sin \phi \tag{7.86}$$

We see that the three defined power quantities are related by

$$\mathbf{P}_{\text{app}} = \mathbf{P} + j\mathbf{Q} \tag{7.87}$$

Since

$$\begin{aligned} \mathbf{P}_{\text{app}} &= V_{\text{eff}} I_{\text{eff}} \cos \phi + j V_{\text{eff}} I_{\text{eff}} \sin \phi \\ &= V_{\text{eff}} I_{\text{eff}} (\cos \phi + j \sin \phi) \\ &= V_{\text{eff}} I_{\text{eff}} e^{j\phi} \\ \mathbf{P}_{\text{app}} &= V_{\text{eff}} I_{\text{eff}} \measuredangle \phi \end{aligned} \tag{7.88}$$

Hence,

$$\begin{aligned} \mathbf{P} &= Re\,\{\mathbf{P}_{\text{app}}\} \\ \mathbf{Q} &= Im\,\{\mathbf{P}_{\text{app}}\} \end{aligned}$$

A simple example summarizes these results.

Example 7.17. Consider the $R - L$ circuit of Figure 7.41. We can immediately establish phasor diagrams showing the impedances of the circuit and the variables.

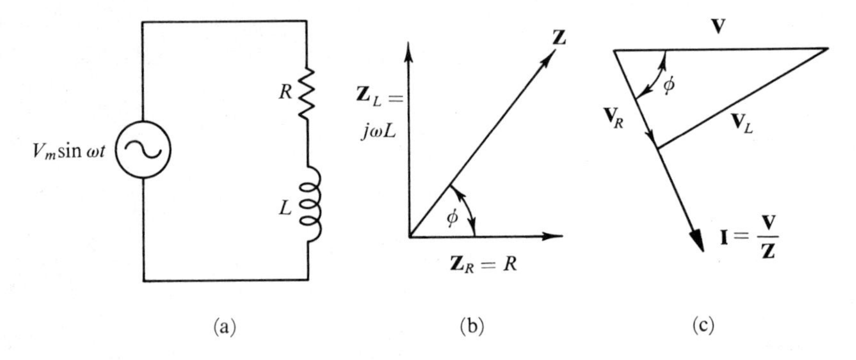

Fig. 7.41. (a) *Simple circuit;* (b) *impedance phasors;* (c) *voltage-current phasors.*

$$\begin{aligned} \mathbf{Z} &= \sqrt{R^2 + \omega^2 L^2} \measuredangle \phi \\ \mathbf{I} &= \frac{V_n \measuredangle 0^\circ}{\sqrt{R^2 + \omega^2 L^2} \measuredangle \phi} = \frac{V_m}{\sqrt{R^2 + \omega^2 L^2}} \measuredangle -\phi \\ \mathbf{V}_R &= R\mathbf{I} = RI \measuredangle -\phi \\ \mathbf{V}_1 &= \omega L \measuredangle 90^\circ \cdot \mathbf{I} = \omega LI \measuredangle 90^\circ - \phi \end{aligned}$$

Now calculate the true power flow into the components

$$\begin{aligned} \mathbf{P} &= \frac{V_m}{\sqrt{2}} \cdot \frac{I_m}{\sqrt{2}} \cos \phi \\ &= V_{\text{eff}}^2 \frac{\cos \phi}{\sqrt{R^2 + (\omega L)^2}} \end{aligned}$$

But from Figure 7.41(b)

$$\cos\phi = \frac{R}{R^2 + (\omega L)^2}$$

so that

$$\mathbf{P} = V_{\text{eff}}^2 \frac{R}{\sqrt{R^2 + (\omega L)^2}}$$

however, since

$$V_{\text{eff}} = I_{\text{eff}} \sqrt{R^2 + (\omega L)^2}$$

we may also express the true power by

$$\mathbf{P} = I_{\text{eff}}^2 R$$

Thus, the true power is determined by the power flow into the dissipative component. Of course, this result is expected; in fact, it holds in general, since the true power, P, is the sum of the power flow into each dissipative component in a system.

The reactive power, Q, is now determined.

$$\mathbf{Q} = \frac{V_m}{\sqrt{2}} \cdot \frac{I_m}{\sqrt{2}} \sin\phi$$

$$= V_{\text{eff}}^2 \frac{\sin\phi}{\sqrt{R^2 + (\omega L)^2}}$$

but

$$\sin\phi = \frac{\omega L}{\sqrt{R^2 + (\omega L)^2}}$$

$$\mathbf{Q} = V_{\text{eff}}^2 \frac{\omega L}{R^2 + (\omega L)^2}$$

or

$$\mathbf{Q} = I_{\text{eff}}^2 \omega L$$

Hence,

$$\mathbf{P}_{\text{app}} = P + jQ$$

$$= I_{\text{eff}}^2 (R + j\omega L)$$

$$= I_{\text{eff}}^2 \sqrt{R^2 + (\omega L)^2}\, e^{j\phi}$$

$$\mathbf{P} = I_{\text{eff}} I_{\text{eff}} \sqrt{R^2 + (\omega L)^2} \measuredangle \phi$$

$$\mathbf{P} = I_{\text{eff}} V_{\text{eff}} \measuredangle \phi$$

This last result is in the form of Equation 7.88.

In order to maximize the power flow into a system, the power factor should be as close to unity as possible. Since most single-phase utility systems are resistive and inductive, the power factor is inherently less than unity. Such lagging power factors can be compensated for by the addition of suitable selected capacitors. The net effect of the capacitor is to cancel the lagging phase characteristics of the inductor. Consider, for instance, the power system shown in Figure 7.42.

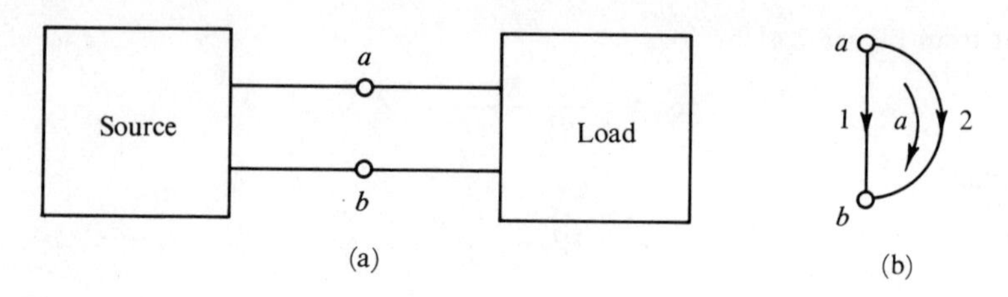

Fig. 7.42. *Power system.*

The system consists of a source to which a load is connected. It is operated at a constant frequency. We wish to determine conditions under which the power transfer to the load can be maximized.

Let the source have the terminal characteristics

$$\mathbf{V}_1 = \mathbf{Z}_1\mathbf{I}_1 + \mathbf{V}_G \tag{7.89}$$

It is assumed that the source has an internal impedance

$$\mathbf{Z}_1 = |\,\mathbf{Z}_1\,| \measuredangle \phi_1$$

ϕ_1 may be a leading or lagging phase angle, but is usually leading due to source inductance.

The load is represented by

$$\mathbf{V}_2 = \mathbf{Z}_2\mathbf{I}_2$$
$$\text{where } \mathbf{Z}_2 = |\mathbf{Z}_2| \measuredangle \phi_2$$

When the source and load are connected, this mesh equation results:

$$\mathbf{V}_G = (\mathbf{Z}_1 + \mathbf{Z}_2)\mathbf{I}_a \tag{7.90}$$

from which

$$\mathbf{I}_a = \frac{\mathbf{V}_G}{\mathbf{Z}_1 + \mathbf{Z}_2} = \frac{V_G \measuredangle 0^\circ}{|\,\mathbf{Z}_1 + \mathbf{Z}_2\,| \measuredangle \phi_{12}}$$
$$= I_a \measuredangle -\phi_{12}$$

Note that all variables are effective quantities.

The negative phase angle here indicates a typical situation, a lagging phase angle. The total true power delivered by the source is

$$\mathbf{P}_G = V_G \cdot I_a \cos \phi_{12} \tag{7.91}$$

The power flow into the load is

$$\mathbf{P}_L = I_a^2 \operatorname{Re}\{\mathbf{Z}_2\}$$

or

$$\mathbf{P}_L = I_a V_2 \cos \phi_{12}$$

since

$$I_a \operatorname{Re}\{\mathbf{Z}_2\} = V_2 \cos \phi_{12}$$

In practice, the power factor correction is accomplished by adding a bank of one or more capacitors in parallel with the load, as shown in Figure 7.43.

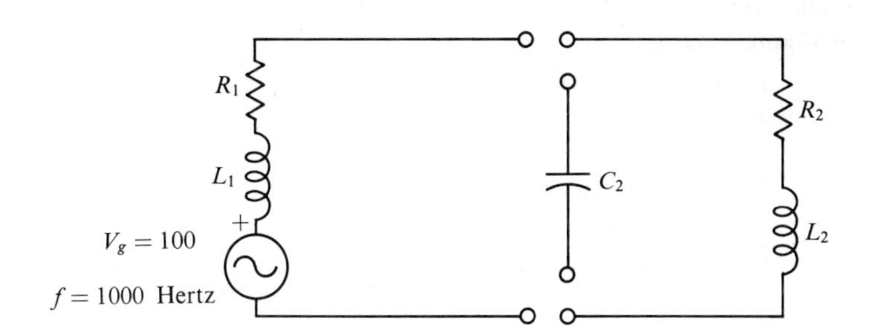

Fig. 7.43. *Example in power transmission.*

Both the source and lead impedances are shown as a series resistance and inductance. The problem is one of finding a suitable capacitor such that the power factor is unity or $\phi_{12} = 0$. Without the capacitor, the power factor is found by considering

$$\mathbf{Z}_1 + \mathbf{Z}_2 = R_1 + R_2 + j\omega(L_1 + L_2)$$

Then

$$\text{P. F.} = \cos \phi_{12} = \frac{R_1 + R_2}{\sqrt{(R_1 + R_2)^2 + \omega^2(L_1 + L_2)^2}} \tag{7.92}$$

We may also write

$$\tan \phi_{12} = \frac{-\omega(L_1 + L_2)}{R_1 + R_2} = \frac{-\operatorname{Im}[\mathbf{Z}_1 + \mathbf{Z}_2]}{\operatorname{Re}[\mathbf{Z}_1 + \mathbf{Z}_2]} \tag{7.93}$$

where Im and Re mean the "imaginary" and "real part of," respectively. For unity power factor,

$$\phi_{12} = \tan \phi_{12} = 0 = \operatorname{Im}[\mathbf{Z}_1 + \mathbf{Z}_2]$$

The imaginary part of $\mathbf{Z}_1$ is ωL_1; therefore, for unity power factor,

$$\omega L_1 + \operatorname{Im}[\mathbf{Z}_2] = 0$$

In Figure 7.43, $\mathbf{Z}_2$ is modified by the capacitance C_2 to be

$$\mathbf{Z}_2(j\omega) = \left(\frac{1}{R_2 + j\omega L_2} = + j\omega C_2\right)^{-1}$$

$$= \frac{R_2 + j\omega L_2}{1 - \omega^2 L_2 C_2 + j\omega R_2 C_2} \tag{7.94}$$

The imaginary part of $\mathbf{Z}_2$ is found by rationalizing the impedance, giving the result

$$\text{Im}\,[\mathbf{Z}_2] = \frac{-\omega[R_2^2\,C_2 + L_2(\omega^2 L_2 C_2 - 1)]}{(1 - \omega^2 L_2 C_2)^2 + \omega^2 R_2^2\,C_2^2} \tag{7.95}$$

The solution for C_2 requires a solution of a quadratic equation in C_2. The smaller positive solution is usually the better of the two possible solutions.

Example 7.18.

In Figure 7.43, let

$$\begin{aligned} R_1 &= 1 \text{ ohm} \\ R_2 &= 5 \text{ ohms} \\ L_1 &= 1 \text{ millihenry} \\ L_2 &= 3 \text{ millihenries} \\ f &= 1000 \text{ Hertz} \\ V_g &= 100 \text{ volts} \\ \mathbf{Z}_1 &= 1 + j\,6.28 \qquad \text{and} \qquad \text{Im}\,[\mathbf{Z}_1] = \omega L_1 = 6.28 \\ \omega L_2 &= 18.84 \end{aligned}$$

Let $\omega C_2 = 1/X_c$, where X_c is the capacitive reactance of C_2; then for unity factor power,

$$\frac{R_2^2}{X_c} + \omega L_2\left(\frac{\omega L_2}{X_c} - 1\right) = \omega L_1\left[\left(1 - \frac{\omega L_2}{X_c}\right)^2 + \frac{R_2^2}{X_c^2}\right]$$

Clearing of fractions,

$$X_c^2[\omega L_2 + \omega L_1] - X_c[R_2^2 + (\omega L_2)^2 + 2\omega^2 L_1 L_2] + \omega L_1[R_2^2 + (\omega L_2)^2] = 0$$

Substituting for ω, L_1, L_2, R_1, and R_2, we have

$$25.1 X_c^2 - 617 X_c + 2380 = 0$$

from which

$$X_c = 16.3,\ 9.75$$

Since $X_c = 1/\omega C_2$, the smaller value of C_2 is found from the larger value of X_c: $X_c = 16.3$. Then

$$C_2 = \frac{1}{\omega X_c} = 9.75 \cdot 10^{-6} \text{ farad} = 9.75 \text{ microfarad}$$

The line current, which is the current at the generator terminals, is found by finding

$$\begin{aligned} \text{Re}\,[\mathbf{Z}_1 + \mathbf{Z}_2] &= \frac{R_2}{(1 - \omega^2 L_2 C_2)^2 + \omega^2 R_2^2\,C_2^2} + R_1 \\ &= 1 + \frac{5}{(1 - 1.16)^2 + (0.306)^2} = 43.5 \text{ ohm} \end{aligned}$$

Because $\text{Im}\,[\mathbf{Z}_1 + \mathbf{Z}_2] = 0$,

$$\mathbf{I}_a = \frac{V_g}{\text{Re}\,[\mathbf{Z}_1 + \mathbf{Z}_2]} = 2.30 \measuredangle 0° \text{ ampere}$$

The power in the load is found by the equation

$$\mathbf{P}_L = \text{Re}\,[\mathbf{Z}_2]I^2 = 42.5(2.30)^2 = 225 \text{ watts}$$

Without the parallel capacitor, C_2, the power in the load is

$$\mathbf{P}_L = I_a^2 R_2$$

where

$$\mathbf{I}_a = \frac{V_g}{\mathbf{Z}_1 + \mathbf{Z}_2} = \frac{100}{6 + j\,25.12} = 3.86 \measuredangle -76.6^\circ$$

$P_L = 74.5$ watts, a decrease of a factor of 3 from the power-factor-corrected value.

Polyphase Systems

Polyphase Systems, in contrast to single-phase systems, are driven by more than one source voltage at different phases but at the same frequency. The most common polyphase system which is used industrially is the three-phase system. The three voltage sources are represented on a phasor diagram at angles of 120° from each other.

Some of the advantages of three-phase systems are:

1. Three-phase generators are more economical and efficient than single-phase generators.
2. Three-phase motors require no special starting windings and are smaller for the same horsepower relative to single-phase motors.
3. For the same voltage regulation and efficiency of transmission, smaller conductors are required to transmit polyphase power.
4. There is greater flexibility of available generated voltages.

Two-phase systems in which there are two voltage sources at a phase angle of 90° (or 270°) are frequently used to control two-phase motors

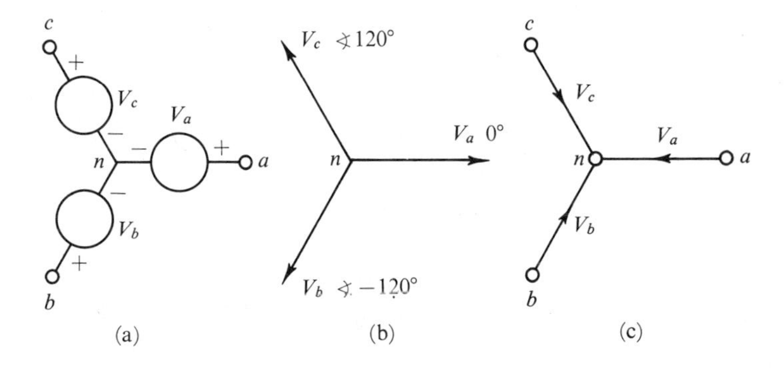

Fig. 7.44. (a) *Y connection of voltage generators;* (b) *phasor diagram;* (c) *linear graph representation.*

in servo control systems. Six-phase systems are in use in some geographical areas, and circuits with as high as 180 phases have been used in rectifier systems to convert ac power to dc power.

Three-phase voltages may be generated either Y or Δ, as illustrated in Figures 7.44 and 7.45.

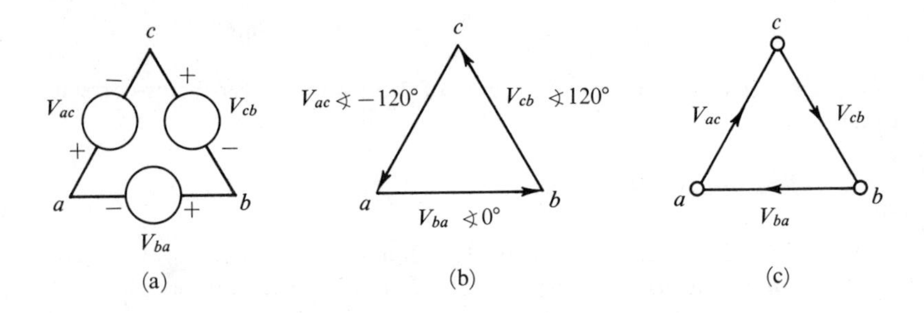

Fig. 7.45. (a) *Δ connection of voltage generators;* (b) *phasor diagram;* (c) *linear graph representation.*

The loads may also be connected to the generators in Y or Δ, giving the four possible connections Y − Y, Y − Δ, Δ − Y or Δ − Δ, where the first symbol represents the generator connection and the second the load connection. One of the simpler connections is the Δ − Δ shown in Figure 7.46.

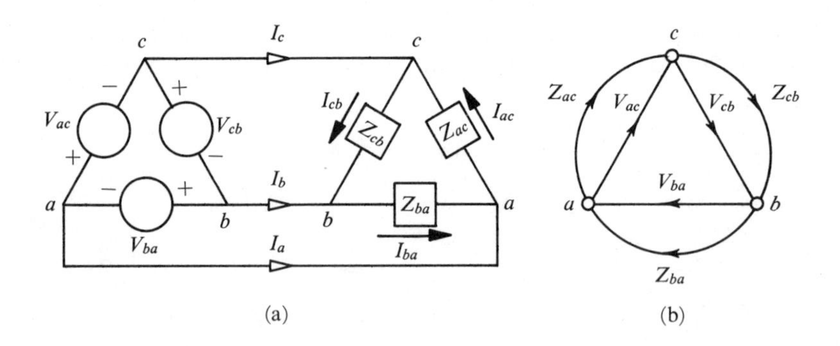

Fig. 7.46. *Generators and loads connected in Δ, with linear graph representation.*

The three phase currents can be calculated independently. Using phasor notation,

$$\mathbf{I}_{cb} = \frac{V_{cb} \measuredangle 120^\circ}{|Z_{cb}| \measuredangle \phi_{cb}}$$

$$\mathbf{I}_{ba} = \frac{V_{ba} \measuredangle 0^\circ}{|Z_{ba}| \measuredangle \phi_{ba}}$$

$$\mathbf{I}_{ac} = \frac{V_{ac} \measuredangle -120^\circ}{|Z_{ac}| \measuredangle \phi_{ba}}$$

where ϕ_{cb}, ϕ_{ba}, and ϕ_{ac} are the arguments of $\mathbf{Z}_{cb}$, $\mathbf{Z}_{ba}$, and $\mathbf{Z}_{ac}$, respectively. The line currents, $\mathbf{I}_a$, $\mathbf{I}_b$, and $\mathbf{I}_c$ are the vector sums

$$\begin{aligned} \mathbf{I}_a &= \mathbf{I}_{ac} - \mathbf{I}_{ba} \\ \mathbf{I}_b &= \mathbf{I}_{ba} - \mathbf{I}_{cb} \\ \mathbf{I}_c &= \mathbf{I}_{cb} - \mathbf{I}_{ac} \end{aligned} \tag{7.97}$$

If the three-phase system is " balanced " the three loads are equal, that is $\mathbf{Z}_{ac} = \mathbf{Z}_{ba} = \mathbf{Z}_{cb}$. For this case the three phase currents and line currents are equal in magnitude respectively, but are 120° apart in phase. This is shown in Figure 7.47. In this figure the three voltage phasors are connected as shown for convenience in drawing the diagram. The angle ϕ is the argument of the impedances.

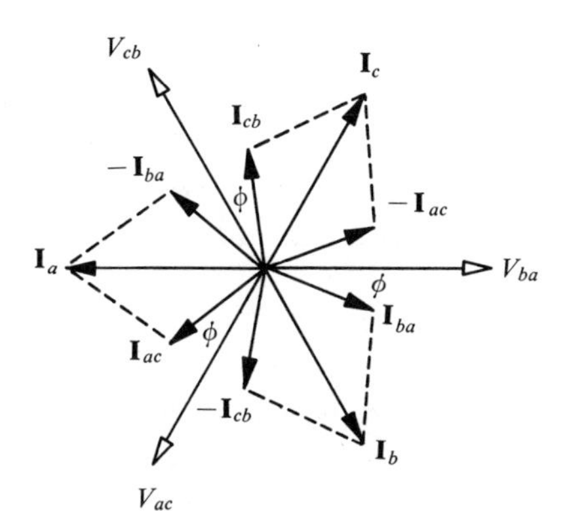

Fig. 7.47. *Phasor diagram of a three phase Δ − Δ system.*

In this case each line current is uniquely related to each phase current. For example,

$$\begin{aligned} \mathbf{I}_b &= |I_{ba}| \measuredangle -\phi - |I_{cb}| \measuredangle 120^\circ - \phi \\ &= |I_{ba}| \measuredangle -\phi + |I_{ba}| \measuredangle -60^\circ - \phi \\ &= 2|I_{ba}| \cos 30^\circ = \sqrt{3}\,|I_{ba}| \end{aligned} \tag{7.98}$$

or in general $|I_L| = \sqrt{3}\,|I_P|$. The line currents are $\sqrt{3}$ times the phase currents. If we define the line voltages as the voltage between lines going to the load, then for the Δ connection the line and phase voltages are equal.

The true power in each phase load is

$$\mathbf{P}_P = |V_P||I_P| \cos \phi \tag{7.100}$$

The total power is therefore

$$\mathbf{P}_T = 3|V_P||I_P| \cos \phi = \sqrt{3}\,|V_L||I_L| \cos \phi \tag{7.101}$$

If the load impedances are not equal, the relatively simple relationships just derived are not valid. For unbalanced loads, the individual phase currents can be easily found and a phasor diagram drawn. The line currents may then be found analytically, or graphically as shown in the next example.

Example 7.19. For the system shown in Figure 7.47, find all phase and line currents. What is the total load power?

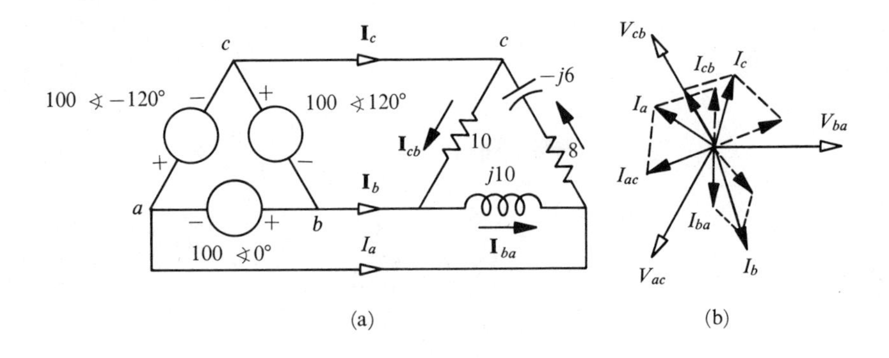

Fig. 7.48. *A three phase unbalanced system with phasor diagram.*

$$\mathbf{I}_{cb} = \frac{100\measuredangle 120^\circ}{10\measuredangle 0^\circ} = 10\measuredangle 120^\circ = -5 + j\,8.66$$

$$\mathbf{I}_{ba} = \frac{100\measuredangle 0^\circ}{10\measuredangle 90^\circ} = 10\measuredangle -90^\circ = -j10$$

$$\mathbf{I}_{ac} = \frac{100\measuredangle -120^\circ}{10\measuredangle -36.8^\circ} = 10\measuredangle -156.8^\circ = -9.2 - j3.94$$

$$\mathbf{I}_a = \mathbf{I}_{ac} - \mathbf{I}_{ba} = -9.2 - j3.94 + j10 = -9.2 + j6.06 = 11.0\measuredangle 146.6^\circ$$

$$\mathbf{I}_b = \mathbf{I}_{ba} - \mathbf{I}_{cb} = -j10 + 5 - j8.66 = 5 - j18.66 = 19.3\measuredangle -75^\circ$$

$$\mathbf{I}_c = \mathbf{I}_{cb} - \mathbf{I}_{ac} = -5 + j8.66 + 9.2 + j3.94 = 4.2 + j14.6 = 15.2\measuredangle 74^\circ$$

$$\mathbf{P}_T = |V_{cb}||I_{cb}| \cos 0^\circ + |V_{ba}||I_{ba}| \cos 90^\circ + V_{ac}||I_{ac}| \cos 36.8^\circ$$
$$= 1000 + 0 + 600 = 1600 \text{ watts}$$

Most three-phase systems are Y-Y connected with a fourth wire or neutral wire connected to the common point of the three voltages and three loads. One then has a choice of three-phase voltage—the line-to-line voltages or the line-to-neutral voltages. A common arrangement is illustrated in Figure 7.49. The line-to-neutral voltage of 120 volts is the normal industrial or residential supply voltage and the loads of a building are divided equally among the three phases. The line-to-line voltage of 208 volts is sometimes used for three-phase loads designed for 220 volts.

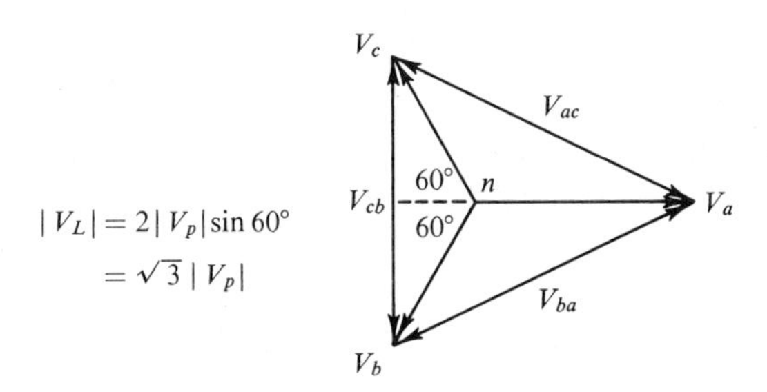

Fig. 7.49. *Relationship between line and phase voltages of a Y-connected system.*

The current in the neutral or ground wire is the vector sum of the three phase currents and for a balanced load this vector sum is zero. Therefore, in a perfectly balanced Y-Y connected system, a neutral wire is not needed. In practice, the loads are seldom balanced and the neutral wire is used to connect the neutral points of the generator and the load. This is known as a Y-Y connection with neutral.

In a power distribution system, transformers are used first to step voltages up from the generators to the transmission lines which operate at relatively high voltages (2200 volts to 500,000 volts). High voltages on lines are necessary to keep line resistance (I^2R) power losses low for the transmission of power over long distances. Since power is basically the product of voltage and current, high line voltages mean low line currents for the same transmitted power. Transformers are used at the load end to reduce the line voltage to various voltage levels depending on the eventual user's requirements. The transformers also may have the four possible connections from primary to secondary including the Y-Y, Y-Δ, Δ-Y, Δ-Δ connections. The choice of connection is based on the economics of the particular system. Natural voltage increases and reductions of $\sqrt{3}$ are possible using transformer windings with a 1:1 turns ratio. An advantage of the Δ-Δ connection is that if one transformer fails it can be removed and the two remaining transformers will continue to supply all or part of the original three-phase load. This is an " open Δ " configuration.

As a final example, consider a Y-connected load without a neutral wire. In this case the load neutral potential will be different from the generator reference potential.

Example 7.20. Find the load currents and voltages for the Y-Y system of Figure 7.50. What is the total power consumed?

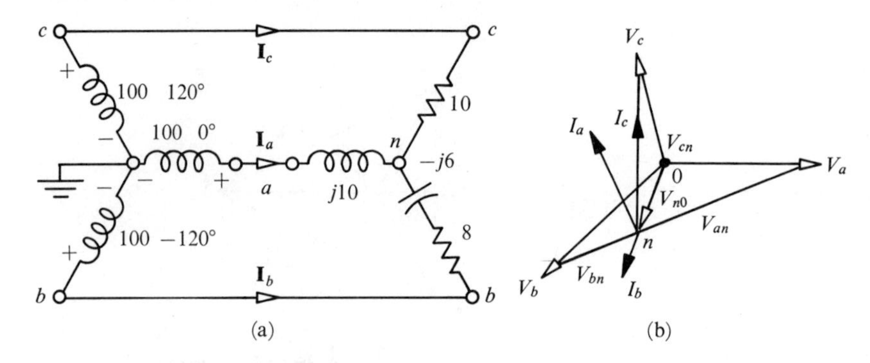

Fig. 7.50. *Unbalanced three-phase load system and phasor diagram.*

We first need to find the voltage of the load neutral with respect to the transformer neutral, which is usually grounded. This is easily done with a single node equation at n relative to O. After transforming the impedances to admittances:

$$\mathbf{Y}_a = \frac{1}{\mathbf{Z}_a} = -j0.1$$

$$\mathbf{Y}_b = \frac{1}{\mathbf{Z}_b} = \frac{1}{8 - j6} = 0.08 + j0.06$$

$$\mathbf{Y}_c = \frac{1}{\mathbf{Z}_c} = 0.1$$

we have

$$\begin{aligned}(-j0.1 + 0.08 + j0.06 + 0.1)\mathbf{V}_{no} &= -j0.1(100\angle 0°) + 0.1(100\angle 120°) \\ &\quad + (0.08 + j0.06)(100\angle -120°) \\ (0.18 - j0.04)\mathbf{V}_{no} &= -j10 - 5 + j8.66 + 1.2 - j9.9 \\ (0.185\angle -12.5°)\mathbf{V}_{no} &= -3.8 - j11.24 = 11.85\angle -118.7° \\ \mathbf{V}_{no} &= 64\angle -106.2° = -17.8 - j61.4\end{aligned}$$

Then, by referring to Figure 7.50(b),

$$\begin{aligned}\mathbf{V}_{an} = \mathbf{V}_a - \mathbf{V}_{no} &= 100 - (-17.8 - j61.4) = 117.8 + j61.4 = 133\angle 27.5° \\ \mathbf{V}_{bn} = \mathbf{V}_b - \mathbf{V}_{no} &= -50 - j86.6 - (-17.8 - j61.4) \\ &= 32.2 - j25.2 = 41\angle -142° \\ \mathbf{V}_{cn} = \mathbf{V}_c - \mathbf{V}_{no} &= -50 + j86.6 - (-17.8 - j61.4) \\ &= 32.2 + j148 = 152\angle 102.3°\end{aligned}$$

These are the three load voltages. The load currents are

$$\mathbf{I}_a = \frac{\mathbf{V}_{an}}{\mathbf{Z}_a} = \frac{133\measuredangle 27.5^\circ}{10\measuredangle -90^\circ} = 13.3\measuredangle 117.5^\circ$$

$$\mathbf{I}_b = \frac{\mathbf{V}_{bn}}{\mathbf{Z}_b} = \frac{41\measuredangle -142^\circ}{10\measuredangle -36.8^\circ} = 4.1\measuredangle -105.2^\circ$$

$$\mathbf{I}_c = \frac{\mathbf{V}_{cn}}{\mathbf{Z}_c} = \frac{152\measuredangle 102.3^\circ}{10\measuredangle 0^\circ} = 15.2\measuredangle 102.3^\circ$$

The total power is

$$\begin{aligned}\mathbf{P}_T &= |V_{an}|\,|I_a| \cos 90^\circ + |V_{bn}|\,|I_b| \cos 36.8^\circ + |V_{cn}|\,|I_c| \cos 0^\circ \\ &= 0 + 142 + 2300 = 2442 \text{ watts}\end{aligned}$$

A comparison of this solution to the equivalent unbalanced system solution of Example 7.18 shows that there can be a large difference in both the magnitude and direction of the load voltages and currents if there is no neutral wire. Most loads are designed for a certain voltage and would be damaged if over voltages occurred. A neutral wire is therefore required in a general Y-Y system.

Summary

In this chapter we have briefly considered some of the classical concepts in the general area of systems frequency response. Included were the following topics: graphical and phasor display of frequency response, frequency response of first- and second-order systems, the phenomenon of resonance, and a brief survey of ac circuit steady-state power analysis techniques. For the student who is more interested in ac systems many excellent texts are available. Some are listed at the end of this chapter.

ADDITIONAL READINGS

Cannon, Robert H., Jr., *Dynamics of Physical Systems,* New York: McGraw-Hill Book Co., 1967.

Fitzgerald, A.E., D.E. Higginbotham, and A. Grabel, *Basic Electrical Engineering,* New York: McGraw-Hill Book Co., 1967.

Guillemin, E., *Theory of Linear Physical Systems,* New York: John Wiley & Sons, Inc., 1963.

Le Page, W., *Analysis of Alternating Current Circuits,* New York: McGraw-Hill Book Co., 1958.

Lynch, W. A., and J. G. Truxal, *Introductory System Analysis,* New York: McGraw-Hill Book Co., 1961.

Pfeiffer, P. E., *Linear System Analysis,* New York: McGraw-Hill Book Co., 1961.

Woodruff, L. F., *Electrical Power Transmission,* New York: John Wiley & Sons, Inc., 1938.

PROBLEMS

7.1. For the differential equation

$$\dot{x} + 5x = \sin \omega t$$

determine the complete solution by the Laplace-Transform method. Verify the steady-state solution by the application of Equation 7.14.

7.2. For a system described by the differential equation

$$2\frac{dx_o}{dt} + 3x_o = 10x_i + 20\frac{dx_i}{dt}$$

find $G(j\omega)$, $R(\omega)$, and $I(\omega)$ if the system input is $\sin 2t$.

7.3.

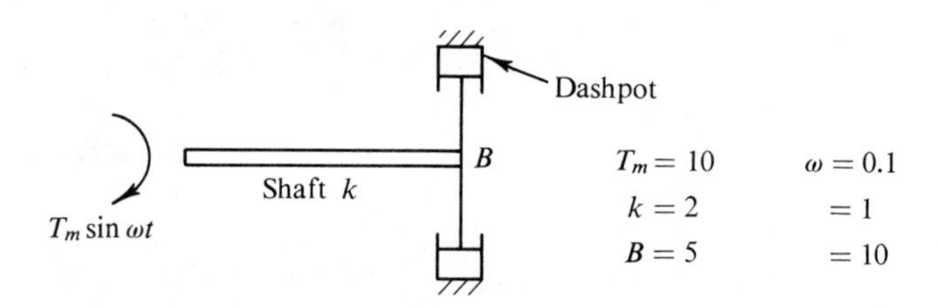

Fig. P 7.3.

For the torsional system shown in Figure P 7.3, calculate the velocity of the rotational dashpot for the sinusoidal state. Sketch Bode plots of the result showing magnitude and phase angle.

7.4.

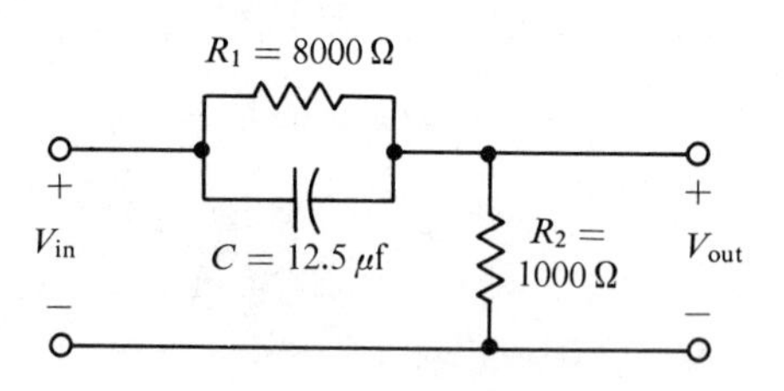

Fig. P 7.4.

For the network shown in Figure P 7.4:

a) Find the output to input transfer function;
b) Sketch the phase and amplitude Bode plots of $G(j\omega)$;
c) Calculate the frequency at which Arg $[G(j\omega)]$ is its maximum positive.

Hint: Differentiate Arg $[G(j(\omega)]$ to find minimum or maximum.

7.5.

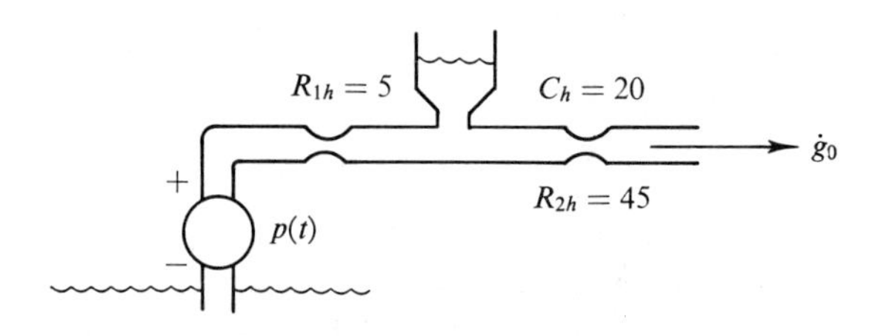

Fig. P 7.5.

In the hydraulic system sketched in Figure P 7.5, let the pump pressure be $p(t) = 100 + 10 \sin (0.01)t$. Find the total output flow $\dot{g}_0(t)$ in the steady state.

7.6. Calculate the phasors representing the voltages of all components in the circuit of Figure P 7.6. Show on a phasor diagram that the sum of the voltages is zero.

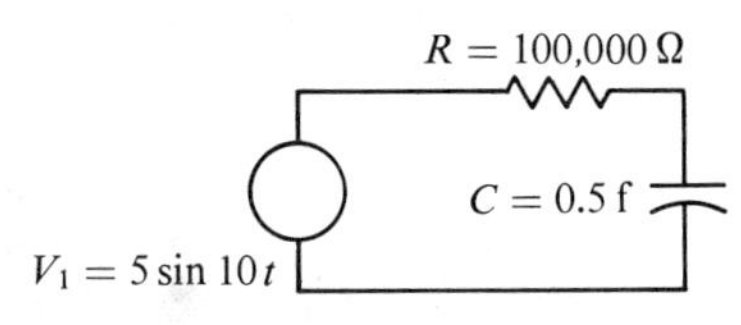

Fig. P 7.6.

7.7. Calculate the magnitudes and phase angles of the voltage V_a, V_b, and V_c. Show a phasor diagram of the five voltages in Figure P 7.7.

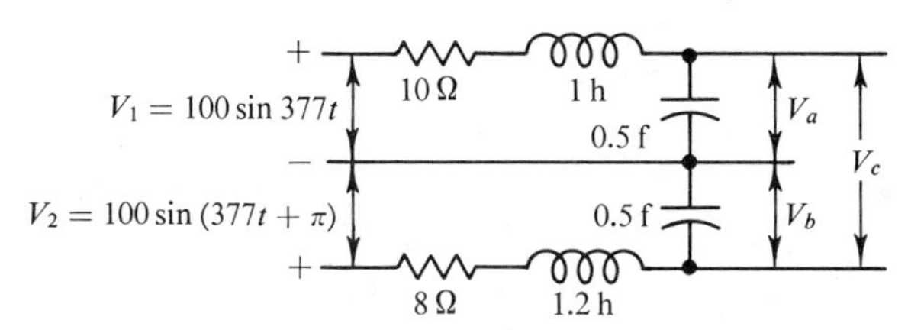

Fig. P 7.7.

7.8. Calculate the sinusoidal impedances or admittances of the circuits in Figure P 7.8 ($\omega = 2\pi \times 60$).

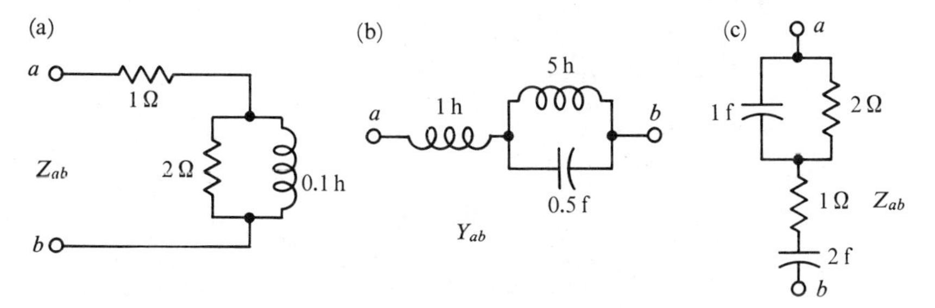

Fig. P 7.8.

7.9. Calculate the frequency at which the output is in phase with the input of the circuit shown in Figure P 7.9.

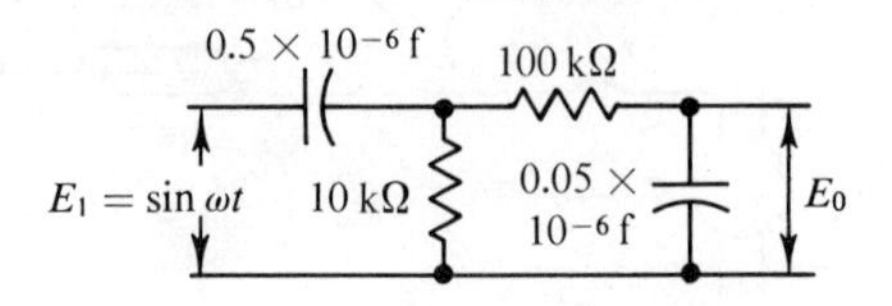

Fig. P 7.9.

7.10. Draw a phasor diagram of the three voltages

$$V_a = 208 \sin 377t$$

$$V_b = 208 \sin\left(377t + \frac{2\pi}{3}\right)$$

$$V_c = 208 \sin\left(377t - \frac{2\pi}{3}\right)$$

Calculate and draw as phasor quantities the voltages

$$\mathbf{V}_1 = \mathbf{V}_a - \mathbf{V}_b, \quad \mathbf{V}_2 = \mathbf{V}_b - \mathbf{V}_c, \quad \mathbf{V}_3 = \mathbf{V}_c - \mathbf{V}_a$$

7.11.

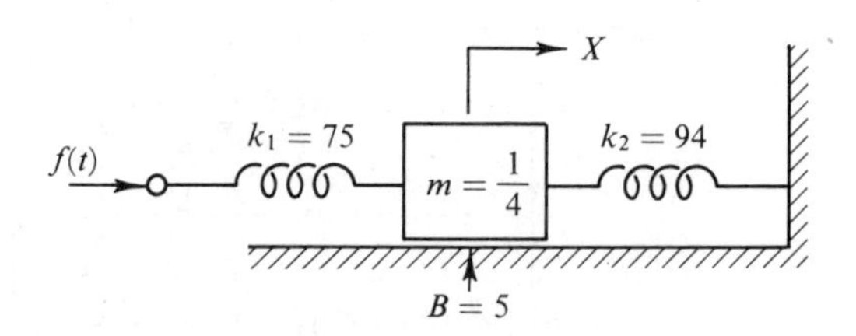

Fig. P 7.11.

In the mechanical system sketched in Figure P 7.11, let the input force $f(t) = F \sin \omega t$. If the displacement of the mass is the output,

a) What is the undamped natural frequency of the system?
b) What is the damping ratio, ζ?
c) What is the resonant frequency of the system?
d) What is the quality factor, Q?
e) Locate and sketch the poles of the system in the s-plane.

7.12. Three voltage generators and a resistance of 10 ohms are all connnected in series. Let the generated voltages be

$$v_1(t) = 10 \sin (t + 10°) \quad v_2(t) = 20 \sin (2t - 20°) \quad v_3 = -5$$

Find the effective value of voltage across and current through the resistance. What is the power consumed?

7.13.

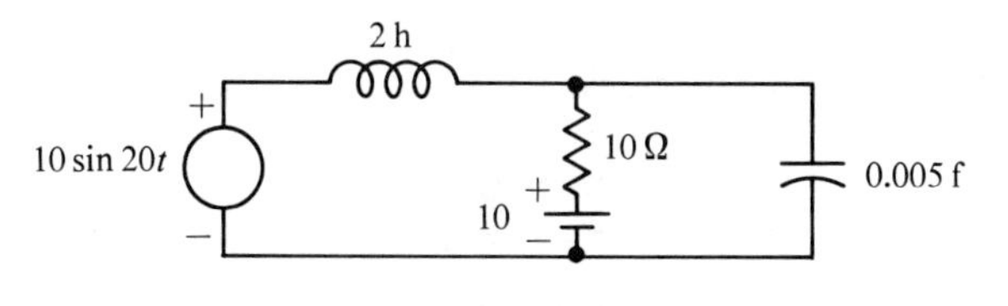

Fig. P 7.13.

Find the effective value of current through the resistor for the circuit sketched in Figure P 7.13.

7.14. Find the total power consumed in the circuit shown in Figure P 7.14

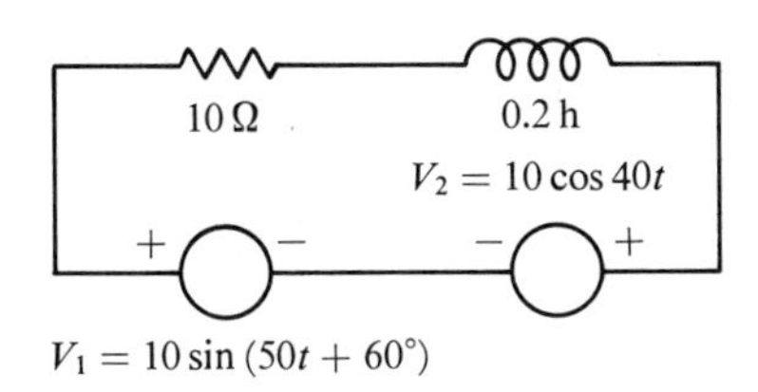

Fig. P 7.14.

7.15. A three-wire 115/230 volt single phase circuit supplies two loads: (a) on side *A* there are six 60 watt and two 50 watt lamps; (b) on side ***B*** there is a motor drawing 600 volt-amperes at 60 per cent power factor. Calculate the current in all three lines, and total power.

7.16.

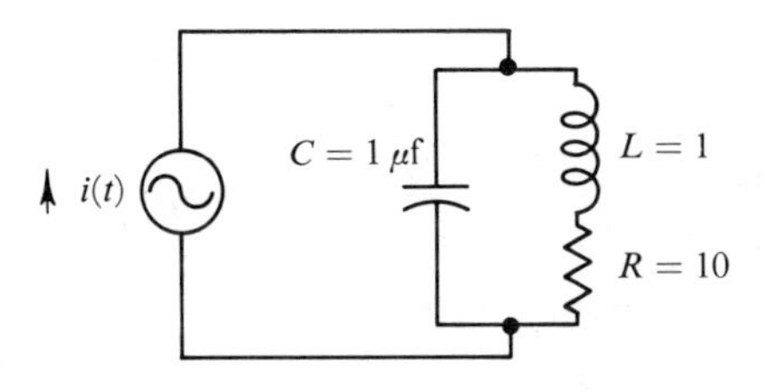

Fig. P 7.16.

The parallel *L-C* circuit in Figure P 7.16 is excited by a current source, $i(t) = 0.01 \cos \omega t$. Find

a) The resonant frequency
b) The voltage across the tuned circuit at resonance
c) The power consumed by the circuit at resonance

d) The parallel impedance of the circuit at resonance
e) The quality factor, Q, of the circuit

7.17. Three equal impedances, each of $12 + j16$ ohms are connected in Y. A balanced three-phase source with a line-to-line voltage of 208 volts is connected to the Y. Determine the magnitudes of the phase voltage, the phase current, the line current, and the total power.

7.18. Compute the power into R for the circuit shown in Figure P 7.18. (Answer: 1000 watts.)

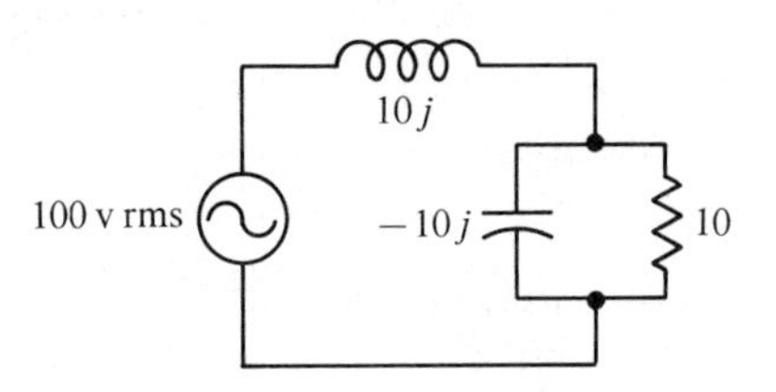

Fig. P 7.18.

7.19. Calculate $\mathbf{I}_1$, $\mathbf{I}_2$, $\mathbf{I}_g$ of the system shown in Figure P 7.19 and plot as phasors.

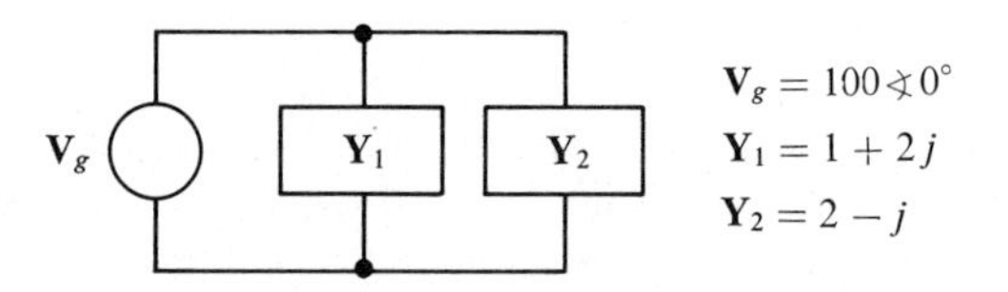

Fig. P 7.19.

7.20.

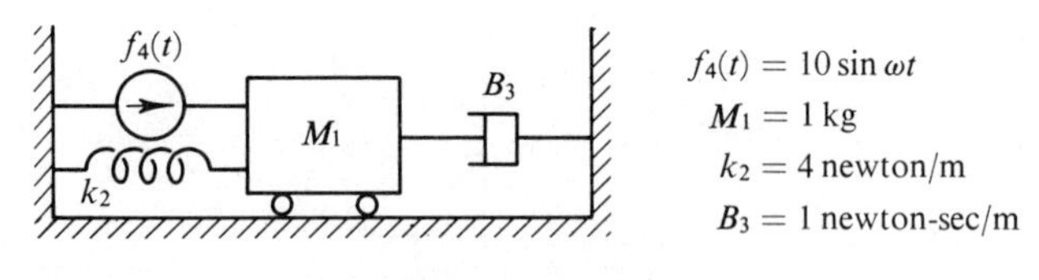

Fig. P 7.20.

Calculate phasor relations for the displacement of the mass δ_a, (Figure P 7.20) the forces f_1, f_2, and f_3 as a function of $f_4(t)$ for the following values of ω:

$$\omega = \begin{cases} \frac{1}{2} \text{ radian/second} \\ 2.2 \text{ radian/second} \\ 8 \text{ radian/second} \end{cases}$$

Draw a phasor diagram in each case. Show graphically that the vectorial sum $f_1 + f_2 + f_3 + f_4 = 0$, that is, the phasors $\mathbf{F}_1$, $\mathbf{F}_2$, $\mathbf{F}_3$, and $\mathbf{F}_4$ should add vectorially to zero.

7.21.

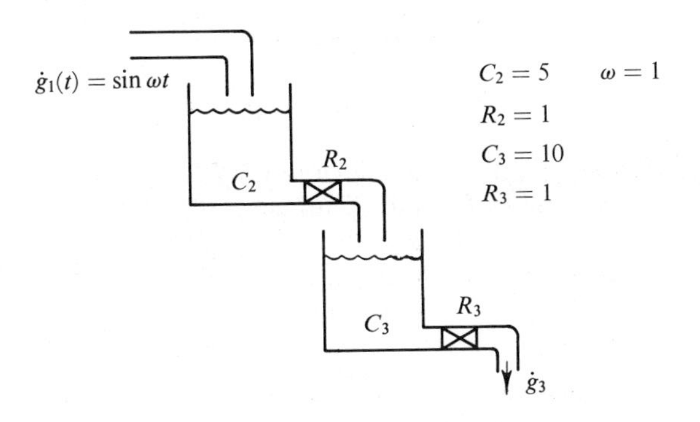

Fig. P 7.21.

For the system of Figure P 7.21, calculate $\dot{g}_3(t)$ as a function of $\dot{g}_1(t)$ (s-domain). Determine the phasor $\dot{G}_3$ and draw a phasor diagram.

7.22.

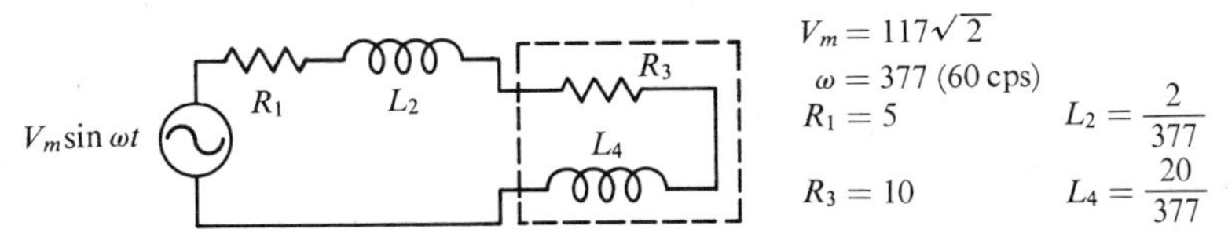

Fig. P 7.22.

For the system shown in Figure P 7.22, calculate current phasor, real power into load, and real power loss in line. Determine the latter two by *two* different approaches.

7.23. For the system shown in Figure P 7.23, find $\mathbf{I}_1$, $\mathbf{I}_2$; $\mathbf{E}_a$; and apparent, real, and reactive power supplied by generator.

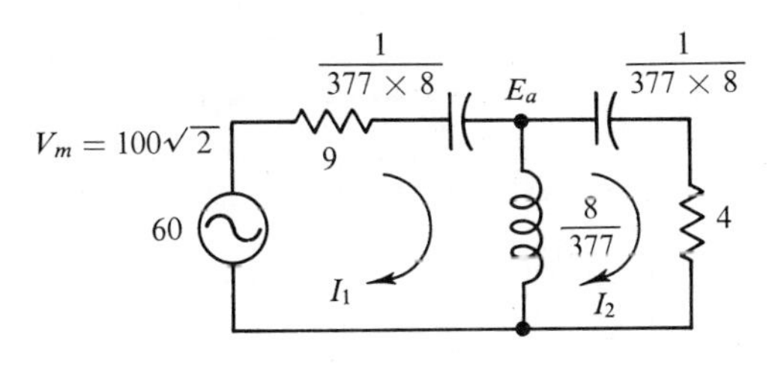

Fig. P 7.23.

7.24.

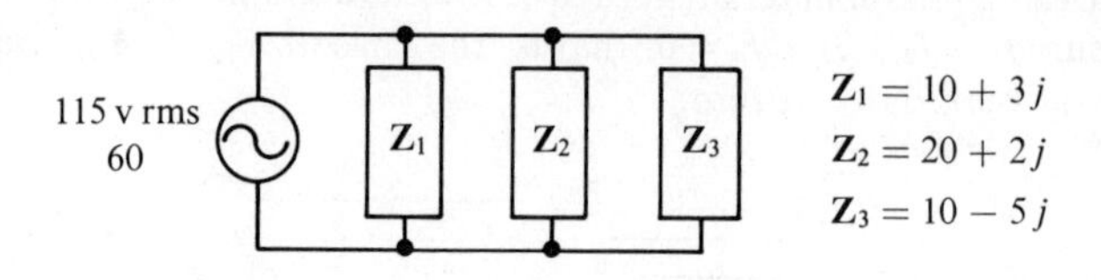

Fig. P 7.24.

For the system shown in Figure P 7.24:

a) Find **P**, **Q**, and$\mathbf{P}_{app}$ for generator.

b) Find $\mathbf{P}_1$, $\mathbf{P}_2$, and $\mathbf{P}_3$.

c) Find power factor of each load and generator.

b) Is $\mathbf{P} = \mathbf{P}_1 + \mathbf{P}_2 + \mathbf{P}_3$?

Repeat parts a) through d) with Z_3 removed. Explain the result.

7.25. Determine $A(\omega)$and $\phi(\omega)$ for the displacement of M_2 in Figure P 7.25. Is there a frequency at which $\delta_2 = 0$? Make plots of $A(\omega)$ versus ω and $\phi(\omega)$ versus ω on rectangular coordinates, and $A(\omega)$ versus $\phi(\omega)$ on polar coordinates.

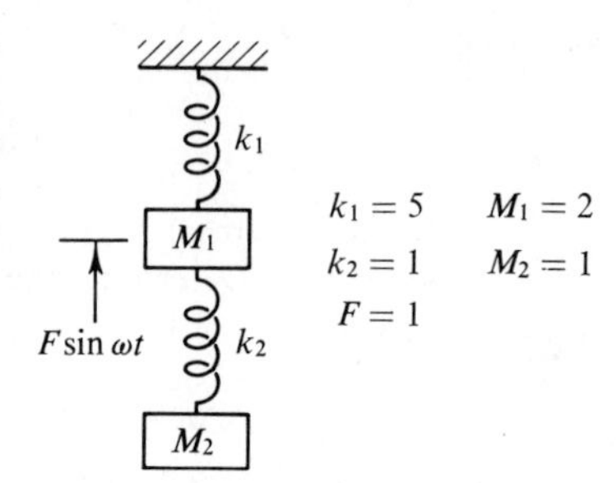

Fig. P 7.25.

7.26. Determine the resonant frequency of the circuits of Figure P 7.26.

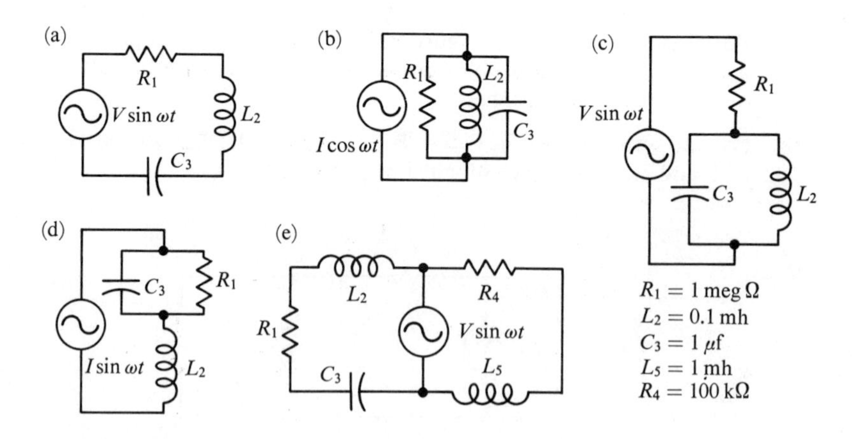

Fig. P 7.26.

7.27.

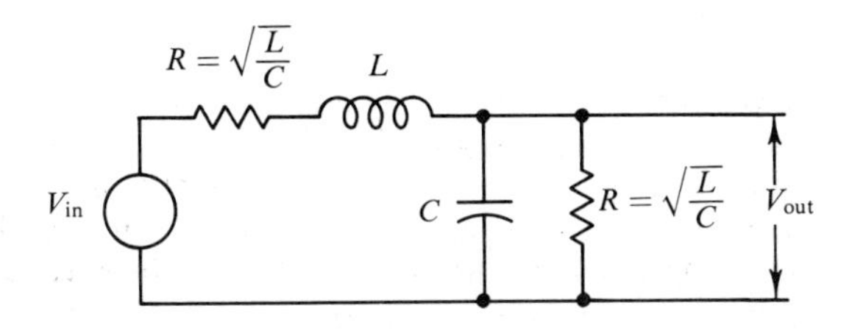

Fig. P 7.27.

a) For the low-pass filter of Figure P 7.27, determine the transfer function V_{out}/V_{in} and locate the zeros and poles.
b) Find $A(\omega) = |G(j\omega)|$.
c) Determine the rate of attenuation of $A(\omega)$ in decibels/decade for $\omega >> 1/\sqrt{LC}$.
d) Let $L = 0.1$ henry, $C = 0.01$ microfarad, and determine the polar plot of $G(j\omega)$.

7.28. Show that $Q = 1/2\zeta$ for any *R-L-C* circuit. Verify for two examples.

7.29. Calculate the maximum current flow in the circuit of Figure P 7.29 for $\omega = \omega_p$; ω_p is resonant frequency.

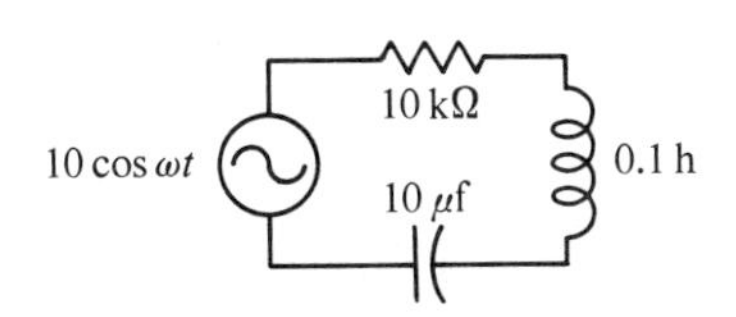

Fig. P 7.29.

7.30.

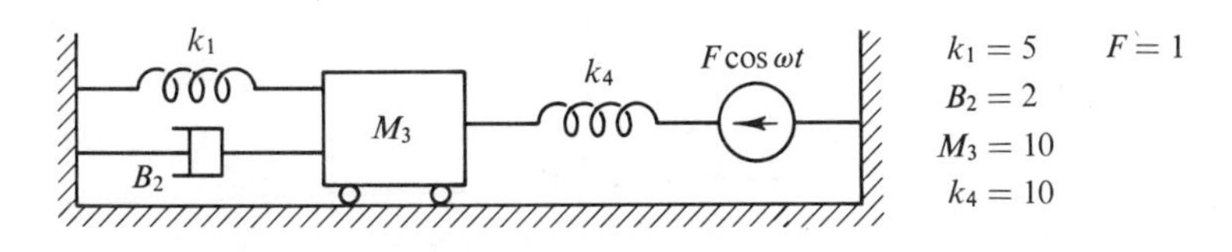

Fig. P 7.30.

For the system shown is Figure P 7.30, derive an expression that relates the combined force of spring k_1 and dashpot B_2 to the applied force. This is the transmitted force F_t. For what frequency is F_t/F a maximum? Show F_t and F on a phasor diagram.

7.31 A system has a transfer function

$$G(s) = \frac{5}{(s+2+5j)(s+2-5j)}$$

a) Determine $A(\omega)$ and $\phi(\omega)$ by graphical procedures.
b) What is ω_p, $A(\omega_p)$, $\phi(\omega_p)$?
c) What is ζ and ω_n? ω_n is natural resonant frequency.
d) Let the poles of the transfer function be moved in the negative real direction on the lines $\pm 5j$. What is the effect on ζ, ω_p and ω_n?

8 Multiterminal Components

8.1 Introduction

Our presentation of system analysis has been limited so far to assemblies of two-terminal components in order to permit a more careful introduction to the elementary principles of system analysis: modeling, formulation, and solution. It is, however, very uncommon to find systems which are performing a useful function that consist of only two-terminal components. One only has to consider electronic circuits which contain vacuum tubes and transistors; mechanical systems which contain gears, levers, and pulleys; control systems which contain electric motors and hydraulic actuators; all of which are components with three, four, or more terminals. It therefore becomes essential to consider multiterminal components.

This chapter deals with the development of mathematical models of multiterminal components. The discussion will be confined to those components whose characteristics are essentially linear or may be approximated by linear models for small signal operation. To become properly oriented in obtaining mathematical models of physical components, let us briefly review the modeling concepts as they apply to two-terminal components. A two-terminal component can be symbolically represented as shown in Figure 8.1.

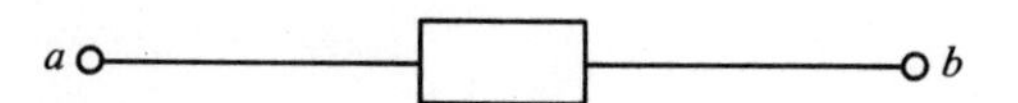

Fig. 8.1. *Symbolic representation of two-terminal components.*

Furthermore, there exists a unique relationship between the across and through variables:

$$x = F_1(y) \tag{8.1}$$

or

$$y = F_2(x) \tag{8.2}$$

where the variables x and y are in a one-to-one correspondence with measurements made at points a and b, and the relationship between x and y reflects the physical property which is characteristic of the component.

The mathematical model of the two-terminal component is complete in defining the orientation of variables x and y with respect to the terminals a and b of the component. The orientation is defined through use of the terminal graph shown in Figure 8.2.

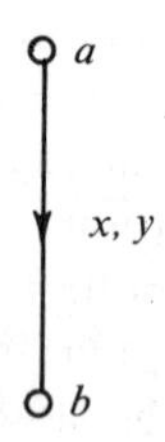

Fig. 8.2. *Linear graph defining orientation of variables.*

It is very important that the mathematical model of the component include both Equation 8.1 or 8.2 expressing an observable physical relationship *and* the linear graph defining the orientation of the variables as well as the points of measurement.

8.2 Terminal Graphs of Three- and Four-Terminal Components

The modeling of multiterminal components is dependent upon an extension of the basic modeling concepts developed for the two-terminal component. The thoroughness with which those concepts were developed in Chapter 2 will now be of great benefit in the modeling of multiterminal components. Primary emphasis will be placed on three- and

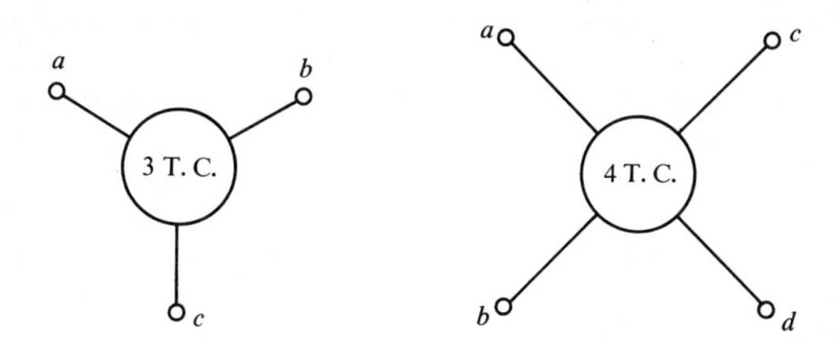

Fig. 8.3. *Symbolic representation of three- and four-terminal components.*

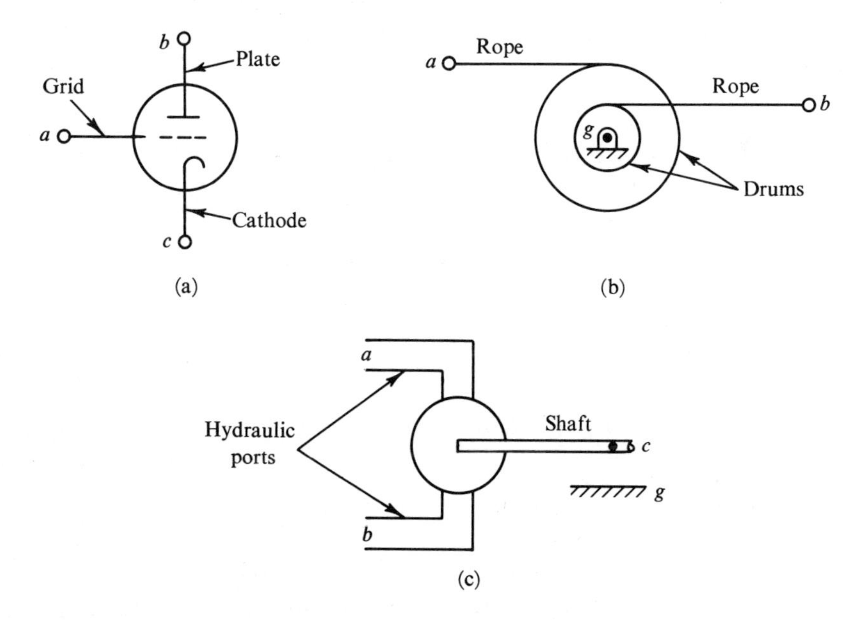

Fig. 8.4. *Illustrations of multiterminal components:* (a) *triode;* (b) *pulley;* (c) *hydraulic motor.*

four-terminal components due to their relative importance in the design of engineering systems.

We identify as a three-terminal (four-terminal) component a physical device which has three (four) points to which, under normal application, connections are made by other components. They are represented symbolically as shown in Figure 8.3. Components may have all electrical terminals, as does a triode; or they may be all mechanical, as they are in a pulley; or two of the terminals of a four-terminal component may be hydraulic, while the other two are mechanical, as in a hydraulic motor. These illustrative examples are shown in Figure 8.4.

The development of the mathematical model of a multiterminal component requires a statement regarding the physical properties of the component, as does the two-terminal component. This statement consists of a set of terminal equations interrelating terminal variables, and a terminal graph showing the orientation of such variables. From the study of two-terminal components we have learned that the mathematical model consists of exactly one equation, and a terminal graph with exactly one element. This equation relates a pair of variables, both of which are defined between *two* points. It appears, then, that the complexity of the mathematical model of multiterminal components is determined simply by the number of pairs of variables that can be specified for the component. For the three-terminal component there are three such pairs; for the four-terminal component, there are six, as shown in Figure 8.5.

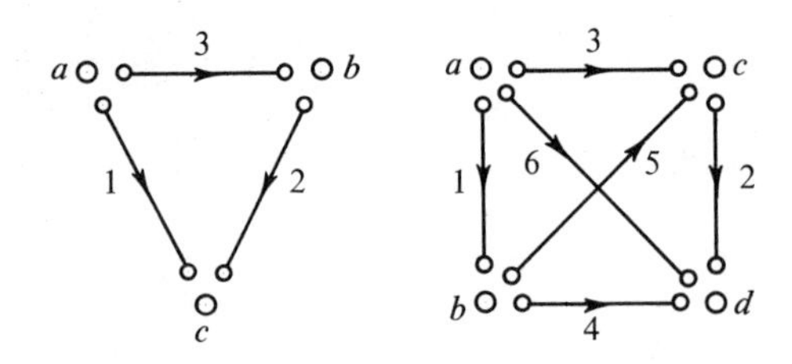

Fig. 8.5. *Variable pairs for multiterminal components.*

The following pairs of variables are identified:

Three-terminal	Four-terminal
x_1, y_1—element 1	x_1, y_1—element 1
x_2, y_2—element 2	x_2, y_2—element 2
x_3, y_3—element 3	x_3, y_3—element 3

x_4, y_4—element 4

x_5, y_5—element 5

x_6, y_6—element 6

In the process of specifying and defining these pairs of variables by linear graphs, we have generated an interconnected set of elements similar to a system graph. The variables associated with the elements are subject to the constraints imposed by the circuit laws and vertex laws by being joined together. Of particular interest in this case is the circuit law. For the three-terminal component it states

$$-x_1 + x_2 + x_3 = 0 \tag{8.3}$$

This relation implies that the across variables x_1, x_2, and x_3 are linearly dependent. One can express any one of the three in terms of the other two; for instance,

$$x_3 = x_1 - x_2 \tag{8.4}$$

Thus, of the three across variables that can be measured between the three pairs of terminals, one is redundant in that it introduces no new information regarding the component. Similarly, one can demonstrate that only three across variables are independent for the four-terminal component. For an n-terminal component, $n - 1$ across measurements are sufficient to determine all definable across variables. This development leads to the statement that for an n-terminal component a terminal graph consisting of exactly $n - 1$ elements is sufficient to define a set of independent across variables. We will see later that, due to peculiarities of actual components, not all $n - 1$ elements are necessary. Thus, a terminal graph constructed for this purpose is characterized by three important features:

1. It contains no circuits; the existence of a circuit would render one of the across variables dependent.
2. It contains all vertices; all component terminals are significant.
3. It contains, at most, $n - 1$ elements.

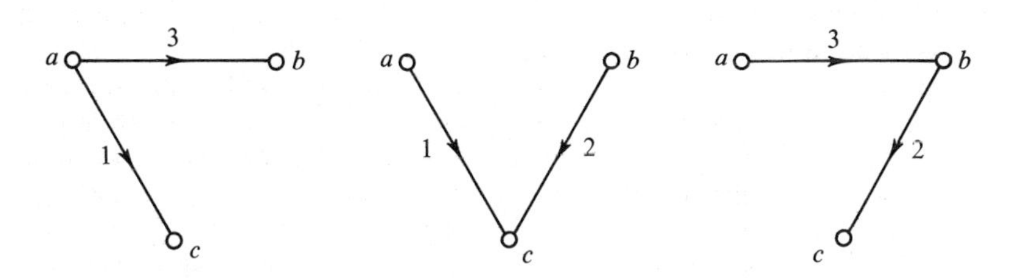

Fig. 8.6. *Terminal graphs for three-terminal components.*

When a terminal graph contains exactly $n - 1$ elements, it is called a *tree-graph,* in reference to the special graph introduced in Chapter 6.

A three-terminal component permits the selection of three different terminal graphs, as identified in Figure 8.6. Each one of these defines a different set of across variables that may be used to measure the properties of the component.

It will be helpful at this point to consider a number of typical components to illustrate the selection of terminal graphs.

Example 8.1. Show suitable terminal graphs for the three components shown in Figure 8.4.

a. The triode is a three-terminal component. One mode of application views the terminal pair *a-c* as input and the terminal pair *b-c* as output. Thus, a most suitable terminal graph is that shown in Figure 8.7 (a).

b. The pulley is also a three-terminal component whose terminals *a-g* may be viewed as input and whose terminals *b-g* may be viewed as output. Its terminal graph is shown in Figure 8.7 (b).

c. The hydraulic motor is a four-terminal component. The hydraulic ports *a*, *b* form one pair of terminals, while the shaft *c* and the reference *g* form another, as shown in Figure 8.7 (c).

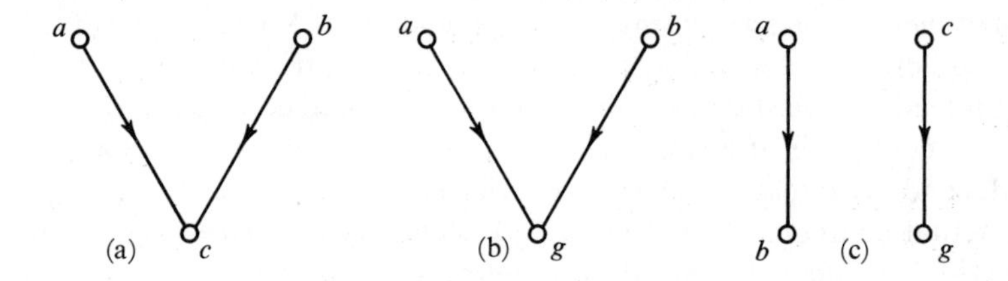

Fig. 8.7. *Terminal graphs of components of Figure 8.4.*

The terminal graphs corresponding to the triode and pulley are tree-graphs, while the hydraulic motor does not have a tree-graph. The explanation for this is simple: it is meaningless to add a third element to the terminal graph of the hydraulic motor since it would define a pair of variables which are mixed mechanical and hydraulic. In other words, one cannot make a measurement between two terminals which are not physically alike.

We have seen how the desire to describe the characteristics of an n-terminal component in a complete but non-redundant manner leads to the selection of no more than $n-1$ across variables as terminal variables. There exist no similar limitations on the selection of suitable through variables for the mathematical model of a multiterminal component, other than the requirement to associate one through variable with each across variable. In summary, we can state that it is sufficient (but not always necessary) to select $n-1$ pairs of terminal variables, which are interrelated by the component properties, to establish a complete representation of an n-terminal component. The choice of terminal graph in each case is greatly dependent on the nature of the component. No general rules can be given for its selection. When two terminals are selected to define an element in the terminal graph, we call that pair of terminals a *port*. Consequently, an n-port terminal representation has exactly n terminal equations.

8.3 The Determination of Characteristics of Three- and Four-Terminal Components

Let us investigate next the actual procedure of determining the relations between the terminal variables of a multiterminal component. Consider again a three-terminal component. It has two ports. Let the terminal graph be selected, as shown in Figure 8.8 (b). Accordingly,

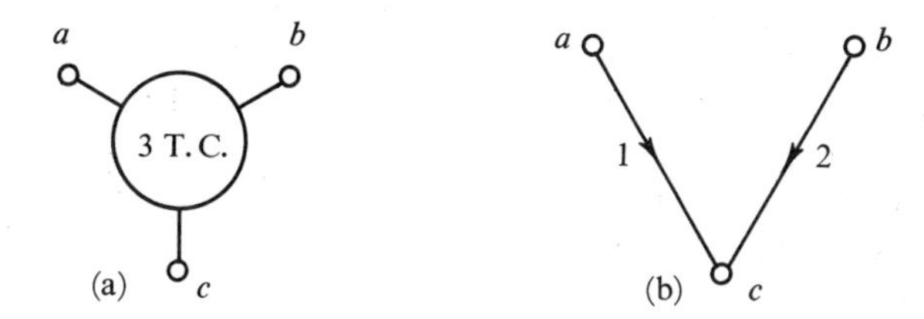

Fig. 8.8. *Three-terminal component:* (a) *symbolic representation;* (b) *terminal graph.*

we will apply suitable across and through measurements to determine the relationships between the two pairs of variables (x_1, y_1) and (x_2, y_2). These variables are uniquely defined by the terminal graph. In Figure 8.9, the component is shown with two across-meters and two through-meters, together with two through drivers, connected to it. The orien-

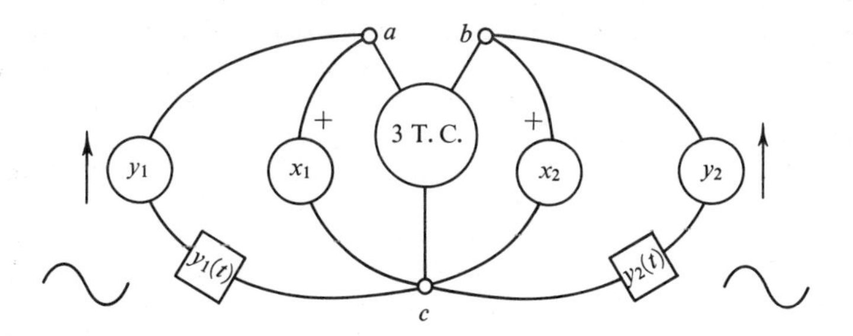

Fig. 8.9. *Experimental test for determining physical properties of three-terminal component.*

tation of the meters is in accordance with the orientation of the elements of the terminal graph of Figure 8.8 (b). The selection of through drivers to excite the component is made on the assumption that the through variables y_1 and y_2 may be specified arbitrarily.* On this basis, it should be possible to determine functional relationships of the form

$$x_1 = F_1(y_1, y_2)$$
$$x_2 = F_2(y_1, y_2) \tag{8.5}$$

where the functions are indicative of the physical properties of the component.

The form of Equations 8.5 indicates that y_1 and y_2 are independent variables and x_1 and x_2 are dependent variables. The experimental procedure for determining these relations is straightforward: x_1 and x_2 are measured as a function of y_1 (or y_2) with y_2 (or y_1) being constant. In this manner, families of curves which are displayed effectively on x-y plots, as shown in Figure 8.10, are generated. The curves may indicate a nonlinear functional relationship [see Figure 8.10 (a)] or a linear relationship [see Figure 8.10 (b)]. When nonlinear relationships are involved, it is generally very difficult to determine a corresponding analytical expression. However, in the case of linear relations, an analytical expression is readily obtained. For the second of Equations 8.5, a linear form may be adopted:

$$x_2 = z_{21}y_1 + z_{22}y_2 \tag{8.6}$$

The constants z_{21} and z_{22} are determined by prescribing the following test conditions:

$$z_{21} = \left.\frac{x_2}{y_1}\right]_{y_2=0} \tag{8.7a}$$

$$z_{22} = \left.\frac{x_2}{y_2}\right]_{y_1=0} \tag{8.7b}$$

Notice that this procedure is based upon the principle of superposition.

Suppose now that the function $F_1(y_1, y_2)$ is also linear such that

$$x_1 = z_{11}y_1 + z_{12}y_2 \tag{8.8}$$

where

$$z_{11} = \left.\frac{x_1}{y_1}\right]_{y_2=0} \tag{8.9a}$$

$$z_{12} = \left.\frac{x_1}{y_2}\right]_{y_1=0} \tag{8.9b}$$

Equations 8.6 and 8.8 may be combined as a matrix equation. Then the mathematical model of the component may be stated as

* This is not possible for many physical components, as will be demonstrated later.

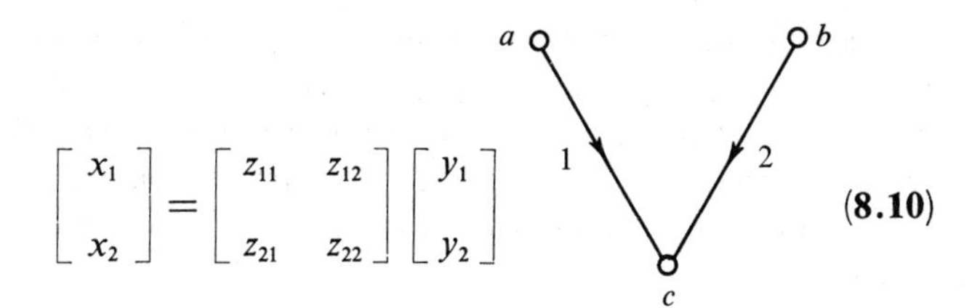

$$\begin{bmatrix} x_1 \\ x_2 \end{bmatrix} = \begin{bmatrix} z_{11} & z_{12} \\ z_{21} & z_{22} \end{bmatrix} \begin{bmatrix} y_1 \\ y_2 \end{bmatrix} \quad \textbf{(8.10)}$$

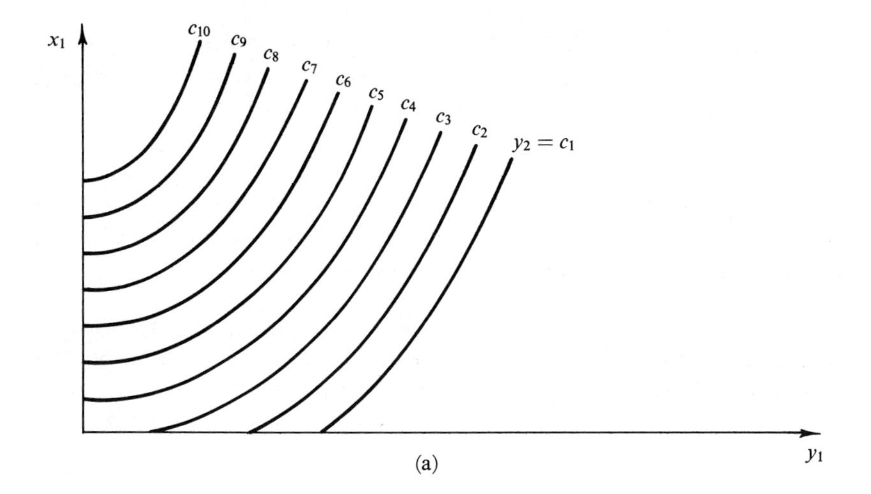

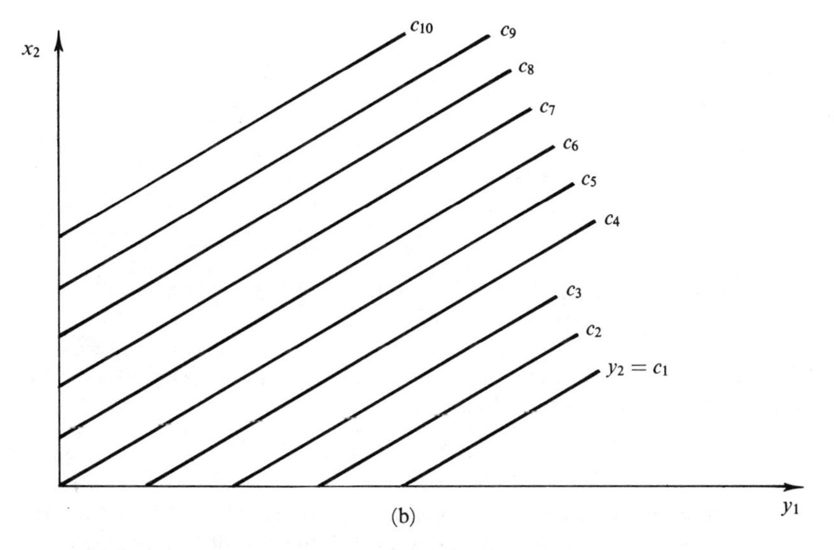

Fig. 8.10. *Typical characteristics of a three-terminal component:* (a) *nonlinear;* (b) *linear.*

Thus, if the component is linear (the terminal variables are interrelated linearly), a matrix equation which is representative of the component may be determined. If the component is nonlinear, a matrix representation is not possible because superposition does not apply, and the mathematical model can only be given in functional form as

$$x_1 = F_1(y_1, y_2)$$
$$x_2 = F_2(y_1, y_2) \tag{8.11}$$

However, regardless of whether or not the component is linear, the terminal variables are identical. Our attention will be initially directed at components with linear characteristics.

Example 8.2. Determine the terminal equations of the two-resistor network of Figure 8.11 (a) according to the terminal graph of Figure 8.11 (b). As indicated by the terminal graph, the resistor network is to be viewed as a three-terminal component. In terms of applications, one can define input and

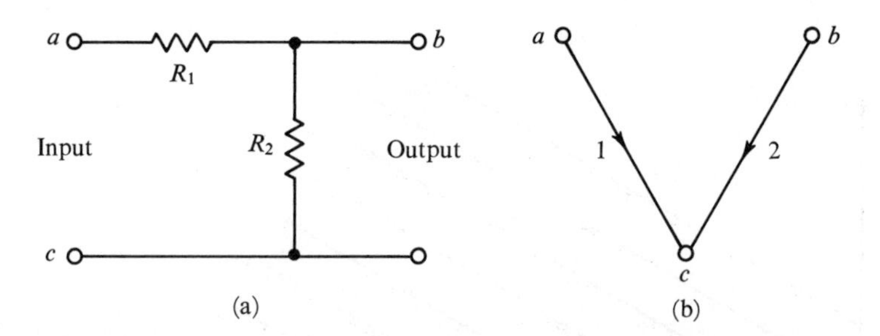

Fig. 8.11. *Three-terminal networks:* (a) *physical schematic;* (b) *terminal graph.*

output terminals as indicated. Let us assume that we can determine the terminal equation in the form of Equations 8.10. Thus

$$\begin{bmatrix} v_1 \\ v_2 \end{bmatrix} = \begin{bmatrix} z_{11} & z_{12} \\ z_{21} & z_{22} \end{bmatrix} \begin{bmatrix} i_1 \\ i_2 \end{bmatrix} \tag{8.12}$$

To determine the four coefficients of the matrix, selected measurements must be carried out according to Equations 8.7 and 8.9. To determine z_{11} we specify that $i_2 = 0$, which means that no connections are made to the output terminals. On the other hand a current source, representing i_1, is connected to the input terminals. In addition, a voltmeter is connected across the input to measure v_1. This is shown in Figure 8.12.

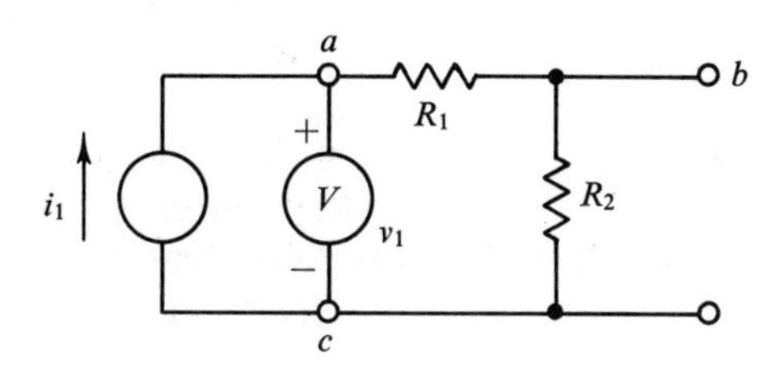

Fig. 8.12. *Test connection to determine z_{11}.*

It is clear that

$$v_1 = (R_1 + R_2)i_1 \tag{8.13}$$

by consideration of a simple mesh equation.

If we also connect a voltmeter across the output we can meaure that

$$v_2 = R_2 i_1 \tag{8.14}$$

This, of course, determines the coefficient z_{21}. To determine the remaining coefficients of the matrix of Equation 8.12 it is only necessary to repeat the above procedure and apply a current source at the output, leave the input terminals unconnected, and measure v_1 and v_2. Then

$$v_1 = R_2 i_2 \tag{8.15}$$

and

$$v_2 = R_2 i_2$$

Consequently, the overall result is

$$\begin{bmatrix} v_1 \\ v_2 \end{bmatrix} = \begin{bmatrix} R_1 + R_2 & R_2 \\ R_2 & R_2 \end{bmatrix} \begin{bmatrix} i_1 \\ i_2 \end{bmatrix} \tag{8.16}$$

We have so far assumed that the terminal equations involve only algebraic interrelationship of the variables. This, however, is a rather restrictive condition. Very frequently, the terminal characteristics of multiterminal components involve differential equations. The principle of superposition is still applicable as long as the differential equations are linear. For a three-terminal component, the mathematical model may then be given symbolically as

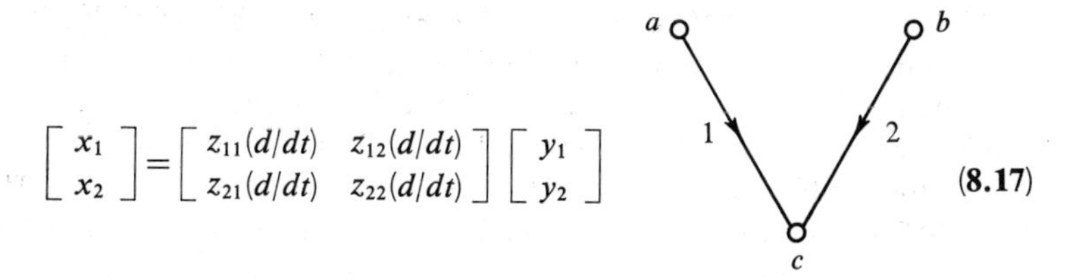

(8.17)

The component model may also be given in the s-domain. The form of the equations then is

$$\begin{bmatrix} X_1 \\ X_2 \end{bmatrix} = \begin{bmatrix} Z_{11}(s) & Z_{12}(s) \\ Z_{21}(s) & Z_{22}(s) \end{bmatrix} \begin{bmatrix} Y_1 \\ Y_2 \end{bmatrix} \tag{8.18}$$

The total number of equations contained in a mathematical model of a multiterminal component is equal to the number of elements in the terminal graph for which unique terminal variables can be defined. Thus, the maximum number of equations is $n - 1$. For instance, the model of a four-terminal component may contain as many as three equations; that is,

$$\begin{bmatrix} y_1 \\ y_2 \\ y_3 \end{bmatrix} = \begin{bmatrix} w_{11} & w_{12} & w_{13} \\ w_{21} & w_{22} & w_{23} \\ w_{31} & w_{32} & w_{33} \end{bmatrix} \begin{bmatrix} x_1 \\ x_2 \\ x_3 \end{bmatrix} \tag{8.19}$$

where the variables are defined by the terminal graph,

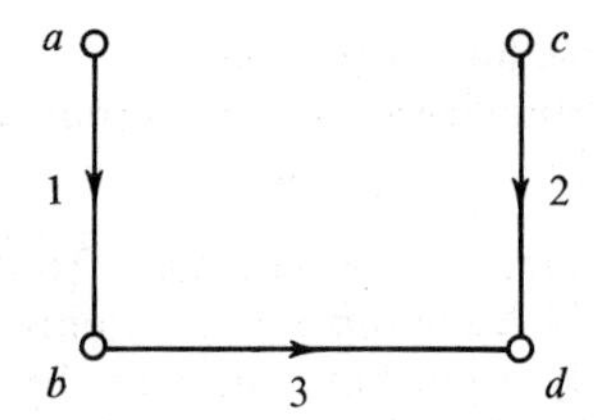

The matrix coefficients of Equation 8.19 are determined again by superposition, that is, by specifying alternately the following test conditions:

$$\begin{bmatrix} y_1 \\ y_2 \\ y_3 \end{bmatrix} = \begin{bmatrix} w_{11} \\ w_{21} \\ w_{31} \end{bmatrix} x_1, \qquad \begin{matrix} x_2 = 0 \\ x_3 = 0 \end{matrix} \tag{8.20}$$

etc.

8.4 Classification of Models of Multiterminal Components

The mathematical models of linear multiterminal components may assume a variety of forms. To investigate these forms and explain the process of their generation, consider an n-terminal component. We wish to derive a terminal representation according to the terminal graph of Figure 8.13. Specified drivers are applied at each of the ports for which elements representing terminal variables are selected. Depending upon the component, these drivers may be across or through drivers. The unspecified covariables are then expressed as linear combinations of the specified variables.

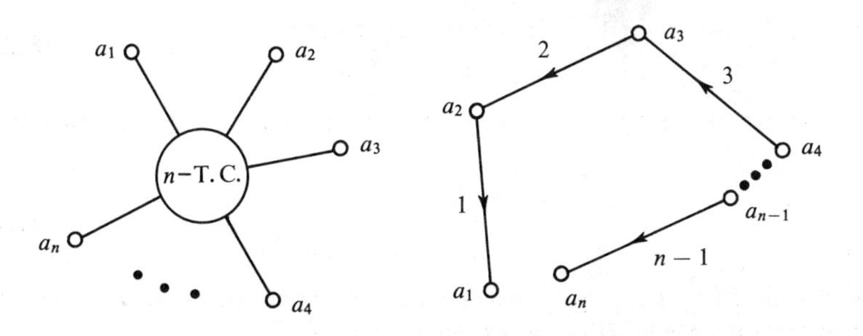

Fig. 8.13. *n-terminal component.*

$$\begin{bmatrix} y_1 \\ x_2 \\ x_3 \\ \cdot \\ \cdot \\ y_{n-1} \end{bmatrix} = \begin{bmatrix} c_{11} & c_{12} & c_{13} \cdots c_{1,\,n-1} \\ c_{21} & c_{22} & c_{23} \cdots c_{2,\,n-1} \\ \cdot & & \\ \cdot & & \\ \cdot & & \\ c_{n-1,1} & c_{n-1,2} & \cdots\cdots c_{n-1,\,n-1} \end{bmatrix} \begin{bmatrix} x_1 \\ y_2 \\ y_3 \\ \cdot \\ \cdot \\ x_{n-1} \end{bmatrix} \tag{8.21}$$

variables corresponding to measurements (↑ left) — variables corresponding to drivers (↑ right)

To evaluate the coefficients c_{ij} in the resulting matrix, one specifies the appropriate test conditions that all drivers except the jth are set to zero. For instance,

$$c_{13} = \left.\frac{y_1}{y_3}\right]_{x_1,\, y_2,\, \cdots,\, x_{n-1}=0} \tag{8.22}$$

A test condition corresponding to setting a specified across variable to zero is called a *short-circuit* test; an *open-circuit* test results when a specified through variable is zero. For the coefficient c_{13} defined by Equation 8.22 above, the open-circuit test condition is $x_1 = 0$, the short-circuit test condition is $y_2 = 0$, etc. All these test conditions must be realizable simultaneously; this requirement is a *necessary condition* to permit the form of the terminal equations. Whether or not a chosen combination of test conditions is realizable depends entirely upon the characteristics of a given component.

A number of special forms for component models are encountered for three-terminal components and four-terminal components which have only two ports. Because of their frequent occurrence, it is convenient to define special terms for the coefficients of the matrices.

a. *Open-circuit parameters.* When all test conditions are open-circuit tests, the general form of the equations is

$$\begin{bmatrix} x_1 \\ x_2 \end{bmatrix} = \begin{bmatrix} z_{11}(d/dt) & z_{12}(d/dt) \\ z_{21}(d/dt) & z_{22}(d/dt) \end{bmatrix} \begin{bmatrix} y_1 \\ y_2 \end{bmatrix} \tag{8.23}$$

If s-domain format is chosen to represent these characteristics they would be

$$\begin{bmatrix} X_1 \\ X_2 \end{bmatrix} = \begin{bmatrix} Z_{11}(s) & Z_{12}(s) \\ Z_{21}(s) & Z_{22}(s) \end{bmatrix} \begin{bmatrix} Y_1 \\ Y_2 \end{bmatrix} \tag{8.24}$$

The coefficients of the matrix are called the *open-circuit parameters*. An example will help to illustrate these definitions.

Example 8.3. Determine the open-circuit parameters of the three-terminal network shown in Figure 8.14.

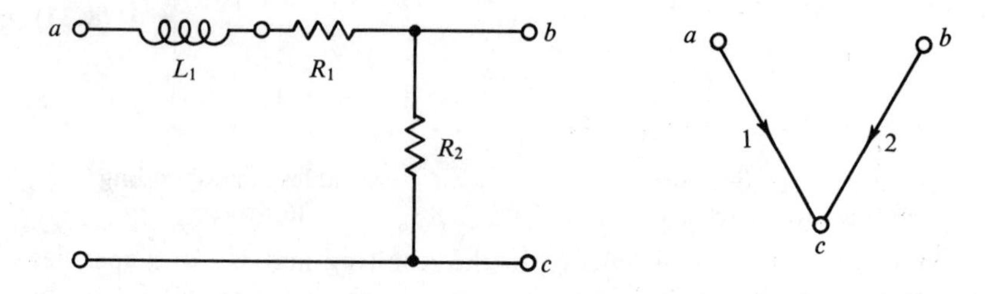

Fig. 8.14. *Three-terminal network.*

A comparison of this network with that of Example 8.2 shows that the only difference is the addition of the inductor. Furthermore, the same test conditions that applied in Example 8.2 may be used here. Following through, we realize that only the z_{11} coefficient will be affected by the addition of the inductor; that is,

$$v_1 = \left(R_1 + L_1\frac{d}{dt}\right)i_1, \qquad i_2 = 0$$

Hence the desired model will be

$$\begin{bmatrix} v_1 \\ v_2 \end{bmatrix} = \begin{bmatrix} \left(R_1 + L_1\frac{d}{dt}\right) & R_2 \\ R_2 & R_2 \end{bmatrix} \begin{bmatrix} i_1 \\ i_2 \end{bmatrix} \tag{8.25}$$

or when transformed into the s-domain

$$\begin{bmatrix} V_1 \\ V_2 \end{bmatrix} = \begin{bmatrix} R_1 + L_1 s & R_2 \\ R_2 & R_2 \end{bmatrix} \begin{bmatrix} I_1 \\ I_2 \end{bmatrix} \tag{8.26}$$

b. *Short-circuit parameters.* All test conditions are short-circuit tests; the form of the equations is

$$\begin{bmatrix} y_1 \\ y_2 \end{bmatrix} = \begin{bmatrix} w_{11}(d/dt) & w_{12}(d/dt) \\ w_{21}(d/dt) & w_{22}(d/dt) \end{bmatrix} \begin{bmatrix} x_1 \\ x_2 \end{bmatrix} \tag{8.27}$$

or

$$\begin{bmatrix} Y_1 \\ Y_2 \end{bmatrix} = \begin{bmatrix} W_{11}(s) & W_{12}(s) \\ W_{21}(s) & W_{22}(s) \end{bmatrix} \begin{bmatrix} X_1 \\ X_2 \end{bmatrix} \tag{8.28}$$

The coefficients of these matrices are called the short-circuit parameters.

Example 8.4. Determine the short-circuit parameters of the mechanical network shown in Figure 8.15.

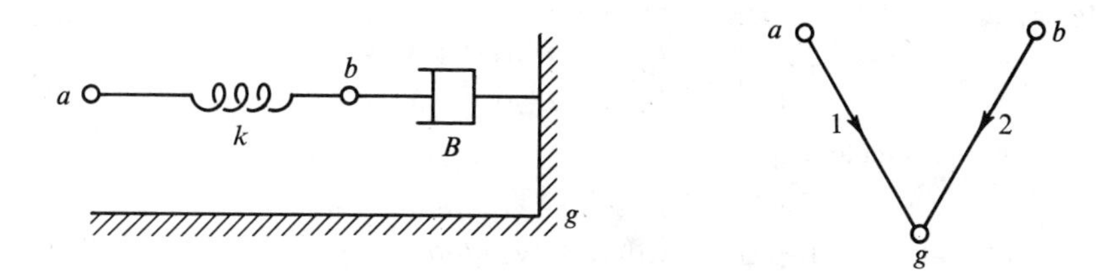

Fig. 8.15. *Three-terminal mechanical network and terminal graph.*

To establish $w_{11}(d/dt)$ we set $\delta_2 = 0$ and measure f_1 upon application of the driver $\delta_1(t)$. Under these conditions we have simply

$$f_1 = k\delta_1 \tag{8.29}$$

Also, the $w_{21}(d/dt)$ coefficient may be determined from the same test. It is

$$f_2 = -k\delta_1 \tag{8.30}$$

Similarly, the coefficients of the second column of the matrix are obtained by setting $\delta_1 = 0$ and applying the driver $\delta_2(t)$. Then force measurements will show that

$$\begin{bmatrix} f_1 \\ f_2 \end{bmatrix} = \begin{bmatrix} -k \\ k + B\dfrac{d}{dt} \end{bmatrix} \delta_2 \tag{8.31}$$

Upon combining Equations 8.29, 8.30, and 8.31, we have the complete three-terminal model

$$\begin{bmatrix} f_1 \\ f_2 \end{bmatrix} = \begin{bmatrix} k & -k \\ -k & k + B\dfrac{d}{dt} \end{bmatrix} \begin{bmatrix} \delta_1 \\ \delta_2 \end{bmatrix} \tag{8.32}$$

or

$$\begin{bmatrix} F_1 \\ F_2 \end{bmatrix} = \begin{bmatrix} k & -k \\ -k & k+Bs \end{bmatrix} \begin{bmatrix} \Delta_1 \\ \Delta_2 \end{bmatrix}$$

We note that if a component or a network can be modeled both in terms of open-circuit and short-circuit parameters, then the two matrices involved are inverses of one another. However, when the coefficients are expressed in terms of differential equations, like Equations 8.23 and 8.27, then inverses cannot be obtained. The Laplace transform of these equations is required first. Hence, in general it is possible to change Equations 8.24 into a short-circuit parameter model or change Equations 8.28 into an open-circuit parameter model.

c. *Hybrid parameters.* When the test conditions consist of one open-circuit and one short-circuit condition, two forms of equations are possible:

The h-parameters

$$\begin{bmatrix} x_1 \\ y_2 \end{bmatrix} = \begin{bmatrix} h_{11}(d/dt) & h_{12}(d/dt) \\ h_{21}(d/dt) & h_{22}(d/dt) \end{bmatrix} \begin{bmatrix} y_1 \\ x_2 \end{bmatrix} \tag{8.33}$$

or

$$\begin{bmatrix} X_1 \\ Y_2 \end{bmatrix} = \begin{bmatrix} H_{11}(s) & H_{12}(s) \\ H_{21}(s) & H_{22}(s) \end{bmatrix} \begin{bmatrix} Y_1 \\ X_2 \end{bmatrix} \tag{8.34}$$

The g-parameters

$$\begin{bmatrix} y_1 \\ x_2 \end{bmatrix} = \begin{bmatrix} g_{11}(d/dt) & g_{12}(d/dt) \\ g_{21}(d/dt) & g_{22}(d/dt) \end{bmatrix} \begin{bmatrix} x_1 \\ y_2 \end{bmatrix} \tag{8.35}$$

or

$$\begin{bmatrix} Y_1 \\ X_2 \end{bmatrix} = \begin{bmatrix} G_{11}(s) & G_{12}(s) \\ G_{21}(s) & G_{22}(s) \end{bmatrix} \begin{bmatrix} X_1 \\ Y_2 \end{bmatrix} \tag{8.36}$$

Again, it is obvious that the h-parameters and g-parameters of the components are inverses of one another when they exist.

In addition to the four forms listed above, a fifth form finds occasional usage in system analysis.

d. *Cascade parameters.*

$$\begin{bmatrix} x_1 \\ y_1 \end{bmatrix} = \begin{bmatrix} A & B \\ C & D \end{bmatrix} \begin{bmatrix} x_2 \\ -y_2 \end{bmatrix} \tag{8.37}$$

These parameters *cannot* be directy determined by measurement. It is physically impossible to specify one variable at a port while still retaining arbitrary control over its covariable. The cascade parameters can be determined by rewriting the terminal equations of other forms. It is left as an exercise to the reader to demonstrate this.

e. *State models.* In connection with the introduction of state variable techniques as a tool in systems analysis, yet another form is available for the modeling of three- and four-terminal components. Before a state model is defined let us consider the following introductory development.

Suppose we solve the second of Equations 8.32 for the derivative $d/dt\ \delta_2$,

$$\frac{d}{dt}\delta_2 = -\frac{k}{B}\delta_2 + \frac{k}{B}\delta_1 + \frac{1}{B}f_2 \tag{8.38}$$

and form the following two equations:

$$\left.\begin{aligned} f_1 &= -k\delta_2 + k\delta_1 \\ \delta_2 &= \delta_2 \end{aligned}\right] \tag{8.39}$$

Then we may view Equation 8.38 as a state equation in the state variable δ_2 with inputs δ_1 and f_2, and Equations 8.39 as output equations. Upon combining these equations and letting $x = \delta_2$, we have

$$\begin{bmatrix} \frac{d}{dt}x \\ f_1 \\ \delta_2 \end{bmatrix} = \begin{bmatrix} -\frac{k}{B} & \frac{k}{B} & \frac{1}{B} \\ -k & +k & 0 \\ 1 & 0 & 0 \end{bmatrix} \begin{bmatrix} x \\ \delta_1 \\ f_2 \end{bmatrix} \tag{8.40}$$

Equations 8.40 will be referred to as the state model of the three-terminal network of Figure 8.15. By letting $\delta_2 = x$ we emphasize the fact that the differential equations used to describe the component characteristics are "internal." Only the terminal variables are "external" to the the component.

The general state model of a three- or four-terminal component is given as

$$\begin{bmatrix} \frac{d}{dt}\mathbf{x} \\ \hdashline y_i \\ x_o \end{bmatrix} = \begin{bmatrix} \mathbf{A} & \mathbf{B}_1 & \mathbf{B}_2 \\ \hdashline \mathbf{C}_1 & d_{11} & d_{12} \\ \mathbf{C}_2 & d_{21} & d_{22} \end{bmatrix} \begin{bmatrix} \mathbf{x} \\ \hdashline x_i \\ y_o \end{bmatrix} \tag{8.41}$$

where $\mathbf{x}$ is state vector with n components, x_1, y_1 are input terminal variables, x_o, y_o are output terminal variables, A is $n \times n$ matrix, B_1, B_2 are $n \times 1$ matrices, C_1, C_2 are $1 \times n$ matrices.

The number of state variables, n, in the state vector x depends entirely upon the number of memory states in the components or network.

8.5 Linear Models of Multiterminal Components

The process of assuming the form of the terminal equations for a particular component is somewhat arbitrary. For each pair of terminal variables a choice exists in the selection of an appropriate test condition. Usually, the peculiarities of the component dictate the choice. This section deals with the derivation of models of actual components.

A variety of physical components will be discussed in order to demonstrate the principles of modeling of multiterminal components.

Rotational Dashpot

The first component to be considered is a rotational dashpot, shown in Figure 8.16 (a). It consists, in principle, of two cylindrical cups, whose inertias are not negligible,* nested in one another. The two cups are closely fitted, leaving a small clearance which is filled with oil. The primary physical property of the dashpot is the viscous friction torque generated by a relative velocity between the two cups. Three

* If the inertias are negligible, the dashpot is simply a two-terminal component.

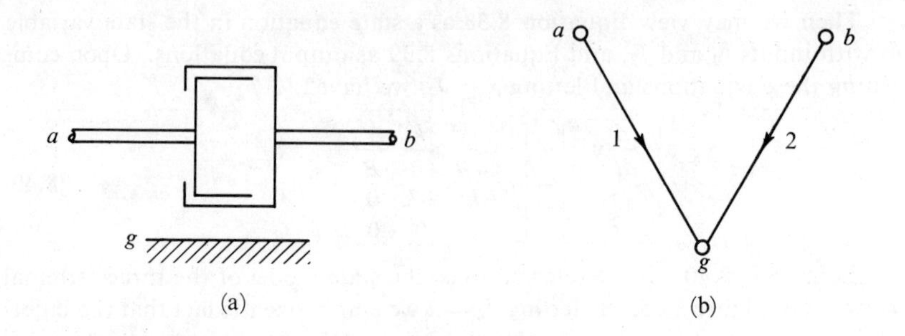

Fig. 8.16. *Rotational dashpot:* (a) *schematic;* (b) *terminal graph.*

terminals are identified on the component to which connections may be made: two shafts, labeled a and b, and the mechanical ground, g.

It is generally considered good practice to express the component characteristics in terms of directly identifiable physical properties of the component, called the *device parameters*. In other words, an effort should be made to involve the device parameters as directly as possible. For the rotational dashpot we can identify three device parameters:

J_1—inertia of first cup
J_2—inertia of second cup
B_{12}—relative friction coefficient

The three parameters are related to the terminal variables defined by the terminal graph of Figure 8.16 (b) in terms of the following equations:

$$\tau_1 = J_1\, d/dt\, \dot{\varphi}_1 \tag{8.42a}$$

$$\tau_2 = J_2\, d/dt\, \dot{\varphi}_2 \tag{8.42b}$$

$$\tau_{12} = B_{12}(\dot{\varphi}_1 - \dot{\varphi}_2) \tag{8.42c}$$

In view of these equations, it would be desirable to derive the terminal equations with the variables τ_1 and τ_2 explicit. Therefore, the suggested form is

$$\begin{bmatrix} \tau_1 \\ \tau_2 \end{bmatrix} = \begin{bmatrix} z_{11}(d/dt) & z_{12}(d/dt) \\ z_{21}(d/dt) & z_{22}(d/dt) \end{bmatrix} \begin{bmatrix} \dot{\varphi}_1 \\ \dot{\varphi}_2 \end{bmatrix} \tag{8.43}$$

These will be the short-circuit parameters. To determine the coefficients of the first column, the test condition $\dot{\varphi}_2 = 0$ is required and a driver $\dot{\varphi}_1$ is applied between terminals a and g, as shown in Figure 8.17. Since under the condition $\dot{\varphi}_2 = 0$ both τ_1 and τ_2 are measured, two torquemeters are connected in addition. Under the action of the driver, the first cup will rotate while the second remains locked. Thus, the following test results will occur:

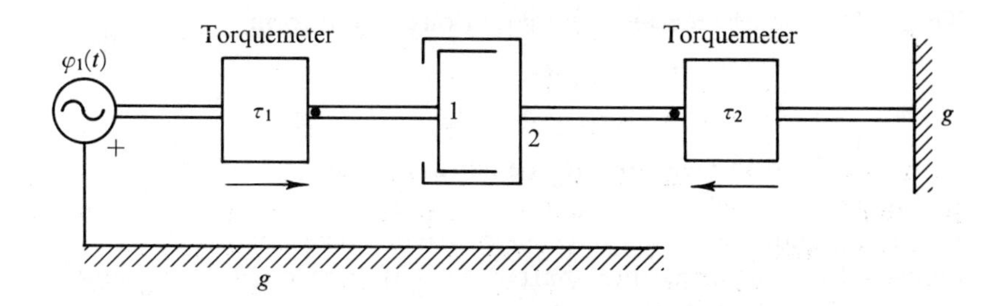

Fig. 8.17. *Test conditions for dashpot.*

$$\left.\begin{aligned}\tau_1 &= (J_1\, d/dt + B_{12})\dot{\varphi}_1 \\ \tau_2 &= -B_{12}\,\dot{\varphi}_1\end{aligned}\right]\dot{\varphi}_2 = 0$$

Note that the minus sign in the second result is a consequence of the orientation of the meter, which in turn is specified by the terminal graph. An entirely symmetrical setup results for the implementation of the test condition $\dot{\varphi}_1 = 0$. Hence, one may write immediately

$$\left.\begin{aligned}\tau_1 &= -B_{12}\,\dot{\varphi}_2 \\ \tau_2 &= (J_2\, d/dt + B_{12})\dot{\varphi}_2\end{aligned}\right\}\dot{\varphi}_1 = 0$$

Hence, a possible model for the dashpot is

$$\begin{bmatrix}\tau_1 \\ \tau_2\end{bmatrix} = \begin{bmatrix} J_1\, d/dt + B_{12} & -B_{12} \\ -B_{12} & J_2\, d/dt + B_{12}\end{bmatrix}\begin{bmatrix}\dot{\varphi}_1 \\ \dot{\varphi}_2\end{bmatrix} \tag{8.44}$$

These are the short-circuit parameters of the dashpot; as planned, they involve the device parameters in a most simple manner.

It is of course of interest to determine whether Equations 8.44 offer the most convenient form for the terminal representation of the dashpot. The present form may be changed in two ways: (1) the terminal graph; or (2) the form of the equations.

With regard to the first, for instance, we may attempt to determine a set of terminal equations associated with the terminal graph

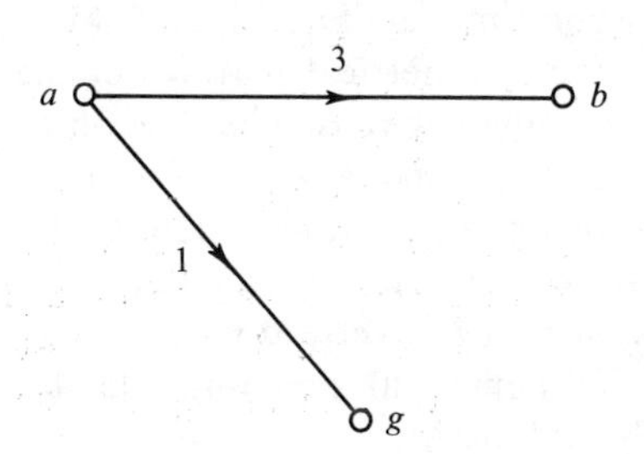

To do this, we assume terminal equations of the form

$$\begin{bmatrix} \tau_1 \\ \tau_3 \end{bmatrix} = \begin{bmatrix} z_{11}(d/dt) & z_{13}(d/dt) \\ z_{31}(d/dt) & z_{33}(d/dt) \end{bmatrix} \begin{bmatrix} \dot{\varphi}_1 \\ \dot{\varphi}_3 \end{bmatrix}$$

A test setup to measure the coefficients of the first column is shown in Figure 8.18. The test condition requires $\dot{\varphi}_3 = 0$, τ_1 and τ_3 to be measured, and $\dot{\varphi}_1(t)$ to be a specified driver. The condition $\dot{\varphi}_3 = 0$ is realized by short-circuiting shaft a to shaft b through a torquemeter. Upon excitation of the test system by $\dot{\varphi}_1(t)$, the meter will indicate that

$$\tau_1 = (J_1 + J_2)d/dt\,\dot{\varphi}_1$$
$$\tau_3 = -J_2\,d/dt\,\dot{\varphi}_1$$

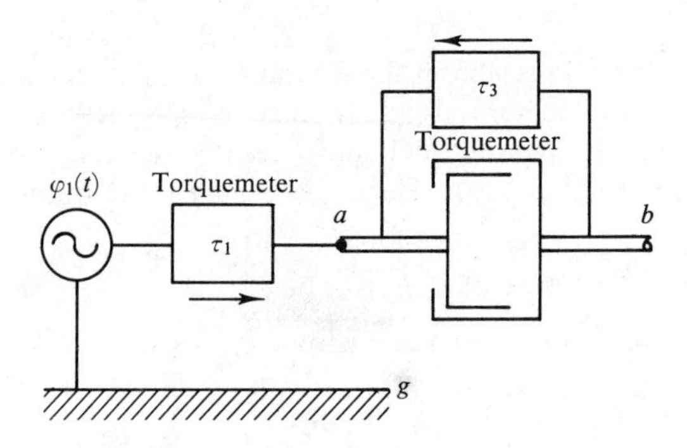

Fig. 8.18. *Test condition for dashpot.*

It is left as an exercise for the reader to select a suitable test setup to determine the coefficients of the second column. The complete model is derived as

$$\begin{bmatrix} \tau_1 \\ \tau_3 \end{bmatrix} = \begin{bmatrix} (J_1 + J_2)d/dt & -J_2\,d/dt \\ -J_2\,d/dt & J_2\,d/dt + B_{12} \end{bmatrix} \begin{bmatrix} \dot{\varphi}_1 \\ \dot{\varphi}_3 \end{bmatrix} \qquad \mathbf{(8.45)}$$

It is easily agreed that the first model, Equations 8.44, is more readily obtained than the second model, Equations 8.45. Furthermore, Equations 8.44 illustrate the symmetrical features of the component.

Alternate models to the above two may be obtained by investigating other forms for the terminal equations. For instance, one might be asked to determine the open-circuit parameters. To do this, one simply considers the inverse of Equations 8.44. With Equations 8.44 in the present form, however, the inverse does not exist, since division by a derivative has no mathematical meaning. If the equations are first transformed into the s-domain,

$$\begin{bmatrix} T_1 \\ T_2 \end{bmatrix} = \begin{bmatrix} J_1 s + B_{12} & -B_{12} \\ -B_{12} & J_2 s + B_{12} \end{bmatrix} \begin{bmatrix} \dot{\Phi}_1 \\ \dot{\Phi}_2 \end{bmatrix} \tag{8.46}$$

the inverse is easily obtained. It is

$$\begin{bmatrix} \dot{\Phi}_1 \\ \dot{\Phi}_2 \end{bmatrix} = \frac{1}{\Delta(s)} \begin{bmatrix} J_2 s + B_{12} & B_{12} \\ B_{12} & J_1 s + B_{12} \end{bmatrix} \begin{bmatrix} T_1 \\ T_2 \end{bmatrix} \tag{8.47}$$

where $\Delta(s) = s[(J_1 + J_2)B_{12} + J_1 J_2 s]$. Again, it is agreed that this variation in the component model is more cumbersome than the first form.

Alternatively, we may wish to derive the terminal characteristics of the rotational dashpot in terms of a state model. This may be done by conversion of the short-circuit parameter model, Equations 8.44, and the terminal graph of Figure 8.16 (b). Writing the terminal equations in derivative form,

$$\frac{d}{dt}\dot{\varphi}_1 = -B/J_1(\dot{\varphi}_1 - \dot{\varphi}_2) + \frac{1}{J_1}\tau_1$$

$$\frac{d}{dt}\dot{\varphi}_2 = -B/J_2(\dot{\varphi}_2 - \dot{\varphi}_1) + \frac{1}{J_2}\tau_2$$

Letting $\dot{\varphi} = x_1$ and $\dot{\varphi}_2 = x_2$, and adding the output equations

$$\dot{\varphi}_1 = x_1$$

$$\dot{\varphi}_2 = x_2$$

yields the state model

$$\begin{bmatrix} \frac{d}{dt}x_1 \\ \frac{d}{dt}x_2 \\ \hdashline \dot{\varphi}_1 \\ \dot{\varphi}_2 \end{bmatrix} = \begin{bmatrix} -B/J_1 & B/J_1 & 1/J_1 \\ B/J_2 & -B/J_2 & 1/J_2 \\ \hdashline 1 & 0 & 0 \\ 0 & 1 & 0 \end{bmatrix} \begin{bmatrix} x_1 \\ x_2 \\ \hdashline \tau_1 \\ \tau_2 \end{bmatrix} \tag{8.48}$$

The Transformer

The transformer is a four-terminal component. It consists of two coils of wire which are wound on a closed loop iron core, as shown in Figure 8.19.

In developing a mathematical model according to the terminal graph of Figure 8.19 (b), it is immediately evident that the variables v_3 and i_3 as defined by the element between b and d in the terminal graph are identically zero since the two coils are isolated from one another. Therefore, the terminal graph reduces to one containing two elements only. The transformer thus is an example of a component whose

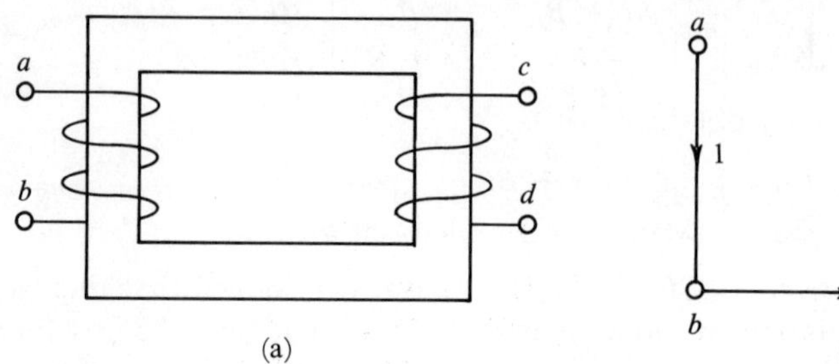

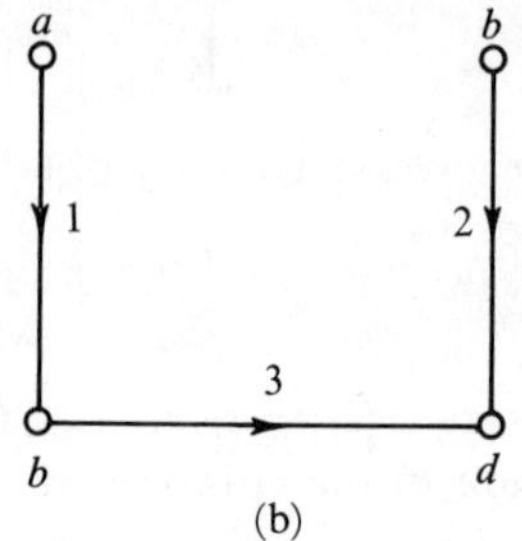

Fig. 8.19. *Transformer:* (a) *schematic;* (b) *terminal graph.*

terminal graph has less than the maximum possible number of elements. It is a two-port component.

The following device parameters may be identified:

R_1, L_1—resistance and inductance of coil 1
R_2, L_2—resistance and inductance of coil 2
M—mutual inductance between coil 1 and coil 2

In an effort to introduce these parameters into the terminal equations in the most direct manner, the open-circuit parameters are suggested as a possible format. One has

$$\begin{bmatrix} v_1 \\ v_2 \end{bmatrix} = \begin{bmatrix} z_{11}(d/dt) & z_{12}(d/dt) \\ z_{21}(d/dt) & z_{22}(d/dt) \end{bmatrix} \begin{bmatrix} i_1 \\ i_2 \end{bmatrix}$$

An experimental setup leading to the determination of the coefficients of the first column is shown in Figure 8.20. Two voltmeters are applied to measure v_1 and v_2; $i_1(t)$ is specified. The terminals c and d are open-circuited to satisfy the condition $i_2 = 0$.

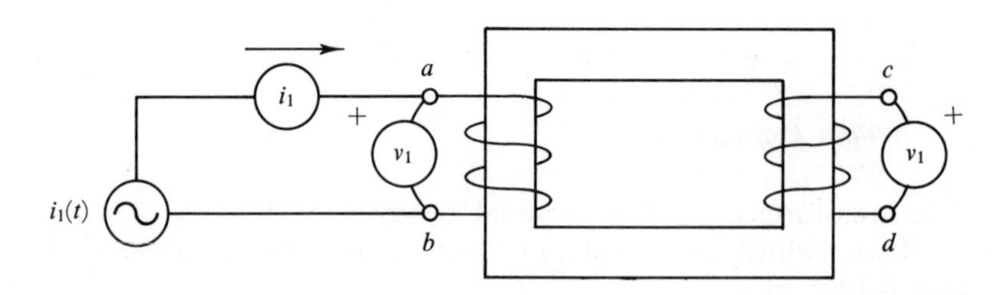

Fig. 8.20. *Experimental setup for transformer measurements.*

The information obtained is

$$\left.\begin{aligned} v_1 &= (R_1 + L_1\, d/dt) i_1 \\ v_2 &= M\, d/dt\, i_1 \end{aligned}\right\} i_2 = 0$$

And, by symmetry, one also has

$$\left.\begin{aligned} v_1 &= M\,d/dt\,i_2 \\ v_2 &= R_2 + L_2\,d/dt\,i_2 \end{aligned}\right\} i_1 = 0$$

Hence, all open-circuit parameters are easily identified from these experimental results and the terminal equations are

$$\begin{bmatrix} v_1 \\ v_2 \end{bmatrix} = \begin{bmatrix} R_1 + L_1\,d/dt & M\,d/dt \\ M\,d/dt & R_2 + L_2\,d/dt \end{bmatrix} \begin{bmatrix} i_1 \\ i_2 \end{bmatrix} \qquad \textbf{(8.49)}$$

The reader may wish to verify that this form is the most convenient obtainable.

Next, consider an alternate derivation of Equations 8.49 in order to permit a closer look at the interrelations between the device parameters. In this alternate approach we "tear" the transformer into two parts, as shown in Figure 8.21. We will then derive mathematical models for

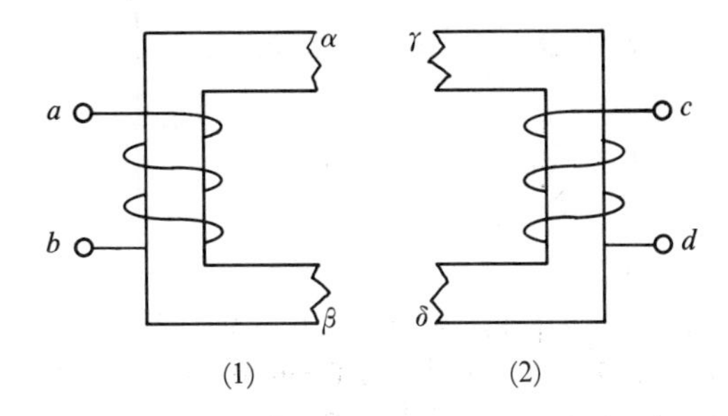

Fig. 8.21. *Transformer as an assembly of two parts.*

each part and later assemble the parts mathematically. Each part in itself is a four-terminal component and the terminal variables involved are voltage and current at one pair of terminals, flux λ and magneto-

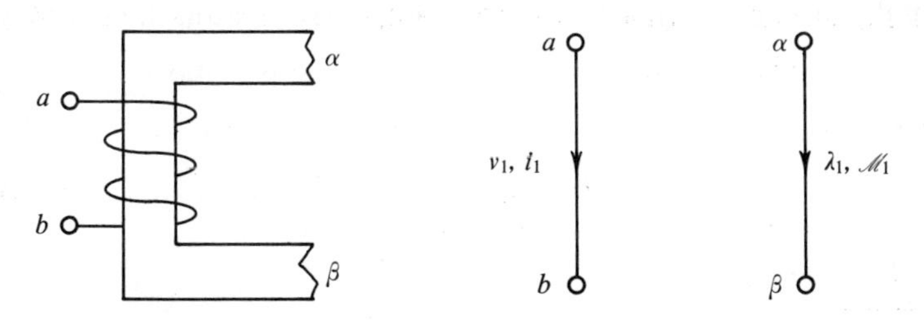

Fig. 8.22. *Halftransformer and terminal graph.*

motive force $\mathscr{M}$ at the other pair.* To establish the terminal equations of this component we investigate the relationship among these four variables. Figure 8.22 shows one half of the transformer and the terminal graph. In order to determine a suitable form for the terminal equations we consider the following device parameters:

resistance of the coil R_1
reluctance of the magnetic core $\mathscr{R}_1$
number of turns of coil n_1

These are related to the variables by the following equations:

$$\begin{bmatrix} v_1 \\ \mathscr{M}_1 \end{bmatrix} = \begin{bmatrix} R_1 & n_1 \dfrac{d}{dt} \\ -n_1 & \mathscr{R}_1 \end{bmatrix} \begin{bmatrix} i_1 \\ \lambda_1 \end{bmatrix} \tag{8.50}$$

It is left as an exercise to specify suitable test conditions to verify Equations 8.50. Similarly,

$$\begin{bmatrix} \mathscr{M}_2 \\ v_2 \end{bmatrix} = \begin{bmatrix} \mathscr{R}_2 & -n_2 \\ n_2 \dfrac{d}{dt} & R_2 \end{bmatrix} \begin{bmatrix} \lambda_2 \\ i_2 \end{bmatrix} \tag{8.51}$$

α, $\mathscr{M}_2$, λ_2, δ — c, v_2, i_2, d

Now combine Equations 8.50 and 8.51. We recognize that the terminal graphs of the two halftransformers are joined in a one-to-one correspondence with the physical components.

Since $\mathscr{M}$ is a through variable and λ an across variable, we have

$$\mathscr{M}_1 + \mathscr{M}_2 = 0 \tag{8.52a}$$

$$\lambda_1 = \lambda_2 \tag{8.52b}$$

These two equations express the assumption that the two half-trans formers are *perfectly coupled*;* hence our derivation will lead to a model which is called the *perfect transformer*. Combining Equations 8.52a with the second of Equations 8.50 and the first of Equations 8.51 yields

$$\mathscr{M}_1 + \mathscr{M}_2 = -n_1 i_1 + \mathscr{R}_1 \lambda_1 + \mathscr{R}_2 \lambda_2 - n_2 i_2 = 0$$

But $\lambda_1 = \lambda_2 = \lambda$, therefore

$$\lambda = \frac{n_1 i_1 + n_2 i_2}{\mathscr{R}_1 + \mathscr{R}_2} = \frac{n_1 i_1 + n_2 i_2}{\mathscr{R}} \tag{8.53}$$

where $\mathscr{R} = \mathscr{R}_1 + \mathscr{R}_2$.

* See Problem 2.4.
* This means that there is no flux loss.

Substituting Equation 8.53 into the remaining equations of Equations 8.50 and 8.51 yields the model

$$\begin{bmatrix} v_1 \\ v_2 \end{bmatrix} = \begin{bmatrix} R_1 + \dfrac{n_1^2}{\mathscr{R}}\dfrac{d}{dt} & \dfrac{n_1 n_2}{\mathscr{R}}\dfrac{d}{dt} \\ \dfrac{n_1 n_2}{\mathscr{R}}\dfrac{d}{dt} & R_2 + \dfrac{n_2^2}{\mathscr{R}}\dfrac{d}{dt} \end{bmatrix} \begin{bmatrix} i_1 \\ i_2 \end{bmatrix} \tag{8.54}$$

These equations constitute the mathematical model of a perfect transformer. The procedure used in deriving Equations 8.45 is characteristic of interconnecting two-ports. It is an important technique which will be investigated in greater detail in Chapter 11.

Upon comparing Equations 8.49 and 8.54, we can state the conditions for a perfect transformer in terms of the device parameters L_1, L_2 and M.

$$\left.\begin{aligned} L_1 &= \frac{n_1^2}{\mathscr{R}} \\ L_2 &= \frac{n_2^2}{\mathscr{R}} \\ M &= \frac{n_1 n_2}{\mathscr{R}} \end{aligned}\right] \tag{8.55}$$

These conditions may also be stated in an aggregate manner:

$$M^2 = L_1 L_2 \tag{8.56}$$

Let us consider one further simplification in the model of the transformer dealing with the effect of neglecting the properties of resistance and reluctance. To assume that resistance and reluctance are negligible we must set $R = 0$ and $\mathscr{R} = 0$. Setting $R = 0$ produces no problems. But the same is not true for $\mathscr{R}$. The difficulty may be avoided if we find a different form for the terminal equations. Let us first set $R_1 = R_2 = 0$ in Equation 8.54. This yields

$$\begin{bmatrix} v_1 \\ v_2 \end{bmatrix} = \begin{bmatrix} \dfrac{n_1^2}{\mathscr{R}}\dfrac{d}{dt} & \dfrac{n_1 n_2}{\mathscr{R}}\dfrac{d}{dt} \\ \dfrac{n_1 n_2}{\mathscr{R}}\dfrac{d}{dt} & \dfrac{n_2^2}{\mathscr{R}}\dfrac{d}{dt} \end{bmatrix} \begin{bmatrix} i_1 \\ i_2 \end{bmatrix}$$

Next, change these equations into hybrid format. To do this, take the Laplace transform, yielding

$$\begin{bmatrix} V_1 \\ V_2 \end{bmatrix} = \begin{bmatrix} \dfrac{n_1^2}{\mathscr{R}}s & \dfrac{n_1 n_2}{\mathscr{R}}s \\ \dfrac{n_1 n_2}{\mathscr{R}}s & \dfrac{n_2^2}{\mathscr{R}}s \end{bmatrix} \begin{bmatrix} I_1 \\ I_2 \end{bmatrix}$$

and the hybrid format is

$$\begin{bmatrix} V_1 \\ \\ I_2 \end{bmatrix} = \begin{bmatrix} 0 & +\dfrac{n_1}{n_2} \\ -\dfrac{n_1}{n_2} & \dfrac{\mathscr{R}}{n_2^2}s \end{bmatrix} \begin{bmatrix} I_1 \\ \\ V_2 \end{bmatrix}$$

Now letting $\mathscr{R} \to 0$ we have

$$\begin{bmatrix} V_1 \\ I_2 \end{bmatrix} = \begin{bmatrix} 0 & n_1/n_2 \\ -n_1/n_2 & 0 \end{bmatrix} \begin{bmatrix} I_1 \\ V_2 \end{bmatrix} \tag{8.57}$$

Equation 8.57 is the mathematical model of an *ideal* transformer. The matrix associated with this model is called a *skew-symmetric* matrix.

A component for which a mathematical model of the form illustrated by Equations 8.57 can be generated under ideal conditions is called an *ideal transducer*. We will investigate the characteristics of a few more components, many of which can be reduced to ideal transducer models. It will then be appropriate to examine the conditions that lead to the development of ideal transducers.

It is of interest to attempt the derivation of a state model for the transformer. Upon inspection of Equation 8.49 or 8.54, it is clear that these equations cannot be solved for the derivative terms. Therefore, a state model as such cannot be established for the transformer. We will return to this problem at a later time.

The Hydraulic Transformer

As the next example, examine the characteristics of a component called the *hydraulic transformer*, whose physical schematic is shown in Figure 8.23. The hydraulic transformer consists of a two-faced piston with cross-sectional areas A_1 and A_2 and mass M_p.

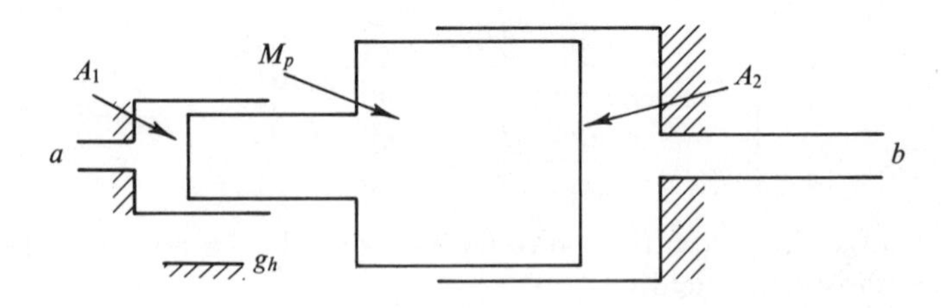

Fig. 8.23. *Hydraulic transformer.*

The terminal equations to be derived are associated with the terminal graph

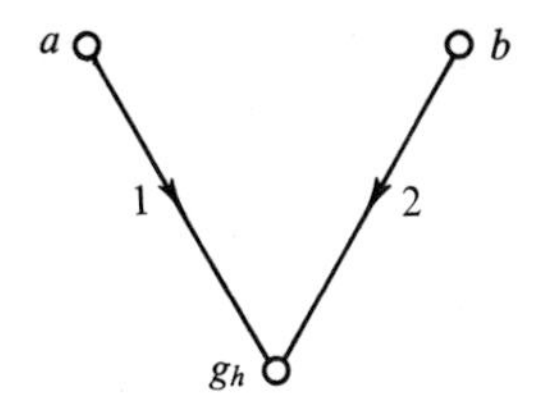

Thus, the terminal variables are p_1 and p_2, and $\dot{g}_1$ and $\dot{g}_2$; they represent the pressures and flows at ports a and b measured with respect to g_h, the hydraulic "ground" reference.

Perhaps the most difficult problem in the process of modeling the characteristics of an unfamiliar component is the choice of the form of the terminal equations. In the previous two examples, some guidance was provided by the obvious physical properties, corresponding to the so-called device parameters. Frequently, however, knowledge about other similar components offers some insight. We will rely on information of the latter kind to help select a suitable form for the terminal equations in this example. As was seen in the case of the electrical transformer, the hybrid form provided an excellent means for emphasizing the "transforming" features of the component in directly relating the output through variable to the input through variable, and the input across variable to the output across variable. On the basis of the similar types of components involved, we will assume a hybrid form. Thus, we select the equations in the form

$$\begin{bmatrix} p_1 \\ \dot{g}_2 \end{bmatrix} = \begin{bmatrix} h_{11}(d/dt) & h_{12}(d/dt) \\ h_{21}(d/dt) & h_{22}(d/dt) \end{bmatrix} \begin{bmatrix} \dot{g}_1 \\ p_2 \end{bmatrix}$$

Appropriate test conditions to determine the coefficients of the first column are shown in Figure 8.24. Provision is made for the condition

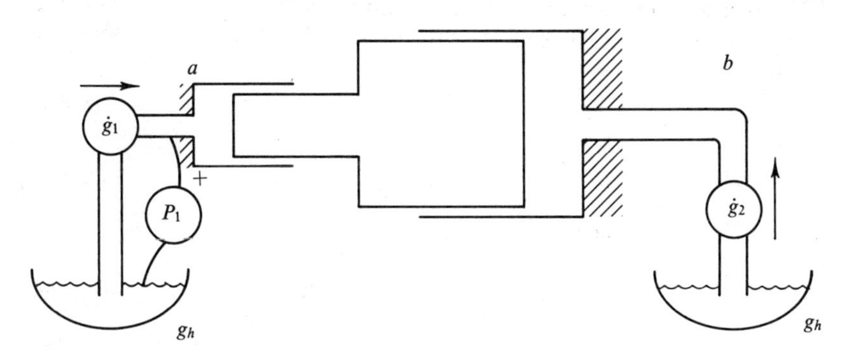

Fig. 8.24. *Test setup for hydraulic transformer.*

$p_2 = 0$ by short-circuiting port b through a flowmeter to the reference g_h. Furthermore, a flow driver $\dot{g}_1(t)$ and a pressure-meter are connected from a to g_h. This test condition is referred to as a "no-load" condition since zero pressure is developed at b during the test. Measurements will show the following relations:

$$p_1 = (R_1 + I_1\, d/dt)\dot{g}_1 \qquad \textbf{(8.58a)}$$

$$\dot{g}_2 = -A_2/A_1\, \dot{g}_1 \qquad \textbf{(8.58b)}$$

where R_1 is an aggregate fluid resistance and I_1 is an aggregate fluid inertance. Both of these terms collectively include *all* frictional effects and inertial effects present in the component as measured between a and g_h.

We now alter the test conditions to obtain the second column coefficients as shown in Figure 8.25.

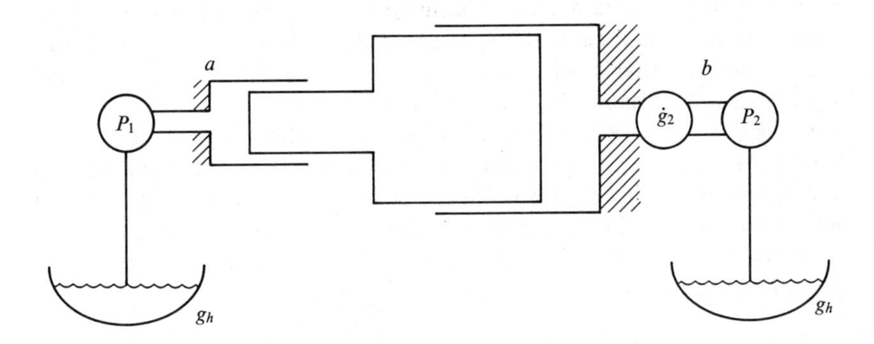

Fig. 8.25. *Test setup for hydraulic transformer.*

The test condition $\dot{g}_1 = 0$ specifies blocking of any flow at port a. Therefore an attempt to force fluid through port b under action of pressure p_2 must fail as long as the fluid is incompressible. We have, therefore,

$$\dot{g}_2 = 0 \qquad \textbf{(8.58c)}$$

and

$$p_1 = A_2/A_1\, p_2 \qquad \textbf{(8.58d)}$$

The complete model is

$$\begin{bmatrix} p_1 \\ \dot{g}_2 \end{bmatrix} = \begin{bmatrix} R_1 + I_1\, d/dt & A_2/A_1 \\ -A_2/A_1 & 0 \end{bmatrix} \begin{bmatrix} \dot{g}_1 \\ p_2 \end{bmatrix} \qquad \textbf{(8.59)}$$

An interesting result develops when the component is idealized (all resistive and inertive properties are neglected). One simply has

$$\begin{bmatrix} p_1 \\ \dot{g}_2 \end{bmatrix} = \begin{bmatrix} 0 & A_2/A_1 \\ -A_2/A_1 & 0 \end{bmatrix} \begin{bmatrix} \dot{g}_1 \\ p_2 \end{bmatrix} \quad \textbf{(8.60)}$$

which are the equations representative of an ideal transducer.

It is left to the reader as a problem to show that in Equations 8.59

$$R_1 = R_h + R_p/A_1^2 \quad \textbf{(8.61a)}$$

$$I_1 = I_h + M_p/A_1^2 \quad \textbf{(8.61b)}$$

where R_h is hydraulic resistance, R_p is mechanical friction, I_h is fluid inertance, and M_p is mass of piston.

It can be easily shown that a state model for the hydraulic transformer is given by

$$\begin{bmatrix} \frac{d}{dt}x \\ \dot{g}_1 \\ \dot{g}_2 \end{bmatrix} = \begin{bmatrix} -R_1/I_1 & 1/I_1 & -A_2/A_1 \\ 1 & 0 & 0 \\ -A_2/A_1 & 0 & 0 \end{bmatrix} \begin{bmatrix} x \\ p_1 \\ p_2 \end{bmatrix} \quad \textbf{(8.62)}$$

Gear Box

Having studied the characteristics of a number of components and ways of describing them, we may now assume some familiarity with the basic considerations of the modeling process. The gear box will be used to demonstrate the possibility of encountering awkward situations when the general guidelines established in the previous examples are ignored. At this point, unsuccessful attempts to achieve a convenient model should not be disturbing; it is likely that a suitable model can be found.

Consider now the gear box whose schematic is shown in Figure 8.26 (a). The terminal graph is selected as shown in Figure 8.26 (b).

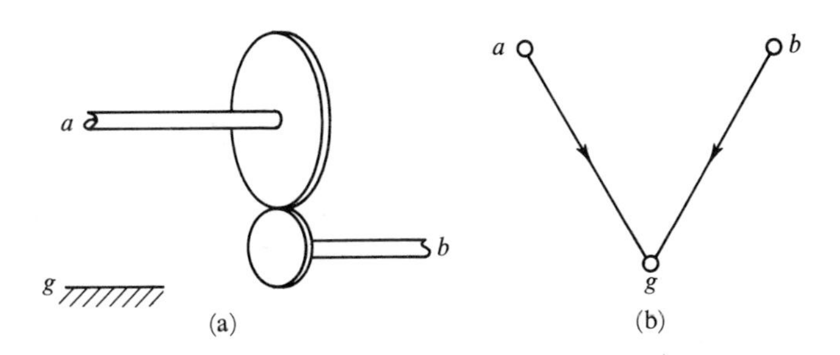

Fig. 8.26. *Gear box:* (a) *schematic;* (b) *terminal graph.*

Without first giving any consideration to the physical properties of the components, the following form of equations is attempted:

$$\begin{bmatrix} \varphi_1 \\ \varphi_2 \end{bmatrix} = \begin{bmatrix} z_{11}(d/dt) & z_{12}(d/dt) \\ z_{21}(d/dt) & z_{22}(d/dt) \end{bmatrix} \begin{bmatrix} \tau_1 \\ \tau_2 \end{bmatrix}$$

A maximum of two terminal equations are required since the terminal graph contains two elements. The appropriate test conditions of the measurement of the coefficients of the first column require that no load be applied to the shaft marked *b*, or $\tau_2 = 0$, and that τ_1 be specified. However, any attempt made at measuring φ_1 and φ_2 as a function of τ_1,

$$\varphi_1 = F_1(\tau_1)$$
$$\varphi_2 = F_2(\tau_2)$$

will be impossible as differential equations due to the presence of inertia and friction. The assumption of a different form for the terminal equations is therefore advised. Instead of the open-circuit parameters, we will try to determine the short-circuit parameters as indicated by Equations 8.63,

$$\begin{bmatrix} \tau_1 \\ \tau_2 \end{bmatrix} = \begin{bmatrix} w_{11}(d/dt) & w_{12}(d/dt) \\ w_{21}(d/dt) & w_{22}(d/dt) \end{bmatrix} \begin{bmatrix} \dot{\varphi}_1 \\ \dot{\varphi}_2 \end{bmatrix} \qquad \textbf{(8.63)}$$

Figure 8.27 shows the test condition necessary to determine $w_{11}(d/dt)$ and $w_{12}(d/dt)$. Shaft *b* is blocked so that $\dot{\varphi}_2 = 0$ is satisfied. In addition, a velocity driver, $\dot{\varphi}_1(t)$, and two torquemeters to measure τ_1 and τ_2 are applied. According to the form of Equations 8.63, the following functional relations are to be measured:

$$\left.\begin{array}{l} \tau_1 = G_1(\dot{\varphi}_1) \\ \tau_1 = G_2(\dot{\varphi}_1) \end{array}\right\} \dot{\varphi}_2 = 0$$

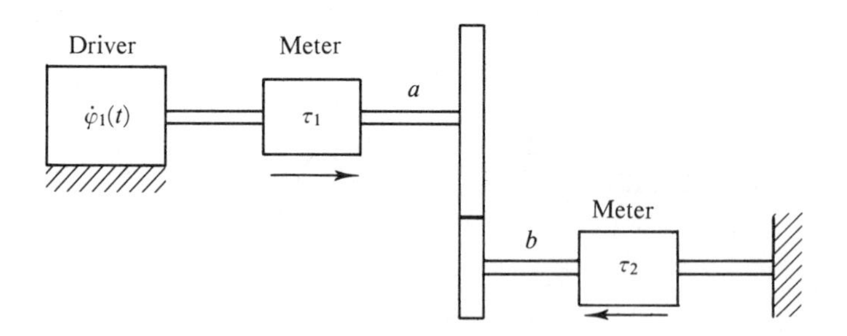

Fig. 8.27. *Test condition for gear box.*

An inspection of the test condition will reveal that only trivial relations can be determined, since both shaft torques cannot be related to $\dot{\varphi}_1(t)$ when $\dot{\varphi}_2 = 0$—nothing will move.

So far, the two attempted forms for the terminal equations have failed to yield a meaningful mathematical model for the component. Consider now a hybrid model of the form

$$\begin{bmatrix} \tau_1 \\ \dot{\varphi}_1 \end{bmatrix} = \begin{bmatrix} g_{11}(d/dt) & g_{12}(d/dt) \\ g_{21}(d/dt) & g_{22}(d/dt) \end{bmatrix} \begin{bmatrix} \dot{\varphi}_1 \\ \tau_2 \end{bmatrix} \tag{8.64}$$

We select test conditions according to Figure 8.28 to determine that

$$\left. \begin{aligned} \tau_1 &= (J_1\, d/dt + B_1)\dot{\varphi}_1 \\ \dot{\varphi}_2 &= -k_{21}\,\dot{\varphi}_1 \end{aligned} \right\} \tau_2 = 0 \tag{8.65a}$$

and

$$\left. \begin{aligned} \tau_1 &= +k_{21}\,\tau_2 \\ \dot{\varphi}_2 &= 0 \end{aligned} \right\} \dot{\varphi}_1 = 0 \tag{8.65b}$$

where J_1 is aggregate inertia at shaft *a*, B_1 is aggregate friction at shaft *a*, and k_{21} is a constant.

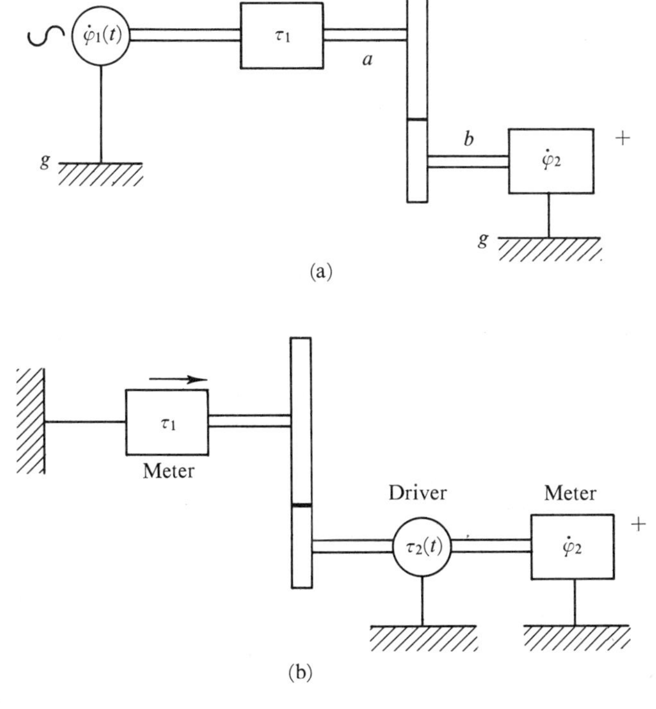

Fig. 8.28. *Test conditions for gear box:* (a) *first column;* (b) *second column.*

The complete model is thus given as

$$\begin{bmatrix} \tau_1 \\ \dot{\varphi}_2 \end{bmatrix} = \begin{bmatrix} J_1 \, d/dt + B_1 & +k_{21} \\ -k_{21} & 0 \end{bmatrix} \begin{bmatrix} \dot{\varphi}_1 \\ \tau_2 \end{bmatrix} \tag{8.66}$$

With the hybrid form, the test conditions are easily realized. Indeed, the resulting relations as given by Equations 8.66 are very closely related to the device parameters J_a and J_b, inertias of gear a and gear b, and N_2/N_1, gear ratio. It is left to the reader to show that

$$J_1 = J_a + \left(\frac{N_1}{N_2}\right)^2 J_b \tag{8.67a}$$

and

$$k_{21} = N_2/N_2 \tag{8.67b}$$

As with previous components, we will investigate the component under ideal conditions (friction and inertia neglected). The ideal transducer property of the gear box is immediately evident from Equations 8.68:

$$\begin{bmatrix} \tau_1 \\ \dot{\varphi}_2 \end{bmatrix} = \begin{bmatrix} 0 & +N_2/N_1 \\ -N_2/N_1 & 0 \end{bmatrix} \begin{bmatrix} \dot{\varphi}_1 \\ \tau_2 \end{bmatrix} \tag{8.68}$$

If, at the beginning of this development, it had been recognized that the primary function of the gear box is to couple two shafts, the immediate choice of equation form should have been the hybrid form.

8.6 Summary of Linear Models of Multiterminal Components

This section contains a summary of the mathematical models of system components most frequently encountered in the study of systems. The survey is limited to components for which linear models are a reasonable approximation. The model will include all significant physical properties. A second model, where appropriate, shows a reduced version of the first by neglecting all loss effects. Development of the models is not discussed. The reader is encouraged to investigate suitable test conditions to determine the component model coefficients in each case.

1. Autotransformer

Complete model:

$$\begin{bmatrix} v_1 \\ v_2 \end{bmatrix} = \begin{bmatrix} R_1 + L_1 \, d/dt & M_{12} \, d/dt \\ M_{12} \, d/dt & R_2 + L_2 \, d/dt \end{bmatrix} \begin{bmatrix} i_1 \\ i_2 \end{bmatrix} \tag{8.69a}$$

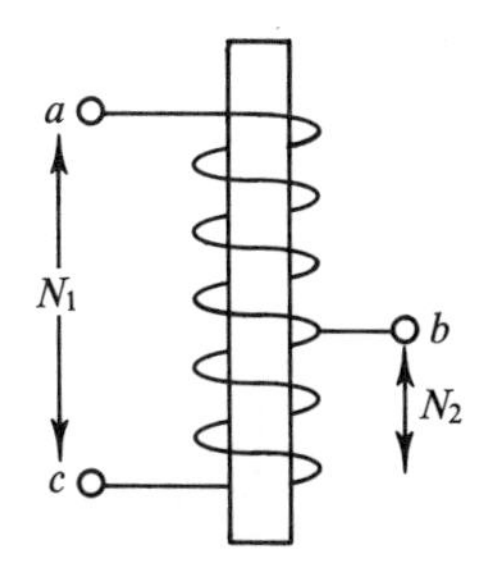

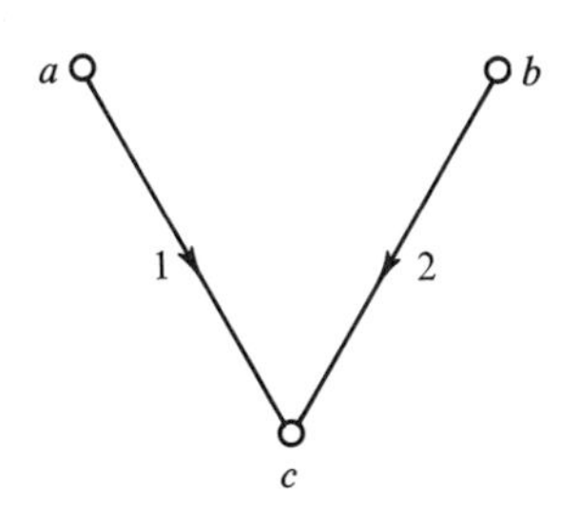

Ideal model:

$$\begin{bmatrix} i_1 \\ v_2 \end{bmatrix} = \begin{bmatrix} 0 & -N_2/N_1 \\ N_2/N_1 & 0 \end{bmatrix} \begin{bmatrix} v_1 \\ i_2 \end{bmatrix} \qquad \textbf{(8.69b)}$$

2. *Three Terminal T-Network*

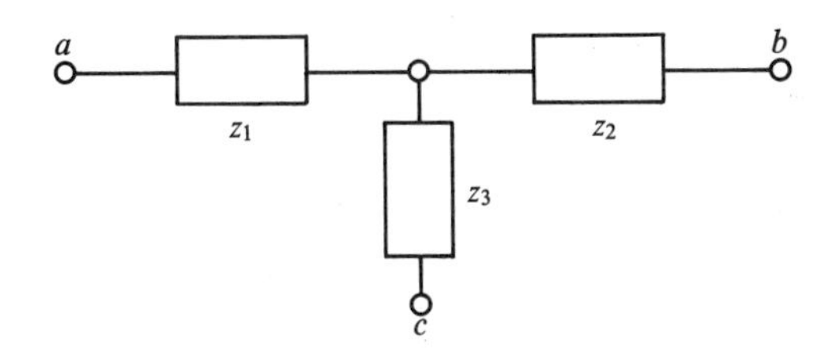

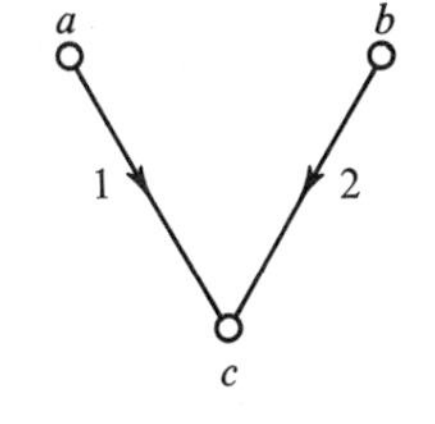

$$\begin{bmatrix} v_1 \\ v_2 \end{bmatrix} = \begin{bmatrix} Z_1 + Z_3 & Z_3 \\ Z_3 & Z_2 + Z_3 \end{bmatrix} \begin{bmatrix} i_1 \\ i_2 \end{bmatrix} \qquad \textbf{(8.70)}$$

Z_1, Z_2, Z_3 are impedances.

3. *Three Terminal Pi-Network*

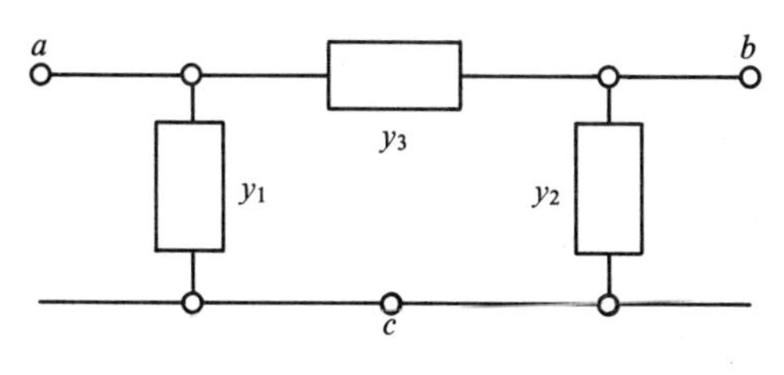

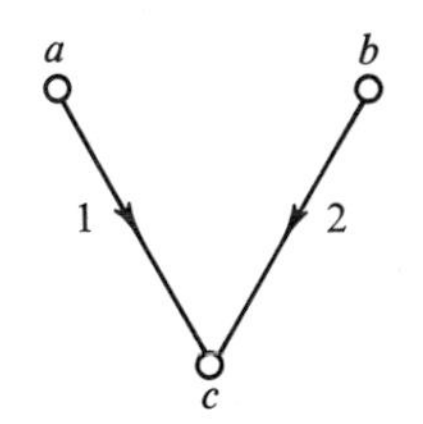

$$\begin{bmatrix} i_1 \\ i_2 \end{bmatrix} = \begin{bmatrix} Y_1 + Y_3 & -Y_3 \\ -Y_3 & Y_2 + Y_3 \end{bmatrix} \begin{bmatrix} v_1 \\ v_2 \end{bmatrix} \qquad \textbf{(8.71)}$$

Y_1, Y_2, Y_3 are admittances.

4. *Hydraulic Cylinder*

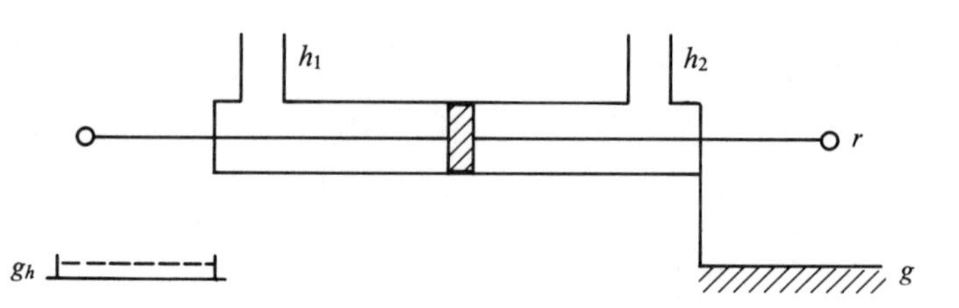

Complete model:

$$\begin{bmatrix} \dot{g}_1 \\ \dot{g}_2 \\ f_3 \end{bmatrix} = \begin{bmatrix} C\,d/dt & 0 & A_p \\ 0 & C\,d/dt & -A_p \\ -A_p & A_p & M_p\,d/dt + B_p \end{bmatrix} \begin{bmatrix} p_1 \\ p_2 \\ \dot{\delta}_3 \end{bmatrix} \tag{8.72a}$$

where C is piston chamber capacity, A_p is piston area, M_p is piston mass, and B_p is seal friction.

Ideal model:

$$\begin{bmatrix} \dot{g}_1 \\ f_2 \end{bmatrix} = \begin{bmatrix} 0 & A_p \\ -A_p & 0 \end{bmatrix} \begin{bmatrix} p_1 \\ \dot{\delta}_2 \end{bmatrix} \tag{8.72b}$$

5. *Hydraulic Capacitor*

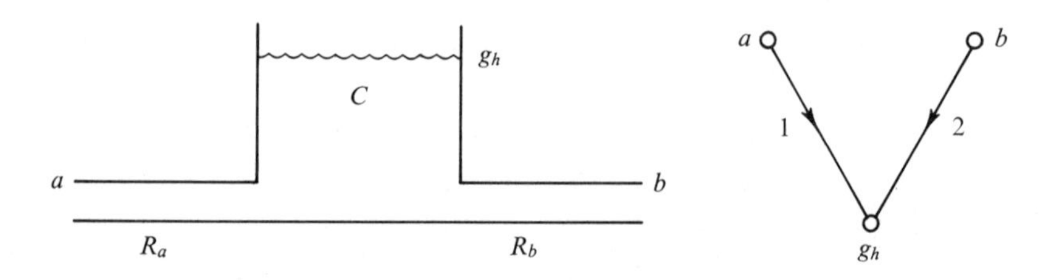

$$\begin{bmatrix} P_1 \\ \\ P_2 \end{bmatrix} = \begin{bmatrix} R_a + \dfrac{1}{Cs} & \dfrac{1}{Cs} \\ \dfrac{1}{Cs} & R_b + \dfrac{1}{Cs} \end{bmatrix} \begin{bmatrix} \dot{G}_1 \\ \\ \dot{G}_2 \end{bmatrix} \tag{8.73}$$

where R_a, R_b are inlet resistances and C is chamber capacity.

6. *Mechanical Lever*

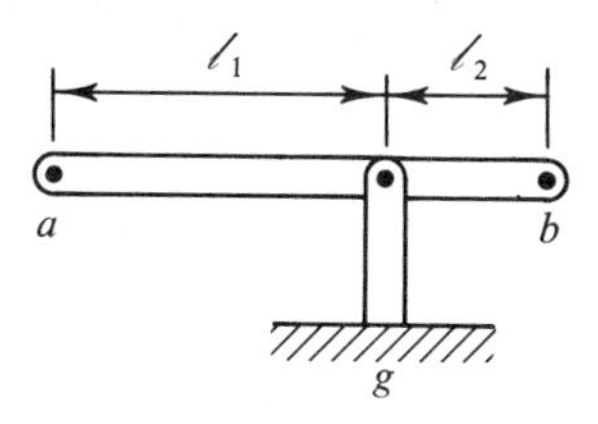

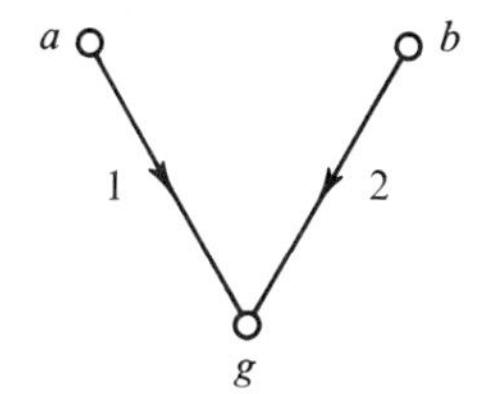

Complete model:

$$\begin{bmatrix} f_1 \\ \delta_2 \end{bmatrix} = \begin{bmatrix} M_1 d^2/dt^2 + B_1 d/dt & l_2/l_1 \\ -l_2/l_1 & \dfrac{1}{k_2} \end{bmatrix} \begin{bmatrix} \delta_1 \\ f_2 \end{bmatrix} \tag{8.74a}$$

where M_1 is total inertia of the lever as seen from terminal a, B_1 is pivot friction as seen from terminal a, and k_2 is elastic coefficient of the lever as seen from terminal b.

Ideal model:

$$\begin{bmatrix} f_1 \\ \delta_2 \end{bmatrix} = \begin{bmatrix} 0 & l_2/l_1 \\ -l_2/l_1 & 0 \end{bmatrix} \begin{bmatrix} \delta_1 \\ f_2 \end{bmatrix} \tag{8.74b}$$

7. *Shaft and Pulley*

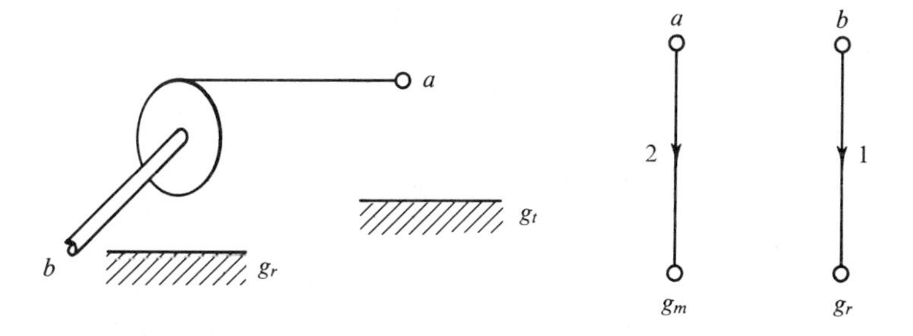

$$\begin{bmatrix} \tau_1 \\ \delta_2 \end{bmatrix} = \begin{bmatrix} J_1 d^2/dt^2 & R \\ -R & R^2/k_2 \end{bmatrix} \begin{bmatrix} \varphi_1 \\ f_2 \end{bmatrix} \tag{8.75a}$$

where J_1 is inertia of shaft and pulley, R is radius of pulley, and k_2 is shaft spring constant.

Ideal model:

$$\begin{bmatrix} \tau_1 \\ \delta_2 \end{bmatrix} = \begin{bmatrix} 0 & R \\ -R & 0 \end{bmatrix} \begin{bmatrix} \varphi_1 \\ f_2 \end{bmatrix} \tag{8.75b}$$

8.7 General Properties of Component Models

In the preceding sections characteristics of a number of typical multiterminal components have been developed or presented. Although most components are physically distinct, certain common mathematical features have become evident. It will be useful to recognize these common features for modeling procedures.

A component with predominantly linear characteristics is modeled as a set of linear algebraic and/or differential equations written in matrix format. The matrix format is helpful in determining the characteristics of the component in an orderly fashion. The entries of the matrix are determined as a result of "pseudo" experimental measurements, which we do not actually carry out, but simulate in thought. Component characteristics are determined under two different test conditions that are physically realizable: (1) open-circuit test conditions, and (2) short-circuit conditions.

In general, combinations of test conditions must be specified for multiterminal components. We call test conditions homogeneous if they are all of the same type, heterogeneous if they are not. Measurements performed under the two types of test conditions will result in a variety of matrix formats, some of which have been classified in Section 8.5. The matrices associated with the terminal equation can be further classified with the specific objective of relating physical component properties to the matrix formats. Our discussion will be confined to two-port components, such as all three-terminal and some four-terminal components.* Appropriate extensions to components with more terminals are certainly possible, and are left as exercises for the reader.

Table 8.1 summarizes the five basic forms of terminal equations.

TABLE 8.1. *Two-port component representations*

Equation	Representation
$\begin{bmatrix} x_1 \\ x_2 \end{bmatrix} = \begin{bmatrix} z_{11} & z_{12} \\ z_{21} & z_{22} \end{bmatrix} \begin{bmatrix} y_1 \\ y_2 \end{bmatrix}$	Open-circuit parameters
$\begin{bmatrix} y_1 \\ y_2 \end{bmatrix} = \begin{bmatrix} w_{11} & w_{12} \\ w_{21} & w_{22} \end{bmatrix} \begin{bmatrix} x_1 \\ x_2 \end{bmatrix}$	Short-circuit parameters

* Later developments will offer further evidence in establishing the terminal representations of two-port components as decidedly the most frequently encountered form.

$$\begin{bmatrix} x_1 \\ y_2 \end{bmatrix} = \begin{bmatrix} h_{11} & h_{12} \\ h_{21} & h_{22} \end{bmatrix} \begin{bmatrix} y_1 \\ x_2 \end{bmatrix} \qquad \text{Hybrid } h\text{-parameters}$$

$$\begin{bmatrix} y_1 \\ x_2 \end{bmatrix} = \begin{bmatrix} g_{11} & g_{12} \\ g_{21} & g_{22} \end{bmatrix} \begin{bmatrix} x_1 \\ y_2 \end{bmatrix} \qquad \text{Hybrid } g\text{-parameters}$$

$$\begin{bmatrix} \frac{d}{dt}\mathbf{x} \\ y_1 \\ x_2 \end{bmatrix} = \begin{bmatrix} \mathbf{A} & \mathbf{B}_1 & \mathbf{B}_2 \\ \mathbf{C}_1 & d_{12} & d_{12} \\ \mathbf{C}_2 & d_{21} & d_{22} \end{bmatrix} \begin{bmatrix} \mathbf{x} \\ x_1 \\ y_2 \end{bmatrix} \qquad \text{State model}$$

Reciprocal Component

Reciprocal components are recognized by inspecting the open-circuit or short-circuit parameters for the condition

$$z_{21} = z_{12} \tag{8.76a}$$

or

$$w_{21} = w_{12} \tag{8.76b}$$

Thus, the matrix associated with a reciprocal component is typically of the form

$$\begin{bmatrix} z_{11} & z_{12} \\ z_{12} & z_{22} \end{bmatrix} \tag{8.77a}$$

or

$$\begin{bmatrix} w_{11} & w_{12} \\ w_{12} & w_{22} \end{bmatrix} \tag{8.77b}$$

The matrix is *symmetric* for a reciprocal component.

Example 8.5. Examine the terminal representation of a transformer when the complete model is considered. We have, from Equations 8.49,

$$\begin{bmatrix} v_1 \\ v_2 \end{bmatrix} = \begin{bmatrix} R_1 + L_1 d/dt & M d/dt \\ M d/dt & R_2 + L_2 d/dt \end{bmatrix} \begin{bmatrix} i_1 \\ i_2 \end{bmatrix}$$

The matrix clearly satisfies the condition of Equation 8.76a; hence, the transformer is a reciprocal component.

Example 8.6. Show that the mechanical lever is a reciprocal component. In order to investigate the lever for reciprocity, it appears necessary to develop a model in either the open- or short-circuit parameters. To obtain either form directly from measurements, it is necessary to consider the lever non-rigid. If we agree to stretch our imaginations a little, we will attempt to achieve such a model.

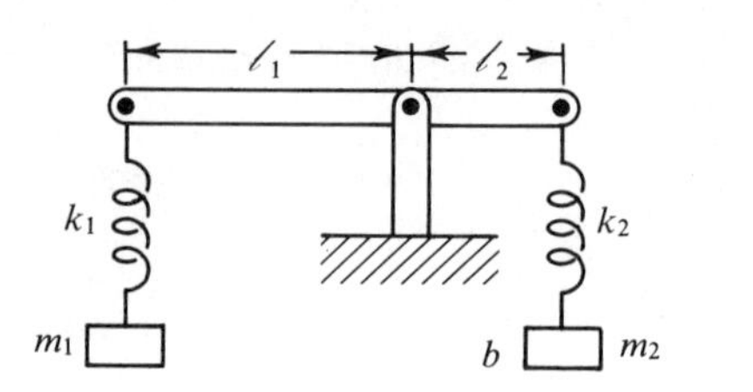

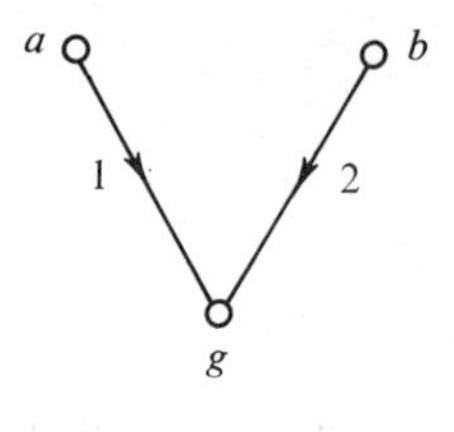

Fig. 8.29. *"Flexible" lever:* (a) *schematic;* (b) *terminal graph.*

In consideration of the device parameters (mass, spring constant, lever ratio), the appropriate choice is the short-circuit parameters, that is,

$$\begin{bmatrix} f_1 \\ f_2 \end{bmatrix} = \begin{bmatrix} w_{11}(d/dt) & w_{12}(d/dt) \\ w_{21}(d/dt) & w_{22}(d/dt) \end{bmatrix} \begin{bmatrix} \delta_1 \\ \delta_2 \end{bmatrix} \tag{8.78}$$

In order to more easily include the non-rigid effects in the model, we will view the lever as an assembly of components, as shown in Figure 8.29. Any attempt to determine the expressions for the matrix coefficients for Equation 8.78 from inspection, however, results in failure because of our inability to clearly simulate the experiment in thought.

It is still possible to obtain a model for the lever in terms of the short-circuit parameters if the hybrid model given by Equations 8.74a is taken as the starting point. We simply solve the second equation for f_2 and substitute the result into the first equation, obtaining

$$\begin{bmatrix} f_1 \\ f_2 \end{bmatrix} = \begin{bmatrix} M_1 d^2/dt^2 + B_1 d/dt + (l_2/l_1)^2 k_2 & l_2/l_1 k_2 \\ l_2/l_1 k_2 & k_2 \end{bmatrix} \begin{bmatrix} \delta_1 \\ \delta_2 \end{bmatrix} \tag{8.79}$$

The form of Equations. 8.79 offers sufficient support for the claims that the lever is a reciprocal component.

A reciprocal component may also be recognized by inspection of the hybrid parameters. Consider the determination of the h-parameters from the open-circuit parameters. This is easily accomplished if it is possible to invert the bottom equation of the reciprocal form

$$\begin{bmatrix} x_1 \\ x_2 \end{bmatrix} = \begin{bmatrix} z_{11} & z_{12} \\ z_{12} & z_{22} \end{bmatrix} \begin{bmatrix} y_1 \\ y_2 \end{bmatrix}$$

We obtain

$$\begin{bmatrix} x_1 \\ y_2 \end{bmatrix} = \begin{bmatrix} z_{11} - \dfrac{z_{12}^2}{z_{22}} & \dfrac{z_{12}}{z_{22}} \\ -\dfrac{z_{12}}{z_{22}} & \dfrac{1}{z_{22}} \end{bmatrix} \begin{bmatrix} y_1 \\ x_2 \end{bmatrix} \tag{8.80}$$

From Equations 8.80, the condition of reciprocity may be specified. In terms of the h-parameters it is

$$h_{12} = -h_{21} \tag{8.81a}$$

Similarly, one may show for the g-parameters that the condition

$$g_{12} = -g_{21} \tag{8.81b}$$

must be satisfied by a reciprocal component. In terms of Equations 8.81, it is readily shown that in Example 8.5 the lever is a reciprocal component. Equations 8.81, however, are *not* sufficient to establish the reciprocity of a component. An explanation for this restriction will be offered later, through the properties of a perfect coupler.

Symmetrical Component

A symmetrical component is a special case of a reciprocal component. In addition to the conditions of Equation 8.77, it is required that

$$z_{11} = z_{22} \tag{8.82a}$$

or

$$w_{11} = w_{22} \tag{8.82b}$$

Physically, we interpret these conditions as an absence of any distinction between the ports of the component. The orientation of the component in a system connection is arbitrary.

Example 8.7. A transformer with identical windings is a symmetrical component. Although the concept of a symmetrical component is of very little practical importance, its theoretical value is significant. A very powerful test for the validity of a developed model for a reciprocal component is offered by physically simulating conditions for symmetry. The equations must bear out the assumed symmetry condition. We can apply this notion immediately by checking the model of the lever.

Example 8.8. Test the validity of Equations 8.79 by a symmetry test. When the lever is physically symmetrical, the significance of the subscripts on the parameters vanishes and Equations 8.79 reduce to

$$\begin{bmatrix} f_1 \\ f_2 \end{bmatrix} = \begin{bmatrix} Md^2/dt^2 + Bd/dt + k & k \\ k & k \end{bmatrix} \begin{bmatrix} \delta_1 \\ \delta_2 \end{bmatrix} \tag{8.83}$$

But Equations 8.83 fail to verify the hypothesized symmetry of the lever! The discrepancy must be immediately explained as an inaccurately established model for the lever in hybrid parameters. Our physical intuition has failed us. The need for more effective techniques of modeling is indicated here. Such techniques will be developed after we have outlined formulation procedures for systems involving multiterminal components. Reciprocal and symmetric components cannot be identified from inspection of the state model.

Transducers

A transducer is normally defined as a component which transmits energy from one system to another. A few examples would be the potentiometer (mechanical to electrical), the motor (electrical to mechanical) and the loudspeaker (electrical to mechanical to acoustical). A transducer can be defined more broadly as any component whose terminal equations can be formulated by the two×two matrix,

$$\begin{bmatrix} L_{11}(d/dt) & N \\ -N & L_{22}(d/dt) \end{bmatrix}$$

where $L_{11}(d/dt)$ and $L_{22}(d/dt)$ are differential operators whose coefficients are dependent on the physical properties of the component, and N is a constant depending upon the geometric properties of the component.

This form may occur in any of the four possible directly measurable two-port component models. Two examples of transducers are the following components: (a) Lever, g-parameters, Equations 8.74; (b) Hydraulic cylinder, short-circuit parameters, Equations 8.72.

Note that if both diagonal entries in the matrix of a transducer are not zero, then the transducer may be modeled as a reciprocal component. As an example, the reader is referred to Equations 8.79, which represent the lever as a reciprocal component. The diagonal entries in the terminal equations of a transducer are functions of the physical properties of a component (such as mass friction and elasticity in a mechanical component). Therefore, whether or not they will be accounted for in the modeling process will depend upon the importance of these properties. If a transducer is modeled with diagonal entries taken as zero, the model is called an ideal transducer.

Ideal Transducer

The ideal transducer is characterized by terminal equations whose matrix is of the form

$$\begin{bmatrix} 0 & N \\ -N & 0 \end{bmatrix}$$

The matrix is skew-symmetric. Examples of an ideal transducer are given by the perfect transformer

$$\begin{bmatrix} i_1 \\ v_2 \end{bmatrix} = \begin{bmatrix} 0 & n_2/n_1 \\ -n_2/n_1 & 0 \end{bmatrix} \begin{bmatrix} v_1 \\ i_2 \end{bmatrix} \quad \textbf{(8.57)}$$

or the ideal shaft and pulley

$$\begin{bmatrix} \tau_1 \\ \delta_2 \end{bmatrix} = \begin{bmatrix} 0 & R \\ -R & 0 \end{bmatrix} \begin{bmatrix} \varphi_1 \\ f_2 \end{bmatrix} \quad \textbf{(8.75)}$$

The fact that ideal transducers are characterized by a skew-symmetric matrix is most useful in the modeling of such components. Nevertheless, the skew-symmetry of ideal transducers is occasionally most puzzling to the student. For that reason, consider this additional evidence in support of this characteristic through a consideration of the power function of an ideal transducer.

The power function for an n-port component is defined as

$$p(t) = \sum_{k=1}^{n} x_{p_k}(t) \cdot y_{p_k}(t) \tag{8.84}$$

where $x_p(t)$ is the principal system across variable and $y_p(t)$ is the principal system through variable. Thus, the power function is the sum of the products formed by the pairs of across and through variables associated by the n ports of the component. The power function for two-port components may be formed in a variety of ways through use of column matrices formed by the component variables. With $n = 2$ in Equation 8.84, we write

$$p(t) = x_1 \cdot y_1 + x_2 \cdot y_2 \tag{8.85}$$

Equation 8.85 may be obtained as a result of the following combinations:

$$[y_1 \quad x_2]\begin{bmatrix} x_1 \\ y_2 \end{bmatrix}, \quad [x_1 \quad y_2]\begin{bmatrix} y_1 \\ x_2 \end{bmatrix}, \quad [x_1 \quad x_2]\begin{bmatrix} y_1 \\ y_2 \end{bmatrix}, \quad [y_1 \quad y_2]\begin{bmatrix} x_1 \\ x_2 \end{bmatrix}$$

For the ideal transducer the power function must vanish, since all physical properties relating to energy dissipation or storage have been neglected in the modeling process. Consider now a component which is modeled as

$$\begin{bmatrix} x_1 \\ y_2 \end{bmatrix} = \begin{bmatrix} 0 & N_{12} \\ N_{21} & 0 \end{bmatrix} \begin{bmatrix} y_1 \\ x_2 \end{bmatrix} \tag{8.86}$$

If Equations 8.86 are the terminal equations of an ideal transducer, the power function should vanish. Hence,

$$\begin{aligned} p(t) &= [y_1 \quad x_2]\begin{bmatrix} x_1 \\ y_2 \end{bmatrix} = [y_1 \quad x_2]\begin{bmatrix} 0 & N_{12} \\ N_{21} & 0 \end{bmatrix}\begin{bmatrix} y_1 \\ x_2 \end{bmatrix} \\ &= x_2 N_{21} y_1 + y_1 N_{12} x_2 \\ &= x_2 y_1 (N_{21} + N_{12}) = 0 \end{aligned}$$

so that

$$N_{21} = -N_{12} \tag{8.87}$$

This substantiates the fact that the matrix of an ideal transducer is skew symmetric.

Bilateral Component

All two-port components whose matrix equations have non-zero entries on all off-diagonal positions are bilateral. A bilateral component may be utilized in a system connection in either direction, resulting in a meaningful system performance.

Unilateral Component

A two-port component is said to be unilateral when one (but not both) of the off-diagonal entries vanishes. An example of such a component has not been discussed so far. Obviously, a unilateral component cannot be connected arbitrarily in a system. Typical unilateral components will have terminal equations of the form

$$\begin{bmatrix} x_1 \\ x_2 \end{bmatrix} = \begin{bmatrix} z_{11}(d/dt) & 0 \\ z_{21}(d/dt) & z_{22}(d/dt) \end{bmatrix} \begin{bmatrix} y_1 \\ y_2 \end{bmatrix} \quad \textbf{(8.88)}$$

or

$$\begin{bmatrix} x_1 \\ y_2 \end{bmatrix} = \begin{bmatrix} h_{11}(d/dt) & 0 \\ h_{21}(d/dt) & h_{22}(d/dt) \end{bmatrix} \begin{bmatrix} y_1 \\ x_2 \end{bmatrix} \quad \textbf{(8.89)}$$

Examples of unilateral components will be presented later.

8.8 Analytical Derivation of Terminal Representations

In the preceding sections we have stressed the derivation of mathematical models of n-terminal components through application of suitable test conditions. The test conditions simulated the application of drivers and measurement of terminal variables. The resulting terminal equations, which are mathematical statements of the relations between the measured variables and drivers, were an expression of the physical and geometric properties of the component. This modeling procedure represents the only means of handling components that are fundamentally constructed as an integral union of physical and geometric properties.

Let us turn our attention now to the analytical derivation of mathematical models of subsystems that are generated by the interconnection of two-terminal components. Specifically, we are interested in treating a system of components as a multiterminal component, as indicated by the schematic of Figure 8.30. A number of two-terminal components are shown (symbolically) in a functional interconnection. We hypothesize this assembly of components to be part of a large system. We wish to use this assembly as a three-terminal component as shown in Figure 8.30 to be completely equivalent to the actual system. We are therefore interested in determining a functional relationship involving two pairs of terminal variables in terms of the component characteristics of

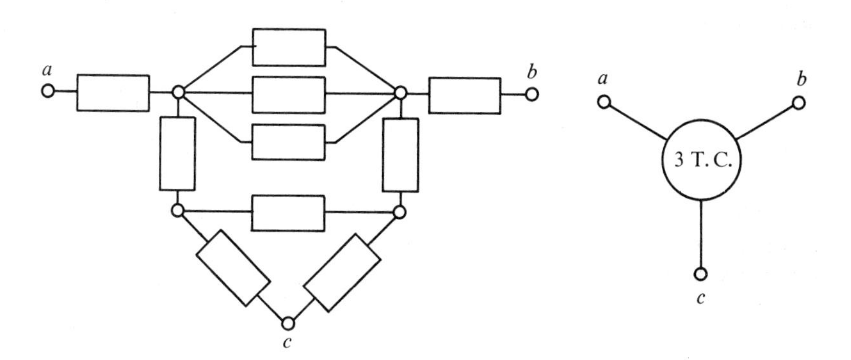

Fig. 8.30. *Subassembly.*

the subassembly. The terminal variables may be defined by any one of three terminal graphs. We will choose here a terminal graph taking vertex c as the common terminal. Following procedures similar in

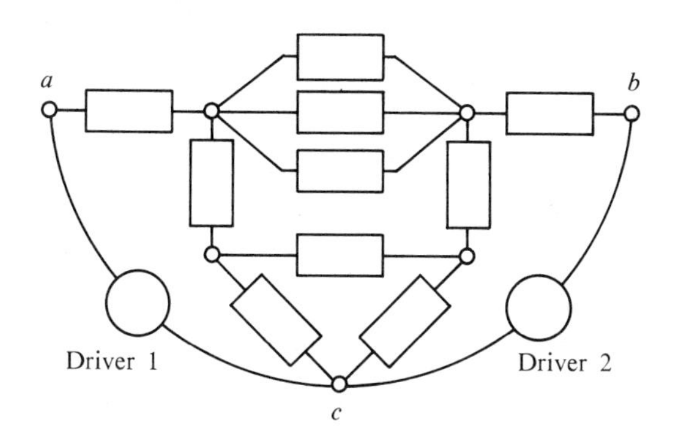

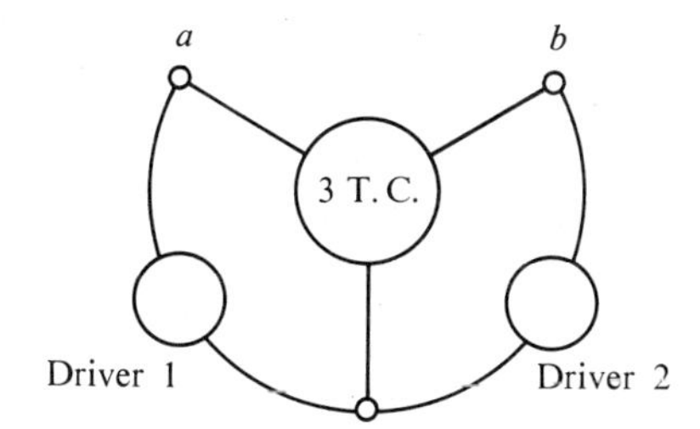

Fig. 8.31. *Application of drivers to calculate equivalent representation of system.*

principle to those used in earlier sections, we apply drivers at the ports of the three terminals a, b, and c of both the subsystem and the three-terminal components, as shown in Figure 8.31.

We then calculate the associated covariables of the drivers, utilizing mesh and node formulation techniques. This will be possible as long as both drivers are of the same type, either both across or both through variables. This analytical task is carried out using the system graphs of Figure 8.32. Elements 1 and 2 specify the variables associated with the drivers, while elements 3 and 4 constitute the desired terminal graph.

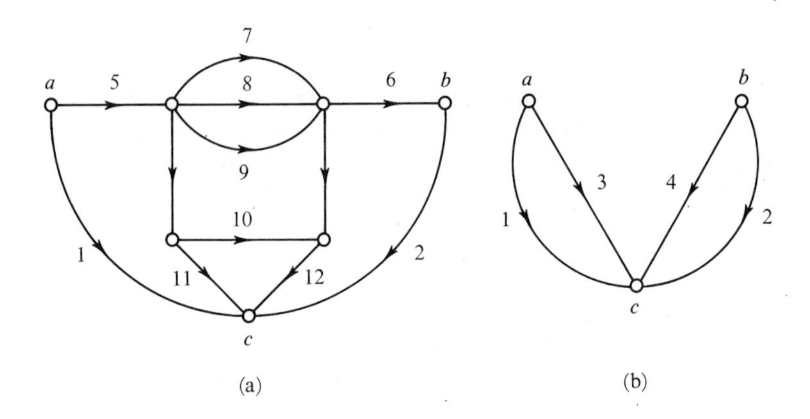

Fig. 8.32. *System graph of* (a) *system and drivers,* (b) *three-terminal equivalent component and drivers.*

Equivalency is established when the covariables of the drivers, identified by elements 1 and 2, are identically related for both the system and the three-terminal component. A variety of examples will illustrate the procedure.

Example 8.9. Develop a mathematical model of the mechanical system shown in Figure 8.33 (a) that will properly represent the system as a three-terminal component according to Figure 8.33 (b). Systems graphs are shown in Figure 8.34. Note the correspondence between drivers represented by elements 6 and 7.

Some consideration must be given to the choice of drivers. If they are taken as through drivers, the through variables of elements 6 and 7 are specified and our task is to formulate a set of equations to determine the associated across variables. The result will then appear in the form indicated by Equations 8.90,

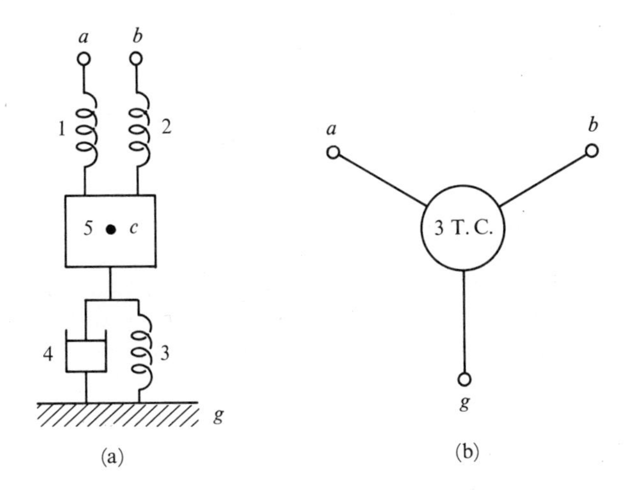

Fig. 8.33. *Mechanical system:* (a) *schematic;* (b) *three-terminal equivalent.*

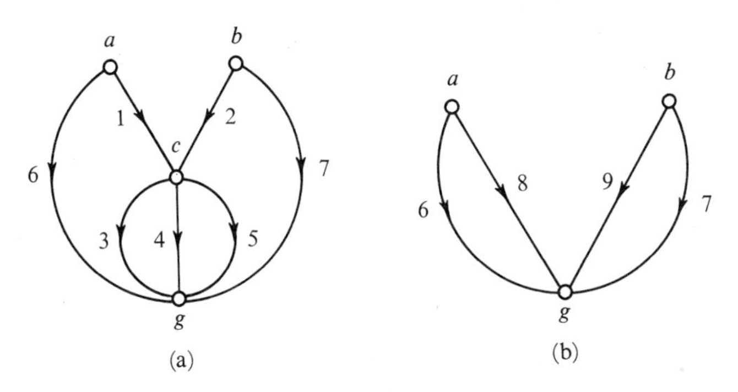

Fig. 8.34. *System graph:* (a) *system and drivers;* (b) *terminal graph and drivers.*

$$\begin{bmatrix} \Delta_6 \\ \Delta_7 \end{bmatrix} = \begin{bmatrix} Z_{11} & Z_{12} \\ Z_{21} & Z_{22} \end{bmatrix} \begin{bmatrix} F_6 \\ F_7 \end{bmatrix} \tag{8.90}$$

They represent an open-circuit parameter model for the equivalent three-terminal component. However, since Equations 8.90 are to be derived analytically, they must be interpreted as a set of mesh equations involving an impedance matrix. It is then realized that in the formulation process leading to that result the component equations are explicitly expressed in the across variable. An identical argument may be made upon interchanging the role of the across and through variables.

The choice of the drivers must therefore be based upon the following three criteria: (a) most convenient form of terminal equations of components; (b) formulation process resulting in least number of simultaneous equations; and (c) final form of desired terminal equations. A judicious application of these three criteria in the choice of drivers will prove to be of great advantage.

The desired terminal representation may be derived in two ways.

Method I, *Node formulation.* There are three nodes. Two of the node variables are known when 6 and 7 are selected as across drivers. The node equations are written from Figure 8.34(a).

$$\begin{bmatrix} k_1 & 0 & -k_1 \\ 0 & k_2 & -k_2 \\ -k_1 & -k_2 & k_1 + k_2 + k_3 + M_3 s^3 + B_4 s \end{bmatrix} \begin{bmatrix} \Delta_a \\ \Delta_b \\ \Delta_c \end{bmatrix} = - \begin{bmatrix} F_6 \\ F_7 \\ 0 \end{bmatrix} \tag{8.91}$$

In Equations 8.91 we find that

$$\begin{bmatrix} \Delta_a \\ \Delta_b \end{bmatrix} = \begin{bmatrix} \Delta_6 \\ \Delta_7 \end{bmatrix} \tag{8.92}$$

In addition, the submatrix

$$\begin{bmatrix} F_6 \\ F_7 \end{bmatrix}$$

contains the covariables of the drivers, which we want to calculate in terms of the drivers only. A set of equations involving just those variables is obtained upon eliminating Δ_c from Equations. 8.91. Solving for Δ_c from the bottom equation of Equations 8.91,

$$\Delta_c = \frac{1}{k_1 + k_2 + Y(s)} \begin{bmatrix} k_1 & k_2 \end{bmatrix} \begin{bmatrix} \Delta_a \\ \Delta_b \end{bmatrix} \tag{8.93}$$

where $y(s) = k_3 + M_5 s^2 + B_4 s$. We substitute Equations 8.93 and 8.92 into 8.91 and obtain

$$\begin{bmatrix} k_1 & 0 \\ 0 & k_2 \end{bmatrix} \begin{bmatrix} \Delta_6 \\ \Delta_7 \end{bmatrix} + \begin{bmatrix} -k_1 \\ -k_2 \end{bmatrix} \left\{ \frac{1}{k_1 + k_2 + Y(s)} \begin{bmatrix} k_1 & k_2 \end{bmatrix} \begin{bmatrix} \Delta_6 \\ \Delta_7 \end{bmatrix} \right\} = - \begin{bmatrix} F_6 \\ F_7 \end{bmatrix}$$

or

$$\frac{1}{k_1 + k_2 + y(s)} \begin{bmatrix} k_1 k_2 + k_1 Y(s) & -k_1 k_2 \\ -k_1 k_2 & k_1 k_2 + k_2 Y(s) \end{bmatrix} \begin{bmatrix} \Delta_6 \\ \Delta_7 \end{bmatrix} = - \begin{bmatrix} F_6 \\ F_7 \end{bmatrix} \tag{8.94}$$

The interrelation between the variables of the drivers and the final terminal graph is obtained from the graph of Figure 8.35(b),

$$\begin{bmatrix} F_8 \\ F_9 \end{bmatrix} = - \begin{bmatrix} F_6 \\ F_7 \end{bmatrix} \quad \text{and} \quad \begin{bmatrix} \Delta_8 \\ \Delta_9 \end{bmatrix} = \begin{bmatrix} \Delta_6 \\ \Delta_7 \end{bmatrix} \tag{8.95}$$

When the change in variables as indicated by Equations 8.95 is perfomed on Equations 8.94, we obtain

$$\begin{bmatrix} F_8 \\ F_9 \end{bmatrix} = \frac{1}{k_1 + k_2 + Y(s)} \begin{bmatrix} k_1 k_2 + k_1 Y(s) & -k_1 k_2 \\ -k_1 k_2 & k_1 k_2 + k_2 Y(s) \end{bmatrix} \begin{bmatrix} \Delta_8 \\ \Delta_9 \end{bmatrix} \tag{8.96}$$

This is the final form of the terminal equations as obtained through node formulation.

Method II, *Mesh formulation.* For mesh formulation, it is expedient to regard components 3, 4 and 5 as a parallel combination. Therefore, only two meshes remain in the system graph. A reduced system graph displaying the orientation of the mesh forces F_a and F_b is shown in Figure 8.35.* Elements 6 and 7 represent through drivers.

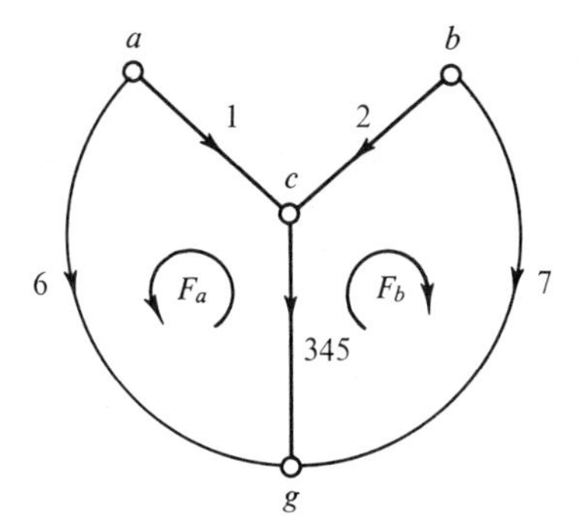

Fig. 8.35. *Reduced system graph with mesh force orientation.*

The mesh equations are

$$\begin{bmatrix} \dfrac{1}{k_1} + \dfrac{1}{Y(s)} & \dfrac{1}{Y(s)} \\ \dfrac{1}{Y(s)} & \dfrac{1}{k_2} + \dfrac{1}{Y(s)} \end{bmatrix} \begin{bmatrix} F_a \\ F_b \end{bmatrix} = - \begin{bmatrix} \Delta_6 \\ \Delta_7 \end{bmatrix} \tag{8.97}$$

where $Y(s) = k_3 + B_4 s + M_5 s^2$. The mesh forces are related to the specified drivers by

$$\begin{bmatrix} F_a \\ F_b \end{bmatrix} = \begin{bmatrix} F_6 \\ F_7 \end{bmatrix}$$

In addition, through use of Equations. 8.95, we again relate the information obtained through application of the drivers and expressed in terms of variables defined by elements 6 and 7 to the final terminal graph variables to obtain,

$$\begin{bmatrix} \Delta_8 \\ \Delta_9 \end{bmatrix} = \frac{1}{Y(s)} \begin{bmatrix} \dfrac{k_1 + Y(s)}{k_1} & 1 \\ 1 & \dfrac{k_2 + Y(s)}{k_2} \end{bmatrix} \begin{bmatrix} F_8 \\ F_9 \end{bmatrix} \tag{8.98}$$

This is the final form of the terminal equations obtained through mesh formulation.

---

* The orientation of the mesh variables is contrary to the previously established convention of making all mesh variables positive in the clockwise direction. For the purpose of deriving terminal representations, it is expedient to orient the mesh variables of driver circuits in accordance with the orientation of the drivers. All other mesh variables may still be taken as positive in the clockwise direction.

We may choose as the terminal representation of the mechanical system Equations 8.96 or Equations 8.98 in connection with the terminal graph of Figure 8.35. The first set of equations is in the form of a short-circuit parameter model, while the second is in terms of an open-circuit parameter model. Since the same terminal graph is used in either case, the terminal variables are identical. Hence, the matrices of Equations 8.96 and 8.98 are inverses of one another. This fact may be readily verified.

It will be of benefit to review the major steps leading to the results in the last example. It is evident that the procedure utilized in the development of the equivalent representation is a special case of the general formulation procedures presented in Chapter 6. On this basis, we view the derivation leading to Equations 8.96 as a node formulation problem with an equation count of one,

$$v - 1 - n_x = 4 - 1 - 2 = 1$$

The count of one has the significance that only one unknown has to be solved. The applied drivers were chosen as across drivers. Had they been chosen as through drivers, the node equation count would be three, resulting in a considerable increase in effort. We further note that the co-variables of the drivers are immediately available as a result of the formulation procedure.

The derivation of Equations 8.98 is viewed as a mesh formulation problem with an equation count of zero,

$$e - v + 1 - n_y = 5 - 4 + 1 - 2 = 0$$

The zero count implies that no equations have to be inverted. Had the drivers been chosen as across drivers, the count would be increased by two.

On the basis of this discussion we are able to make the following observations regarding the formulation of equivalent representations of subsystems consisting of passive two-terminal components.

Method I, *Node formulation.*

1. Node formulation yields a set of equations in the form

$$\begin{bmatrix} \mathbf{Y}_d \\ 0 \end{bmatrix} + \begin{bmatrix} \mathbf{W}_{11} & \mathbf{W}_{12} \\ \mathbf{W}_{21} & \mathbf{W}_{22} \end{bmatrix} \begin{bmatrix} \mathbf{X}_b \\ \mathbf{X}_n \end{bmatrix} = 0 \qquad \textbf{(8.99)}$$

where the subscript d denotes variables associated with drivers and subscript n denotes node variable. The order of $\mathbf{X}_d$ and $\mathbf{Y}_d$ is equal to the number of ports of the terminal representation and the order of $\mathbf{X}_n$ is given by the equation count

$$v - 1 - n_{xd}$$

2. The node variables $\mathbf{X}_n$ are eliminated from Equation 8.99 by

$$\mathbf{X}_n = -\mathbf{W}_{22}^{-1} \quad \mathbf{W}_{21} \quad \mathbf{X}_d \qquad \textbf{(8.100)}$$

3. The drivers are related to the terminal variables by

$$\mathbf{Y}_d = -\mathbf{Y}_t \qquad \text{and} \qquad \mathbf{X}_d = \mathbf{X}_t$$

where t denotes terminal variable.

4. The final model is given by

$$\mathbf{Y}_t = (\mathbf{W}_{11} - \mathbf{W}_{12}\mathbf{W}_{22}^{-1}\mathbf{W}_{21})\mathbf{X}_t \tag{8.101}$$

or the form

$$\mathbf{Y} = \mathbf{W}\mathbf{X} \tag{8.102}$$

a short-circuit representation.

5. In the formulation process, the drivers are chosen as across drivers.
6. All component equations are explicit in the through variable.

Method II, *Mesh formulation.*

1. Mesh formulation yields a set of equations in the form

$$\begin{bmatrix} \mathbf{X}_d \\ 0 \end{bmatrix} + \begin{bmatrix} \mathbf{Z}_{11} & \mathbf{Z}_{12} \\ \mathbf{Z}_{21} & \mathbf{Z}_{22} \end{bmatrix} \begin{bmatrix} \mathbf{Y}_d \\ \mathbf{Y}_m \end{bmatrix} = 0 \tag{8.103}$$

where the subscript d denotes variables associated with drivers and m denotes mesh variable. The order of $\mathbf{X}_d$ and $\mathbf{Y}_d$ is equal to the number of ports of the terminal representation and the order of $\mathbf{Y}_m$ is given by the equation count

$$e - v + 1 - n_{yd}$$

2. The mesh variables $\mathbf{Y}_m$ are eliminated from Equation 8.103 by

$$\mathbf{Y}_m = -\mathbf{Z}_{22}^{-1}\mathbf{Z}_{21}\mathbf{Y}_d \tag{8.104}$$

3. The drivers are related to the terminal variables by

$$\mathbf{Y}_d = -\mathbf{Y}_t \qquad \text{and} \qquad \mathbf{X}_d = \mathbf{X}_t$$

where t denotes terminal variables.

4. The final model is given by

$$\mathbf{X}_t = (\mathbf{Z}_{11} - \mathbf{Z}_{12}\mathbf{Z}_{22}^{-1}\mathbf{Z}_{21})\mathbf{Y}_t \tag{8.105}$$

or the form

$$\mathbf{X} = \mathbf{Z}\mathbf{Y} \tag{8.106}$$

an open circuit representation.

5. In the formulation process, the drivers are chosen as through drivers.
6. All component equations are explicit in the across variable.

These general observations provide answers to the questions raised at the beginning of Example 8.9. The concept of a terminal representation for a subassembly of components may in some cases be successfully applied in obtaining a mathematical model for a multiterminal component. Certain multiterminal components may be viewed as an assembly of two-terminal components, each representing a single physical property. When this can be clearly established, the analytical formulation techniques may be successfully exploited in the modeling of such a component. Consider an example.

Example 8.10. Obtain the mathematical model for a hydraulic capacitor (Equations 8.73) by analytical techniques.

We may view the hydraulic capacitor as consisting of the tank and the fluid resistances of the entrance ports. Under these circumstances, the multiterminal component consists of an assembly of three two-terminal components, as shown in Figure 8.36.

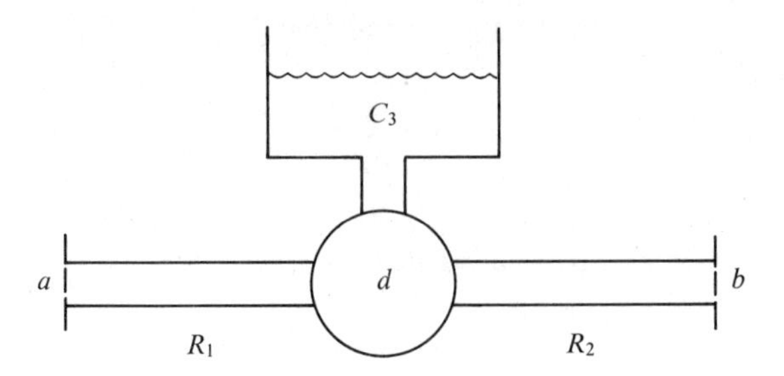

Fig. 8.36. *Hydraulic capacitor as an assembly of two-terminal components.*

Equations 8.73 are given in terms of the open circuit parameter. This suggests that we apply flow drivers and follow mesh formulation. We begin by drawing the system graph of components and drivers, as shown in Figure 8.37(a).

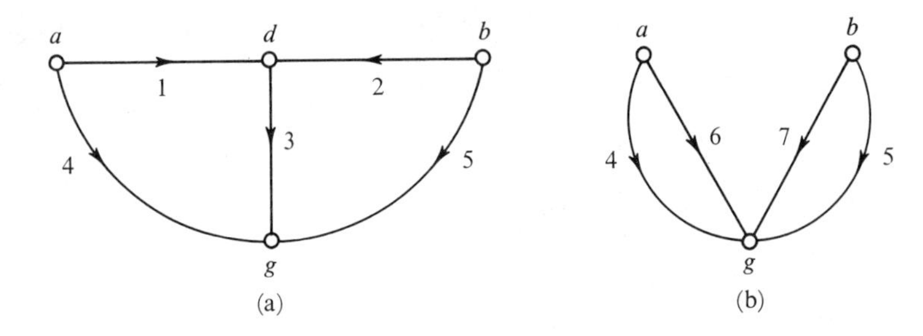

Fig. 8.37. *System graph of* (a) *component and drivers,* (b) *terminal graph and drivers.*

The component equations must be given as

$$\left.\begin{aligned} P_1 &= R_1\dot{G}_1 \\ P_2 &= R_2\dot{G}_2 \\ P_3 &= \frac{1}{C_3 s}\dot{G}_3 \end{aligned}\right] \tag{8.107}$$

The equation count is

$$e - v + 1 - 2 = 0$$

(The zero implies that *no* elimination of variables is required in the derivation.) The mesh equations are

$$\begin{bmatrix} P_4 \\ \\ P_5 \end{bmatrix} + \begin{bmatrix} R_1 + \dfrac{1}{C_3 s} & \dfrac{1}{C_3 s} \\ \dfrac{1}{C_3 s} & R_2 + \dfrac{1}{C_3 s} \end{bmatrix} \begin{bmatrix} \dot{G}_4 \\ \\ \dot{G}_5 \end{bmatrix} = 0 \tag{8.108}$$

In terms of the terminal variables, the final form is

$$\begin{bmatrix} P_6 \\ P_7 \end{bmatrix} = \begin{bmatrix} R_1 + \dfrac{1}{C_3 s} & \dfrac{1}{C_3 s} \\ \dfrac{1}{C_3 s} & R_2 + \dfrac{1}{C_3 s} \end{bmatrix} \begin{bmatrix} \dot{G}_6 \\ \dot{G}_7 \end{bmatrix} \tag{8.109}$$

These equations agree with Equations 8.73.

Another example illustrates the procedure for obtaining terminal representations for subassemblies of two-terminal components. Consider the electrical circuit shown in Figure 8.33(a). This circuit is a filter which is to be inserted into a larger system. It is therefore advantageous to obtain a terminal representation involving those terminals to which other connections are to be made. These terminals are ***a***, *b*, and *c*. Hence, the terminal graph of the desired representation can be chosen as shown in Figure 8.38 (b).

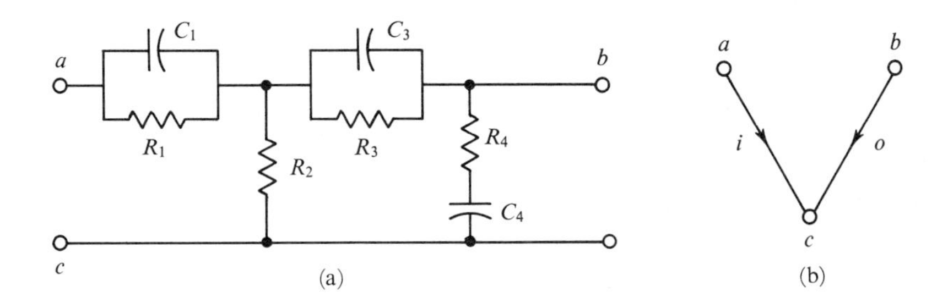

Fig. 8.38. (a) *Filter circuit;* (b) *terminal graph.*

In order to determine the most suitable formulation method, we realize all useful series and parallel combinations resulting in the reduction of the seven components of the filter to four equivalent components, as shown in Figure 8.39. The associated system graph with drivers applied is shown in Figure 8.40.

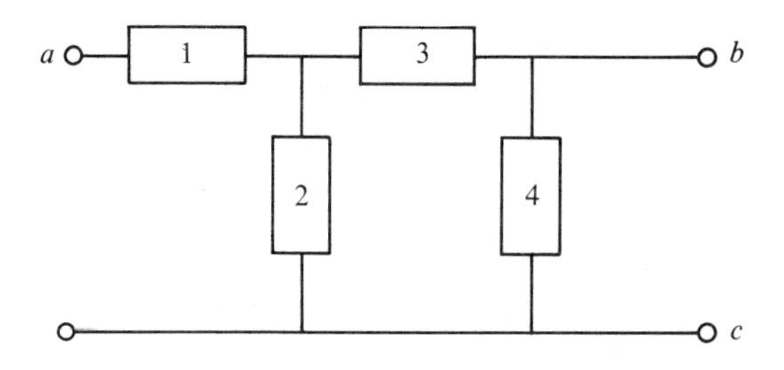

Fig. 8.39. *Reduced filter structure.*

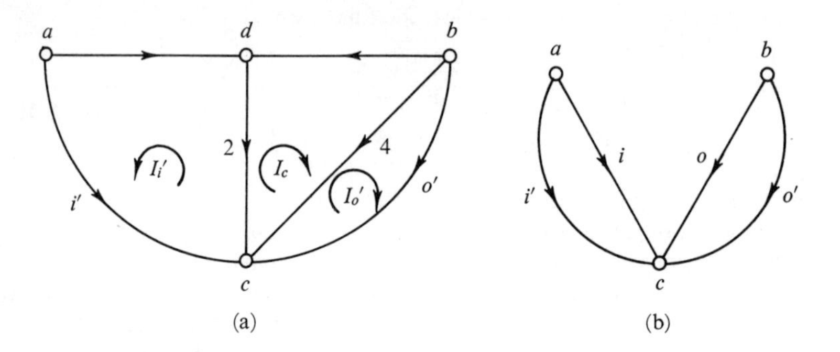

Fig. 8.40. *System graph of* (a) *filter and drivers,* (b) *terminal graph and drivers.*

Check the equation count. Node formulation (across drivers):

$$v - 1 - n_x = 4 - 1 - 2 = 1$$

Mesh formulation (through drivers):

$$e - v + 1 - n_y = 6 - 4 + 1 - 2 = 1$$

The equation count reveals that in both formulation methods, exactly one variable will have to be eliminated. When the equation count yields no decisive information on the choice of the formulation procedure, one should consider in which form the resulting mathematical model is most useful for further system connections. We will assume in this case that an open-circuit parameter model is needed. In order to obtain the open-circuit parameters directly, we choose mesh formulation and select through drivers. The assumed directions of the mesh currents are shown in Figure 8.40(a). It is advantageous to orient the mesh currents associated with the drivers in the direction of the drivers. The three mesh equations are

$$\left.\begin{aligned} V_{i'} + Z_1 I_a + Z_2(I_a + I_c) &= 0 \\ V_{0'} + Z_4(I_b - I_c) &= 0 \\ Z_2(I_c + I_a) + Z_3 I_c + Z_4 (I_c - I_b) &= 0 \end{aligned}\right] \quad (8.110)$$

These equation are written in matrix format:

$$\begin{bmatrix} Z_1 + Z_2 & 0 & +Z_2 \\ 0 & Z_4 & -Z_4 \\ \hline +Z_2 & -Z_4 & Z_2 + Z_3 + Z_4 \end{bmatrix} \begin{bmatrix} I_{i'} \\ I_{o'} \\ \hline I_c \end{bmatrix} = - \begin{bmatrix} V_{i'} \\ V_{o'} \\ \hline 0 \end{bmatrix} \quad (8.111)$$

To achieve the desired equation form for the terminal representation, it is necessary to eliminate I_c. If we write Equations 8.111 in the symbolic form

$$\begin{bmatrix} \mathbf{W}_{11} & \mathbf{W}_{12} \\ \mathbf{W}_{21} & \mathbf{W}_{22} \end{bmatrix} \begin{bmatrix} \mathbf{I}_d \\ \mathbf{I}_m \end{bmatrix} = \begin{bmatrix} \mathbf{V}_d \\ 0 \end{bmatrix} \quad (8.112)$$

When $\mathbf{I}_m$ is eliminated, we have

$$(\mathbf{W}_{11} - \mathbf{W}_{12}\mathbf{W}_{22}^{-1}\mathbf{W}_{21})\mathbf{I}_d = \mathbf{V}_d \quad (8.113)$$

Equation. 8.113 is expessed in terms of the variables and coefficients of Equation. 8.111:

$$\left\{\begin{bmatrix} Z_1 + Z_2 & 0 \\ 0 & Z_4 \end{bmatrix} - \frac{1}{Z_2 + Z_3 + Z_4}\begin{bmatrix} +Z_2 \\ -Z_4 \end{bmatrix}[+Z_2 \quad -Z_4]\right\}\begin{bmatrix} I_{i'} \\ I_{o'} \end{bmatrix} = -\begin{bmatrix} V_{i'} \\ V_{o'} \end{bmatrix}$$

or when multiplied out,

$$\begin{bmatrix} Z_1 + Z_2 - \dfrac{Z_2^2}{Z_2 + Z_3 + Z_4} & \dfrac{+Z_2Z_4}{Z_2 + Z_3 + Z_4} \\ \dfrac{+Z_2Z_4}{Z_2 + Z_3 + Z_4} & Z_4 - \dfrac{Z_4^2}{Z_2 + Z_3 + Z_4} \end{bmatrix}\begin{bmatrix} I_{i'} \\ I_{o'} \end{bmatrix} = -\begin{bmatrix} V_{i'} \\ V_{o'} \end{bmatrix} \tag{8.114}$$

The terminal variables are now introduced through the relations

$$\begin{bmatrix} I_{i'} \\ I_{o'} \end{bmatrix} = -\begin{bmatrix} I_i \\ I_o \end{bmatrix} \quad \text{and} \quad \begin{bmatrix} V_{i'} \\ V_{o'} \end{bmatrix} = \begin{bmatrix} V_i \\ V_o \end{bmatrix}$$

so that the desired model is

$$\begin{bmatrix} V_i \\ V_o \end{bmatrix} = \begin{bmatrix} Z_1 + Z_2 - \dfrac{Z_2^2}{Z_2 + Z_3 + Z_4} & \dfrac{Z_2Z_4}{Z_2 + Z_3 + Z_4} \\ \dfrac{Z_2Z_4}{Z_2 + Z_3 + Z_4} & Z_4 - \dfrac{Z_4^2}{Z_2 + Z_3 + Z_4} \end{bmatrix}\begin{bmatrix} I_i \\ I_o \end{bmatrix} \tag{8.115}$$

where

$$\begin{aligned} Z_1 &= \frac{R_1}{1 + R_1C_1s} \\ Z_1 &= R_2 \\ Z_3 &= \frac{R_3}{1 + R_3C_3s} \\ Z_4 &= \frac{1 + R_4C_4s}{C_4s} \end{aligned} \tag{8.116}$$

Note that the filter is a reciprocal component. Is it also a symmetrical component?

The above procedures may also be applied to derive mathematical models of subassemblies in terms of state models. Two examples will illustrate this.

Example 8.11. Derive the state model of the filter network in Figure 8.41 in hybrid parameter form.

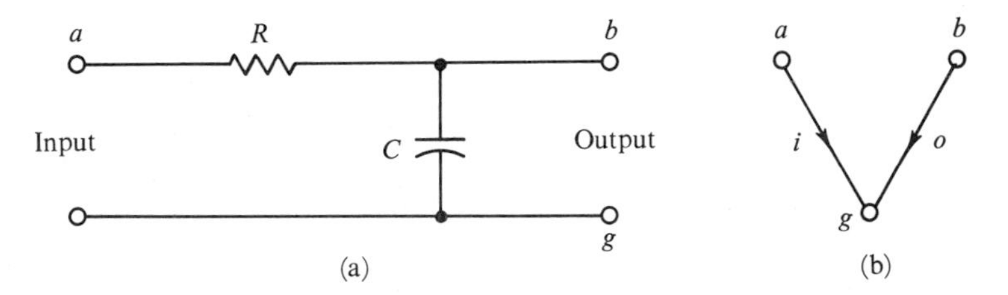

Fig. 8.41. *R-C network and two-port system graph.*

The system graph with augmenting drivers v_i and i_o is shown in Figure 8.42 with tree containing elements i' and 2.

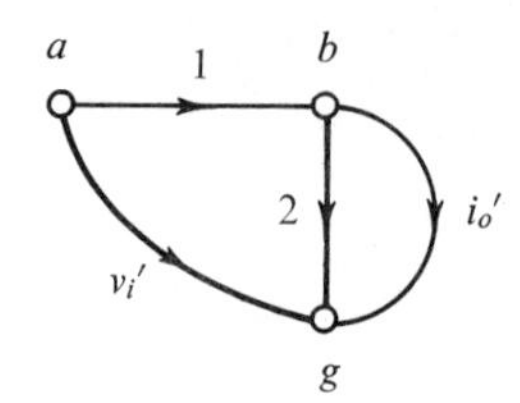

Fig. 8.42. *System graph with augmenting drivers.*

The component equations are

$$\frac{d}{dt}v_2 = \frac{1}{C}i_2$$
$$i_1 = \frac{1}{R}v_1$$

The cutset and circuit equations are

$$i_2 = i_1 - i_{o'}$$
$$i_{i'} = -i_1$$
$$v_1 = v_{i'} - v_2$$
$$v_{o'} = v_2$$

Furthermore,

$$\begin{bmatrix} v_{i'} \\ v_{o'} \end{bmatrix} = \begin{bmatrix} v_i \\ v_o \end{bmatrix} \quad \text{and} \quad \begin{bmatrix} i_i \\ i_o \end{bmatrix} = -\begin{bmatrix} i_{i'} \\ i_{o'} \end{bmatrix}$$

Combining the above equations yields the hybrid parameter model

$$\begin{bmatrix} \frac{d}{dt}v_2 \\ i_i \\ v_o \end{bmatrix} = \begin{bmatrix} -\frac{1}{RC} & \frac{1}{RC} & \frac{1}{C} \\ -\frac{1}{R} & \frac{1}{R} & 0 \\ 1 & 1 & 0 \end{bmatrix} \begin{bmatrix} v_2 \\ v_i \\ i_o \end{bmatrix} \tag{8.117}$$

Example 8.12. Derive a state model for the hydraulic transformer shown in Figure 8.43. The coupling medium in the hydraulic transformer is a two-faced piston with cross sectional areas A_1 and A_2. The forces on this piston must be in balance, thus

$$M\ddot{\delta} + B\dot{\delta} - p_iA_1 + p_oA_2 = 0$$

where M is the mass of the piston, B is the combined viscous friction coefficient, and $\dot{\delta}$ is piston velocity. Solving for the derivative,

$$\frac{d}{dt}\dot{\delta} = -\frac{B}{m}\dot{\delta} + p_iA_1 - p_oA_2 \tag{8.118}$$

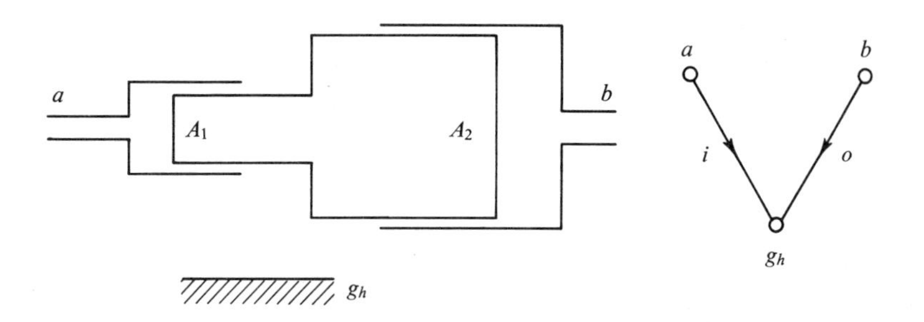

Fig. 8.43. *Hydraulic transformer.*

The following relation exists between the input and output flows and the velocity

$$\left.\begin{aligned} \dot{g}_i &= A_1\dot{\delta} \\ \dot{g}_o &= -A_2\dot{\delta} \end{aligned}\right] \quad (8.119)$$

Combining Equations 8.118 and 8.119 in matrix format yields the desired result

$$\begin{bmatrix} \frac{d}{dt}\dot{\delta} \\ \dot{g}_i \\ \dot{g}_o \end{bmatrix} = \begin{bmatrix} -\frac{B}{M} & A_1 & -A_2 \\ A_1 & 0 & 0 \\ -A_2 & 0 & 0 \end{bmatrix} \begin{bmatrix} \dot{\delta} \\ p_i \\ p_o \end{bmatrix} \quad (8.120)$$

The state model is in short-circuit parameter form. Because of the presence of the zeros it would be impossible to obtain any other form. It is interesting to show, however, that other forms exist when an s-domain model is sought. Equation 8.118, when transformed, becomes

$$(Ms + B)\dot{\Delta} + p_iA_1 - p_oA_2 = 0$$

Solving for $\dot{\Delta}$ and substituting into Equations 8.119 yields

$$\begin{bmatrix} \dot{G}_i \\ \dot{G}_o \end{bmatrix} = \frac{1}{Ms + B} \begin{bmatrix} A_1^2 & -A_1A_2 \\ -A_1A_2 & A_2^2 \end{bmatrix} \begin{bmatrix} P_i \\ P_o \end{bmatrix} \quad (8.121)$$

This is also a short-circuit parameter model. But it may be easily transformed into an h-parameter model.

$$\begin{bmatrix} \dot{G}_i \\ P_o \end{bmatrix} = \begin{bmatrix} 0 & -\frac{A_1}{A_2} \\ \frac{A_1}{A_2} & \frac{Ms + B}{A_2^2} \end{bmatrix} \begin{bmatrix} P_i \\ \dot{G}_o \end{bmatrix} \quad (8.122)$$

8.9 The DC Machine

The direct current machine is an important device in electrical engineering. It serves in a multitude of applications. Under steady-state operating conditions it may be used as a motor where it supplies mechanical power at a given torque level and speed through its shaft, or it may be used as a generator to supply a dc power system. Under transient operating conditions it may be used as a rotational actuator in a control system, or as a shaft speed sensor.

For each of the many applications, appropriate considerations are required to provide the optimum match between design and application. No matter how many physical models of the dc machine are available in the commercial market, they all belong to the same family of physical devices and thus in principle may be characterized by the same mathematical model. It is the objective of this section to present mathematical models which adequately represent the physical principles of the machine. No attempt is made to discuss design considerations, either in general or in particular.

Let us begin with a treatment of a non-commutating dc machine, more commonly known as the galvanometer movement, dynamometer, or torque-motor.

The Dynamometer

Consider the schematic diagram of Figure 8.44. It illustrates a device which consists of a rotor mounted inside a magnetic field. The

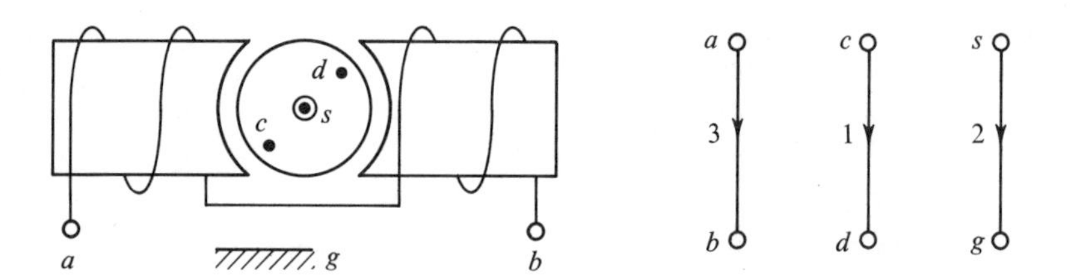

Fig. 8.44. (a) *Dynamometer movement;* (b) *graph defining terminal variables.*

rotor is concentrically mounted and is free to rotate. The magnetic field may be generated by a permanent magnet or by a coil, *a-b*, wound on a core of soft steel. The coil of wire, *c-d*, is wound symmetrically on the rotor. The shaft, *s-g*, is located at the center of rotation of the rotor. Thus the device is a six-terminal component with three separate ports.

For the purpose of deriving the terminal characteristics of the dynamometer, we first consider the device under constant field operation. With this simplification the dynamometer reduces to a four-terminal component. The terminal characteristics of the constant field dynamometer involve the relationship between the rotor voltage and current, v_1 and i_1, and the shaft torque and velocity, τ_2 and $\dot{\varphi}_2$. The equations are given as

$$\begin{bmatrix} v_1 \\ \tau_2 \end{bmatrix} = \begin{bmatrix} R_1 + L_1\dfrac{d}{dt} & k_g \\ k_m & J\dfrac{d}{dt} + B \end{bmatrix} \begin{bmatrix} i_1 \\ \dot{\varphi}_2 \end{bmatrix} \tag{8.123}$$

Under suitable test conditions the entries of the matrix in Equation 8.123 are easily investigated.

1. When the rotor is locked, we have

$$\dot{\varphi}_2 = 0$$

Then

$$v_1 = \left(R_1 + L_1\frac{d}{dt} \right) i_1 \tag{8.124}$$

where R_1 is resistance and L_1 is inductance of the coil c-d. Also

$$\tau_2 = k_m i_1 \tag{8.125}$$

where k_m is the motor constant which is primarily a function of the strength of the magnetic field. Since the rotor is constructed of ferromagnetic material, the constant k_m is also influenced by iron saturation and magnetic hysteresis effects. Typically, an experimental measurement of this effect is illustrated by the curve in Figure 8.45. The curve

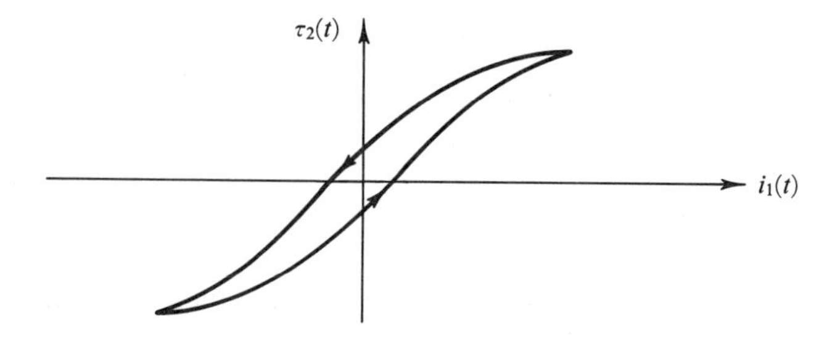

Fig. 8.45. *Torque-current curve and locked rotor conditions.*

is the result of measuring $\tau_2(t)$ as a function of $i_1(t)$ which is varied sinusoidally at low frequency. To consider k_m a constant, therefore, requires a linear approximation to the curve.

In addition to being a function of the ferromagnetic characteristics, k_m is also a function of the position of the shaft. If $i_1(t) =$ constant, and the torque is measured for a variety of locked positions, a torque versus position curve as shown in Figure 8.46 will result. The torque

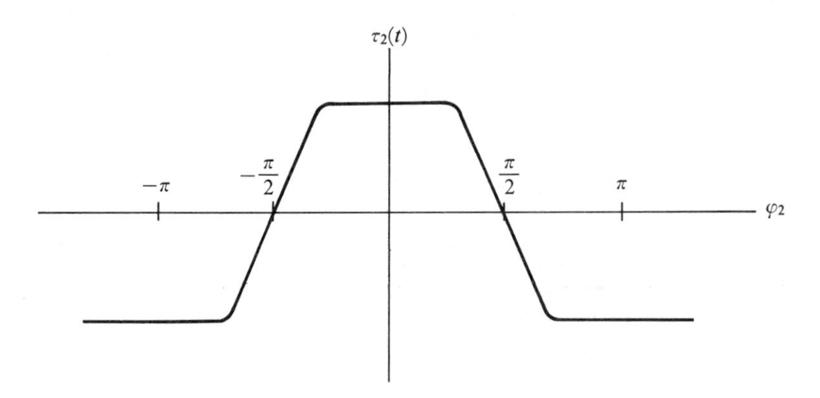

Fig. 8.46. *The dependence of dynamometer torque on the position of the rotor.*

developed by a given current is seen to be a periodic function of the position. In fact, the average torque over one cycle is zero. The dependence of torque on angular position is a direct consequence of the fact that the rotor magnetic field as induced by $i_1(t)$ is changing its orientation with respect to the fixed magnetic field, as generated by the permanent magnet or coil *a-b*. When the angular position of the dynamometer is restricted to within approximately $\pm\pi/4$, the torque is independent of the position and Equation 8.125 is an adequate representation of the relation between torque and current. The range $\pm\pi/4$ evidently is the useful range of a dynamometer.

2. When the current in the rotor is

$$i_1 = 0$$

we have from Equation 8.123

$$v_1 = k_g\dot{\varphi}_2 \tag{8.126}$$

When $\dot{\varphi}_2(t)$ is varied sinusoidally, a voltage is generated which is proportional to the magnitude of the shaft speed. Thus k_g is appropriately called the generator constant. It is subject to the same dependence of magnetic field orientation as is k_m, that is, the angular range over which Equation 8.126 applies is restricted to $\pm\pi/4$ and magnetic saturation and hysteresis effects are present. Also

$$\tau_2 = \left(B + J\frac{d}{dt}\right)\dot{\varphi}_2 \tag{8.127}$$

where J is rotor inertia and B is rotor-bearing viscous friction. It is important to note that k_m and k_g are of approximately the same numerical value in a typical dynamometer. Their difference is caused by a number of nonlinear effects, including saturation and hysteresis, and is usually approximately 10 per cent. When the dynamometer is idealized, R_1, L_1, J and B are neglected and the terminal equations become

$$\begin{bmatrix} v_1 \\ \tau_2 \end{bmatrix} = \begin{bmatrix} 0 & k_g \\ k_m & 0 \end{bmatrix} \begin{bmatrix} i_1 \\ \dot{\varphi}_2 \end{bmatrix} \tag{8.128}$$

Under these idealized conditions the dynamometer is thus reduced to an ideal transducer, easily identified by the characteristic skew-symmetric component matrix. It is then easily shown that k_m and k_g are identical but of opposite sign. An ideal transducer has no internal power dissipation. Therefore

$$\begin{aligned} 0 = p(t) &= [i_1 \quad \dot{\varphi}_2] \begin{bmatrix} v_1 \\ \tau_2 \end{bmatrix} \\ &= [i_1 \quad \dot{\varphi}] \begin{bmatrix} 0 & k_g \\ k_m & 0 \end{bmatrix} \begin{bmatrix} i_1 \\ \dot{\varphi}_2 \end{bmatrix} \\ &= i_1 \dot{\varphi}_2 (k_m + k_g) \end{aligned}$$

hence

$$k_m = -k_g$$

Therefore Equations 8.128 may be written

$$\begin{bmatrix} v_1 \\ \tau_2 \end{bmatrix} = \begin{bmatrix} 0 & +k_g \\ -k_g & 0 \end{bmatrix} \begin{bmatrix} i_1 \\ \dot{\varphi}_2 \end{bmatrix} \tag{8.129}$$

Because of the relatively slight discrepancy between k_m and k_g, it is often adequate to model the dynamometer ignoring this difference. Thus

$$\begin{bmatrix} v_1 \\ \\ \tau_2 \end{bmatrix} = \begin{bmatrix} R_1 + L_1 \dfrac{d}{dt} & +k_g \\ \\ -k_g & J\dfrac{d}{dt} + B \end{bmatrix} \begin{bmatrix} i_1 \\ \\ \dot{\varphi}_2 \end{bmatrix} \tag{8.130}$$

The constants k_m and k_g represent the electromechanical coupling that exists between the shaft torque and the current, and the voltage and the shaft speed. The coupling medium is provided by the magnetic field. Variations in this field affect the numerical value in an approximately linear manner. When the field is produced by a current through coil *a-b*, $i_f(t)$, we indicate the dependence of the coupling constants on $i_f(t)$ by writing Equations 8.123 as

$$v_1(t) = \left(R_1 + L_1 \frac{d}{dt} \right) i_1(t) + k_{mg} i_3(t) \dot{\varphi}_2(t) \tag{8.131}$$

$$\tau_2(t) = -k_{mg} i_3(t) i_1(t) + \left(B + J\frac{d}{dt}\right)\dot{\varphi}_2(t) \tag{8.132}$$

where k_{mg} is defined such that

$$k_{mg}\, i_{3\max} = k_g$$

Since under these conditions the dynamometer becomes a six-terminal component, we introduce the additional terminal equation

$$v_3(t) = \left(R_3 + L_3\frac{d}{dt}\right) i_3(t) \tag{8.133}$$

Although there is some inductive coupling between coil *a-b* and coil *c-d*, these effects may be neglected.

Devices Related to the Dynamometer

The dynamometer is indicative of the basic principle of operation of a number of other electromechanical transducers. They will be briefly discussed here as being closely related to the dynamometer.

1. Solenoid (Translational Dynamometer)

The solenoid is the translational equivalent of the dynamometer. It is also frequently called a linear actuator. It consists of a ferromagnetic core, *s-g*, which moves freely inside a coil, *a-b*. A current passing through this coil generates a magnetic field which will interact with the field of the core. Figure 8.47 shows a schematic of a solenoid. The

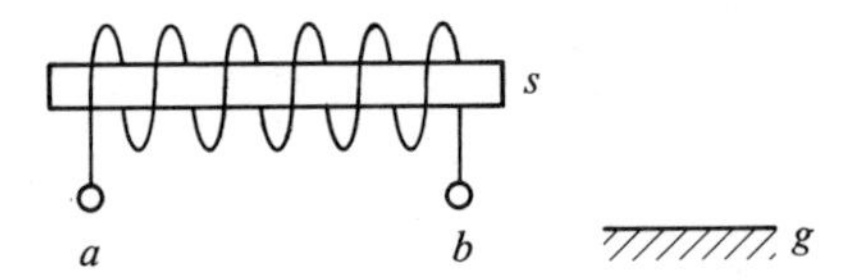

Fig. 8.47. *Schematic of a solenoid.*

solenoid is a four-terminal component with terminal equations

$$\begin{bmatrix} v_1 \\ f_2 \end{bmatrix} = \begin{bmatrix} R_1 + L_1\dfrac{d}{dt} & k_s \\ -k_s & B + M\dfrac{d}{dt} \end{bmatrix} \begin{bmatrix} i_1 \\ \dot{\delta} \end{bmatrix} \tag{8.134}$$

(Terminal graph: edge 1 from a to b; edge 2 from s to g.)

where R_1 is resistance of the coil, L_1 is inductance of the coil, k_s is the coupling coefficient, B is the viscous friction coefficient, and M is mass of the core. These equations are identical in form to that of the dynamometer.

2. Loudspeaker (Electroacoustic transducer)

Figure 8.48 shows the schematic of a loudspeaker. As can be seen, the loudspeaker can be viewed as a solenoid whose core is connected to a membrane

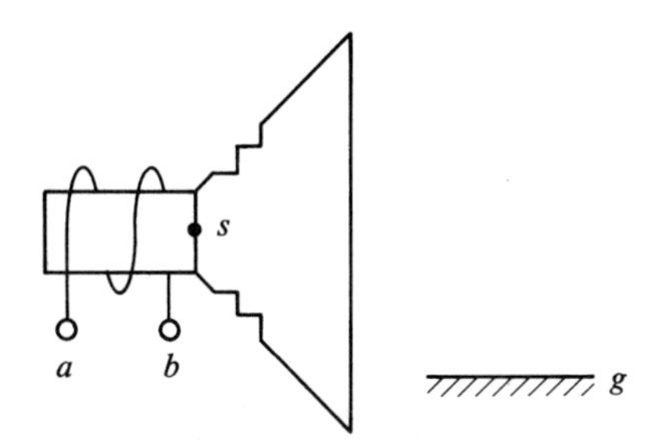

Fig. 8.48. *Schematic of a loudspeaker.*

The equations are

$$\begin{bmatrix} v_1 \\ f_2 \end{bmatrix} = \begin{bmatrix} R + L\dfrac{d}{dt} & k_s\dfrac{d}{dt} \\ -k_s & k_m + B_m\dfrac{d}{dt} + M\dfrac{d^2}{dt^2} \end{bmatrix} \begin{bmatrix} i_1 \\ \delta_2 \end{bmatrix} \tag{8.135}$$

(terminal graph: edge 1 from a to b, edge 2 from s to g)

where k_m is the spring constant of the membrane and B_m is the acoustic damping constant.

The loudspeaker is actually coupled to a column of air whose characteristics will have to be considered to obtain a complete description of a loudspeaker under normal operating conditions. This will be considered later, as it requires additional background in the interconnection of two-port components.

It was shown that the dynamometer has a useful angle of rotation of approximately $\pm\pi/4$. A similar restriction applies to the solenoid and the loudspeaker. Depending upon construction, the useful translational range may vary from a few millimeters to several centimeters.

The Commutating DC Machine

The dc machine is illustrated schematically in Figure 8.49. The armature, *A*, is a cylinder of soft steel laminated to reduce magnetic losses and mounted on a shaft. Embedded in longitudinal slots in the surface of the armature are a number of coils. Current is supplied to these coils through graphite brushes, a_1-a_2, making contact with a segmented cylinder on the shaft called the commutator (not shown). The commutator is an automatic switching arrangement which maintains the current in the armature in a direction to generate a magnetic field which remains fixed in orientation, regardless of the angular position of the armature.

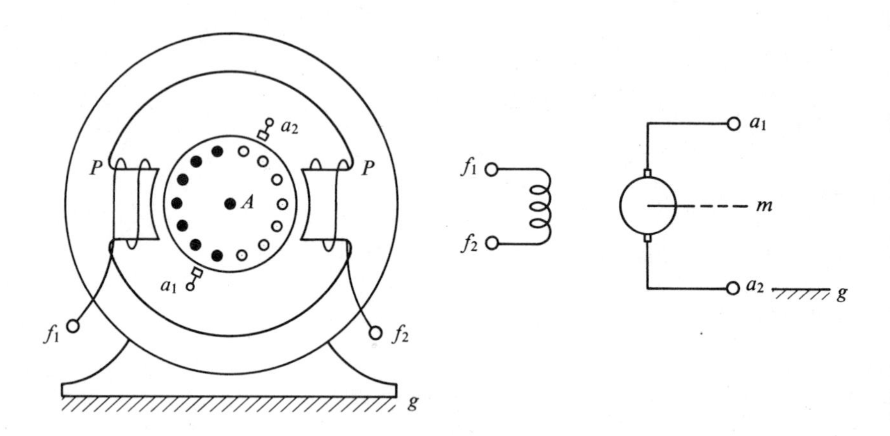

Fig. 8.49. *Schematic of a dc machine and generally adopted symbol.*

A second set of coils, f_1-f_2, wound around two poles, *P*, is mounted on the machine frame. It produces a stationary magnetic field designed to pass through the armature. These coils are usually referred to as the *field* of the machine. In some dc machines the field is provided by permanent magnets.

The terminal characteristics of the dc machine are easily derived from those of the dynamometer. It is readily seen that through the principle of commutation, the dc machine behaves as a dynamometer with the advantage of removing the restrictions on the useful range of rotation. Therefore, if the number of commutator segments is sufficiently large, we may take Equations 8.131 through 8.133 as the form of the terminal equations of the dc machine.

$$v_f = \left(R_f + L_f\frac{d}{dt}\right)i_f$$

$$v_a = \left(R_a + L_a\frac{d}{dt}\right)i_a + k_{mg}i_f\dot{\varphi}_m \qquad (8.136)$$

$$\tau_m = \left(R_m + L_m\frac{d}{dt}\right)\dot{\varphi}_m - k_{mg}i_f i_a$$

where the subscripts are used to denote terminal variables, *f*—field, *a*—armature, *m*—shaft.

Laboratory Measurements of Coefficients

The designer of dc machines hopes, of course, that calculations based upon machine dimensions may be made to select suitable numerical values for the coefficients of Equations 8.136. The coefficients can also be obtained from laboratory measurements. The following tests serve this purpose.

1. R_f. The field resistance may be obtained by static resistance measurement.

2. L_f. The field inductance can be measured by recording the exponential rise or decay of the field current as a solution to the differential equation

$$\left(R_f + L_f\frac{d}{dt}\right)i_f(t) = v_f(t)$$

when $v_f(t) = u(t)$. Since the solution is of the form $i_f(t) = e^{-(R/L)t}$ the time constant may be easily measured from the recording.

3. R_a. Although the armature resistance may be obtained by the same technique as R_f, sliding contacts require a more complicated procedure. R_a is best measured when the armature is rotating. This can be accomplished by setting

$$i_f = I_f \qquad \text{constant}$$

$$\dot{\varphi}_m = \dot{\Phi}_m \qquad \text{constant}$$

and connecting a variable resistance across the terminals of the armature. We then plot v_a as a function of i_a for these conditions, which results in a typical curve as shown in Figure 8.50. A straight line approximation to this curve is R_a.

4. L_a. The armature inductance is so small that it may be neglected.

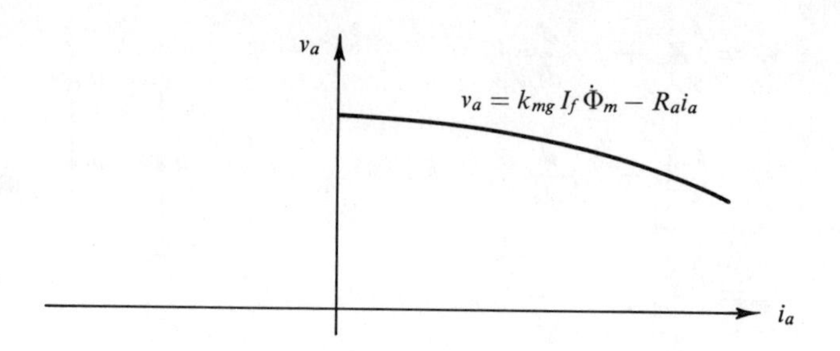

Fig. 8.50. *Typical steady state load curve.*

5. k_{mg}. The electromechanical coupling coefficient may be measured in two independent ways, (a) and (b).

a. By use of the equation

$$v_a = k_{mg} i_f \dot{\varphi}_m + R_a i_a$$

under the test conditions $i_a = 0$, $\dot{\varphi}_m = \dot{\Phi}_m$, constant. The machine is run as a generator under no-load conditions. Typically, a curve as shown in Figure 8.50 will result when $i_f(t) = I_{f\max} \sin \omega t$, a low frequency sinusoidal test function. This test will bring out the saturation and hysteresis properties of the iron core of the armature. A straight line approximation will yield k_{mg}.

b. By use of the equation

$$\tau_m = -k_{mg} i_f i_a + \left(B + J\frac{d}{dt}\right)\dot{\varphi}_m$$

under the test condition $\dot{\varphi}_m = 0$, $i_f = I_f$, constant. The machine is run as a motor, with a constant field. This is called the locked rotor test. When τ_m is plotted versus i_a, a curve very similar to that of Figure 8.51 results. Again, a straight line approximation is used to determine k_{mg}.

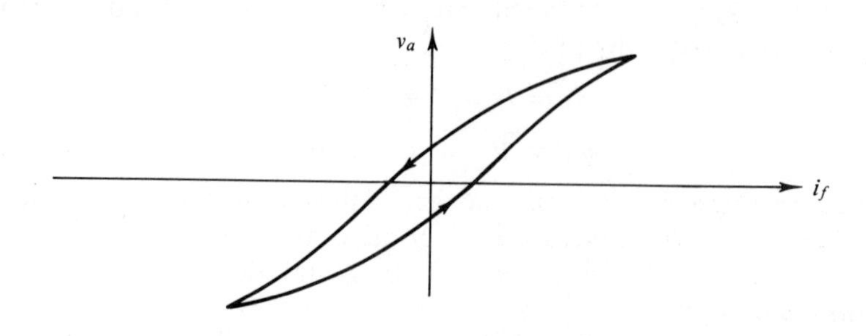

Fig. 8.51. *No-load saturation curve.*

6. *B* and *J*. The mechanical coefficients are measured by driving the machine with an external mechanical source and no electrical connections made. The speed of the mechanical source should be slaved to a periodic triangular function generator of the wave form shown in Figure 8.52.

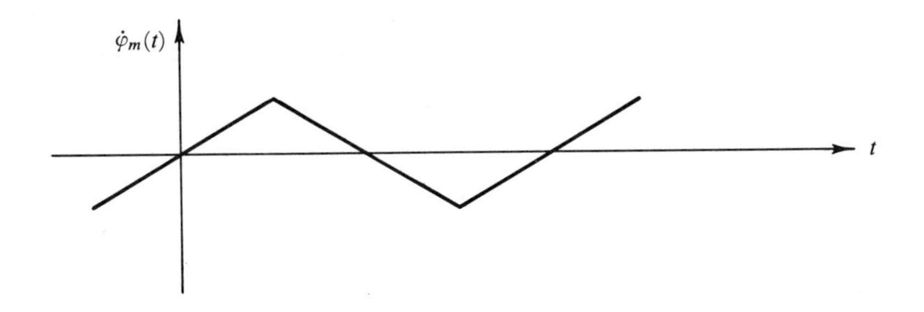

Fig. 8.52. *Wave shape of mechanical driver.*

The torque equation under these test conditions then is

$$\tau_m = J\frac{d}{dt}\dot{\varphi}_m + B\dot{\varphi}_m$$

Since the term $(d/dt)\dot{\varphi}_m$ is of constant magnitude with alternating signs, it is easy to separate the two terms in a recording made of τ_m versus $\dot{\varphi}_m$. A typical curve for the friction being entirely viscous is shown in Figure 8.53. The slope of the dotted line represents the *B* coefficient, while the vertical separation of the recorded plot is twice the term $J(d/d)\dot{\varphi}_m$.

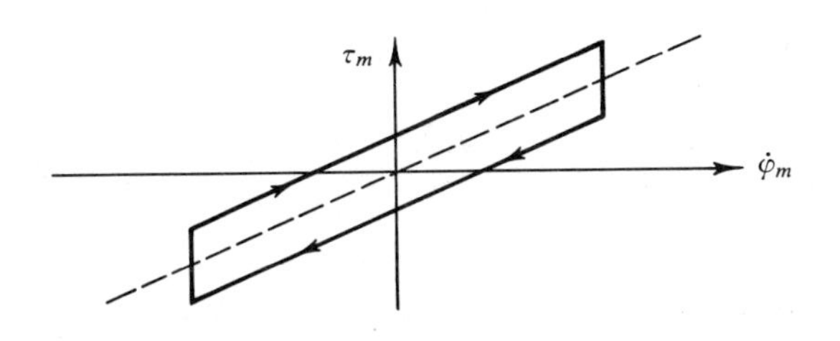

Fig. 8.53. *Mechanical response curve.*

For machines with pronounced coulomb friction properties due to heavy sliding friction of the brushes, a similar technique applies. It is left an an exercise to define a suitable approach under that condition.

Basic Modes of Operation

The terminal characteristics of the dc machine as a general six-terminal component are nonlinear due to the presence of products of terminal variables. However, if the machine is reduced to a four-terminal, two-port component by setting any of the variables i_f, i_a, or $\dot{\varphi}_m$ to zero, the equations become linear. For the three reduced two-port configurations, we associate the following terminal equations.

1. Rotating amplifier: $\dot{\varphi}(t) = \dot{\Phi}$, constant

$$\begin{bmatrix} v_f \\ v_a \end{bmatrix} = \begin{bmatrix} R_f + L_f\frac{d}{dt} & 0 \\ k_{mg}\dot{\Phi} & R_a + L_a\frac{d}{dt} \end{bmatrix} \begin{bmatrix} i_f \\ i_a \end{bmatrix} \tag{8.137}$$

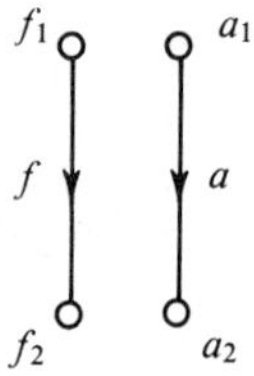

2. Rotational transducer: $i_f = I_f$, constant

$$\begin{bmatrix} v_a \\ \tau_m \end{bmatrix} = \begin{bmatrix} R_a + L_a\frac{a}{dt} & k_{mg}I_f \\ -k_{mg}I_f & B + J\frac{d}{dt} \end{bmatrix} \begin{bmatrix} i_a \\ \dot{\varphi}_m \end{bmatrix} \tag{8.138}$$

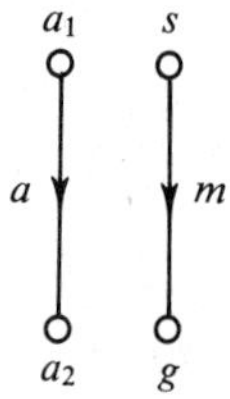

3. Rotational transducer: $i_a = I_a$, constant

$$\begin{bmatrix} v_f \\ \tau_m \end{bmatrix} = \begin{bmatrix} R_f + L_f\frac{d}{dt} & 0 \\ -k_{mg}I_a & B + J\frac{d}{dt} \end{bmatrix} \begin{bmatrix} i_f \\ \dot{\varphi}_m \end{bmatrix} \tag{8.139}$$

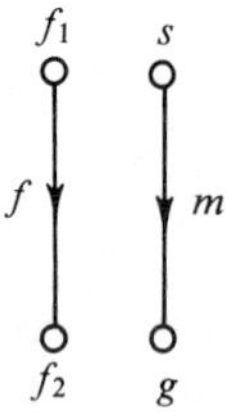

In practical situations it is difficult to realize this latter mode because it requires a constant current source of relatively large magnitude.

The Amplidyne

An interesting and useful variation of the basic dc machine is realized by adding a second set of brushes, called the *direct-axis* brushes,

90° apart from the regular set of brushes (hereafter called the *quadrature-axis* brushes) as shown schematically in Figure 8.54 for a two-pole machine. For reasons that will later become apparent, the main poles are equipped with two sets of windings, the usual field winding and an additional winding called a *compensating winding*. The compensating winding is connected in series with the direct-axis brushes of the

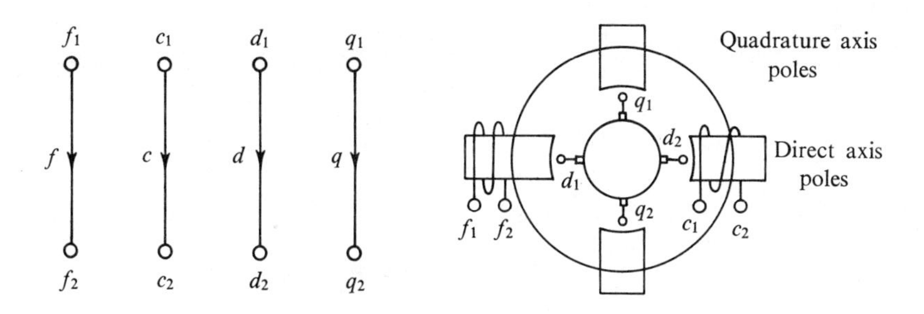

Fig. 8.54. *Schematic and terminal graph of an amplidyne.*

machine. The amplidyne is normally driven at constant speed. By using Equations 8.137 as a guide, the terminal equations of the eight-terminal amplidyne are

$$\begin{bmatrix} v_f \\ v_c \\ v_q \\ v_d \end{bmatrix} = \begin{bmatrix} R_f + L_f\frac{d}{dt} & L_{fc}\frac{d}{dt} & 0 & L_{df}\frac{d}{dt} \\ L_{fc}\frac{d}{dt} & R_c + L_c\frac{d}{dt} & 0 & L_{dc}\frac{d}{dt} \\ \dot{\Phi}k_{qf} & \dot{\Phi}k_{qc} & R_q + L_q\frac{d}{dt} & \dot{\Phi}k_{dq} \\ L_{df}\frac{d}{dt} & L_{dc}\frac{d}{dt} & \dot{\Phi}k_{dq} & R_d + L_d\frac{d}{dt} \end{bmatrix} \begin{bmatrix} i_f \\ i_c \\ i_q \\ i_d \end{bmatrix} \tag{8.140}$$

These equations introduce self and mutual inductance coefficients where appropriate. The quadrature voltage has three generated voltage terms.

The amplidyne is internally connected to operate as a two-stage high-gain power amplifier. The input is provided by field winding, f_1-f_2. Its magnetic field induces a current in the quadrature winding which is short-circuited. The quadrature current produces a magnetic field of considerably greater strength which in turn generates the output at the terminals of the direct axis winding in series with the compensating field winding. The purpose of the compensating field is to cancel out any reduction in the strength of the secondary field due to load current. The amplidyne thus is a two-port component. The system graph in Figure 8.55 shows these connections and the actual terminal graph of the amplidyne.

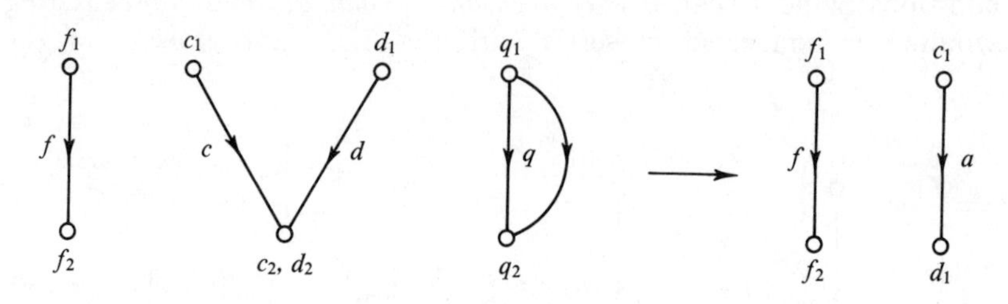

Fig. 8.55. (a) *System graph of amplidyne;* (b) *terminal graph.*

By procedures to be presented in Chapter 11, we reduce Equation 8.140 to obtain the s-domain two-port model

$$\begin{bmatrix} V_f \\ V_a \end{bmatrix} = \begin{bmatrix} R_f + L_f s & 0 \\ k_{\text{ampl}}/(1 + \tau_{\text{ampl}} s) & R_a + L_a s \end{bmatrix} \begin{bmatrix} I_f \\ I_a \end{bmatrix} \tag{8.141}$$

where

$$k_{\text{ampl}} = -\frac{\dot{\Phi}^2 k_{dq} k_{fq}}{R_q}$$

$$\tau_{\text{ampl}} = \frac{L_q}{R_q}$$

and

$$R_a = R_d + R_c$$

The following approximations have also been used

$$L_{fd} = L_{fq}$$

$$L_c + L_d = 2L_{cd}$$

$$K_{qd} = K_{qc}$$

The last relation is under the control of the compensating winding.

State Model of the DC Machine

To obtain a state model of the dc machine, it is only necessary to put the differential equations of the transducer into proper form. From Equations 8.136 we have

$$\left.\begin{aligned}\frac{d}{dt}i_f &= -\frac{R_f i_f}{L_f} + \frac{1 v_f}{L_f}\\ \frac{d}{dt}i_a &= -\frac{R_a i_a}{L_a} + \frac{v_a}{L_a} - \frac{k_{mg} i_f \dot{\varphi}_m}{L_a}\\ \frac{d}{dt}\dot{\varphi}_m &= -\frac{B_m \dot{\varphi}_m}{J_m} + J_m \tau_m + \frac{k_{mg} i_f i_a}{J_m}\end{aligned}\right] \qquad (8.142)$$

Depending upon the mode of operation, one can take two of the above equations, add appropriate algebraic equations for the terminal variables, and generate a two-port state model.

Example 8.13. Obtain the state model corresponding to the rotating amplifier mode as defined by Equations 8.137. With $\dot{\varphi}_m = \dot{\Phi}_m$, constant, the state model is formulated as

$$\begin{bmatrix} \frac{d}{dt}i_f \\ \frac{d}{dt}i_a \\ \hdashline i_{\text{in}} \\ i_{\text{out}} \end{bmatrix} = \begin{bmatrix} -R_f/L_f & 0 & 1/L_f & 0 \\ -\frac{k_{mg}\dot{\Phi}_m}{L_a} & -R_a/L_a & 0 & 1/L_a \\ \hdashline 1 & 0 & 0 & 0 \\ 0 & 1 & 0 & 0 \end{bmatrix} \begin{bmatrix} i_f \\ i_a \\ \hdashline v_{\text{in}} \\ v_{\text{out}} \end{bmatrix} \qquad (8.143)$$

8.10 The Hydraulic Valve

The hydraulic valve is schematically illustrated in Figure 8.54. It consists of an assembly of control spools, S, mounted integrally on a rod. Fluid entering through point h_3 is controlled by the position of the spools. There are four orifices, (1-4), one on each side of a spool through which the fluid passes. If the spools are centered, equal amounts of fluid will pass through each orifice and the pressures

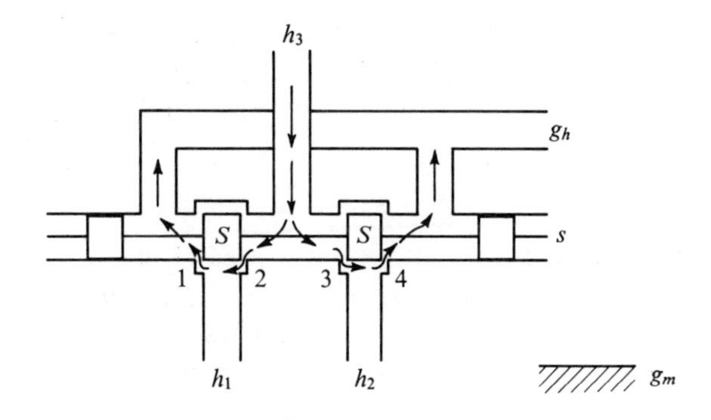

Fig. 8.56. *Hydraulic valve.*

developed at points h_1 and h_2 are equal. If the spools are positioned slightly to the right, more fluid will pass through orifices 1 and 3 than through 2 and 4, and the pressure at h_2 will be larger than at h_1. A valve so constructed is called a four-way valve. It is a most important component in hydraulic control systems. We are interested in developing a mathematical model for a four-way valve. The proposed development can be approached systematically by viewing the valve as a system of four identical four-terminal components, the orifices. Therefore, a discussion of the basic characteristics of an orifices is a good place to begin.

The Control Orifice

A single orifice is shown schematically in Figure 8.57. It is viewed as a two-port component with terminal pairs, h_1-h_2, and v-g. Fluid may pass through h_1-h_2 in either direction, the flow being restricted on

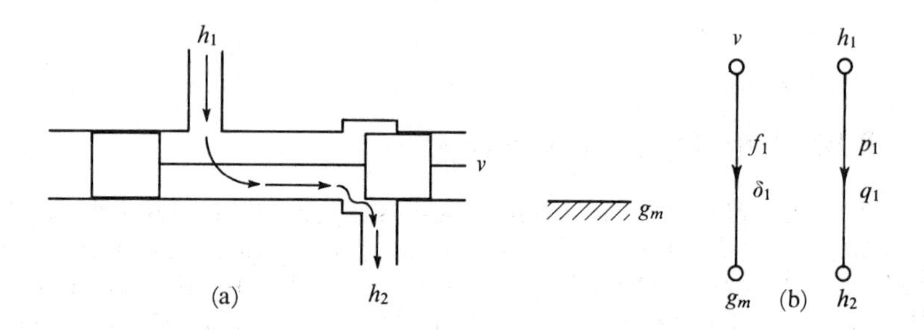

Fig. 8.57. (a) *A single orifice;* (b) *terminal graph.*

a variable basis by the position of the spool. One may interpret the orifice thus described as a variable hydraulic resistor.

The flow through the orifice may be adequately described by the relation

$$\dot{g}_1 = k_o A^{*}\sqrt{p_1} \tag{8.144}$$

where k_o is the orifice coefficient, A is the area of the orifice, and the symbol $^{*}\sqrt{}$ is the sign sensitive square root. Equation 8.144 follows from the steady flow equation in fluid mechanics.

The area A is related to the orifice position by

$$A = F_a(\Delta + \delta_1) \tag{8.145}$$

where F_a is a logic function defined by

$$F_a(x) = x \qquad x \geq 0$$
$$\qquad\quad 0 \qquad x < 0$$

and Δ is "lapping" of the valve, which represents the amount of spool displacement required to close the orifice. Combining Equations 8.144 and 8.145,

$$\dot{g}_1 = k_o F_a(\Delta + \delta_1) {}^*\sqrt{p_1} \tag{8.146}$$

Typically, the flow $\dot{g}_1$ and the pressure p_1 are selected by the plot of Figure 8.58.

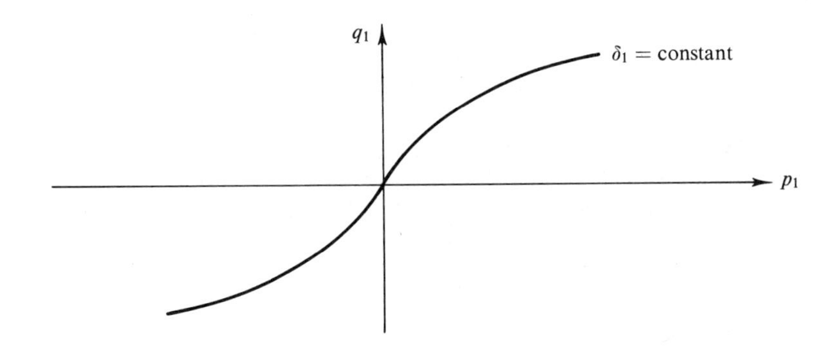

Fig. 8.58. *Relation between q_1 and p_1 for orifice.*

The mechanical variables are related by

$$f_1 = B_1\dot{\delta}_1 + M_1\ddot{\delta}_1 - k_{fb}(\delta_1)p_1 \tag{8.147}$$

where B_1 is the viscous friction coefficient, M_1 is mass of spool and rod, and $k_{fb}(\delta_1)$ is the force reaction coefficient describing the orifice's tendency to open under the action of pressure.

Equations 8.146 and 8.147 represent the terminal equations of the orifice. The two-port model thus derived will now be employed to develop the terminal equations of a four-way valve containing four such orifices.

The Four-Way Valve

In considering the schematic of the four-way valve as given by Figure 8.54, it can be seen that the four orifices contained in it are arranged in a bridge circuit as indicated by Figure 8.59. Only the hydraulic circuit elements, the hydraulic "half" of the orifices, are shown. The mechanical "halves" are connected as shown by Figure 8.60.

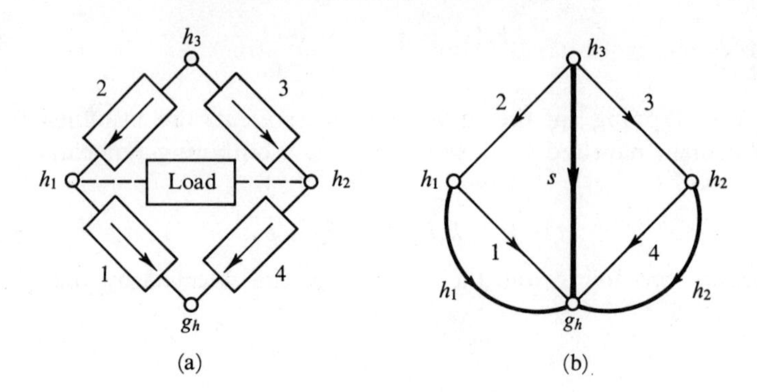

Fig. 8.59. (a) *Schematic of hydraulic bridge circuit;* (b) *System graph.*

Once the correct interconnection of the orifices is recognized, it is a simple matter to derive the overall mathematical model of the valve. We seek the equations associated with the terminal graph of Figure 8.60.

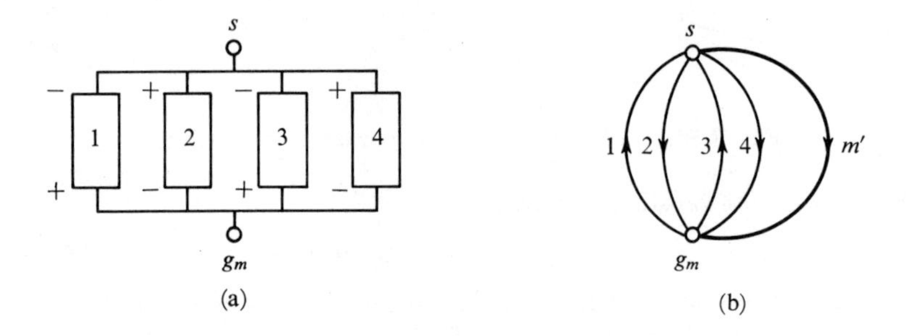

Fig. 8.60. (a) *Schematic of mechanical interconnection of orifices;* (b) *system graph.*

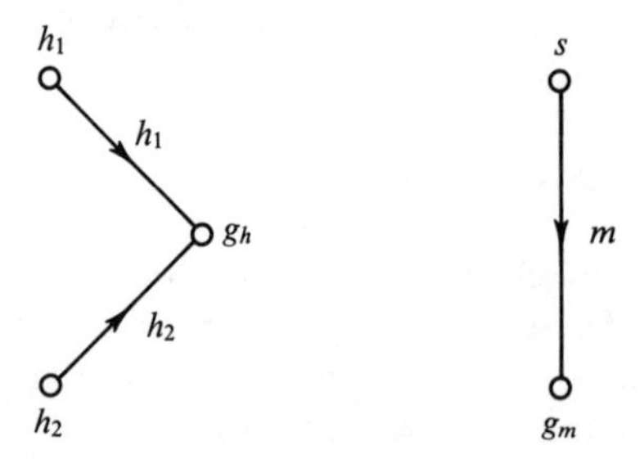

Fig. 8.61. *Terminal graph of four-way valve.*

For the orifices we have the component equations

$$\dot{g}_1 = k_o F_a(\Delta + \delta_1)^* \sqrt{p_1} \qquad f_1 = B\dot{\delta}_1 + M\ddot{\delta}_1 - k_{fb}(\delta_1)p_1$$
$$\dot{g}_2 = k_o F_a(\Delta + \delta_2)^* \sqrt{p_2} \qquad f_2 = B\dot{\delta}_2 + M\ddot{\delta}_2 - k_{fb}(\delta_2)p_2$$
$$\dot{g}_3 = k_o F_a(\Delta + \delta_3)^* \sqrt{p_3} \qquad f_3 = B\dot{\delta}_3 + M\ddot{\delta}_3 - k_{fb}(\delta_3)p_3$$
$$\dot{g}_4 = k_o F_a(\Delta + \delta_4)^* \sqrt{p_4} \qquad f_4 = B\dot{\delta}_4 + M\ddot{\delta}_4 - k_{fb}(\delta_4)p_4$$

For the system graphs we have

$$\dot{g}_{h_1} = -\dot{g}_{h_1'} = -(\dot{g}_2 - \dot{g}_1) \quad \text{and} \quad \dot{g}_{h_2} = -\dot{g}_{h_2'} = -(\dot{g}_3 - \dot{g}_4)$$
$$p_1 = p_{h_1} \qquad \delta_1 = -\delta_m$$
$$p_2 = p_3 - p_{h_1} \qquad \delta_2 = \delta_m$$
$$p_3 = p_s - p_{h_2} \qquad \delta_3 = -\delta_m$$
$$p_4 = p_{h_2} \qquad \delta_4 = \delta_m$$

also

$$f_m = -f_{m'} = -f_1 + f_2 - f_3 + f_4$$

Upon combining the component equations with the cutset and circuit equations above we obtain

$$\begin{aligned} \dot{g}_{h_1} &= k_o[F_a(\Delta + \delta_m)^* \sqrt{p_{h_1} - p_s} + F_a(\Delta - \delta_m)^* \sqrt{p_{h_1}}] \\ \dot{g}_{h_2} &= k_o[F_a(\Delta - \delta_m)^* \sqrt{p_{h_2} - p_s} + F_a(\Delta + \delta_m)^* \sqrt{p_{h_2}}] \end{aligned} \tag{8.148}$$

and

$$\begin{aligned} f_m &= 4B\dot{\delta}_m + 4M\ddot{\delta}_m + k_v\delta_m \\ &= B_v\dot{\delta}_m + M_v\ddot{\delta}_m + k_v\delta_m \end{aligned} \tag{8.149}$$

where

$$B_v = 4B$$
$$M_v = 4M$$

and k_v is the equivalent spring constant, formed by the addition of the flow-reaction forces which cancel one another except for a residual axial force which tends to center the spools.

Equations 8.148 and 8.149 represent the terminal equations of a four-way hydraulic valve. The equations pertaining to the hydraulic variables are extremely nonlinear. They may be simplified when two special designs which are frequently employed are considered.

Two Modes of Design

The design parameter Δ representing the lapping of the valve may be selected to yield two different designs. That in itself is not sufficiently significant to warrant mention; but when the lapping is chosen such that $\Delta > \delta_{\max}$, the equations may be linearized.

1. $\Delta = 0$: zero-lapped valve. For this selection of Δ it can easily be shown that Equations 8.148 reduce to

$$\left.\begin{aligned} \dot{g}_{h_1} &= k_o|\delta_m|^*\sqrt{p_{h_1} - F_s(\delta_m)p_s} \\ \dot{g}_{h_2} &= k_o|\delta_m|^*\sqrt{p_{h_2} - F_s(-\delta_m)p_s} \end{aligned}\right] \tag{8.150}$$

where a new logic function is introduced as

$$\begin{aligned} F_s(x) &= 1 \qquad x \geq 0 \\ &= 0 \qquad x < 0 \end{aligned}$$

The terminal equations, although simplified, are still very nonlinear. Ironically, the zero-lap design is the one most widely employed in hydraulic control valves. It is preferred because it permits the design of extremely stiff control systems.

2. $\Delta > \delta_{\max}$. When Δ is greater than zero the valve is said to be underlapped. A very good linear approximation for the terminal characteristics of an underlapped valve may be obtained as long as the valve spool motion is small, such that $\delta_{\max} < \Delta$. In obtaining the linear approximation, we expand Equations 8.148 in a Taylor series about an operating point and retain the first-order term only.

The operating point is selected as

$$\delta_m]_{\text{op. pt.}} = \delta_{m_o} = 0$$

most frequently encountered in steady state. Furthermore, if

$$p_{h_1} + p_{h_2} = p_s$$

and

$$p_{h_1} - p_{h_2} = p_L$$

load pressure in steady state, then

$$p_{h_1}\Big]_{\text{op. pt.}} = p_{1_o} = \frac{p_s + p_L}{2}$$

$$p_{h_2}\Big]_{\text{op. pt.}} = p_{2_o} = \frac{p_s + p_L}{2}$$

The flows $\dot{g}_{h_1}$ and $\dot{g}_{h_2}$ are functions of the two variables δ_m and p_{h_1}, and δ_m and p_{h_2}, respectively. So we may write

$$\begin{aligned} \dot{g}_{h_1} &= F_1(\delta_{m_1} p_{h_1}) \\ \dot{g}_{h_2} &= F_2(\delta_{m_1} p_{h_2}) \end{aligned}$$

A first-order Taylor series expansion for the first equation is

$$F_1(\delta_{m_1} p_{h_1}) = F_1\Big|_{\text{op. pt.}} + \frac{\partial F_1}{\partial \delta_m}\Big|_{\text{op. pt.}}(\delta_m - \delta_{m_o}) + \frac{\partial F_1}{\partial p_{h_1}}\Big|_{\text{op. pt.}}(p_{h_1} - p_{1_o}) \tag{8.151}$$

A series expansion similar to Equation 8.151 may be written for $F_2(\delta_m, p_{h_2})$.

Evaluating the partial derivatives of the series expansion yields the linear approximation

$$\dot{g}_{h_1} = Q_o + k_\delta \delta_m + G p_{h_1} \tag{8.152}$$

$$\dot{g}_{h_2} = Q_o - k_\delta \delta_m + G p_{h_2} \tag{8.153}$$

where

$$Q_o = F_1(\delta_{m_o}, p_{1_o}) = \frac{k_o \Delta}{2}(\sqrt{p_{1_o}} - \sqrt{p_{2_o}})$$

$$k_\delta = \left.\frac{\partial F_1}{\partial \delta_m}\right|_{\delta_{m_o},\, p_{1_o}} = -\frac{k_o}{2}(\sqrt{p_{1_o}} - \sqrt{p_{2_o}})$$

$$G = \left.\frac{\partial F_1}{\partial p_{h_1}}\right|_{\delta_{m_o},\, p_{1_o}} = \frac{k_o \Delta}{2}\left(\frac{1}{\sqrt{p_{1_o}}} + \frac{1}{\sqrt{p_{2_o}}}\right)$$

When operating an underlapped valve in a linear range it is convenient to eliminate the hydraulic reference from the terminal graph. Thus we derive the equivalent representation according to the system graph of Figure 8.62 (a) to be associated with the terminal graph of Figure 8.62 (b).

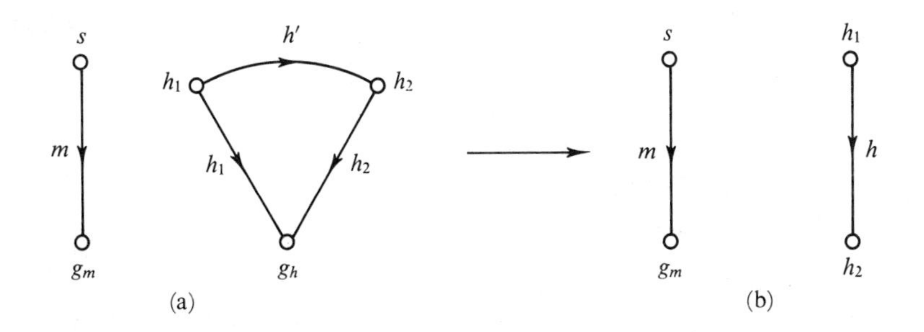

Fig. 8.62. (a) *System graph;* (b) *terminal graph for the reduction of the hydraulic valve to a two-port.*

In the proposed reformulation it is necessary to solve Equations 8.152 and 8.153 for the pressure variables so that use can be made of the relation

$$p_h = p_{h_1} - p_{h_2}$$

and

$$\dot{g}_h = \dot{g}_{h_1} = -\dot{g}_{h_2}$$

The resulting two-port model is

$$\begin{bmatrix} f_m \\ \dot{g}_h \end{bmatrix} = \begin{bmatrix} B_v\frac{d}{dt} + M_v\frac{d^2}{dt^2} + k_v & 0 \\ k_\delta & G/2 \end{bmatrix} \begin{bmatrix} \delta_m \\ p_h \end{bmatrix} \tag{8.154}$$

Although it is possible to determine the coefficients k_δ and G in Equations 8.154 analytically, it is often more convenient and perhaps more reliable to obtain numerical values for these coefficients from performance curves. These can be obtained through laboratory measurements, and they play a role similar to the performance curves for vacuum tubes and transistors. Such curves will be discussed in the next section.

Laboratory Measurement of Valve Characteristics

Simple laboratory test conditions may be specified to obtain numerical values for the coefficients used in the valve equations. First consider Equations 8.148. Only one coefficient needs to be determined; k_o. Taking the first of the two equations, we recall that $\dot{g}_{h_1}$ represents the net flow into the valve port h_1 and p_{h_1} represents the pressure at that same port with respect to the hydraulic reference which is taken as atmospheric pressure. We then connect a variable pressure supply between h_1 and g_h which will specify p_{h_1}. Thus laboratory measurements can be made to determine a set of curves which are plotted as shown in Figure 8.63. These curves are indicated by the solid lines. The dashed

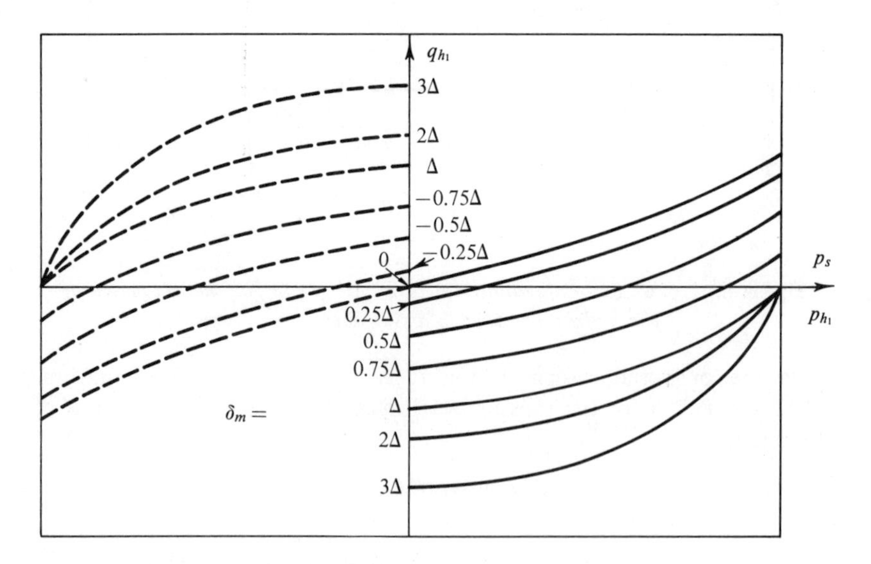

Fig. 8.63. *Flow plotted against pressure for an underlapped four-way valve.*

lines for negative valve openings are shown for convenience. They are extrapolated from the measured curves by argument of symmetry.

Figure 8.63 may serve two purposes: (1) k_o may be determined; and (2) the partial derivatives required for the linearization of Equations 8.148 may be determined graphically.

Although the curves shown in Figure 8.63 are obtained for an underlapped valve, those curves for which $\delta_m \geq \Delta$ are identical to curves corresponding to a zero-lap valve. Notice that the curves marked Δ, 2Δ, and 3Δ are square root curves with a common zero flow point. This result corresponds to considering the first equation of Equations 8.148 for $\delta_m \geq \Delta$

$$\dot{g}_{h_1} = k_o(\Delta + \delta_m)\, {}^{*}\!\sqrt{p_{h_1} - p_s} \tag{8.155}$$

which clearly represents a family of square root curves with $(\Delta + \delta_m)$ as a parameter.

To obtain numerical values for the mechanical coefficients we employ two measurements.

1. k_v. Test condition: Short circuit h_1 and h_2, operate the valve with constant supply pressure p_s, and measure the force required to obtain a certain valve displacement. When measurements are plotted, a curve as shown in Figure 8.63 typically results. When care is taken

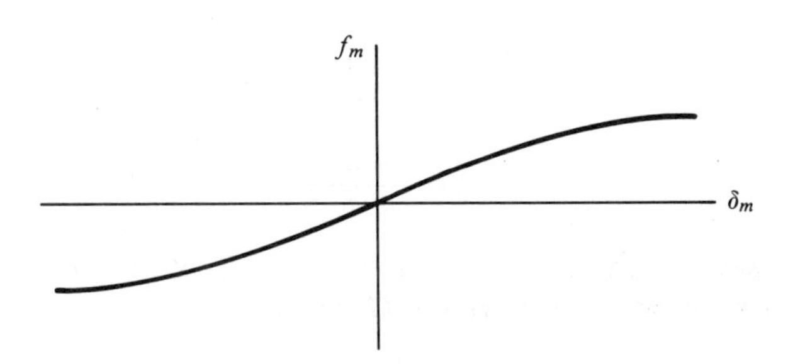

Fig. 8.64. *Static axial force versus displacement for valve.*

to assure that $\dot{\delta} = 0$, the resulting curve represents the static axial force. A straight line approximation yields k_v.

2. B_v and M_v. These coefficients are most effectively obtained by employing frequency response methods. Taking the Laplace transform of Equation 8.149,

$$F_m(s) = (M_v s^2 + B_v s + k_v)\Delta_m(s)$$

or

$$\Delta_m(s) = \frac{F_m(s)}{M_v s^2 + B_v s + k_v} \tag{8.156}$$

If $f_m(t) = \sin \omega t$ then

$$\delta(t) = \frac{1}{\sqrt{(k_v - M_v\omega^2)^2 + (B_v\omega)^2}} \sin(\omega t - \phi(\omega)) \tag{8.157}$$

where

$$\phi(\omega) = \tan^{-1} \frac{B_v\omega}{k_v - M_v\omega^2}$$

Equation 8.157 is the frequency response to a typical second-order transfer function. To make the interpretation of the experimental frequency response easier, we introduce the parameters ω_n and ζ, the natural frequency and damping factors, respectively. Thus Equation 8.157 becomes

$$\delta_m(t) = \frac{\omega_n^2}{\sqrt{[1 - (\omega/\omega_n)^2] + (2\zeta\omega/\omega_n)^2}} \sin[\omega t - \phi(\omega)]$$

where

$$\phi(\omega) = \tan^{-1} \frac{2\zeta\omega/\omega_n}{1 - (\omega/\omega_n)^2} \tag{8.158}$$

and

$$\omega_n = \sqrt{\frac{k_v}{M_v}}$$

$$\zeta = \frac{B_v}{2\sqrt{k_v M_v}}$$

The parameters ω_n and ζ may be determined from the frequency plot, and knowing k_v one may solve for M_v and B_v.

Summary

This chapter has presented procedures and notions basic to the modeling of multiterminal components of primarily linear characteristics. The developed procedures apply to two groups of components: (1) components that are formed as an integral aggregate of physical and geometric properties; and (2) components that may be viewed as a synthesized combination of two-terminal components or components that are a subsystem of two-terminal components. The modeling process for components of the first type is based upon experimental techniques by identifying the coefficients of the resulting equations through simulated measurements. Analytical procedures derived from mesh and node formulation techniques form the basis on which components of the second type are modeled.

The mathematical models of components of either type are of the same general form, consisting of two parts: (1) a set of linear algebraic and/or differential equations involving terminal variables; and (2) a terminal graph specifying the definition and orientation of the terminal variables. Treatment of multiterminal component modeling was limited to linear components. The terminal equations associated with such components are normally written in matrix format.

The modeling procedures associated with the second type of multiterminal components, which are actually equivalent representations of systems, are limited to systems of two-terminal components, as presented in this chapter. It is left to the next chapters to develop more extensive procedures that will permit the inclusion of multiterminal components in systems for which system models or equivalent terminal representations are to be obtained.

ADDITIONAL READINGS

Cannon, Robert H., Jr., *Dynamics of Physical Systems*, New York: McGraw-Hill Book Co., 1967.

Firestone, F. A., "A New Analogy between Mechanical and Electrical Systems," *J. Acoust. Soc. Am.* 4, 1932–33.

Harman, W. W., and D. W. Lytle, *Electrical and Mechanical Networks*, New York: McGraw-Hill Book Co., 1962.

Huelsman, L., *Circuits, Matrices, and Linear Vector Spaces*, New York: McGraw-Hill Book Co., 1963.

Koenig, Herman E., and William A. Blackwell, *Electromechanical System Theory*, New York: McGraw-Hill Book Co., 1961.

Kuo, Benjamin C., *Linear Networks and Systems*, New York: McGraw-Hill Book Co., 1967.

Schwarz, R. J., and B. Friedland, *Linear Systems*, New York: McGraw-Hill Book Co., 1965.

Seshu, S., and M. B. Reed, *Linear Graphs and Electrical Networks*, Reading, Mass: Addison-Wesley Publishing Co., Inc., 1961.

Van Valkenburg, M. E., *Network Analysis*, 2nd ed., Englewood Cliffs, New Jersey: Prentice-Hall, Inc, 1964.

Zadeh, L. A., and C. A. Desoer, *Linear System Theory*, New York: McGraw-Hill Book Co., 1963.

PROBLEMS

8.1. Express the short-circuit parameters in terms of the open-circuit parameters. Express the open-circuit parameters in terms of the h-parameters. Express the cascade parameters in terms of the g-parameters.

8.2. Obtain the terminal equations of the rotational dashpot in Figure P 8.2 in terms of the h-parameters according to the terminal graph shown.

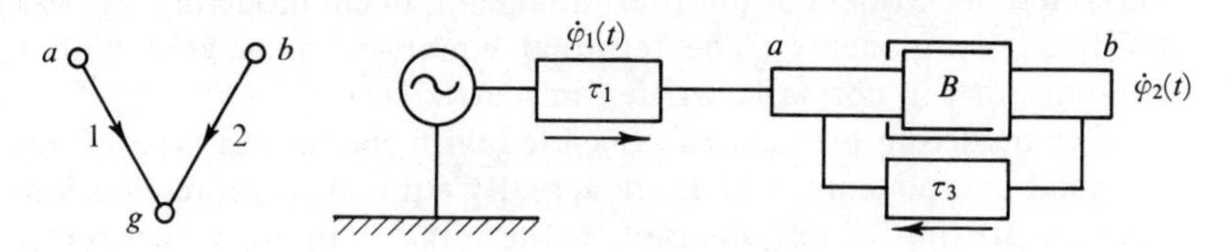

Fig. P 8.2.

8.3. Consider the rotational dashpot as being driven at shaft a by a sinusoidal driver (velocity)

$$\dot{\varphi}_1(t) = \sin \omega t$$

a) If there are no connections made to the other shaft, calculate the frequency response of $\dot{\varphi}_2(t)$.

b) Calculate the power required to maintain the input amplitude at a constant level for all frequencies.

8.4. Repeat a) and b) of Problem 8.3 when first $J_1 = 0$ or $J_2 = 0$; both $J_1 = 0$ and $J_2 = 0$ where J_1 and J_2 are inertias connected to a and b, respectively.

8.5. For the conditions of Problem 8.4 let

$$\dot{\varphi}_1(t) = u(t)$$

Calculate $\dot{\varphi}_2(t)$ (transient).

8.6. Explain the minus sign in Equation (2) of Figure P 8.6.

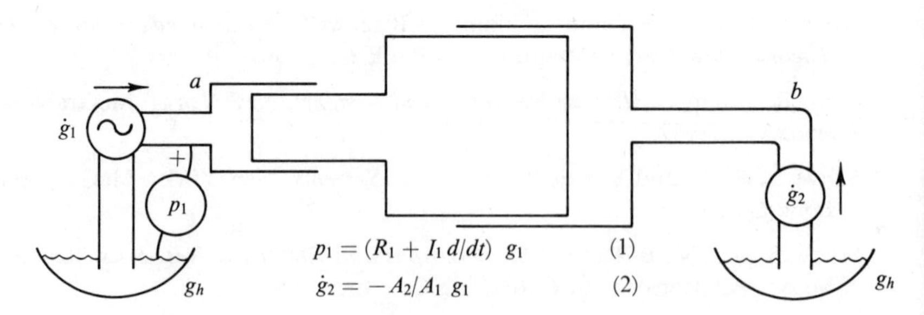

Fig. P 8.6. *Test setup for hydraulic transformer.*

8.7. Show in Figure P 8.6 that $R_1 = R_h + R_p/A_1^2$ and $I_1 = I_h + M_p/A_1^2$ where R_h = hydraulic resistance, R_p = mechanical friction, I_h = fluid inertance, and M_p = mass of piston.

8.8. Derive the terminal representation for the network of two-terminal components in Figure P 8.8.

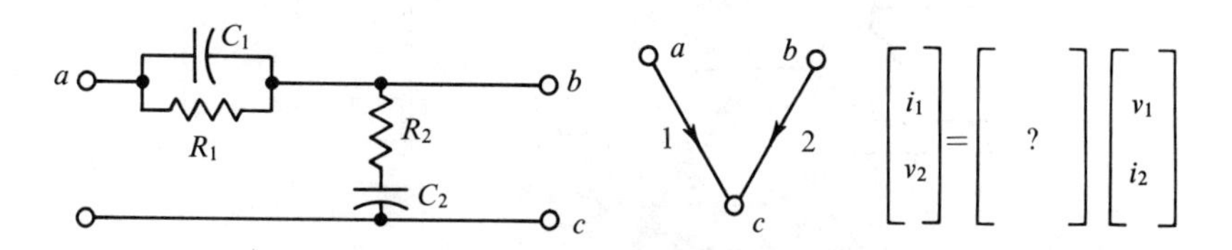

Fig. P 8.8. *An electrical network.*

Derive the open-circuit representation (mesh formulation) and the short-circuit representation (node formulation) and show that they are inverses of one another.

8.9. Derive the terminal representations for the assemblies of two-terminal components in Figure P 8.9.

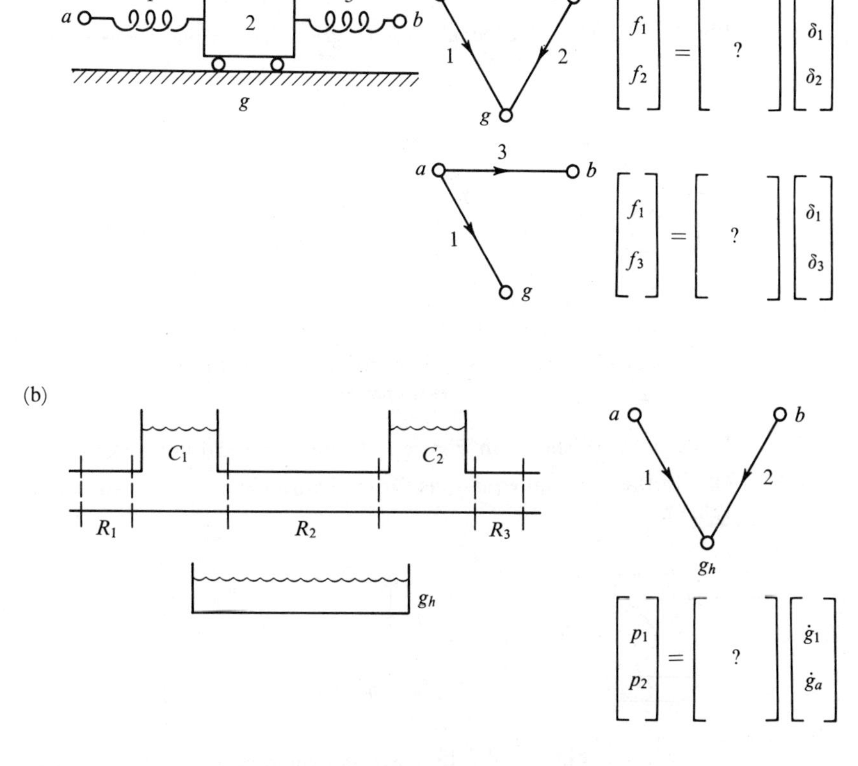

Fig. P 8.9. (a) *A mechanical assembly;* (b) *a hydraulic assembly.*

8.10.

Fig. P 8.10. *A hydraulic motor with four-terminal representation.*

Specify a test condition for the hydraulic motor shown in Figure P 8.10 suitable to determine boxed-in coefficient.

8.11. Model the rack and pinion shown in Figure P 8.11 as an ideal transducer.

Fig. P 8.11. *Rack and pinion with four-terminal representation.*

8.12.

Fig. P 8.12. *An electrical network with three-terminal representation.*

Is the network shown in Figure P 8.12 a reciprocal network?

8.13. Obtain the terminal equations for the hydraulic motor shown in Figure P 8.13.

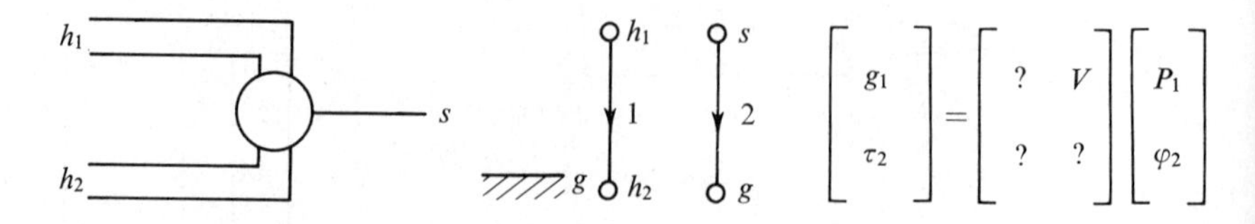

Fig. P 8.13. *A hydraulic motor.*

8.14. Develop the terminal equations of a gear box by viewing the component as an assembly of two components. The terminal equations are

$$\begin{bmatrix} \tau_1 \\ \dot{\varphi}_2 \end{bmatrix} = \begin{bmatrix} J_1 d/dt + B_1 & +k_{21} \\ -k_{21} & 0 \end{bmatrix} \begin{bmatrix} \dot{\varphi}_1 \\ \tau_2 \end{bmatrix}$$

8.15. Let the three winding transformer of Figure P 8.15 be ideal. Determine a suitable mathematical model according to the terminal graph shown.

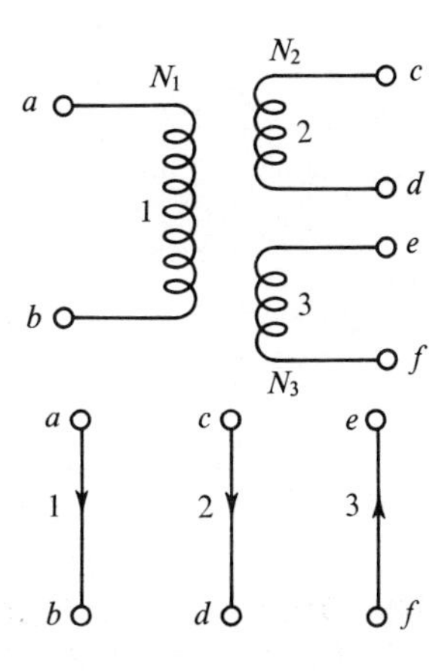

Fig. P 8.15. *Three winding transformer.*

8.16.

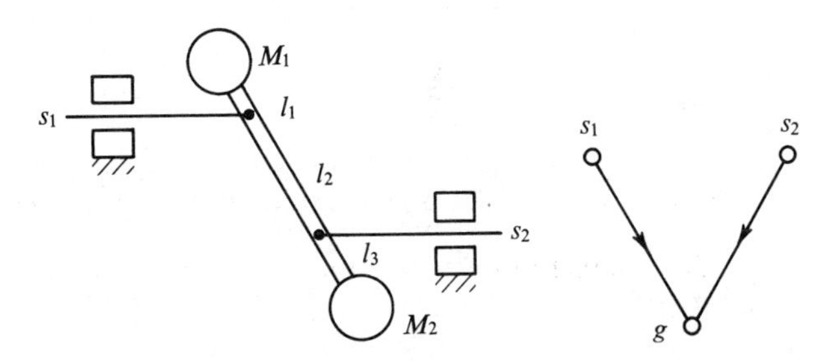

Fig. P 8.16. *A coupled pendulum system.*

Determine a mathematical model for the "coupled pendulum" shown in Figure P 8.16.

8.17. View the dashpot of Figure P 8.17 as an assembly of three two-terminal components.

a) Draw a system graph of the three components.
b) Derive Equations (1) according to the terminal graph of Figure P 8.17 (b).
c) Derive Equations (2) according to the terminal graph of Figure P 8.17 (c).

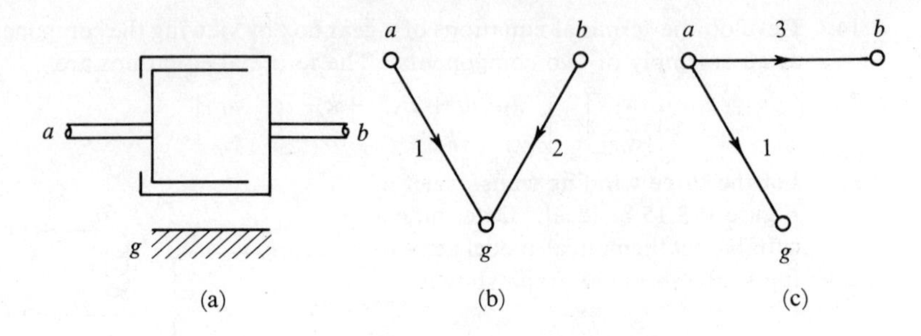

Fig. P 8.17. *Rotational dashpot:* (a) *schematic;* (b) *terminal graph; and* (c) *terminal graph.*

$$\begin{bmatrix} \tau_1 \\ \tau_2 \end{bmatrix} = \begin{bmatrix} J_1 d/dt + B_{12} & -B_{12} \\ -B_{12} & J_2 d/dt + B_{12} \end{bmatrix} \begin{bmatrix} \varphi_1 \\ \varphi_2 \end{bmatrix} \tag{1}$$

$$\begin{bmatrix} \tau_1 \\ \tau_3 \end{bmatrix} = \begin{bmatrix} (J_1 + J_2) d/dt & -J_2 d/dt \\ -J_2 d/dt & J_2 d/dt + B_{12} \end{bmatrix} \begin{bmatrix} \varphi_1 \\ \varphi_3 \end{bmatrix} \tag{2}$$

8.18. Derive the terminal equations for the free lever shown in Figure P 8.18. Assume small angles of rotation.

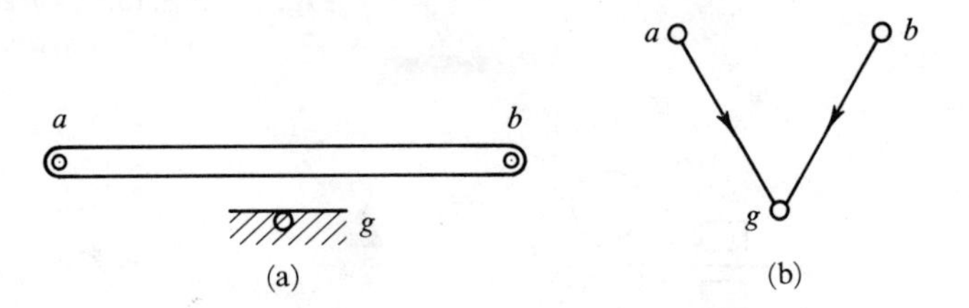

Fig. P 8.18. (a) *A free lever and* (b) *terminal graph.*

8.19. Derive the terminal equations for the pulley and lever system shown in Figure P 8.19.

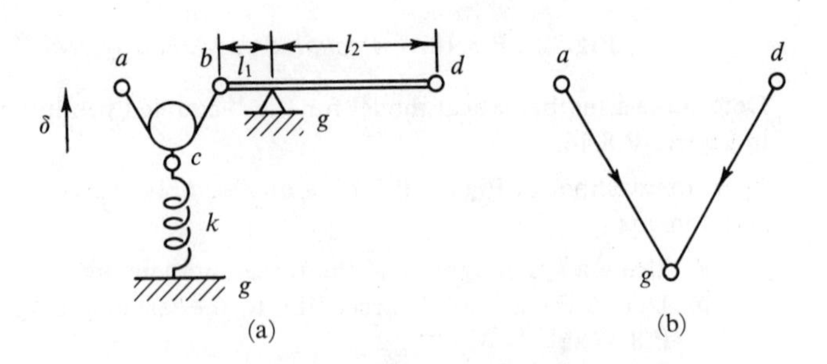

Fig. P 8.19. (a) *Pulley-lever system;* (b) *terminal graph.*

8.20. Derive the common-base and common-collector terminal graph equations of the transistor shown in Figure P 8.20 from the given common-emitter terminal equations.

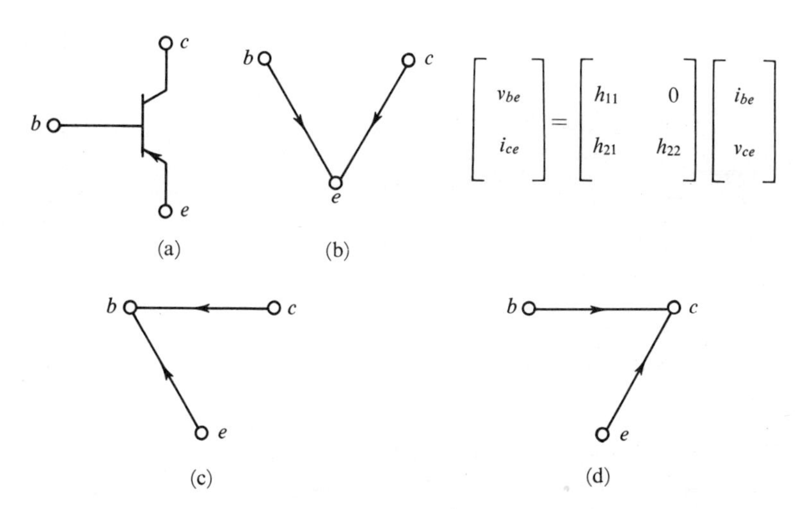

Fig. P 8.20. (a) *Transistor;* (b) *common-emitter terminal graph and equations;* (c) *common-base terminal graph;* (d) *common-collector terminal graph.*

8.21. a) Derive the indicated three-terminal representation of the vacuum tube system of Figure P 8.21.

b) Determine the input conductance and gain coefficient when the output current is zero.

c) Determine the output resistance when the input is short-circuited.

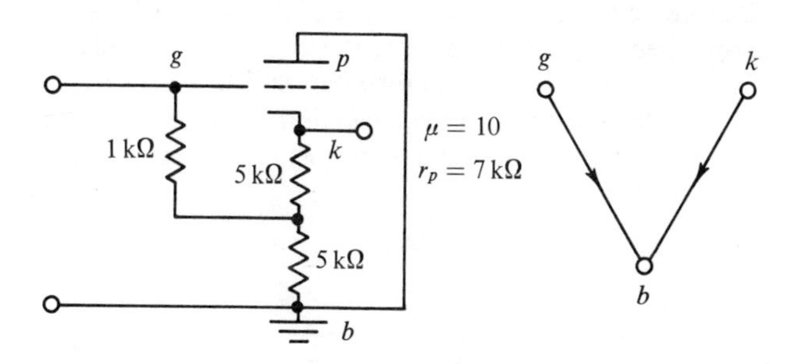

Fig. P 8.21. *Vacuum tube circuit.*

8.22. Determine the terminal equations (open-circuit parameters) of the two-resistor network according to the two terminal graphs shown in Figure P 8.22

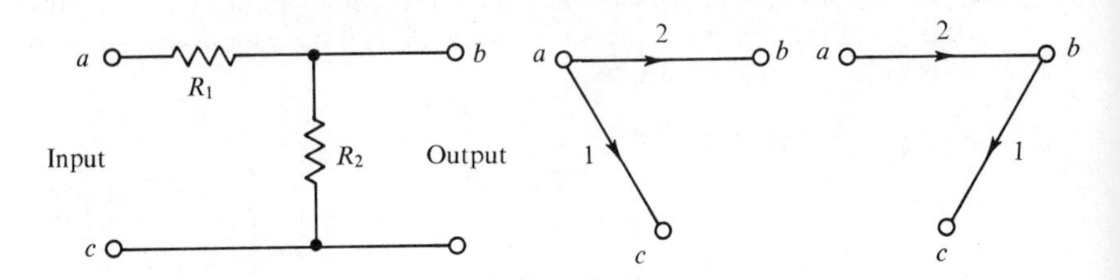

Fig. P 8.22.

Carefully show all measurements.

8.23.

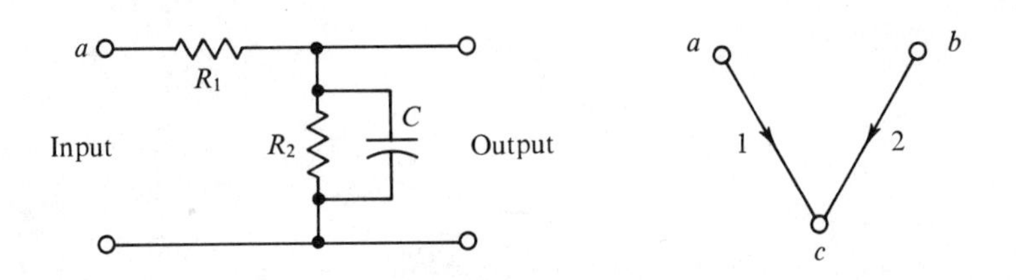

Fig. P 8.23.

Determine the short-circuit parameter terminal equations for the *R-C* network according to the terminal graph shown in Figure P 8.23.

8.24. Determine the open-circuit, short-circuit, *h*- and *g*-cascade parameters for the three-terminal mechanical network of Figure P 8.37 (c).

8.25. Derive a state model for the circuit of Problem P 8.23.

8.26. Determine suitable terminal equations for the following multiterminal components according to the terminal graphs indicated in Figure P 8.26. In each case, state reasons for your choice.

a) Hydraulic actuator (assume incompressible fluid).

b) Pneumatic actuator—same as a) but assume compressible fluid.

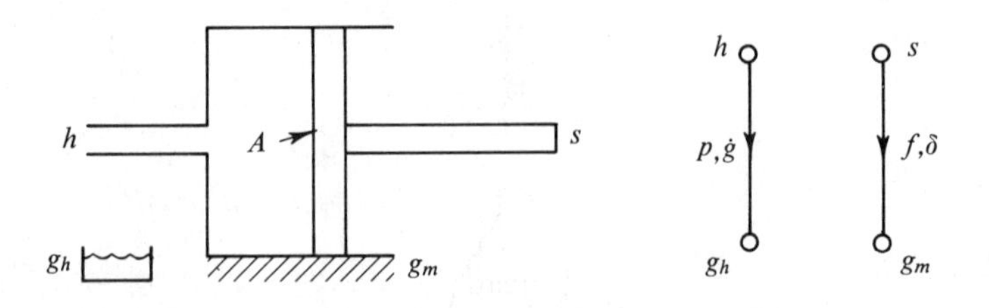

c) String and pulley.

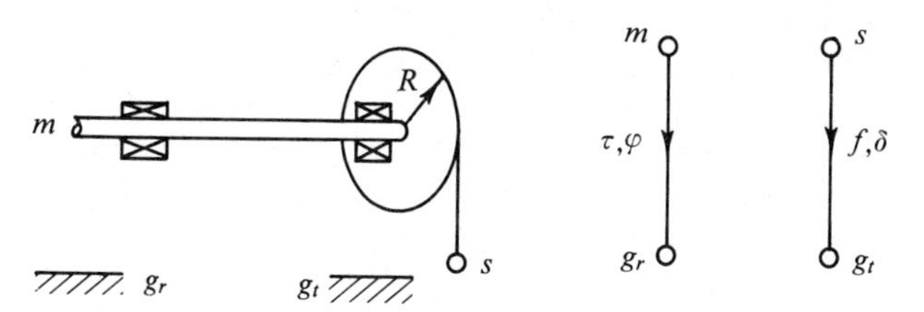

d) Flexible coupling.

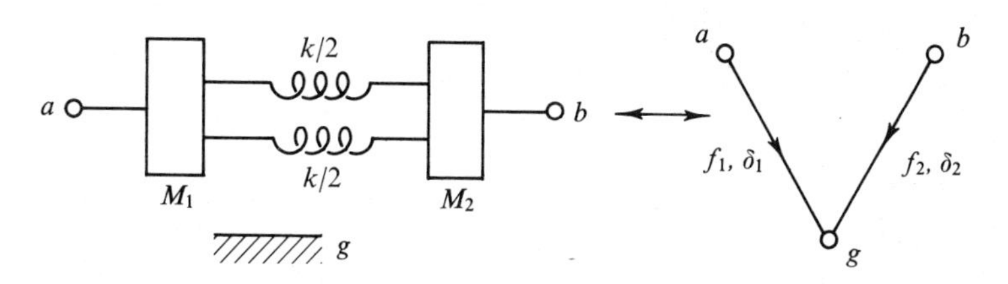

e) Three-winding transformer.

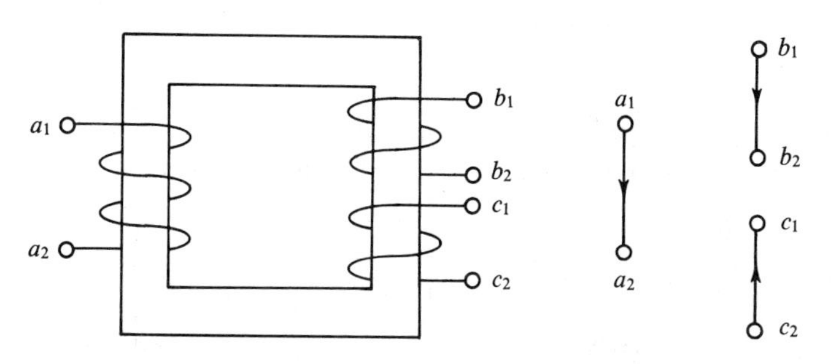

Fig. P 8.26.

8.27. Derive the terminal equations for the hydraulic transformer by viewing it as a cascade assembly of two hydraulic actuators as shown in Figure P 8.27.

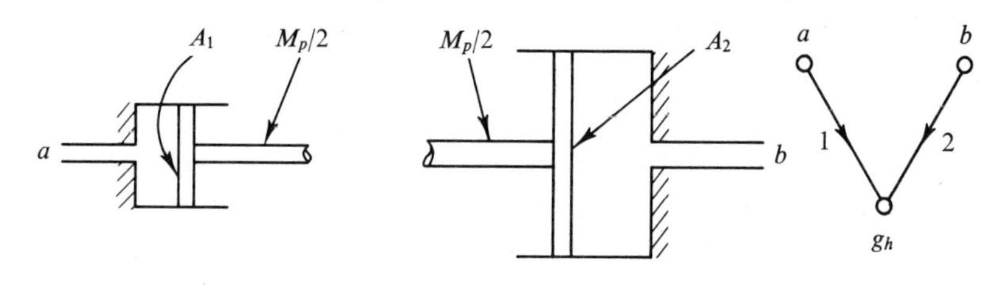

Fig. P 8.27.

8.28. Find the terminal equations of the components of Problem 8.26 when they are treated as ideal components.

8.29. The electrical component called the rotational potentiometer is often used as a component in a system. Many times it is sufficient to view it as a variable resistor. But it also functions as a full-fledged multiterminal component. It is clear then that the resistance of the two sections *a-c*

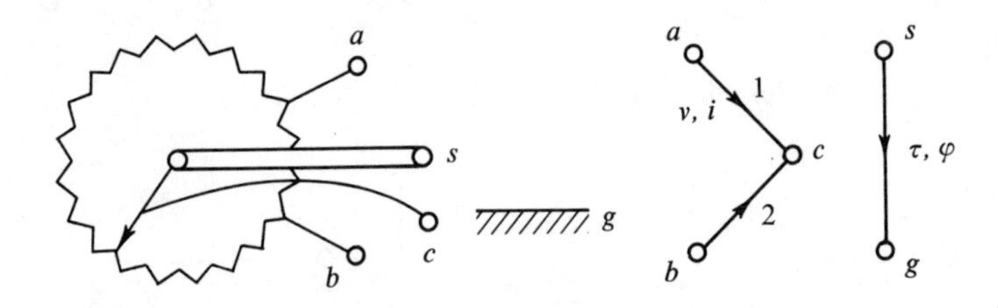

Fig. P 8.29. *Rotational potentiometer.*

and *b-c* become a function of φ, the angular position of c. Develop a model for the rotational potentiometer according to the following form of terminal equations:

$$\begin{bmatrix} \tau \\ v_1 \\ v_2 \end{bmatrix} = \begin{bmatrix} & & \\ & & \\ & & \end{bmatrix} \begin{bmatrix} \varphi \\ i_1 \\ i_2 \end{bmatrix}$$

8.30. Consider the circuit of rotational potentiometers shown in Figure P 8.30. Develop a model according to the equations indicated.

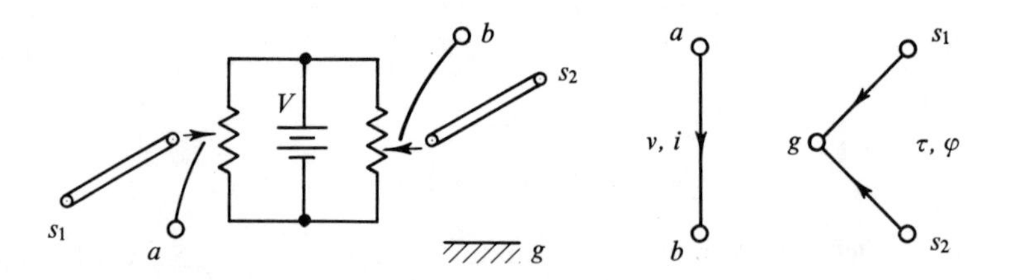

Fig. P 8.30.

$$\begin{bmatrix} \tau_1 \\ \tau_2 \\ v \end{bmatrix} = \begin{bmatrix} & & \\ & & \\ & & \end{bmatrix} \begin{bmatrix} \varphi_1 \\ \varphi_2 \\ i \end{bmatrix}$$

8.31. Show that the hydraulic capacitor is a symmetric component.

8.32. Derive a state model for a hydraulic capacitor.

8.33. A differential gear may frequently be modeled as an ideal transducer when it is used as an error-detection device in a control sysytem. Its model may be given as

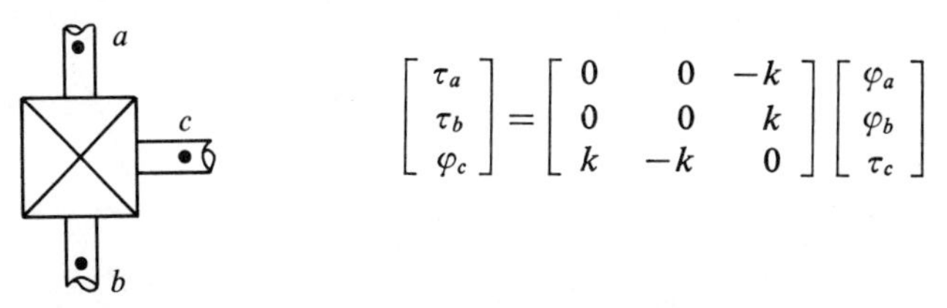

$$\begin{bmatrix} \tau_a \\ \tau_b \\ \varphi_c \end{bmatrix} = \begin{bmatrix} 0 & 0 & -k \\ 0 & 0 & k \\ k & -k & 0 \end{bmatrix} \begin{bmatrix} \varphi_a \\ \varphi_b \\ \tau_c \end{bmatrix}$$

Fig. P 8.33.

Show that its power function is zero.

8.34. Model the differential pulley system shown in Figure P 8.34. Consider the pulley massless.

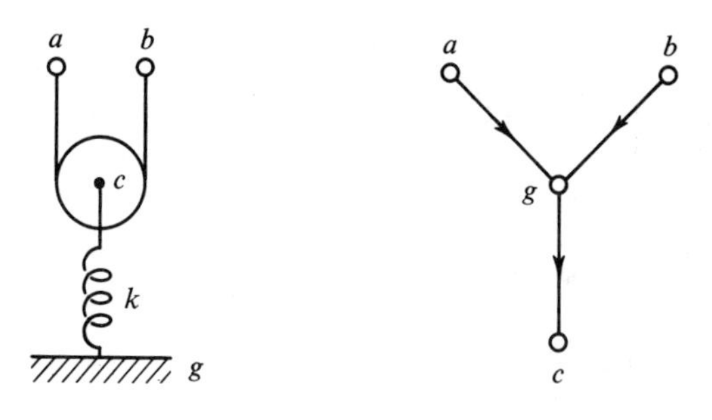

Fig. P 8.34.

8.35. The vacuum triode is a three-terminal component as shown in Figure P 8.35(a) with terminals consisting of the grid, *a*, the plate, *b*, and the cathode, *c*. Electrons which are emitted from the indirectly-heated cathode are attracted by the plate, which is at a high positive potential, and connected plate circuit, thus generating a current. This current may be regulated in magnitude by a suitably selected grid potential which more or less inhibits the flow of electrons. The terminal equations of the triode are nonlinear and may be given as

$$\begin{bmatrix} i_1 \\ i_2 \end{bmatrix} = \begin{bmatrix} 0 \\ G(v_1, v_2) \end{bmatrix}$$

The function $G(v_1, v_2)$ is usually defined graphically by curves as shown in Figure P 8.35(b) and (c).

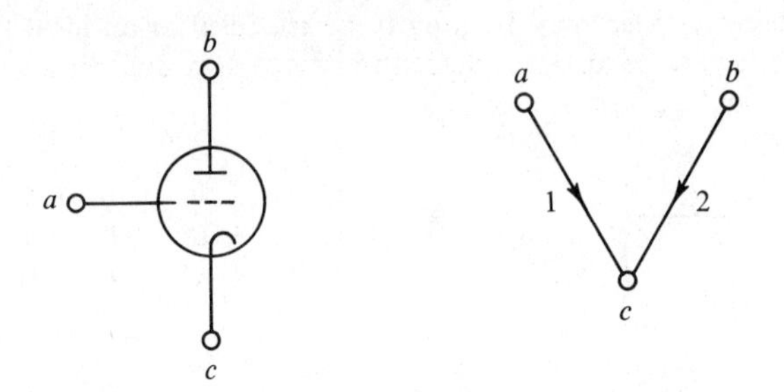

Fig. P 8.35. (a) *Plate characteristics for a (6J6) triode.*

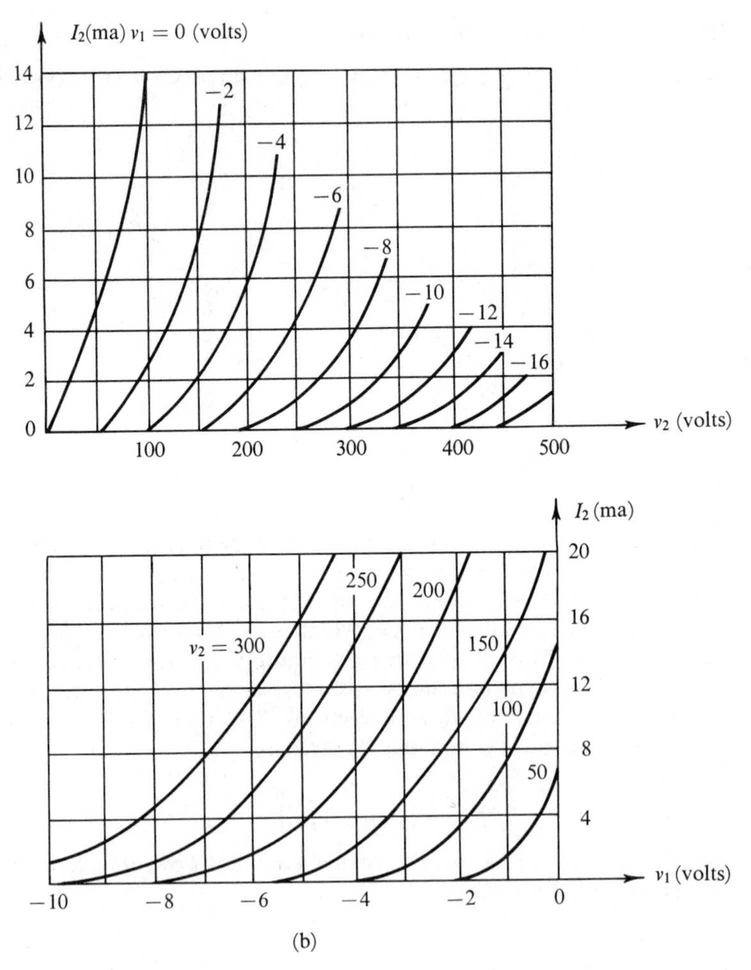

Fig. P 8.35. (b) *Transfer characteristics.*

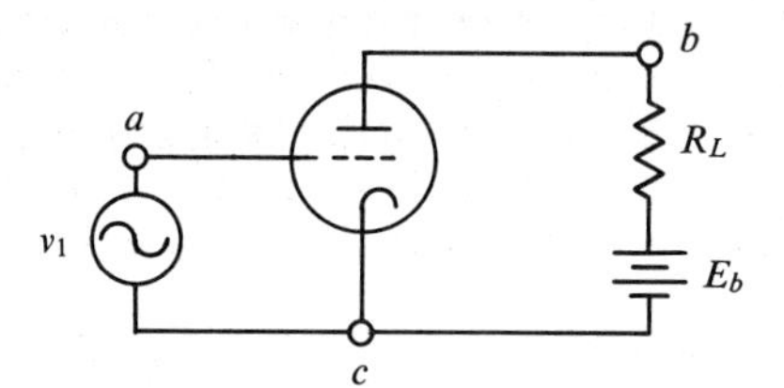

Fig. P 8.35. (c) *Typical circuit.*

(a)

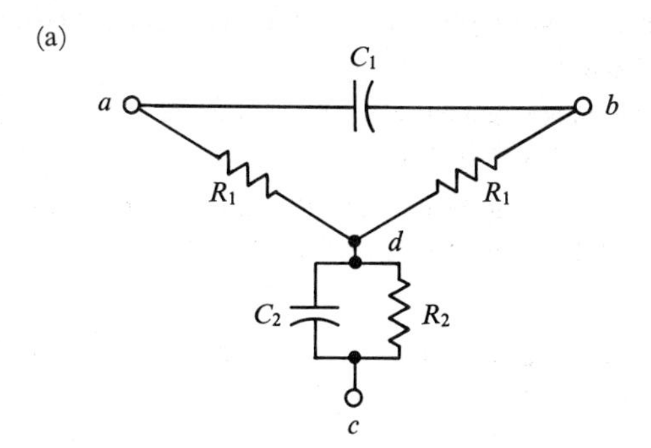

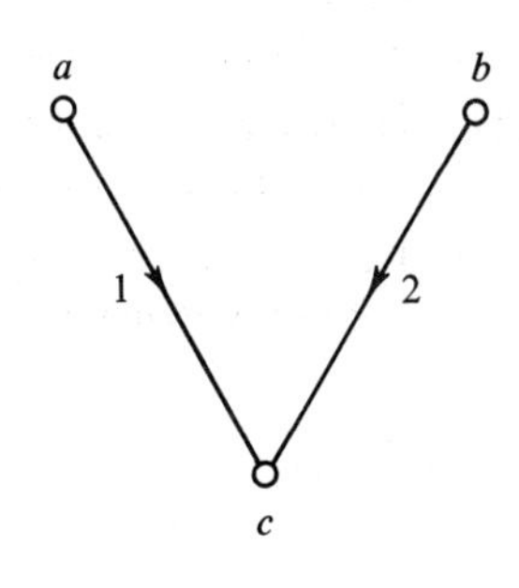

(b) Same network as (a)

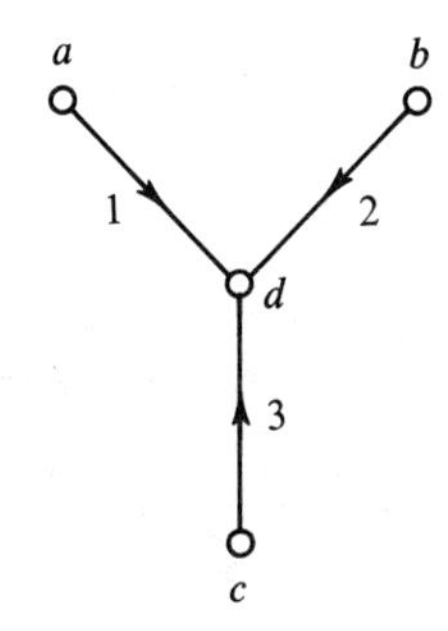

(c)

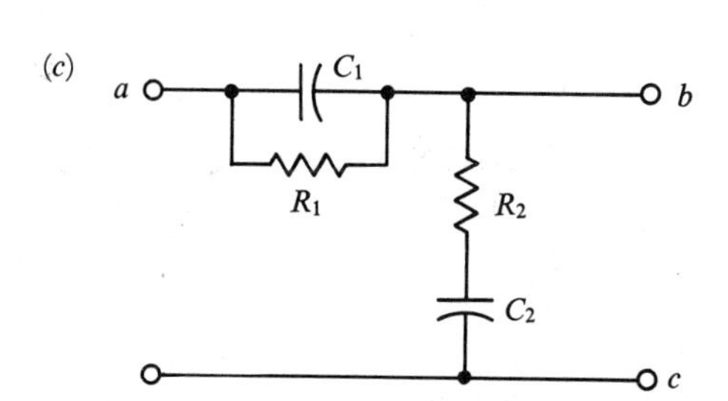

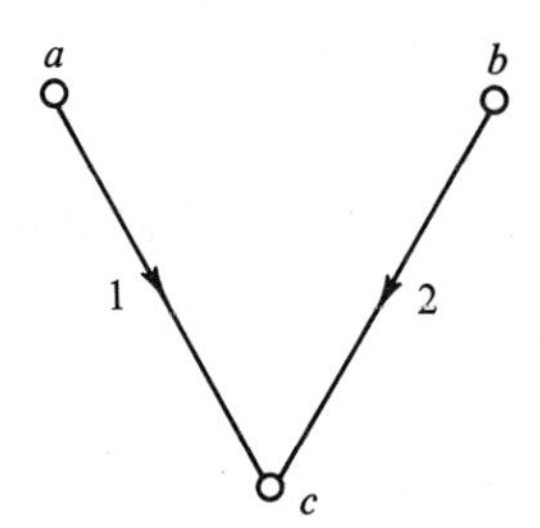

Fig. P 8.36.

Typical application will find the tube operating in a circuit shown in Figure P 8.35(c). A linear operation of the device is possible provided only small signal fluctuations about an operating point take place. If $E_b = 500$ volts, $R_L = 50{,}000$ ohms and $v_1 = -4$ volts, determine this operating point. Find the coefficients of the Taylor series expansion

$$i_2 = G(v_1^*, v_2^*) + \left.\frac{\partial G}{\partial v_1}\right|_{\substack{v_1^* \\ v_2^*}} \Delta v_1 + \left.\frac{\partial G}{\partial v_2}\right|_{\substack{v_1^* \\ v_2^*}} \Delta v_2$$

where v_1^*, v_2^* are the operating voltages and Δv_1 and Δv_2 represent the deviations from these voltages.

3.36. Derive an open-circuit parameter model for the following systems according to the indicated terminal graph in Figure P 8.36.

8.37. Derive a closed-circuit parameter model for the following systems according to the indicated terminal graph in Figure P 8.37.

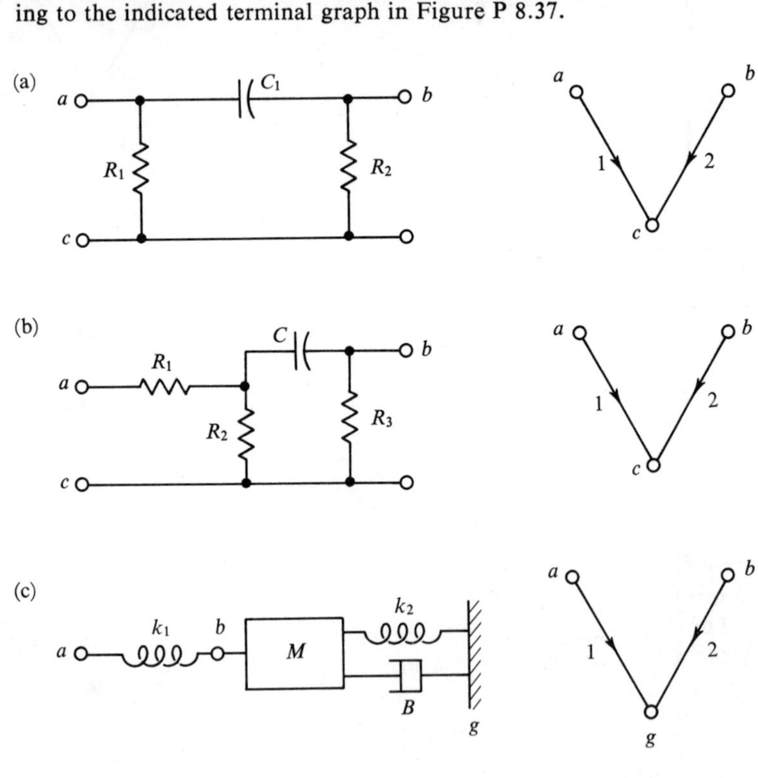

Fig. P 8.37.

8.38. Derive a state model for the twin-tee network shown in Figure P 8.38.

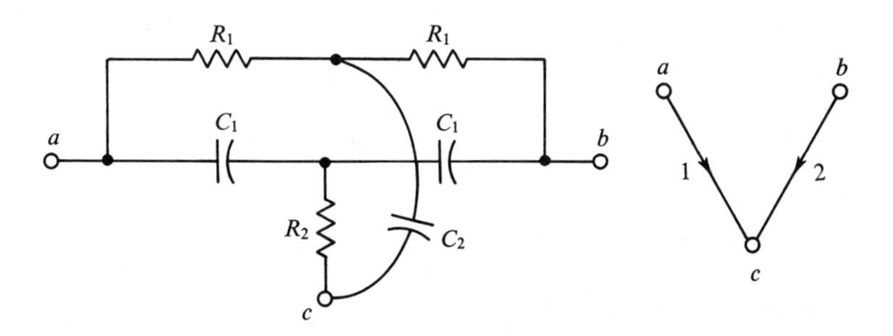

Fig. P 8.38.

8.39. Derive state models for the systems of Problem 8.36(c) and 8.37(c).

9 *Topological Concepts*

The system graph concept was first introduced in Chapter 5, and used in all succeeding chapters. In this graphical representation each component of a system is shown as an oriented line segment or as a set of line segments if the component has more than two terminals. The system graph illustrates the interconnection of the various components. A system analysis consists, then, of combining the component equations with the constraint equations imposed by the interconnections of the system graph. The constraint equations are determined directly from the "topology" of the system graph and are independent of the kinds of components represented therein. An independent study of system topology then leads to some unique methods of writing constraint equations.

These methods of writing constraint equations have been used in previous chapters, and most of the definitions and concepts have already been introduced. The purpose of this chapter is to state and prove the fundamental theorems underlying linear graph theory. We have previously assumed, for example, that the $v - 1$ node equations and $e - v + 1$ mesh equations are an independent set of e equations, but have done so without proof. This chapter, therefore, is not intended to be studied in detail by the student, but is included for completeness.

9.1 A System with Separate Parts

The systems to be studied in succeeding chapters will be more complex and will not only contain multiterminal components but will incorporate more than one system discipline. A hydraulic servomechanism, for example, includes electrical components, hydraulic components, and mechanical components. A system graph of such a system consists of at least three separate parts—one for each system discipline. As an example of a strictly mechanical system which contains multiterminal components and separate parts, consider Figure 9.1. This system represents a signal transmission link which may be used to measure shaft torque.

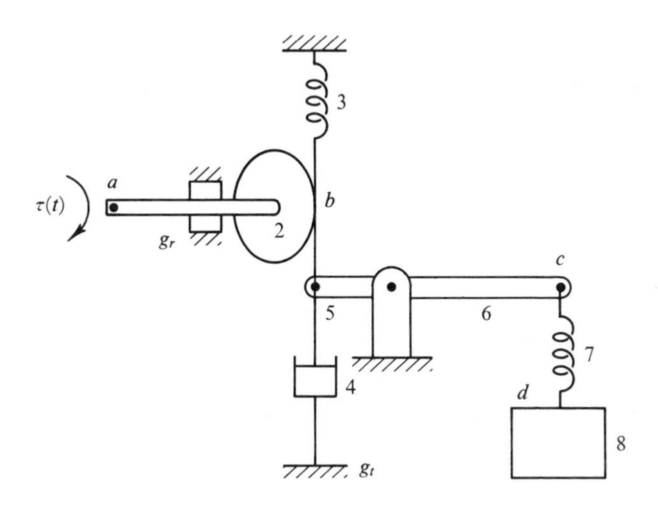

Fig. 9.1. *Mechanical system.*

The system consists of seven components, which are characterized as follows:

(a) Torque driver

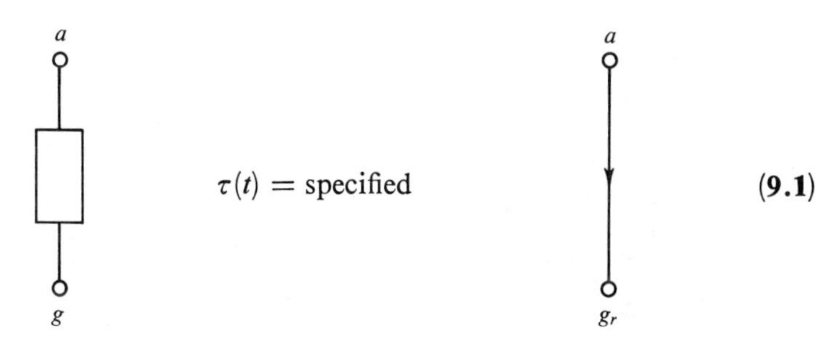

$$\tau(t) = \text{specified} \qquad \textbf{(9.1)}$$

(b) Shaft and pulley

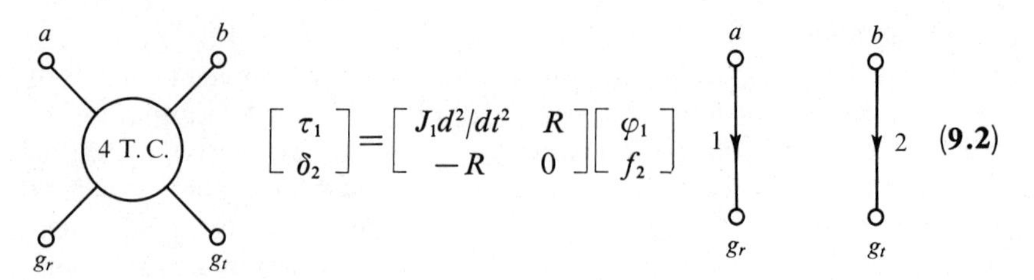

$$\begin{bmatrix} \tau_1 \\ \delta_2 \end{bmatrix} = \begin{bmatrix} J_1 d^2/dt^2 & R \\ -R & 0 \end{bmatrix} \begin{bmatrix} \varphi_1 \\ f_2 \end{bmatrix} \tag{9.2}$$

(c) Springs 3 and 7

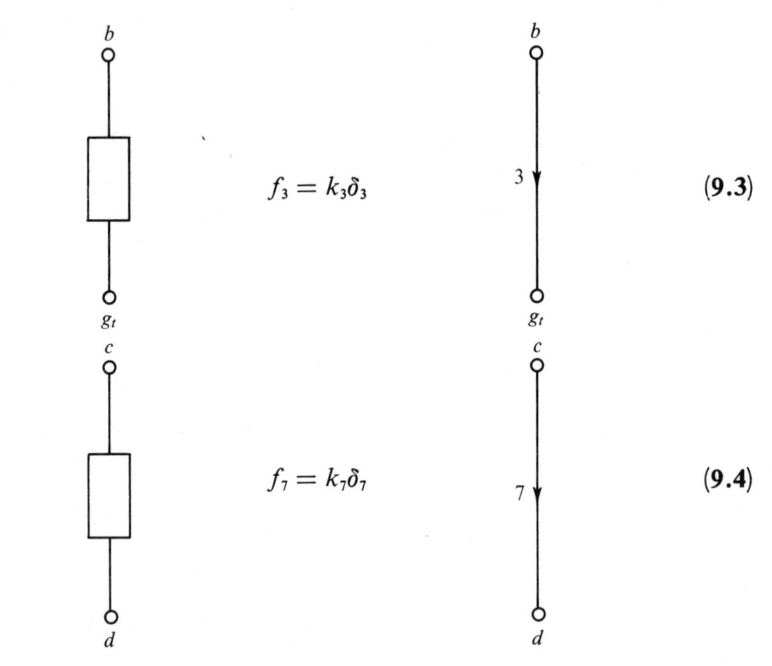

$$f_3 = k_3 \delta_3 \tag{9.3}$$

$$f_7 = k_7 \delta_7 \tag{9.4}$$

(d) Dashpot

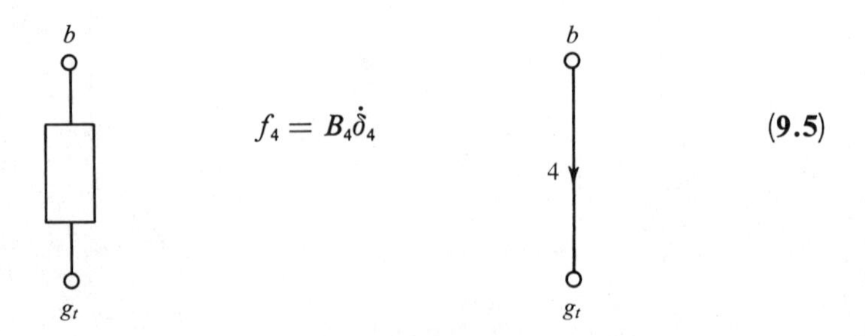

$$f_4 = B_4 \dot{\delta}_4 \tag{9.5}$$

(e) Mass

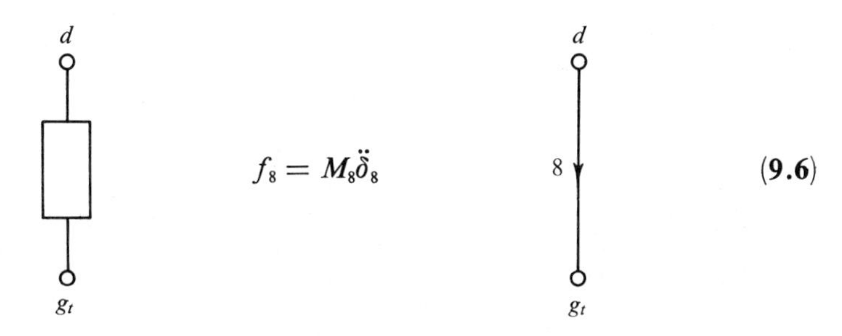

$$f_8 = M_8\ddot{\delta}_8 \tag{9.6}$$

(f) Lever

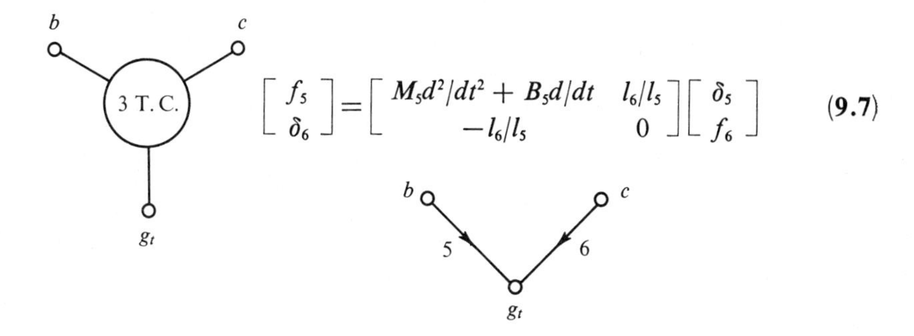

$$\begin{bmatrix} f_5 \\ \delta_6 \end{bmatrix} = \begin{bmatrix} M_5 d^2/dt^2 + B_5 d/dt & l_6/l_5 \\ -l_6/l_5 & 0 \end{bmatrix} \begin{bmatrix} \delta_5 \\ f_6 \end{bmatrix} \tag{9.7}$$

Equations 9.1 through 9.7 are terminal equations of the components. These equations and the associated terminal graphs form the mathematical statement of the component characteristics.

The next step is to obtain a mathematical statement of the compo-

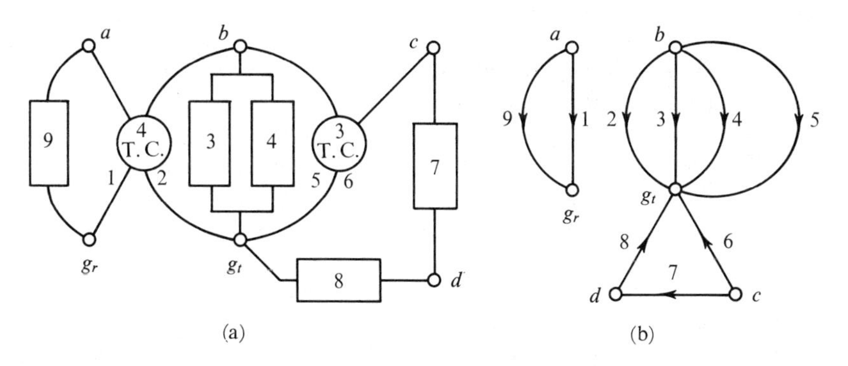

Fig. 9.2. *Mechanical system: (a) interconnection schematic; and (b) system graph.*

nent interconnections by constructing the system graph. We first join the symbolic schematics of the components in a one-to-one correspondence with the physical system. This is shown in Figure 9.2 (a). Subsequently, we establish the system graph shown in Figure 9.2 (b).

As a result of the interconnections, constraints are established on the terminal variables of the components. We have learned to express these constraints in terms of circuit and vertex equations. Two techniques of finding independent circuit and vertex equations were presented in Chapter 6. (1) In formulating mesh and node equations we relied upon expressing the constraints in terms of $e - v + 1$ mesh equations and $v - 1$ node equations. (2) Another technique consisted of finding the $e - v + 1$ fundamental circuit equations and the $v - 1$ fundamental cutset equations from the system graph. The latter method was useful when formulating the state variable equations.

The example selected for the present discussion is not amenable to mesh or node formulation for the following two reasons: (1) the system contains multiterminal components whose terminal equations we are not in a position to process in either of the two formulation procedures; and (2) the system graph appears in two parts, which invalidates the numbers $e - v + 1$ and $v - 1$ used to determine sets of independent equations. However, this example can easily be formulated using the $e - v + p$ fundamental circuit equations and the $v - p$ fundamental cutset equations where p equals the number of separate parts—two in this example.

Before discussing the formulation of systems like this example, let us develop the theoretical structure related to the study of linear graphs. The first objective will be the presentation of a series of useful definitions related to the study of system graphs. In order to be complete, a number of definitions already introduced in Chapter 6 are repeated here.

9.2 Basic Definitions and Elementary Properties of Systems Graphs

Consider the system graph of Figure 9.3 as an example for the following definitions.

Element: An element is an oriented line segment in the system graph (also called an edge).

Vertex: A vertex is the endpoint of an element. A vertex is said to be incident to an element if it is an endpoint of an element.

Subgraph: A subgraph is a graph consisting of a subset of elements which are part of a given graph. *Example:* Elements 4, 6 and 7 comprise a subgraph.

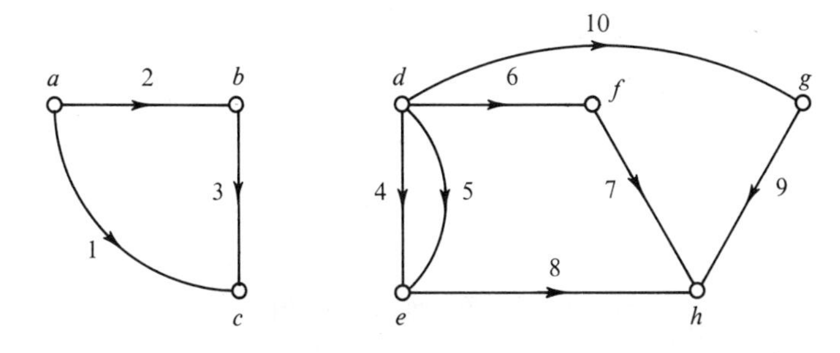

Fig. 9.3. *Typical system graph.*

Path: A path is a subgraph constructed as a sequential assembly of elements of a given graph. The vertices belonging to a path subgraph have exactly two incident elements, and the vertices at the beginning and the end of the path subgraph have exactly one incident element. *Example:* See Figure 9.4.

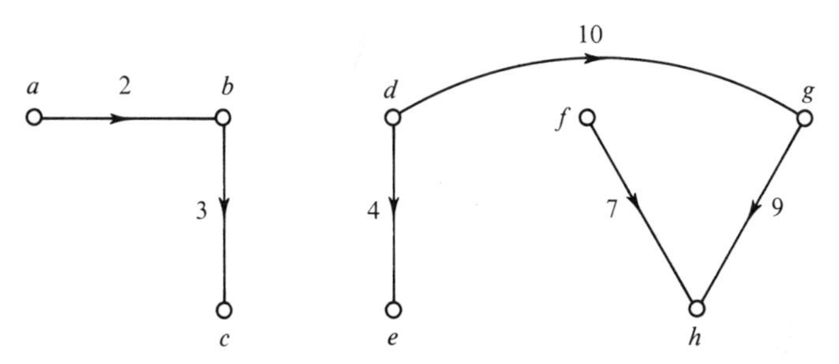

Fig. 9.4. *Example of paths of the graph of Figure 9.3.*

Connected graph: If for a given graph there exists a path between every pair of vertices, then the graph is connected.

Separated graph: If a graph is not a connected graph, it is a separated graph. Each connected subgraph of the separated graph is called a part. *Example:* The system graph of Figure 9.3 is a separated graph consisting of two parts. Each part is a connected subgraph.

Circuit: A circuit is a subgraph consisting of one closed path such that each element in the subgraph has exactly two vertices incident. *Example:* See Figure 9.5.

Tree: A tree T is a subgraph of a given graph G satisfying *all* conditions listed below:

1. It is connected.
2. It contains no circuits.
3. It contains all vertices.

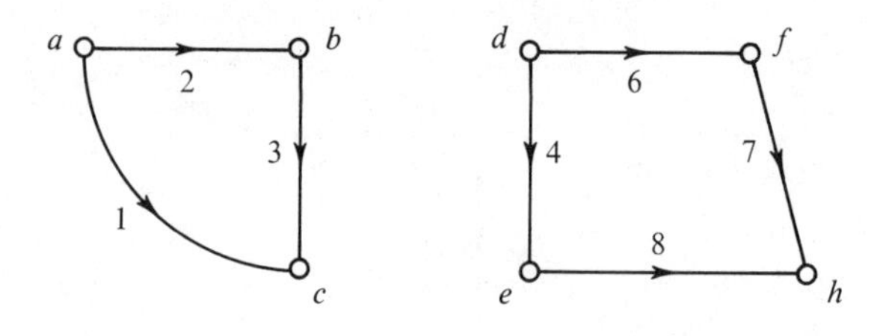

Fig. 9.5. *Examples of circuits.*

The elements of a tree are indicated by heavy lines. *Example:* See Figure 9.6. One of the most important properties of a tree is that there

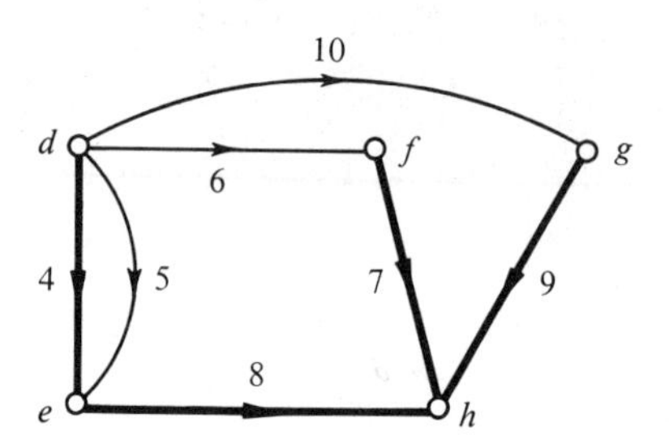

Fig. 9.6. *Example of a tree in a graph.*

exists one and only one path between any two vertices of a tree. In addition, a tree has exactly $v - 1$ elements. There are usually many possibilities for selecting a tree from a graph. However, it is of no particular interest to enumerate these possibilities.

Cotree: A cotree is the subgraph (not necessarily connected) formed when the elements belonging to a tree are deleted from the given graph. For a graph having e elements and v vertices, a tree has $v - 1$ elements and the corresponding cotree has $e - (v - 1) = e - v + 1$ elements. A cotree may be a separated subgraph.

Forest: If a system graph has p parts, then a set of trees corresponding to each part forms a forest. The complement of a forest is a coforest. A forest has $v - p$ elements, while the corresponding coforest has $e - v + p$ elements.

Branches: All elements of a forest are called branches.*

Chords: All elements of a coforest are called chords.

* Some authors refer to all elements of a system graph as branches and define those branches belonging to the chosen forest as "tree branches."

9.3 Matrices of the Graph

Consider the graph shown in Figure 9.7. If we identify it as a system graph, we may associate with each element a pair of variables consisting of an across variable and a through variable. The significance of the system graph is manifested in its role of displaying the continuity

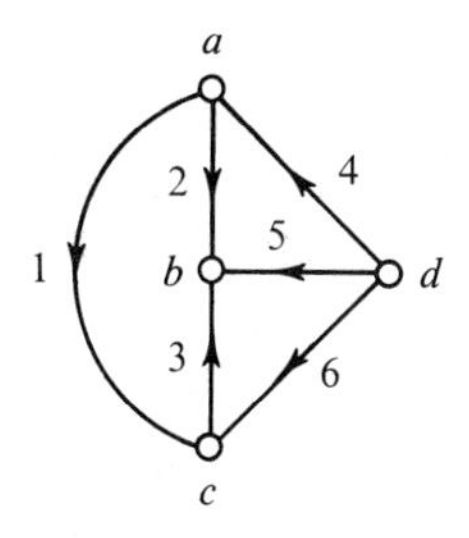

Fig. 9.7. *System graph.*

and compatibility constraints imposed on these variables. We express these constraints in terms of the circuit equations and the vertex equations. The graph of Figure 9.7 contains the following seven circuits involving elements:*

1, 2, 3
1, 4, 6
1, 2, 5, 6
1, 4, 5, 3
2, 4, 5
3, 5, 6
2, 3, 4, 6

For each one of these circuits we may write one circuit equation. If a clockwise orientation is taken as positive, these equations are

$$\left.\begin{aligned} -x_1 + x_2 - x_3 &= 0 \\ -x_1 - x_4 + x_6 &= 0 \\ -x_1 + x_2 - x_5 + x_6 &= 0 \\ -x_1 - x_4 + x_5 - x_3 &= 0 \\ -x_2 - x_4 + x_5 &= 0 \\ x_3 - x_5 + x_6 &= 0 \\ -x_2 + x_3 - x_4 + x_6 &= 0 \end{aligned}\right\} \quad (9.8)$$

* The number of possible circuits—seven in this example—and how to find all of them is not important in this development. Of ultimate importance is the number of *independent* circuits.

If these equations are written in matrix format, we have

$$\begin{bmatrix} -1 & 1 & -1 & 0 & 0 & 0 \\ -1 & 0 & 0 & -1 & 0 & 1 \\ -1 & 1 & 0 & 0 & -1 & 1 \\ -1 & 0 & -1 & -1 & 1 & 0 \\ 0 & -1 & 0 & -1 & 1 & 0 \\ 0 & 0 & 1 & 0 & -1 & 1 \\ 0 & -1 & 1 & -1 & 0 & 1 \end{bmatrix} \begin{bmatrix} x_1 \\ x_2 \\ x_3 \\ x_4 \\ x_5 \\ x_6 \end{bmatrix} = \mathbf{0} \tag{9.9}$$

In a similar fashion, vertex equations may be written for each one of the four vertices. If the orientation away from a vertex is taken as positive, these equations are

$$\left.\begin{array}{ll} \text{vertex a.} & y_1 + y_2 - y_4 = 0 \\ \text{b.} & -y_2 - y_3 - y_5 = 0 \\ \text{c.} & -y_1 + y_3 - y_6 = 0 \\ \text{d.} & y_4 + y_5 + y_6 = 0 \end{array}\right] \tag{9.10}$$

Or in matrix format,

$$\begin{bmatrix} 1 & 1 & 0 & -1 & 0 & 0 \\ 0 & -1 & -1 & 0 & -1 & 0 \\ -1 & 0 & 1 & 0 & 0 & -1 \\ 0 & 0 & 0 & 1 & 1 & 1 \end{bmatrix} \begin{bmatrix} y_1 \\ y_2 \\ y_3 \\ y_4 \\ y_5 \\ y_6 \end{bmatrix} = \mathbf{0} \tag{9.11}$$

The circuit Equations 9.8 are expressed as a matrix equation of the form

$$\mathbf{B}_c\mathbf{X} = \mathbf{0} \tag{9.12}$$

In general, we refer to $\mathbf{B}_c$ as the *circuit matrix* of a graph. $\mathbf{B}_c$ is a matrix of order $n \times e$, where n denotes the number of all possible circuits in a graph and e represents the number of elements; $\mathbf{X}$ is a column vector representing the across variables of the elements. The circuit matrix may be constructed in a formal manner from the graph upon recognizing that the coefficients of the matrix are definable as follows:

$$\mathbf{B}_c = [b_{ij}]_{n \times e} \tag{9.13}$$

where $b_{ij} = +1$ if element j is part of circuit i with a clockwise orientation, $b_{ij} = -1$ if element j is part of circuit i with counterclockwise orientation, and $b_{ij} = 0$ if element j is not part of circuit i.

In a similar fashion, we write the vertex equations as the matrix equation

$$\mathbf{A}_v \mathbf{Y} = 0 \tag{9.14}$$

The matrix $\mathbf{A}_v$ is called the *vertex matrix* of a graph. The order of this matrix is $v \times e$, where v is the number of vertices; $\mathbf{Y}$ is a column vector representing the through variables of the e elements. The vertex matrix may be formally obtained from the graph. We write

$$\mathbf{A}_v = [a_{ij}]_{v \times e} \tag{9.15}$$

where $a_{ij} = +1$ if element j is incident at vertex i and is oriented away from the vertex, $a_{ij} = -1$ if element j is incident at vertex i and is oriented toward the vertex, and $a_{ij} = 0$ if element j is not incident at vertex i.

Both the circuit equations and the vertex equations serve as the basis for the formulation procedures developed in Chapters 5 and 6. It has been pointed out that not all circuit equations or vertex equations are necessary. In fact, there are exactly $e - v + 1$ circuit equations and $v - 1$ vertex equations which must be utilized in a selected formulation procedure. For the purpose of assuring linear dependence for these sets of equations, the node-vertex equations and the mesh-circuit equations were defined. The node-vertex equations are obtained by writing vertex equations for $v - 1$ vertices called the nodes and specifying the vth vertex as the reference node. On the other hand, the mesh-circuit equations are associated with those circuits formed by all " windows " of the graph. It is helpful to define matrices associated with those equations.

For the graph of Figure 9.7 we may write the following mesh-circuit and node-vertex equations. The graph is shown again in Figure 9.8 with the appropriate designation of nodes and meshes.

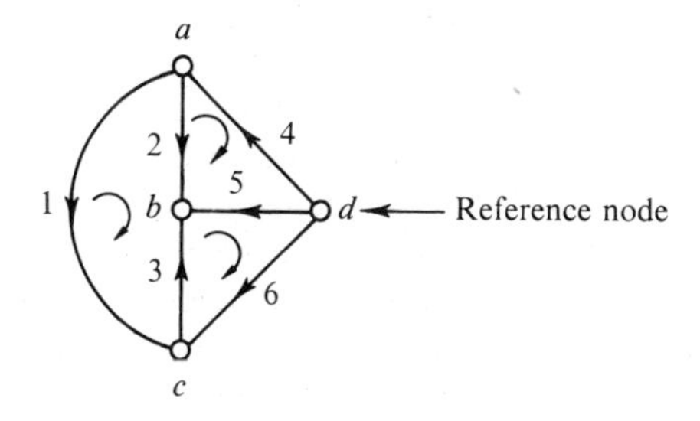

Fig. 9.8. *System graph; selection of nodes and meshes.*

The mesh-circuit equations are written in matrix format

$$\begin{bmatrix} 1 & 1 & -1 & 0 & 0 & 0 \\ 0 & -1 & 0 & -1 & 1 & 0 \\ 0 & 0 & 1 & 0 & -1 & 1 \end{bmatrix} \begin{bmatrix} x_1 \\ x_2 \\ x_3 \\ x_4 \\ x_5 \\ x_6 \end{bmatrix} = 0 \tag{9.16}$$

Or symbolically,

$$\mathbf{B_m X = 0} \tag{9.17}$$

$\mathbf{B_m}$ is called the mesh-circuit matrix. The order of $\mathbf{B_m}$ is $(e-v+1)\times e$. Since the mesh circuits are a subset of all possible circuits, the matrix $\mathbf{B_m}$ is a submatrix of $\mathbf{B_c}$. $\mathbf{B_m}$ is obtained from $\mathbf{B_c}$ by deleting all rows not corresponding to a mesh circuit.

If we choose vertex d as the reference vertex, the node-vertex equations are

$$\begin{bmatrix} 1 & 1 & 0 & -1 & 0 & 0 \\ 0 & -1 & -1 & 0 & -1 & 0 \\ -1 & 0 & 0 & 1 & 0 & -1 \end{bmatrix} \begin{bmatrix} y_1 \\ y_2 \\ y_3 \\ y_4 \\ y_5 \\ y_6 \end{bmatrix} = 0 \tag{9.18}$$

The symbolic form of the node-vertex equations is

$$\mathbf{A_n Y = 0} \tag{9.19}$$

The matrix $\mathbf{A_n}$ is called the node-vertex matrix. The order of this matrix is $(v-1)\times e$. $\mathbf{A_n}$ is a submatrix of $\mathbf{A_v}$. $\mathbf{A_n}$ may be obtained from $\mathbf{A_v}$ by simply deleting the row corresponding to the reference vertex.

Any vertex equation or circuit equation associated with the matrices defined above is a mathematical statement of constraints generated through the interconnection of components. In a formulation process, be it node-formulation or mesh-formulation or any other formulation procedure to be presented later, we depend upon expressing these constraints in terms of just the number of equations which are both necessary and sufficient. The condition of sufficiency is satisfied when all possible circuit and vertex equations are considered; the condition of necessity is satisfied when no redundancy exists among the circuit and vertex equations. These extremely important points will be clarified by examining the linear independence of the circuit and vertex equations in terms of the ranks of the circuit matrix and the vertex matrix.

In Chapter 6 the linear dependence of a set of row vectors was defined: A set of row vectors, $\mathbf{C}_1, \mathbf{C}_2, \cdots, \mathbf{C}_m$ is linearly dependent if there exist m constants, $k_1, k_2, \cdots, k_m$, not all zero such that

$$k_1\mathbf{C}_1 + k_2\mathbf{C}_2 + \cdots + k_m\mathbf{C}_m = \mathbf{0} \tag{9.19}$$

Otherwise, the vectors are linearly independent. Using Equation 9.9 as an illustration, the m vectors are

$$\begin{array}{l} \mathbf{C}_1 = [-1 \quad 1 \quad -1 \quad 0 \quad 0 \quad 0] \\ \mathbf{C}_2 = [-1 \quad 0 \quad 0 \quad -1 \quad 0 \quad 1] \\ \mathbf{C}_3 = [-1 \quad 1 \quad 0 \quad 0 \quad -1 \quad 1] \\ \mathbf{C}_4 = [-1 \quad 0 \quad -1 \quad -1 \quad 1 \quad 0] \\ \mathbf{C}_5 = [\ 0 \quad -1 \quad 0 \quad -1 \quad 1 \quad 0] \\ \mathbf{C}_6 = [\ 0 \quad 0 \quad 1 \quad 0 \quad -1 \quad 1] \\ \mathbf{C}_7 = [\ 0 \quad -1 \quad 1 \quad -1 \quad 0 \quad 1] \end{array} \tag{9.9}$$

For such a large number of vectors, the use of the definition to establish how many and which of these vectors are linearly independent is quite impractical. If, however, we know the rank of the matrix containing these row vectors, we immediately know the number of independent vectors as stated by the following theorem.

Theorem 9.1 Given a matrix of m vectors of n components whose rank is $r < m$, there are exactly r vectors which are linearly independent. Furthermore, the remaining $m - r$ vectors can be expressed as a linear combination of these r vectors

Proof: Consider the matrix $\mathbf{C}$ of Equations 9.20. For this matrix, $m \leq n$. Since the rank of the matrix is r, one may interchange rows and columns necessary to bring an r-order submatrix in the upper left-hand corner with rank r. If all rows and columns are then renumbered in natural order, we have

$$\mathbf{C} = \left[\begin{array}{cccc|ccc} c_{11} & c_{12} & \cdots & c_{1r} & c_{1r+1} & \cdots & c_{1n} \\ c_{21} & c_{22} & \cdots & c_{2r} & c_{2r+1} & \cdots & c_{2n} \\ \cdot & & & & & & \\ \cdot & & & & & & \\ \cdot & & & & & & \\ c_{r1} & c_{r2} & \cdots & c_{rr} & c_{rr+1} & \cdots & c_{rn} \\ \hline \cdot & & & & & & \\ \cdot & & & & & & \\ c_{m1} & c_{m2} & \cdots & c_{mr} & c_{mr+1} & & c_{mn} \end{array}\right] \tag{9.20}$$

The r-order submatrix $\mathbf{D}_r$ has a nonvanishing determinant, *i.e.*,

$$|\mathbf{D_r}| = \begin{vmatrix} c_{11} & c_{12} & \cdots & c_{1r} \\ c_{21} & c_{22} & \cdots & c_{2r} \\ \cdot & & & \\ \cdot & & & \\ \cdot & & & \\ c_{r1} & c_{r2} & \cdots & c_{rr} \end{vmatrix} \neq 0 \tag{9.21}$$

Consider now an $(r + 1)$ order submatrix, $\mathbf{D_{r+1}}$. We have

$$|\mathbf{D_{r+1}}| = \begin{vmatrix} c_{11} & c_{12} & \cdots & c_{1r} & c_{1q} \\ c_{21} & c_{22} & \cdots & c_{2r} & c_{2q} \\ \cdot & & & & \\ \cdot & & & & \\ \cdot & & & & \\ c_{r1} & c_{r2} & \cdots & c_{rr} & c_{rq} \\ c_{p1} & c_{p2} & \cdots & c_{pr} & c_{pq} \end{vmatrix} = 0 \tag{9.22}$$

where the added row and column respectively are not a row or column of $\mathbf{D_r}$. Now select the constants $k_1, k_2, \cdots, k_{r+1}$ as the respective cofactors of the last column vector of $\mathbf{D_{r+1}}$ and note that $k_{r+1} = |\mathbf{D_r}|$. Recall that the value of the determinant of $\mathbf{D_{r+1}}$ may be obtained by forming the sum of the products obtained by multiplying each element of a column of $\mathbf{D_{r+1}}$ by its factors. Therefore

$$k_1c_{1q} + k_2c_{2q} + \cdots + k_rc_{rq} + k_{r+1}c_{pq} = |\mathbf{D_{r+1}}| = 0 \tag{9.23}$$

Now if the last column of $\mathbf{D_{r+1}}$ is replaced by another column of $\mathbf{C}$ not previously used, say column s, then we may also write

$$k_1c_{1s} + k_2c_{2s} + \cdots + k_{r+1}c_{ps} = 0 \tag{9.24}$$

since the cofactors are identical to the k's obtained above. Thus, for all columns not included in $\mathbf{D_r}$,

$$k_1c_{1t} + k_2c_{2t} + \cdots + k_rc_{rt} + k_{r+1}c_{pt} = 0, \quad t = r + 1 \cdots n \tag{9.25}$$

We further recall that the sum of the products formed by multiplying the elements of a column of $\mathbf{D_{r+1}}$ by the corresponding cofactors of another column vanishes. Hence, we have

$$k_1c_{1i} + k_2c_{2i} + \cdots + k_rc_{ri} + k_{r+1}c_{pi} = 0, \quad i = 1, 2, \cdots, r \tag{9.26}$$

After combining this result with Equation 9.25, we have

$$k_1c_{1t} + k_2c_{2t} + \cdots + k_rc_{rt} + k_{r+1}c_{r+1t} = 0, \quad t = 1, 2, \cdots, n \tag{9.27}$$

Upon summing over all t,

$$k_1\mathbf{C_1} + k_2\mathbf{C_2} + \cdots + k_r\mathbf{C_r} + k_{r+1}\mathbf{C_p} = \mathbf{0} \tag{9.28}$$

Since $k_{r+1} = |\mathbf{D}| \neq 0$, $\mathbf{C_p}$ is a linear combination of the r vectors $\mathbf{C_1}$, $\mathbf{C_2}, \cdots, \mathbf{C_r}$. Since $\mathbf{C_p}$ was arbitrarily selected from the m-r vectors not included in $\mathbf{D}$, any of these m-r vectors can be expressed as a linear combination of the r vectors $\mathbf{C_1}, \mathbf{C_2}, \cdots, \mathbf{C_r}$.

It remains to be shown that the r vectors $\mathbf{C_1}, \mathbf{C_2}, \cdots, \mathbf{C_r}$ are linearly independent. Since the components of $\mathbf{C_p}$ are not all zero, we have

$$k_1\mathbf{C_1} + k_2\mathbf{C_2} + \cdots + k_r\mathbf{C_r} \neq \mathbf{0} \tag{9.29}$$

This proves the theorem.

Corollary 9.1. The m vectors (rows or columns) of an $m \times n$ matrix of rank $m \leq n$ are linearly independent.

Example 9.1. Find the rank of the matrix consisting of the row vectors in Equation (9.9). By the following elementary matrix transformations we obtain a unit matrix of rank 3.

1. Multiply first row by -1.
2. Replace column 2 by column 2 plus column 1.
3. Replace column 3 by column 3 minus column 1.

We then have

$$\mathbf{C}' = \begin{bmatrix} 1 & 0 & 0 & 0 & 0 & 0 \\ -1 & -1 & 1 & -1 & 0 & 1 \\ -1 & 0 & 1 & 0 & -1 & 1 \\ -1 & -1 & 0 & -1 & 1 & 0 \\ 0 & -1 & 0 & -1 & 1 & 0 \\ 0 & 0 & 1 & 0 & -1 & 1 \\ 0 & -1 & 1 & -1 & 0 & 1 \end{bmatrix}$$

4. Multiply second row by -1.
5. Replace column 1 by column 1 minus column 2.
6. Replace column 3 by column 3 plus column 2.
7. Replace column 4 by column 4 minus column 2.
8. Replace column 6 by column 6 plus column 2.

Then

$$\mathbf{C}'' = \begin{bmatrix} 1 & 0 & 0 & 0 & 0 & 0 \\ 0 & 1 & 0 & 0 & 0 & 0 \\ -1 & 0 & 1 & 0 & -1 & 1 \\ 0 & -1 & -1 & 0 & 1 & -1 \\ 1 & -1 & -1 & 0 & 1 & -1 \\ 0 & 0 & 1 & 0 & -1 & 1 \\ 1 & -1 & 0 & 0 & 0 & 0 \end{bmatrix}$$

9. Replace column 1 by column 1 plus column 3.
10. Replace column 5 by column 5 plus column 3.
11. Replace column 6 by column 6 minus column 3.

Then

$$\mathbf{C}''' = \begin{bmatrix} 1 & 0 & 0 & 0 & 0 & 0 \\ 0 & 1 & 0 & 0 & 0 & 0 \\ 0 & 0 & 1 & 0 & 0 & 0 \\ -1 & -1 & -1 & 0 & 0 & 0 \\ 0 & -1 & -1 & 0 & 0 & 0 \\ 1 & 0 & 1 & 0 & 0 & 0 \\ 1 & -1 & 0 & 0 & 0 & 0 \end{bmatrix}$$

Finally,

12. Replace row 4 by row 4 plus rows 1, 2, and 3.
13. Replace row 5 by row 5 plus rows 2 and 3.
14. Replace row 6 by row 6 minus rows 1 and 3.
15. Replace row 7 by row 7 minus row 1 plus row 2.

The end result is the matrix

$$\begin{bmatrix} 1 & 0 & 0 & 0 & 0 & 0 \\ 0 & 1 & 0 & 0 & 0 & 0 \\ 0 & 0 & 1 & 0 & 0 & 0 \\ 0 & 0 & 0 & 0 & 0 & 0 \\ 0 & 0 & 0 & 0 & 0 & 0 \\ 0 & 0 & 0 & 0 & 0 & 0 \\ 0 & 0 & 0 & 0 & 0 & 0 \end{bmatrix}$$

which has rank 3. Therefore there are three linearly independent vectors in the matrix **C**.

We have already suspected that the rank is three because there are three meshes, but the mesh-circuits are not the only set of circuits which are linearly independent. As will be shown later, the mesh circuits always are linearly independent, but these may not be the most useful set to use for a system solution. For non-planar networks, that is, networks which cannot be drawn on a plane without crossovers, all meshes may be hard to identify. The following sections lead up to the concept of fundamental circuits. Such circuits are easy to identify from the system graph and are proven to be linearly independent.

We connect the result to Theorem 9.1 with the objective of investigating the linear independence of the circuit and vertex equations. We wish to show that exactly $e - v + 1$ properly chosen circuit equations and any $v - 1$ vertex equations are independent. The property of independence of a set of simultaneous equations is related entirely to the coefficient matrix of the equations. Therefore, the results of Theorem 9.1 now permit a restatement of this objective. We need to show that the rank of the circuit matrix is exactly $e - v + 1$ and the rank of the vertex matrix is exactly $v - 1$.

9.4 Rank of the Vertex Matrix

The vertex matrix is the coefficient of the vertex equations. They are written on the basis of the algorithm defined by Equations 9.15. The vertex matrix equation is

$$\mathbf{A}_v\mathbf{Y} = \mathbf{0}$$

It is our objective in this section to investigate the rank of the matrix $\mathbf{A}_v$.

Theorem 9.2 The rank of the vertex matrix of a connected graph G is exactly $v - 1$.

Proof: Consider the structure of $\mathbf{A}_v$ for a connected graph. Each row corresponds to a vertex and each column corresponds to an element. Since the graph is connected, each vertex has at least one element incident, leaving no row vector void. Furthermore, each column, say the ith column, has exactly two entries corresponding to the ith element. Let this element be incident at vertices j and k with orientation from j to k. Then the ith column contains a $(+1)$ in the jth row and a (-1) in the kth row. This is true of all columns. The sum of the v row vectors vanishes since there is exactly one (-1) and one $(+1)$ in each column. This implies a linear dependence of the v row vectors. By Theorem 9.1, the rank of $\mathbf{A}_v$ can at most be $v - 1$. This constitutes an upper bound of the rank.

Consider also the sum of $v - 1$ row vectors formed by deleting the jth row, which itself contains at least one non-zero entry. Let one non-zero entry of the jth row be in the ith column. Then the ith column contains exactly one other non-zero entry, say in the kth row. Hence, the sum of the $v - 1$ row vectors cannot vanish. Indeed, no linear combination of any $v - 1$ row vectors is linearly independent. We conclude that the rank of $\mathbf{A}_v$ is at least $v - 1$ by Theorem 9.1. This constitutes a lower bound on the rank. The two bounds on the rank intersect at $v - 1$. This proves the theorem.

If a graph is not connected, but consists of p parts, then by repeated application of Theorem 9.2 we may show that the rank of the vertex matrix for the graph is $v - p$.

9.5 Orthogonality Relation of Vertex and Circuit Matrix

A useful property of the matrices $\mathbf{A}_v$ and $\mathbf{B}_c$ will be developed here. This property deals with the relation

$$\mathbf{A}_v\mathbf{B}_c' = \mathbf{0} \tag{9.30}$$

or

$$\mathbf{B}_c\mathbf{A}_v' = \mathbf{0} \tag{9.30}$$

where the prime means the transpose of the respective matrix.

If the order in which the column vectors of the two matrices are arranged is identical, Equations 9.30 hold. We call this property the orthogonality relation of $\mathbf{A_v}$ and $\mathbf{B_c}$. This relation is easily verified for the vertex and circuit equations for the graph of Figure 9.7 as given by Equations 9.9 and 9.11. When the matrices associated with these equations are multiplied as dictated by Equations 9.30, we have

$$\begin{bmatrix} -1 & 1 & -1 & 0 & 0 & 0 \\ -1 & 0 & 0 & -1 & 0 & 1 \\ -1 & 1 & 0 & 0 & -1 & 1 \\ -1 & 0 & -1 & -1 & 1 & 0 \\ 0 & -1 & 0 & -1 & 1 & 0 \\ 0 & 0 & 1 & 0 & -1 & 1 \\ 0 & -1 & 1 & -1 & 0 & 1 \end{bmatrix} \begin{bmatrix} 1 & 0 & -1 & 0 \\ 1 & -1 & 0 & 0 \\ 0 & -1 & 1 & 0 \\ -1 & 0 & 0 & 1 \\ 0 & -1 & 0 & 1 \\ 0 & 0 & -1 & 1 \end{bmatrix} = \mathbf{0} \qquad (9.31)$$

that is,

$$\mathbf{B_c} \times \mathbf{A'_v} = \mathbf{0}$$

The reader may also verify that $\mathbf{A_v B'_c} = \mathbf{0}$ for the numerical cases above.

Theorem 9.3 (Orthogonality relation) Any row vector $\mathbf{B_i}$ of $\mathbf{B_c}$ and any row vector $\mathbf{A_k}$ of $\mathbf{A_v}$ are mutually orthogonal, provided the components of the vectors are arranged in an order corresponding to the same elements.

Proof: Consider the ith circuit and the kth vertex of the subgraph shown in Figure 9.9.

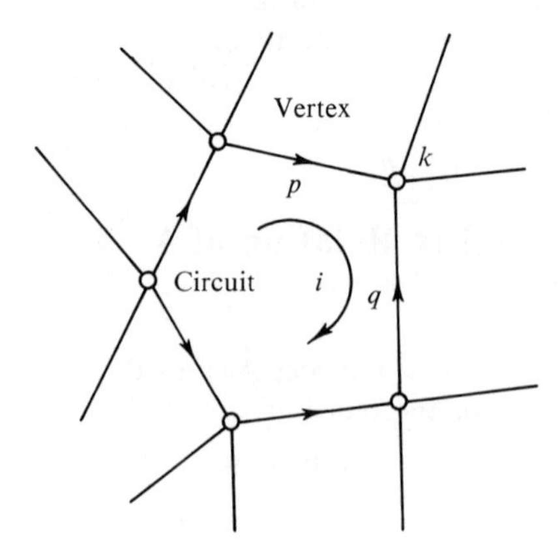

Fig. 9.9. *Subgraph containing i^{th} circuit and k^{th} vertex.*

The row vector $\mathbf{B_i}$ is given as

$$\mathbf{B_i} = [\beta_{i1}, \beta_{i2}, \cdots, \beta_{ij}, \cdots, \beta_{ie}] \tag{9.32}$$

where $\beta_{ij} = +1, -1$, or 0; $j = 1, 2, \cdots, e$. The row vector $\mathbf{A_k}$ is given as

$$\mathbf{A_k} = [\alpha_{k1}, \alpha_{k2}, \cdots, \alpha_{kj}, \cdots, \alpha_{ke}] \tag{9.33}$$

where $\alpha_{jk} = +1, -1$, or 0; $j = 1, 2, \cdots, e$. We form the product

$$\mathbf{B_i A_k'} = [\beta_{i1}, \beta_{i2}, \cdots, \beta_{ij}, \cdots, \beta_{ie}] \begin{bmatrix} \alpha_{k1} \\ \alpha_{k2} \\ \cdot \\ \cdot \\ \cdot \\ \alpha_{kj} \\ \cdot \\ \cdot \\ \cdot \\ \alpha_{ke} \end{bmatrix}$$

$$= \sum_{j=1}^{e} \beta_{ij} \alpha_{kj} \tag{9.34}$$

And, similarly,

$$\mathbf{A_k B_i'} = \sum_{j=1}^{e} \beta_{ij} \alpha_{kj}$$

Consider the following cases to show that

$$\sum_{j=1}^{e} \beta_{ij} \alpha_{kj} = 0$$

(a) Element j incident at k^{th} vertex, but not part of ith circuit. Then

$$\alpha_{kj} \neq 0$$

and

$$\beta_{ij} = 0$$

so that

$$\beta_{ij} \alpha_{kj} = 0$$

(b) Element j part of ith circuit but not incident at k^{th} vertex. Then

$$\beta_{ij} \neq 0$$

and

$$\alpha_{kj} = 0$$

so that

$$\beta_{ij}\alpha_{kj} = 0$$

(c) Of all e elements there are only two, say $j = p$ and $j = q$, that are *both* incident at vertex k *and* part of circuit i. This follows from the definition of the circuit. In view of the results of cases a and b above, it remains to be shown that

$$\sum_{j=1}^{e} \beta_{ij}\alpha_{kj} = \beta_{ip}\alpha_{kp} + \beta_{iq}\alpha_{kq} = 0$$

For a given orientation of circuit i and elements p and q, we may have: If

$$\beta_{ip} = \pm 1 \qquad \text{and} \qquad \beta_{iq} = \mp 1$$

then

$$\alpha_{kp} = \pm 1 \qquad \text{and} \qquad \alpha_{kq} = \pm 1$$

Indeed,

$$\sum_{j=1}^{e} \beta_{ij}\alpha_{kj} = 0 \qquad j = 1, 2, \cdots, e$$

Theorem 9.3 is repeatedly applied to each possible product of the row vectors of $\mathbf{B_c}$ and $\mathbf{A_v}$ to establish Equations 9.30 as valid.

The orthogonality relation is effectively applied in inferring an upper bound on the rank of the circuit matrix. This is considered in the next section.

9.6 The Rank of the Circuit Matrix—the Fundamental Circuit Matrix

The orthogonality relation states that

$$\mathbf{A_v}\mathbf{B'_c} = 0$$

or

$$\mathbf{B_c}\mathbf{A'_v} = 0$$

This relation is useful in establishing the rank of the circuit matrix $\mathbf{B_c}$. An important property relating to the combined rank of the product of two matrices will now be presented.

Theorem 9.4 Rank of an Orthogonal Product

Let $\mathbf{P}$ be an $m \times p$ matrix of rank $r < p$, and $\mathbf{Q}$ be a $p \times n$ matrix. Suppose $\mathbf{PQ} = \mathbf{0}$. Then the rank of $\mathbf{Q}$ cannot exceed $p - r$.

Proof: By hypothesis, $\mathbf{P}$ is of rank r. We may therefore form a non-singular submatrix $\mathbf{P_{11}}$ of $\mathbf{P}$ by elementary row and column operations such that

$$\mathbf{P} = \begin{bmatrix} \mathbf{P}_{11} & \mathbf{P}_{12} \\ \mathbf{P}_{21} & \mathbf{P}_{22} \end{bmatrix}$$

$\mathbf{P}_{11}$ of order r. We also write $\mathbf{Q}$ in the form

$$\mathbf{Q} = \begin{bmatrix} \mathbf{Q}_{11} \\ \mathbf{Q}_{21} \end{bmatrix}$$

where $\mathbf{Q}_{21}$ is of order $(p - r) \times n$. Then, by application of $\mathbf{PQ} = \mathbf{0}$, we have

$$\begin{bmatrix} \mathbf{P}_{11} & \mathbf{P}_{12} \\ \mathbf{P}_{21} & \mathbf{P}_{22} \end{bmatrix} \begin{bmatrix} \mathbf{Q}_{11} \\ \mathbf{Q}_{21} \end{bmatrix} = \mathbf{0}$$

from which

$$\mathbf{P}_{11}\mathbf{Q}_{11} + \mathbf{P}_{12}\mathbf{Q}_{21} = \mathbf{0}$$

or

$$\mathbf{Q}_{11} = -\mathbf{P}_{11}^{-1}\mathbf{P}_{12}\mathbf{Q}_{21} \tag{9.35}$$

Now premultiply $\mathbf{Q}$ by a non-singular matrix. This operation does not change the rank of $\mathbf{Q}$. If we choose this matrix as

$$\mathbf{R} = \begin{bmatrix} \mathbf{U} & \mathbf{P}_{11}^{-1}\mathbf{P}_{12} \\ \mathbf{O} & \mathbf{U} \end{bmatrix}$$

the matrix $\mathbf{Q}$ is transformed into

$$\mathbf{RQ} = \begin{bmatrix} \mathbf{Q}_{11} + \mathbf{P}_{11}^{-1}\mathbf{P}_{12}\mathbf{Q}_{21} \\ \mathbf{Q}_{21} \end{bmatrix} = \begin{bmatrix} \mathbf{O} \\ \mathbf{Q}_{21} \end{bmatrix}$$

The last equality is established by virtue of Equation 9.35. Since $\mathbf{Q}_{21}$ is of order $(p - r) \times n$, its rank cannot exceed $p - r$. Hence, the rank of $\mathbf{Q}$ cannot exceed $p - r$.

Now apply the result of Theorem 9.4 to the product of the circuit matrix and the vertex matrix. Consider

$$\mathbf{A}_v\mathbf{B}_c' = \mathbf{0}$$

$\mathbf{A}_v$ is of rank $v - 1$, order $v \times e$, and $\mathbf{B}_c'$ is of order $e \times n$. The rank of $\mathbf{B}_c'$ is at most $e - (v - 1)$. Since the rank of a matrix is not changed upon taking the transpose, we have proved the following theorem.

Theorem 9.5(a) The rank of the circuit matrix of a connected graph G is at most $e - v + 1$.

This result establishes an upper bound on the number of independent circuit equations associated with a connected graph. The rank of the circuit matrix will be established when the maximum number of independent circuit equations is determined. To aid in the realization of this objective the following are defined.

*Fundamental circuit**

A fundamental circuit of a connected graph G is formed by one element of the co-tree, called a *chord,* and those elements of the tree, called *branches,* which form a path between the vertices at which the chord is incident. The orientation of a fundamental circuit is that of the chord element.

This notion is illustrated by the graph of Figure 9.10.

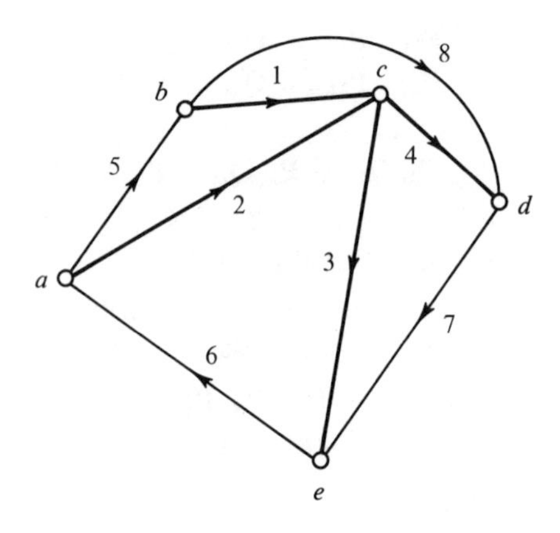

Fig. 9.10. *System graph.*

The graph has eight elements and five vertices. The tree is selected arbitrarily as containing elements

1, 2, 3, 4—branches

leaving a co-tree containing elements

5, 6, 7, 8—chords

The graph has four chords, permitting the definition of four fundamental circuits.

Chord	Branches
5	1, 2
6	2, 3
7	3, 4
8	4, 1

* Many authors call fundamental circuits "fundamental tiesets."

The chords of a graph assume a unique role in the definition of a fundamental circuit. There is exactly one fundamental circuit for each chord. Since there are $e - v + 1$ chords in a connected graph, it follows that one can define $e - v + 1$ fundamental circuits.

Set of fundamental circuits

The $e - v + 1$ fundamental circuits associated with a co-tree T' of a connected graph G form a set of fundamental circuits.

Fundamental circuit equations

The circuit equations associated with a set of fundamental circuits are called the fundamental circuit equations. There are $e - v + 1$ for a given tree.

The fundamental circuit equations of the graph of Figure 9.10 for the tree selected are given as

$$\left.\begin{aligned} x_5 + x_1 - x_2 &= 0 \\ x_6 + x_2 + x_3 &= 0 \\ x_7 - x_3 + x_4 &= 0 \\ x_8 - x_4 - x_1 &= 0 \end{aligned}\right] \tag{9.36}$$

These equations are written in matrix format

$$\begin{bmatrix} 1 & -1 & 0 & 0 & 1 & 0 & 0 & 0 \\ 0 & 1 & 1 & 0 & 0 & 1 & 0 & 0 \\ 0 & 0 & -1 & 1 & 0 & 0 & 1 & 0 \\ -1 & 0 & 0 & -1 & 0 & 0 & 0 & 1 \end{bmatrix} \begin{bmatrix} x_1 \\ x_2 \\ x_3 \\ x_4 \\ x_5 \\ x_6 \\ x_7 \\ x_8 \end{bmatrix} = \mathbf{0} \tag{9.37}$$

In general, fundamental circuit equations are written in the form

$$\mathbf{BX} = \mathbf{0} \tag{9.38}$$

where $\mathbf{B}$ is called the fundamental circuit matrix. $\mathbf{B}$ is of order $(e - v + 1) \times e$ such that

$$\mathbf{B} = [b_{ij}]_{(e-v+1)\times e}$$

where $b_{ij} = +1$ if the jth element is contained in the ith fundamental circuit with an orientation identical to that of the chord; $b_{ij} = -1$ if the jth element is contained in the ith fundamental circuit with an orientation opposite to that of the chord; $b_{ij} = 0$ if the jth element is not contained in the ith fundamental circuit.

If the columns of the fundamental circuit matrix are arranged in two sets corresponding to branches and chords and the branch set is placed first, the fundamental circuit equations can be symbolically written in the form

$$[\mathbf{B}_1 \,\vdots\, \mathbf{U}]\begin{bmatrix} \mathbf{X}_b \\ \mathbf{X}_c \end{bmatrix} = 0 \tag{9.40}$$

where $\mathbf{X}_b$ is the branch variable vector and $\mathbf{X}_c$ is the chord variable vector. An illustration of this arrangement is shown by the numbering of the elements in Figure 9.10 and Equations 9.37.

The fundamental circuit matrix thus appears in partitioned form as

$$\mathbf{B} = [\mathbf{B}_1 \,\vdots\, \mathbf{U}] \tag{9.41}$$

The presence of the unit matrix of order $e - v + 1$ leads immediately to the conclusion that the fundamental circuit equations form a set of $e - v + 1$ linearly independent circuit equations. We may therefore state the following theorem.

Theorem 9.5(b) The rank of the circuit matrix of a connected graph is at least $e - v + 1$.

Proof: $\mathbf{B}$ is a submatrix of $\mathbf{B}_c$. $\mathbf{B}$ is of rank $e - v + 1$.

Theorems 9.5(a) and 9.5(b) permit the statement of the following theorem on the rank of the circuit matrix.

Theorem 9.6 The rank of the circuit matrix $\mathbf{B}_c$ of a connected graph is exactly $e - v + 1$. If the graph consists of p parts, repeated application of Theorem 9.5 sets the rank of the circuit matrix at $e - v + p$.

9.7 Additional Properties of the Vertex Matrix—the Fundamental Cutset Matrix

In this section further properties of the vertex matrix will be explored—in particular, the relation between the vertex matrix and the tree of a graph. In preparation, let us prove the following theorem.

Theorem 9.7 If G is a connected graph with v vertices and G_T is a subgraph of G with $v - 1$ elements containing no circuits, then G_T is a tree of G.

Proof: Assume G_T consists of p parts, identified as $S_1, S_2, \cdots, S_i, \cdots, S_p$. Consider one such subgraph, say S_i, containing v_i vertices.

By hypothesis, S_i is connected and contains no circuits; hence, it is its own tree containing $v_i - 1$ elements. Note that

$$\sum_{i=1}^{p} v_i = v$$

since the subgraphs have no common elements. In addition, the number of elements in G_T is

$$\sum_{i=1}^{p} (v_i - 1) = v - p$$

But by hypothesis G_T contains exactly $v - 1$ elements. This contradicts our assumption that G_T consists of p parts. Hence, G_T is connected and contains all vertices of G. The subgraph G_T is a proper tree of G.

With the help of theorem 9.7, let us prove the following theorem.

Theorem 9.8 A square matrix $\mathbf{A_T}$ of $\mathbf{A_v}$ of order $v - 1$ is nonsingular if and only if the elements corresponding to the columns of the submatrix constitute a tree of a connected graph G.

Proof: Since the theorem involves an " if and only if " statement, we need to show that the conditions required are both necessary and sufficient. The theorem will be proved in two parts.

1. Necessity. Since a tree of a connected graph has $v - 1$ elements, it is necessary to consider a submatrix of order $v - 1$. Furthermore, a submatrix of order $v - 1$ is the largest nonsingular submatrix of $\mathbf{A_v}$ that can be found.

2. Sufficiency. Let $v - 1$ column vectors $\mathbf{A_1}, \mathbf{A_2}, \cdots, \mathbf{A_{v-1}}$ of $\mathbf{A_v}$ form a nonsingular submatrix. These form a set of linearly independent vectors. Associated with the $v - 1$ column vectors are $v - 1$ elements forming a subgraph G_T.

Consider now the relation existing between all column vectors of $\mathbf{A_v}$ and a circuit of the graph. We have from Theorem 9.3 that for the rth circuit

$$[\beta_{r1} \quad \beta_{r2} \quad \cdots \quad \beta_{re}] \begin{bmatrix} \mathbf{A}_1' \\ \mathbf{A}_2' \\ \cdot \\ \cdot \\ \cdot \\ \mathbf{A}_e' \end{bmatrix} = \mathbf{0}$$

When multiplied out, this yields

$$\beta_{r1} \mathbf{A}_1' + \beta_{r2} \mathbf{A}_2' + \cdots + \beta_{re} \mathbf{A}_e' = \mathbf{0}$$

which implies that

$$\beta_{r1}\mathbf{A_1} + \beta_{r2}\mathbf{A_2} + \cdots + \beta_{re}\mathbf{A_e} = \mathbf{0}$$

If now elements $i_1, i_2, \cdots, i_k$ are in circuit r, $\beta_{ri_1}, \beta_{ri_2}, \cdots, \beta_{ri_k}$ are nonzero constants; all other β_r's are zero. Hence,

$$\beta_{ri_1}\mathbf{A_{i_1}} + \beta_{ri_2}\mathbf{A_{i_2}} + \cdots + \beta_{ri_k}\mathbf{A_{i_k}} = \mathbf{0}$$

We conclude that the column vectors corresponding to the elements of a circuit are linearly dependent. However, the $v - 1$ column vectors of the submatrix $\mathbf{A_T}$ are linearly independent; hence, the subgraph G_T cannot contain a circuit.

We have thus shown that the subgraph G_T has no circuits and has $v - 1$ elements. Hence, by Theorem 9.7, it is connected and constitutes a proper tree of G.

Consider now the vertex matrix $\mathbf{A_v}$ of a connected graph G. We delete one row of this matrix, leaving a matrix of order $(v - 1) \times e$ and rank $v - 1$. We call this matrix the reduced vertex matrix and denote it by $\mathbf{A}$. Let the columns of the reduced vertex matrix be arranged according to the branches and chords of the graph G such that

$$\mathbf{A} = [\mathbf{A_T} \mid \mathbf{A_c}] \tag{9.42}$$

where $\mathbf{A_T}$ is a square matrix of order $v - 1$ and $\mathbf{A_c}$ is of order $(v - 1) \times (e - v + 1)$. By Theorem 9.8, $\mathbf{A_T}$ is nonsingular matrix. We may therefore determine $\mathbf{A_T^{-1}}$ and premultiply Equation 9.42 by it. We have

$$\mathbf{A_T^{-1}A} = [\mathbf{A_T^{-1}A_T} \mid \mathbf{A_T^{-1}A_c}] = [\mathbf{U} \mid \mathbf{A_T^{-1}A_c}] \tag{9.43}$$

The right side of Equation 9.43 is identified by a new symbol $\mathscr{A}$ such that

$$\mathscr{A} = \mathbf{A_T^{-1}A} \tag{9.44}$$

and

$$\mathscr{A} = [\mathbf{U} \mid \mathbf{A_T^{-1}A_c}] \tag{9.45}$$

As an illustration of these concepts, consider the system linear graph of Figure 9.11 with the elements 1, 2, 3, 4, and 5, and vertices a, b, c, and d.

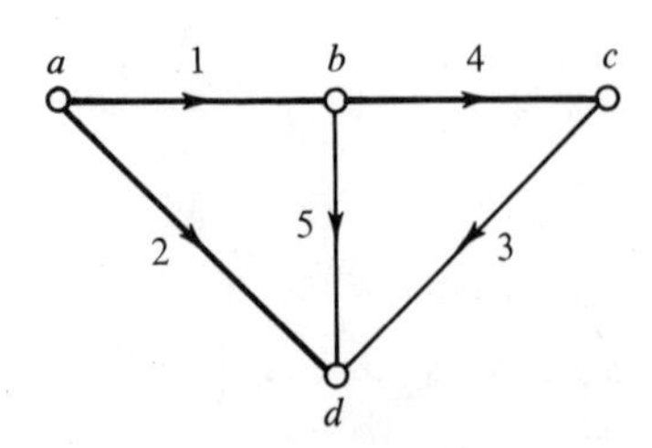

Fig. 9.11. *A system graph.*

The vertex matrix $\mathbf{A}_v$ is found by the summation of flows at each vertex—flows away considered positive.

$$\begin{array}{l} \text{Vertex } a. \\ \text{Vertex } b. \\ \text{Vertex } c. \\ \text{Vertex } d. \end{array} \begin{bmatrix} 1 & 1 & 0 & 0 & 0 \\ -1 & 0 & 0 & 1 & 1 \\ 0 & 0 & 1 & -1 & 0 \\ 0 & -1 & -1 & 0 & -1 \end{bmatrix} = \mathbf{A}_v$$

Since elements 1, 2, and 4 are branches, delete the last row arbitrarily and rearrange columns in the order 1–2–3–4–5; then

$$\mathbf{A}_v = \left[\begin{array}{ccc:cc} 1 & 1 & 0 & 0 & 0 \\ -1 & 0 & 1 & 0 & 1 \\ 0 & 0 & -1 & 1 & 0 \end{array}\right] = [\mathbf{A}_T \mid \mathbf{A}_c]$$

We are assured that $\mathbf{A}_T$ is nonsingular by Theorem 9.8; therefore

$$\mathbf{A}_T^{-1} = \begin{bmatrix} 1 & 1 & 0 \\ -1 & 0 & 1 \\ 0 & 0 & -1 \end{bmatrix}^{-1} = \begin{bmatrix} 0 & -1 & -1 \\ 1 & 1 & 1 \\ 0 & 0 & -1 \end{bmatrix}$$

and

$$\mathscr{A} = [\mathbf{A}_T^{-1}\mathbf{A}_T \mid \mathbf{A}_T^{-1}\mathbf{A}_c] = \left[\begin{array}{ccc:cc} 1 & 0 & 0 & -1 & -1 \\ 0 & 1 & 0 & 1 & 1 \\ 0 & 0 & 1 & -1 & 0 \end{array}\right]$$

The newly formed matrix* $\mathscr{A}$ is related to the reduced vertex matrix $\mathbf{A}$ by a nonsingular transformation as defined by Equation 9.44. Hence, the continuity constraints may be expressed as a set of independent equations in either of the two forms

$$[\mathbf{A}_T \mid \mathbf{A}_c] \begin{bmatrix} \mathbf{Y}_b \\ \hdashline \mathbf{Y}_c \end{bmatrix} = \mathbf{0} \tag{9.46}$$

or

$$[\mathbf{U} \mid \mathbf{A}_T^{-1} \mathbf{A}_c] \begin{bmatrix} \mathbf{Y}_b \\ \hdashline \mathbf{Y}_c \end{bmatrix} = \mathbf{0} \tag{9.47}$$

where both matrices ($\mathbf{A}$ and $\mathscr{A}$) are of maximum rank $v - 1$. Both sets of equations may serve as a mathematical statement of the continuity constraints.

So far, our discussion appears to attach only academic interest to the development of the matrix $\mathscr{A}$. In fact, no advantage is offered in

* $\mathscr{A}$ will shortly be identified as the fundamental cutset matrix.

expressing the continuity constraints in terms of Equation 9.47 rather than Equation 9.46; to obtain the $\mathscr{A}$ matrix, the vertex matrix must be determined anyway. A procedure by which the $\mathscr{A}$ matrix can be obtained directly from the system graph, in a manner similar in concept to the fundamental circuit matrix, will now be defined. In support of this objective, note the following definitions.

Cutset

A cutset is a set of elements of a connected graph which are cut by drawing a closed line through the graph. Figure 9.12 shows an illustration of a cutset containing elements 2, 7, 8, 5.

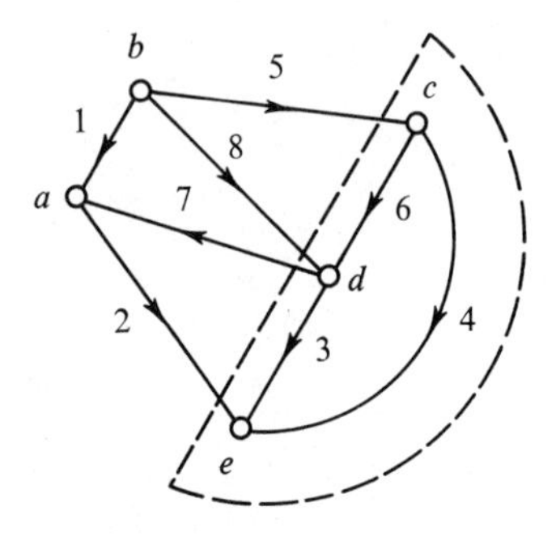

Fig. 9.12. *A cutset.*

A cutset has the property of splitting the vertices of the graph into two sets, called vertex sets. For the cutset containing elements 2, 5, 7, 8, as illustrated by Figure 9.12, the two sets of vertices are vertex set (a, b) and vertex set (c, d, e).

Cutset Equations

A cutset equation is generated by summing the vertex equations of one of the two vertex sets formed by the cutset. The cutset equation associated with vertex set (a, b) of Figure 9.12 is generated by summing the vertex equations of vertices a and b. We have at vertex a:

$$-y_1 + y_2 - y_7 = 0$$

at vertex b:

$$y_1 + y_5 + y_8 = 0$$

Sum:

$$y_2 + y_5 - y_7 + y_8 = 0 \tag{9.48}$$

Note that Equation 9.48 is identical to the equation formed by summing the through variables associated with the elements of the cutset with a positive orientation taken toward vertex set (a, b). Thus a cutset equation has the physical significance that the through variables associated with the elements of a cutset are in mutual equilibrium. The cutsets differ from the vertex equations in that one sums the through variables out of (or into) a region containing a set of vertices rather than always just one vertex. If the cutset region contains just one vertex, then the cutset and vertex equations are the same with the possible exception of a sign reversal.

Fundamental Cutset

A cutset is called a fundamental cutset if exactly one element is a branch while the remaining elements are chords. This concept can be illustrated by defining a tree for the graph of Figure 9.12. A proper tree consisting of elements 1, 2, 3, and 4 is shown in Figure 9.13.

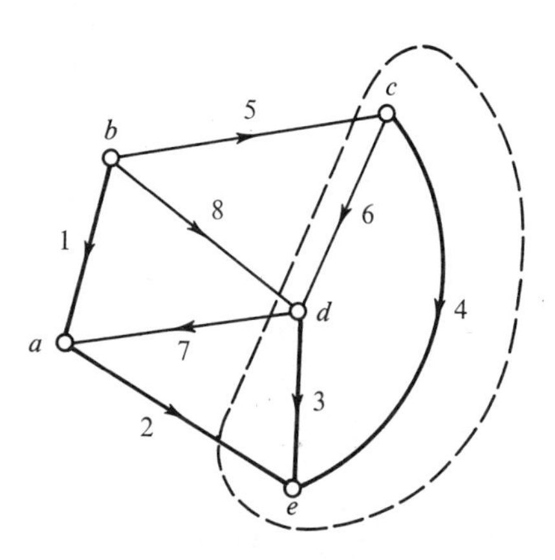

Fig. 9.13. *Graph and tree with fundamental cutset.*

A fundamental cutset is formed by branch 2 and chords 7, 8, and 5, for example. It is seen that the branch assumes a unique role in the definition of a fundamental cutset. There are $v - 1$ fundamental cutsets in a graph for a given tree. A fundamental cutset derives its orientation from the branch.

Set of Fundamental Cutsets

A set of fundamental cutsets consists of the $v - 1$ fundamental cutsets that correspond to the branches of the graph. For the graph of Figure 9.13 there are four fundamental cutsets. They are

branch	chords
1	8, 5
2	7, 8, 5
3	7, 8, 6
4	5, 6

Fundamental Cutset Equations

With each cutset a cutset equation similar to Equation 9.48 is associated. The cutset equations corresponding to a set of fundamental cutsets are called the fundamental cutset equations. For a connected graph, there are exactly $v - 1$ fundamental cutset equations. For the graph of Figure 9.13, the fundamental cutset equations are given in matrix form as

$$\left[\begin{array}{cccc|cccc} 1 & 0 & 0 & 0 & 1 & 0 & 0 & 1 \\ 0 & 1 & 0 & 0 & 1 & 0 & -1 & 1 \\ 0 & 0 & 1 & 0 & 0 & -1 & 1 & -1 \\ 0 & 0 & 0 & 1 & -1 & 1 & 0 & 0 \end{array}\right] \left[\begin{array}{c} y_1 \\ y_2 \\ y_3 \\ y_4 \\ \hline y_5 \\ y_6 \\ y_7 \\ y_8 \end{array}\right] = \mathbf{0} \qquad (9.49)$$

If the columns of the fundamental cutset equations are arranged according to the branches first and the chords last, then the form of the equation is symbolically

$$[\mathbf{U} \mid \mathscr{A}_2] \left[\begin{array}{c} \mathbf{Y}_b \\ \hline \mathbf{Y}_c \end{array}\right] = \mathbf{0} \qquad (9.50)$$

where $\mathbf{Y}_b$ is a vector of branch through variables and $\mathbf{Y}_c$ is a vector of chord through variables. The unit matrix which is present in the leading position of Equation 9.50 indicates that the fundamental cutset equations are linearly independent.

Fundamental Cutset Matrix

Note that Equations 9.50 and Equations 9.47 are identical in structure. Indeed, the fundamental cutset equations offer a procedure by which the $\mathscr{A}$ matrix may be obtained directly from the graph. Hence, we formally identify the matrix

$$\mathscr{A} = [\mathbf{U} \mid \mathbf{A}_{\mathrm{T}}^{-1}\ \mathbf{A}_{\mathrm{c}}] \tag{9.51}$$

as the *fundamental cutset matrix* of a connected graph. Note that the submatrix $\mathscr{A}_2$ is equal to $\mathbf{A}_{\mathrm{T}}^{-1}\ \mathbf{A}_{\mathrm{c}}$,

$$\mathscr{A}_2 = \mathbf{A}_{\mathrm{T}}^{-1}\ \mathbf{A}_{\mathrm{c}} \tag{9.52}$$

Let us verify this equality for the graph of Figure 9.13. The reduced vertex matrix (with vertex e deleted) is

$$\begin{array}{c} \\ \text{a.} \\ \text{b.} \\ \text{c.} \\ \text{d.} \end{array} \begin{array}{c} \begin{array}{cccccccc} 1 & 2 & 3 & 4 & 5 & 6 & 7 & 8 \end{array} \\ \left[\begin{array}{cccc:cccc} -1 & 1 & 0 & 0 & 0 & 0 & -1 & 0 \\ 1 & 0 & 0 & 0 & 1 & 0 & 0 & 1 \\ 0 & 0 & 0 & 1 & -1 & 1 & 0 & 0 \\ 0 & 0 & 1 & 0 & 0 & -1 & 1 & -1 \end{array}\right] \end{array}$$

The submatrix $\mathbf{A}_{\mathrm{T}}$ is composed of the first four columns corresponding to the tree of the graph. The inverse $\mathbf{A}_{\mathrm{T}}^{-1}$ is easily obtained in this case through application of elementary matrix operations. It is

$$\mathbf{A}_{\mathrm{T}}^{-1} = \begin{bmatrix} 0 & 1 & 0 & 0 \\ 1 & 1 & 0 & 0 \\ 0 & 0 & 0 & 1 \\ 0 & 0 & 1 & 0 \end{bmatrix}$$

and

$$\mathbf{A}_{\mathrm{T}}^{-1}\,\mathbf{A}_{\mathrm{c}} = \begin{bmatrix} 0 & 1 & 0 & 0 \\ 1 & 1 & 0 & 0 \\ 0 & 0 & 0 & 1 \\ 0 & 0 & 1 & 0 \end{bmatrix} \begin{bmatrix} 0 & 0 & -1 & 0 \\ 1 & 0 & 0 & 1 \\ -1 & 1 & 0 & 0 \\ 0 & -1 & 1 & -1 \end{bmatrix}$$

$$= \begin{bmatrix} 1 & 0 & 0 & 1 \\ 1 & 0 & -1 & 1 \\ 0 & -1 & 1 & -1 \\ -1 & 1 & 0 & 0 \end{bmatrix}$$

$$= \mathscr{A}_2$$

(from Equations 9.49).

The entries of the fundamental cutset matrix are identified as

$$\mathscr{A} = [a_{ij}]_{v-1,\,e} \tag{9.53}$$

where $a_{ij} = +1$ if the jth element is part of cutset i with orientation according to its branch, $a_{ij} = -1$ if the jth element is part of cutset i with orientation opposite to its branch, and $a_{ij} = 0$ if the jth element is not part of cutset i.

The fundamental cutset equations represent a set of $v - 1$ linearly independent statements of the continuity constraints. Hence, the fundamental cutset equations are totally equivalent to the $v - 1$ vertex equations in serving as a basis for expressing the interrelation between the through variables of a system.

The cutset equation has been defined as the linear combination of the vertex equations associated with those vertices included in one of the vertex sets generated by the cutset. This interpretation may be used in the process of premultiplying the **A** matrix by $\mathbf{A}_{\mathbf{T}}^{-1}$. The entries of $\mathbf{A}_{\mathbf{T}}^{-1}$ are explained as follows:

$$\mathbf{A}_{\mathbf{T}}^{-1} = [a_{ij}]_{v-1} \tag{9.54}$$

where $a_{ij} = -1$ if the vertex set associated with the ith branch contains the jth vertex, the orientation of the ith branch being toward the vertex set containing the vertex not included in the **A** matrix; $a_{ij} = 1$ if the vertex set associated with the ith branch contains the jth vertex, the orientation of the ith branch being away from the vertex set containing the vertex not included in the **A** matrix; and $a_{ij} = 0$ if the vertex set associated with the ith branch does not contain the jth vertex, the orientation of the ith branch being away from the vertex set. Notice that the entries of a given row of $\mathbf{A}_{\mathbf{T}}^{-1}$ are always of the same sign.

Applying the procedure defined by Equation 9.54 to determine $\mathbf{A}_{\mathbf{T}}^{-1}$ for the graph of Figure 9.13, we find that

branch	vertex set	row of $\mathbf{A}_{\mathbf{T}}^{-1}$
1	a	0 1 0 0
2	ab	1 1 0 0
3	d	0 0 0 1
4	c	0 0 1 0

The $\mathbf{A}_{\mathbf{T}}^{-1}$ matrix thus generated is identical to the one previously obtained by an inversion process.

9.8 Relation between the Fundamental Circuit and Cutset Matrices

We have now defined two sets of equations which have been shown to be *complete* mathematical statements of both the compatibility and continuity constraints. They are fundamental circuit equations,

$$[\mathbf{B}_1 \mid \mathbf{U}] \begin{bmatrix} \mathbf{X}_b \\ \mathbf{X}_c \end{bmatrix} = 0 \tag{9.55}$$

and fundamental cutset equations,

$$[\mathbf{U} \mid \mathscr{A}_2] \begin{bmatrix} \mathbf{Y}_b \\ \mathbf{Y}_c \end{bmatrix} = 0 \tag{9.56}$$

Both sets of equations are uniquely related to the tree of a graph. It is by virtue of this relation that unit submatrices are generated in the fundamental cutset and circuit matrices.

Our interest in this section will be focused on investigating the orthogonality relation between the fundamental cutset and circuit matrices. Consider the product of the reduced vertex matrix and the transpose of the fundamental circuit matrix. By Theorem 9.3, we have

$$\mathbf{AB}' = 0 \tag{9.57}$$

Remember that the columns of the **A** and **B** matrices are arranged in the same order. Hence, the columns of **A** are arranged according to branches and chords.

Suppose we premultiply Equation 9.57 by the inverse of the submatrix $\mathbf{A}_T$ corresponding to the branches. We have

$$\mathbf{A}_T^{-1}(\mathbf{AB}') = 0 \tag{9.58}$$

Since products of matrices are associative, we may shift the parentheses in Equation 9.58 such that

$$(\mathbf{A}_T^{-1}\mathbf{A})\mathbf{B}' = 0$$

or

$$\mathscr{A}\mathbf{B}' = 0 \tag{9.59}$$

Equation 9.59 is a statement of the orthogonality relation in terms of the fundamental cutset and circuit equation. Since

$$\mathscr{A} = [\mathbf{U} \mid \mathscr{A}_2]$$

and

$$\mathbf{B} = [\mathbf{B}_1 \mid \mathbf{U}]$$

we may write Equation 9.59 as

$$[\mathbf{U} \mid \mathscr{A}_2] \begin{bmatrix} \mathbf{B}_1' \\ \mathbf{U} \end{bmatrix} = 0 \tag{9.60}$$

or

$$\mathscr{A}_2 = -\mathbf{B}_1'$$

Equation 9.60 also implies that

$$\mathbf{B}_1 = -\mathscr{A}_2' \tag{9.61}$$

Hence, the product of the fundamental circuit matrix and the transpose of the fundamental cutset matrix also vanish, *i.e.*,

$$\mathbf{B}\mathscr{A}' = \mathbf{0} \tag{9.62}$$

Equations 9.60 and 9.61 are significant in that only one of the fundamental matrices has to be determined from the graph. The other one may be obtained from Equation 9.60 or 9.61. This relation will be utilized to great advantage in the formulation techniques to be developed in Chapter 10.

A useful property of the fundamental cutset and circuit equations is realized when Equation 9.55 is solved for $\mathbf{X}_c$. One has

$$\mathbf{X}_c = -\mathbf{B}_1\mathbf{X}_b \tag{9.63}$$

Similarly, if Equation 9.56 is solved for $\mathbf{Y}_b$,

$$\mathbf{Y}_b = -\mathscr{A}_2\mathbf{Y}_c \tag{9.64}$$

We see that the *chord across* variables may be expressed as a linear combination of the *branch across* variables; on the other hand, the *branch through* variables may be expressed as a linear combination of the *chord through* variables. These relations will introduce a significant reduction in complexity in the formulation procedures of Chapter 10.

For the graph and tree shown in Figure 9.13 and Equation 9.49,

$$\mathbf{Y}_b = \begin{bmatrix} y_1 \\ y_2 \\ y_3 \\ y_4 \end{bmatrix} \qquad \mathbf{Y}_c = \begin{bmatrix} y_5 \\ y_6 \\ y_7 \\ y_8 \end{bmatrix} \qquad \mathscr{A}_2 = \begin{bmatrix} 1 & 0 & 0 & 1 \\ 1 & 0 & -1 & 1 \\ 0 & -1 & 1 & -1 \\ -1 & 1 & 0 & 0 \end{bmatrix}$$

We may write the fundamental circuit matrix by inspection:

$$\mathbf{B} = [\mathbf{B}_1 \vdots \mathbf{U}] = \left[\begin{array}{cccc:cccc} -1 & -1 & 0 & 1 & 1 & 0 & 0 & 0 \\ 0 & 0 & 1 & -1 & 0 & 1 & 0 & 0 \\ 0 & 1 & -1 & 0 & 0 & 0 & 1 & 0 \\ -1 & -1 & 0 & 0 & 0 & 0 & 0 & 1 \end{array}\right]$$

then

$$\mathbf{B}_1' = \begin{bmatrix} -1 & 0 & 0 & -1 \\ -1 & 0 & 1 & -1 \\ 0 & 1 & -1 & 1 \\ 1 & -1 & 0 & 0 \end{bmatrix} = -\mathscr{A}_2$$

Deriving both matrices $\mathscr{A}_2$ and $\mathbf{B}_1$ independently provides an accuracy check not obtainable from deriving only one.

9.9 The Rank of the Mesh-Circuit Matrix and the Node-Vertex Matrix

Three brief theorems regarding the linear independence of the node-vertex equations and the mesh-circuit equations are presented in this section. From Equations 9.12 and 9.14 we have

$$\mathbf{B_m X} = \mathbf{0} \tag{9.12}$$

and

$$\mathbf{A_n Y} = \mathbf{0} \tag{9.14}$$

To establish linear independence of these equations, consider the rank of the matrices $\mathbf{B_m}$ and $\mathbf{A_n}$.

Theorem 9.9 The rank of the node-vertex matrix $\mathbf{A_n}$ of a connected graph G is exactly $v - 1$.

Proof: This follows directly from the definition of the node-vertex matrix: The node-vertex matrix is equal to a reduced vertex matrix formed by deleting the vertex defined as the reference node.

Theorem 9.10 There are at least $e - v + 1$ circuits in a connected graph G which correspond to the windows of a graph.

Proof: A proof to this theorem is furnished by repeated application of the definition of a circuit. Consider a connected graph. Let this graph have k windows. We define k subgraphs, $G_1, G_2, \cdots, G_k$ such that G_1 has one window, $G_1 \cup G_2$ has two windows,* $\cdots G_1 \cup G_2 \cup \cdots \cup G_k$ has k windows. G_1 is a circuit containing e_1 elements and v_1 vertices. By definition of a circuit, $e_1 = v_1$ so that for this subgraph, G_1, we have

$$e_1 - v_1 + 1 = 1$$

Consider the union of subgraph G_1 with subgraph G_2. If $G_1 \cup G_2$ is connected, then $G_1 \cap G_2$† may consist of a number of vertices v_1' and elements e_1' of G_1 such that $v_1' - e_1' = 1$. Since $G_2 - (G_1 \cap G_2)$ is the subgraph forming the remainder of the second window with a vertex and element count v_2 and e_2, then

$$e_2 + e_1' = v_2 + v_1'$$

We conclude that

$$e_2 - v_2 = 1$$

* $G_1 \cup G_2$ means the union of G_1 and G_2; that is, all elements and vertices contained in both G_1 and G_2.

† $G_1 \cap G_2$ means the intersection of G_1 and G_2; that is, all elements and vertices common to both G_1 and G_2.

$G_1 \cup G_2$ has two circuits corresponding to two windows and

$$(e_1 - e_2) - (v_1 + v_2) + 1 = 2$$

This process is repeated k times until all subgraphs are added in order. The graph G is then given by $G_1 \cup G_2 \cup \cdots \cup G_k$ and there are k circuits corresponding to k windows such that

$$k = (e_1 + e_2 + \cdots + e_k) - (v_1 + v_2 + \cdots v_k) + 1 = e - v + 1$$

As an example, consider the system graph of Figure 9.14 which has four windows. G_1 consists of three elements, 1, 5, and 6, and three

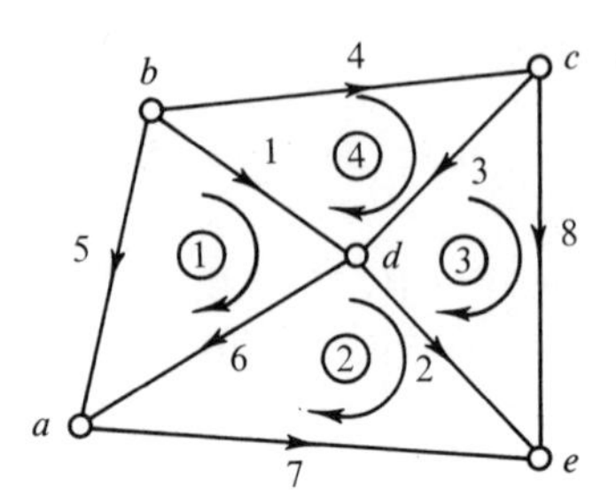

Fig. 9.14. *System graph showing mesh circuits.*

vertices, a, b, and d; $e_1 = 3$, $v_1 = 3$, and $e_1 - v_1 + 1 = 1$. $G_1 \cup G_2$ consists of five elements, 1, 5, 6, 2, and 7, and four vertices, a, b, d, and e. $G_1 \cap G_2$ consists of element 6 and vertices a and d. Then $e_1' = 1$, $v_1' = 2$. G_2 consists of three elements, 2, 6, and 7, and three vertices, a, d, and e. $G_2 - (G_1 \cap G_2)$ consists of elements 2 and 7 and vertex e; $e_2 - v_2 = 1$. Let $G_{12} = G_1 \cup G_2$, which consists of five elements and four vertices. $G_{12} \cap G_3$ consists of element 2 and vertices d and e. Since G_3 consists of three elements, 2, 3, and 8, and three vertices, c, d, and e, then $G_3 - (G_{12} \cap G_3)$ consists of elements 3 and 8 and vertex c; $e_3 - v_3 = 1$. Continuing this procedure, we find that

$$e = e_1 + e_2 + e_3 + e_4 = 3 + 2 + 2 + 1 = 8$$

$$v = v_1 + v_2 + v_3 + v_4 = 3 + 1 + 1 + 0 = 5$$

and

$$e - v + 1 = 4$$

the number of meshes.

Theorem 9.11 The rank of the mesh circuit matrix $\mathbf{B_m}$ of a connected graph is exactly $e - v + 1$.

Proof: By Theorem 9.4(a), the rank of $\mathbf{B_m}$ cannot exceed $e - v + 1$ since $\mathbf{B_m}$ is a submatrix of $\mathbf{B_c}$.

To show that the rank of $\mathbf{B_m}$ is at least $e - v + 1$, consider the process defining the mesh circuits. If the mesh circuits are selected sequentially, it is necessary to include in each new circuit at least one element not previously used in the formation of another mesh circuit. By Theorem 9.10, there are at least $e - v + 1$ such circuits.

Let the columns of $\mathbf{B_m}$ matrix be ordered such that the first element is contained in the first circuit, the second element is contained in the second circuit but not in the first circuit, ···, the $(e - v + 1)^{\text{th}}$ element is contained in the last circuit but not in any of the previous circuits. Then the mesh circuit matrix has the form

$$\mathbf{B_m} = [\mathbf{B_{m1}} \vdots \mathbf{B_{m2}}]$$

where $\mathbf{B_{m1}}$ is a triangular matrix of rank and order $e - v + 1$, such that

$$\mathbf{B_{m1}} = \begin{bmatrix} \pm 1 & 0 & 0 & \cdots & & 0 \\ b_{11} & \pm 1 & 0 & \cdots & & 0 \\ \cdot & & \pm 1 & & & \cdot \\ \cdot & & & \cdot & & \cdot \\ \cdot & & & & \cdot & \cdot \\ \cdot & & & & \cdot & \cdot \\ & & & & \pm 1 & 0 \\ b_{e-v+1,\,1} & & & & b_{e-v+1,\,e-v} & \pm 1 \end{bmatrix}$$

The diagonal consists of entries ± 1 but never 0.

The mesh circuit matrix of Figure 9.14 is, by inspection,

$$\mathbf{B_m} = \left[\begin{array}{cccc:cccc} 1 & 0 & 0 & 0 & -1 & 1 & 0 & 0 \\ 0 & 1 & 0 & 0 & 0 & -1 & -1 & 0 \\ 0 & -1 & -1 & 0 & 0 & 0 & 0 & 1 \\ -1 & 0 & 0 & 1 & 0 & 0 & 0 & 0 \end{array}\right] = [\mathbf{B_{m1}} \vdots \mathbf{B_{m2}}]$$

and its rank is 4.

ADDITIONAL READINGS

Koenig, Herman E., and William A. Blackwell, *Electromechanical System Theory*, New York: McGraw-Hill Book Co., 1961.

Koenig, Herman E., Y. Tokad, and H.K. Kesavan, *Discrete Physical Systems*, New York: McGraw-Hill Book Co., 1966.

Kuo, Benjamin C., *Linear Networks and Systems*, New York: McGraw-Hill Book Co., 1967.

Seshu, S., and N. Balabanian, *Linear Network Analysis,* New York: John Wiley & Sons, Inc., 1959.

Seshu, S., and M.B. Reed, *Linear Graphs and Electrical Networks,* Reading, Mass.: Addison-Wesley Publishing Co., Inc., 1961.

PROBLEMS

9.1. a) What are the trees of the graph shown in Figure P. 9.1?
b) How many circuit equations can one write for the system graph?
c) Write the mesh circuit matrix $\mathbf{B}_m$ and show that it is of maximum rank.
d) Write the node vertex matrix $\mathbf{A}_n$ and shown that it is of maximum rank.

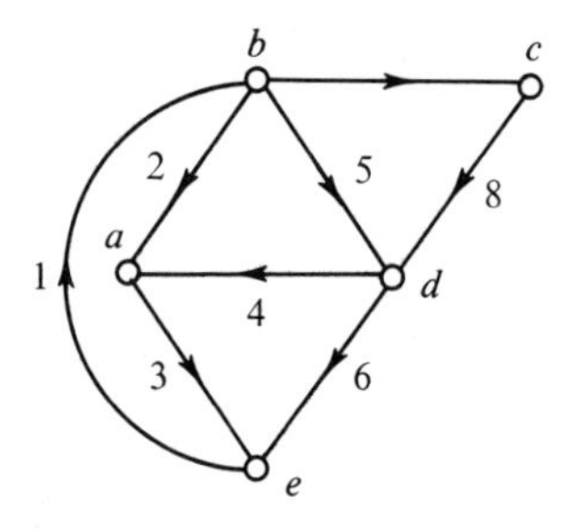

Fig. P 9.1.

9.2. Given are $\nu - 1$ vertex equations corresponding to a graph. Find the graph and the νth vertex equation.

$$\nu - 1 \left\{ \begin{bmatrix} 1 & 0 & 0 & 1 & -1 & 0 \\ -1 & 1 & 0 & 0 & 1 & -1 \\ 0 & 0 & 1 & 0 & 0 & 0 \\ 0 & 0 & 0 & 0 & 0 & 0 \end{bmatrix} \right.$$

9.3. From the graph in Problem 9.1 determine a number of vertex equations and circuit equations. Arrange the terms in each equation in the same order. Show that for any choice of equations

$$[\text{coefficients of circuit equations}] \begin{bmatrix} \swarrow \end{bmatrix} \text{coefficients of vertex equations} = 0$$

9.4. Write the fundamental cutset and circuit equations for the graph in Figure P 9.4.

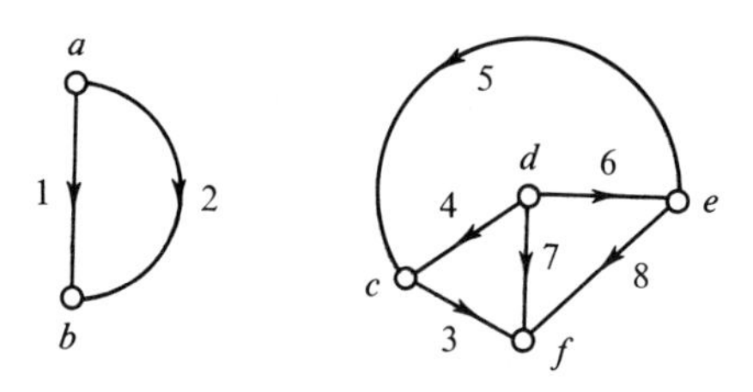

Fig. P 9.4.

9.5. Name two ways in which a submatrix of rank $e - v + 1$ may be determined from the circuit matrix $\mathbf{B}_c$ for a connected graph G.

9.6. List two ways in which the orthogonality relation is useful in the development of matrix equations.

9.7. Draw a system graph for the system shown in Figure P 9.7. Write the fundamental circuit and cutset equations.

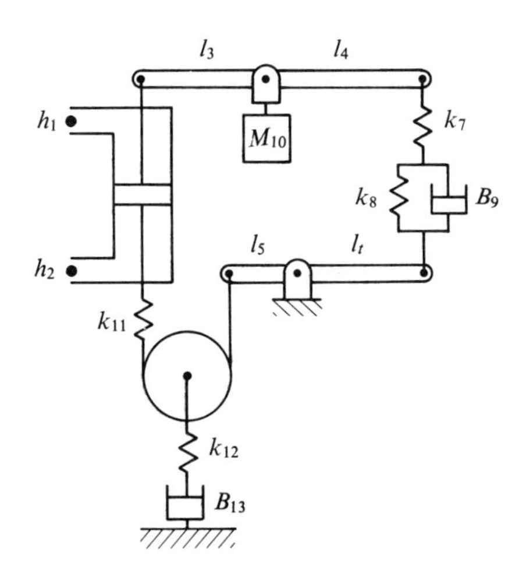

Fig. P 9.7.

9.8. Given the fundamental circuit equations

$$\mathbf{B} = \begin{bmatrix} -1 & 0 & 0 & 0 & 1 & 0 & 0 & 0 \\ 1 & -1 & 0 & 0 & 0 & 1 & 0 & 0 \\ 0 & 0 & -1 & 0 & 0 & 0 & 1 & 0 \\ 0 & 0 & 1 & 1 & 0 & 0 & 0 & 1 \end{bmatrix}$$

find $\mathscr{A}$ and the graph.

9.9. For the graph shown in Figure P 9.9, find

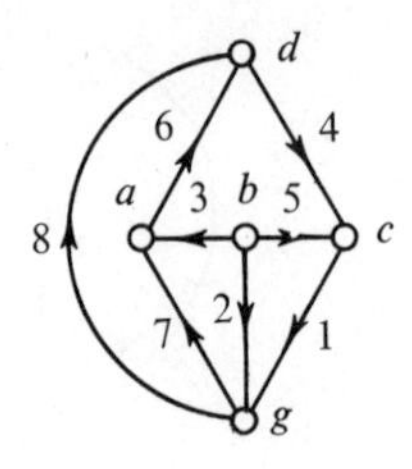

Fig. P 9.9.

a) **B**, $\mathscr{A}$, **A**, $[\mathbf{A}_T : \mathbf{A}_c]$.
b) $\mathbf{A}_T^{-1}$ by two methods.
c) Show that $\mathscr{A} = \mathbf{A}_T^{-1}\mathbf{A}$.

9.10. Summarize the developments leading to these statements.
a) Exactly $e - v + 1$ circuit equations are independent.
b) Exactly $v - 1$ vertex equations are independent.

9.11. Define two independent processes
a) to obtain $e - v + 1$ circuit equations which are independent;
b) to obtain $v - 1$ vertex equations which are independent.

9.12. Draw a system graph for the electrical circuit shown in Figure P 9.12. With elements 1, 3, and 6 forming a tree, write the fundamental cut-set and circuit equations.

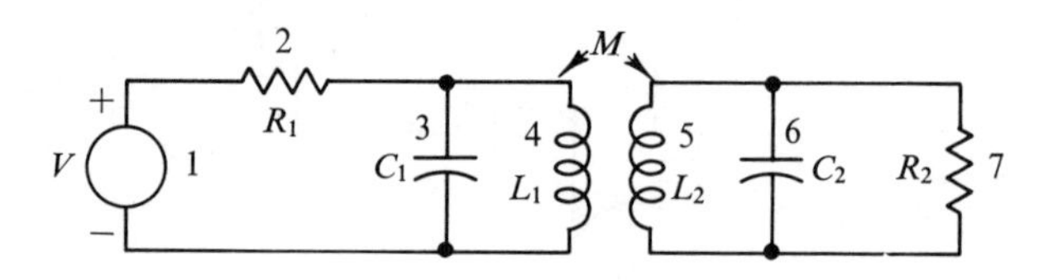

Fig. P 9.12.

9.13. In the system graph shown in Figure P. 9.13, choose an appropriate forest and coforest.

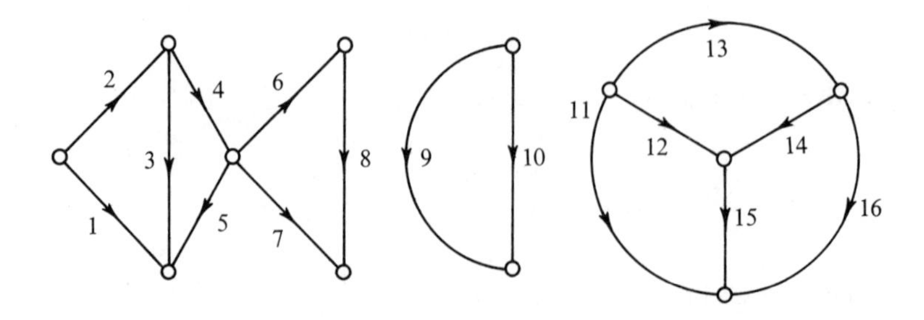

Fig. P 9.13.

a) How many vertex equations are there ?
c) How many meshes are there ?
b) How many independent nodes are there ?
d) How many fundamental circuits are there ?
e) How many fundamental cutsets are there ?

9.14. An electrical network consists of a set of connected resistances along every edge of a cube. The network is driven by a voltage source across diagonally opposite vertices.

a) How many fundamental cutsets are there ?
b) How many fundamental circuits are there ?
c) Describe a procedure for finding all independent meshes.
d) Form a tree and cotree and write all fundamental cutset and circuit equations.

Systems with Multiterminal Components

10

10.1 Introduction

In preceding chapters we have developed the tools necessary to formulate and solve the equations of systems of any complexity. In this chapter a variety of systems which consist of multiterminal components and different system disciplines will be considered.

Three methods of formulating system equations, namely the loop or mesh, node or vertex, and state equation methods have been presented. The number of equations necessary for each method varies; in a system with a connected graph, there are $v - 1$ node equations, $e - v + 1$ loop equations, and a number of state equations normally equal to the number of memory elements. Whichever method leads to the fewer number of equations is generally the preferred method. In large-scale systems whose solution would require a computer, however, the state equations are preferred.

In a large proportion of systems, the node or loop equations are preferred, but their use is difficult if the system consists of separate parts representing more than one system discipline (electromechanical systems, hydromechanical systems, etc.). However, the loop and node equations can be generalized to apply to almost any system. The generalized equations are called chord and branch equations. The number of branch equations in a multipart system graph is $v - p$, where p is the number of separate parts. The branch equations equal the number of fundamental cutsets, and strictly speaking are not node equations because the cutset equations are not vertex equations. The number of chord equations is $e - v + p$, and equals the number of fundamental circuits. Formulation techniques for chord and branch equations will now be presented. To facilitate the discussion, consider Figure 10.1. We will formulate the chord equations for this electrical system.

10.2 Chord Equation Formulation

In Chapter 9 we proved that the fundamental cutsets and circuits are unique, and that the equations can be written in the partitioned forms

$$[\mathbf{U} \,\vdots\, \mathscr{A}] \begin{bmatrix} \mathbf{Y_b} \\ \cdots \\ \mathbf{Y_c} \end{bmatrix} = \mathbf{0}$$

for the fundamental cutsets

$$[\mathbf{B} \,\vdots\, \mathbf{U}] \begin{bmatrix} \mathbf{X_b} \\ \cdots \\ \mathbf{X_c} \end{bmatrix} = \mathbf{0}$$

for the fundamental circuits. Where $\mathbf{Y_b}$ is a column of branch through variables, $\mathbf{Y_c}$ is a column of chord through variables, $\mathbf{X_b}$ is a column of branch across variables, and $\mathbf{X_c}$ is a column of chord across variables.

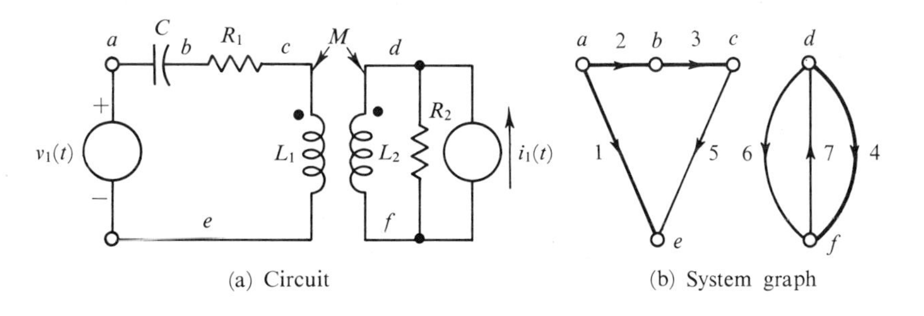

Fig. 10.1. (a) *An electrical system with transformer;* (b) *system graph.*

To obtain the required matrix formats we must first number the branches. For convenience, across or potential sources are numbered first and through or flow sources are numbered last. There are four cutset equations and three circuit equations* and these can be written by inspection as

$$\Bigg[\underbrace{\begin{matrix}1 & 0 & 0 & 0\\ 0 & 1 & 0 & 0\\ 0 & 0 & 1 & 0\\ 0 & 0 & 0 & 1\end{matrix}}_{\mathbf{U}} \;\vdots\; \underbrace{\begin{matrix}1 & 0 & 0\\ -1 & 0 & 0\\ -1 & 0 & 0\\ 0 & 1 & -1\end{matrix}}_{\mathscr{A}}\Bigg]\begin{bmatrix} i_1\\ i_2\\ i_3\\ i_4\\ i_5\\ i_6\\ i_7\end{bmatrix} = \mathbf{0} \qquad (10.1)$$

$$\Bigg[\underbrace{\begin{matrix}-1 & 1 & 1 & 0\\ 0 & 0 & 0 & -1\\ 0 & 0 & 0 & 1\end{matrix}}_{\mathbf{B}} \;\vdots\; \underbrace{\begin{matrix}1 & 0 & 0\\ 0 & 1 & 0\\ 0 & 0 & 1\end{matrix}}_{\mathbf{U}}\Bigg]\begin{bmatrix} v_1\\ v_2\\ v_3\\ v_4\\ v_5\\ v_6\\ v_7\end{bmatrix} = \mathbf{0} \qquad (10.2)$$

A valuable check on the accuracy of these equations is a verification that $\mathscr{A} = -\mathbf{B}^{\mathrm{T}}$. In this example there are two independent circuit equations and the simplest equation formulation involves substitution in these equations by the following steps:

1. Separate off the columns 1 and 7 of $[\mathbf{B} \vdots \mathbf{U}]$ in Equation 10.2 associated with sources.
2. Write the open-circuit-parameter matrix equations for the remaining across variables in the form $\mathbf{X} = [\mathbf{Z}]\mathbf{Y}$. (See Equation 10.3).
3. From the cutset matrix of Equation 10.1, express $\mathbf{Y}$ in step 2 in terms of only the chord through variables.
4. Combine the relations from steps 1, 2, and 3 as shown in Equation 10.5.

In Figure 10.1,

$$\mathbf{X} = \begin{bmatrix} v_2\\ v_3\\ v_4\\ v_5\\ v_6\end{bmatrix}, \qquad \mathbf{Z} = \mathbf{Z}(\mathbf{s}) = \begin{bmatrix} \frac{1}{Cs} & 0 & 0 & 0 & 0\\ 0 & R_1 & 0 & 0 & 0\\ 0 & 0 & R_2 & 0 & 0\\ 0 & 0 & 0 & sL_1 & sM\\ 0 & 0 & 0 & sM & sL_2\end{bmatrix} \qquad (10.3)$$

* It is understood that cutset and circuit mean fundamental cutset and circuit.

$$\mathbf{Y} = \begin{bmatrix} i_2 \\ i_3 \\ i_4 \\ i_5 \\ i_6 \end{bmatrix} = \begin{bmatrix} 1 & 0 & 0 \\ 1 & 0 & 0 \\ 0 & -1 & 1 \\ 1 & 0 & 0 \\ 0 & 1 & 0 \end{bmatrix} \begin{bmatrix} i_5 \\ i_6 \\ i_7 \end{bmatrix} = \mathbf{M}'\mathbf{Y_c} \tag{10.4}$$

The last two equations for i_5 and i_6 are identities. Combining all the solution steps we have

$$\begin{bmatrix} -1 \\ 0 \\ 0 \end{bmatrix} V_1 + \overbrace{\begin{bmatrix} 1 & 1 & 0 & 1 & 0 \\ 0 & 0 & -1 & 0 & 1 \\ 0 & 0 & 1 & 0 & 0 \end{bmatrix}}^{\mathbf{M}} \overbrace{\begin{bmatrix} \frac{1}{Cs} & 0 & 0 & 0 & 0 \\ 0 & R_1 & 0 & 0 & 0 \\ 0 & 0 & R_2 & 0 & 0 \\ 0 & 0 & 0 & sL_1 & sM \\ 0 & 0 & 0 & sM & sL_2 \end{bmatrix}}^{\mathbf{Z}}$$

$$\times \overbrace{\begin{bmatrix} 1 & 0 & 0 \\ 1 & 0 & 0 \\ 0 & -1 & 1 \\ 1 & 0 & 0 \\ 0 & 1 & 0 \end{bmatrix}}^{\mathbf{M}'} \begin{bmatrix} i_5 \\ i_6 \\ i_7 \end{bmatrix} + \begin{bmatrix} 0 \\ 0 \\ 0 \end{bmatrix} v_7 = \mathbf{0} \tag{10.5}$$

Note that the matrix postmultiplying the **Z** matrix is the transpose of the matrix premultiplying **Z**. This results from the known relationship $\mathscr{A} = -\mathbf{B}'$. The reader should verify this. In this example, V_1 and I_7 are known sources, and the solution entails finding I_5 and I_6 (unknown chord through variables) in terms of V_1 and I_7 (sources). After performing the triple matrix multiplication we have

$$\left[\begin{array}{cc:c} \frac{1}{Cs} + R_1 + sL_1 & sM & 0 \\ sM & R_2 + sL_2 & -R_2 \\ \hdashline 0 & -R_2 & R_2 \end{array}\right] \begin{bmatrix} I_5 \\ I_6 \\ I_7 \end{bmatrix} = \begin{bmatrix} 1 \\ 0 \\ 0 \end{bmatrix} V_1 - \begin{bmatrix} 0 \\ 0 \\ 1 \end{bmatrix} V_7 \tag{10.6}$$

Separating the first two equations according to the indicated partitioning of Equations 10.6, we may write

$$\begin{bmatrix} \frac{1}{Cs} + R_1 + sL_1 & sM \\ sM & R_2 + sL_2 \end{bmatrix} \begin{bmatrix} I_5 \\ I_6 \end{bmatrix} = \begin{bmatrix} 1 \\ 0 \end{bmatrix} V_1 - \begin{bmatrix} 0 \\ 0 \end{bmatrix} V_7 + \begin{bmatrix} 0 \\ R_2 \end{bmatrix} I_7 \tag{10.7}$$

Solving for I_5 and I_6, we have

$$\begin{bmatrix} I_5 \\ I_6 \end{bmatrix} = \frac{1}{D(s)} \begin{bmatrix} R_2 + sL_2 & -sM \\ -sM & \frac{1}{Cs} + R_1 + sL_1 \end{bmatrix} \begin{bmatrix} 1 & 0 \\ 0 & R_2 \end{bmatrix} \begin{bmatrix} V_7 \\ I_7 \end{bmatrix} \tag{10.8}$$

where $D(s)$ is the determinant of the matrix whose inverse we have taken. The remaining variables in the system can be found through the cutset and impedance matrices, that is,

$$\begin{bmatrix} I_1 \\ I_2 \\ I_3 \\ I_4 \end{bmatrix} = \begin{bmatrix} -1 & 0 & 0 \\ 1 & 0 & 0 \\ 1 & 0 & 0 \\ 0 & -0 & 1 \end{bmatrix} \begin{bmatrix} I_5 \\ I_6 \\ I_7 \end{bmatrix}$$

from the cutset matrix, and

$$\mathbf{X} = \begin{bmatrix} V_2 \\ V_3 \\ V_4 \\ V_5 \\ V_6 \end{bmatrix} = [\mathbf{Z}] \begin{bmatrix} I_2 \\ I_3 \\ I_4 \\ I_5 \\ I_6 \end{bmatrix}$$

from the open circuit parameter matrix. The remaining variables to be evaluated are the across variables associated with the through sources. In this example we have one,

$$V_7 = R_2(I_7 - I_6)$$

from Equation 10.6.

10.3 Branch Equation Formulation

An alternative method of formulating system equations is the branch method. This is normally used if the number of unknown cutsets is less than the number of unknown circuits. *Known* cutsets are those cutsets defined by branches which are across sources and *known* circuits are those circuits defined by chords which are through sources. In Figure 10.1, chord 7 is a flow source; hence, the number of unknown circuit variables is reduced to two. We may generalize these statements as follows: In a system graph let

$v =$ number of vertices

$e =$ number of elements

$p =$ number of separate parts
$n_x =$ number of across sources
$n_y =$ number of through sources

Then the number of equations to be solved simultaneously is

$$v - p - n_x \tag{10.9a}$$

by the branch method,

$$e - v + p - n_y \tag{10.9b}$$

by the chord method.

As an illustration of a solution using the branch method, consider the following example.

The mechanical system of Figure 10.2 has the appearance of a system of two-terminal components; but both springs and the mass are actually multiterminal components, taking into account that the mass may move in both a translational mode and a rotational mode.

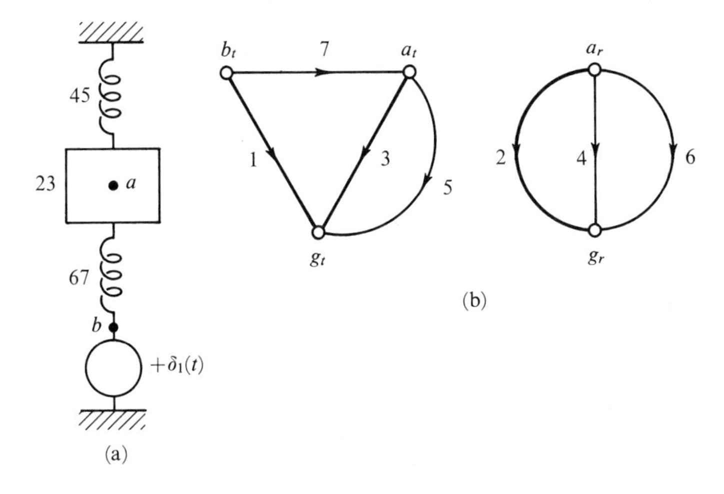

Fig. 10.2. (a) *Dual mode mechanical system;* (b) *system graph.*

The component models are given as
(a) compound springs (subscripts 4, 5 and 6, 7),

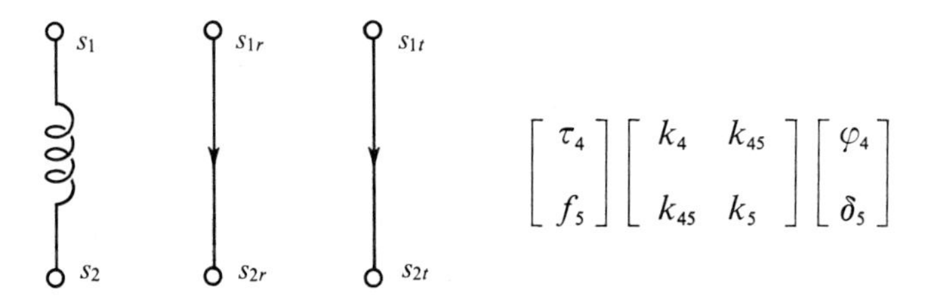

(b) compound mass (subscripts 2, 3),

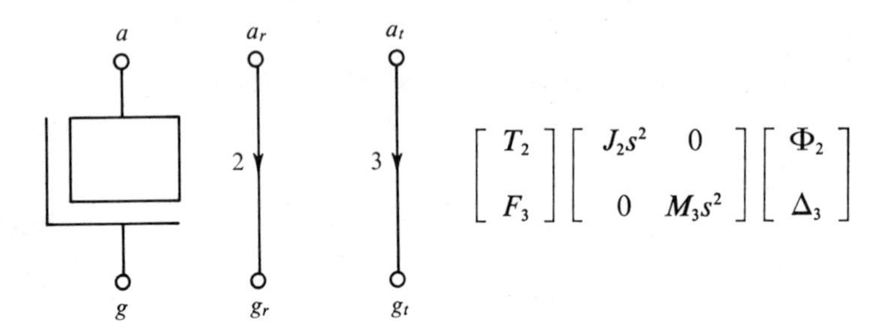

$$\begin{bmatrix} T_2 \\ F_3 \end{bmatrix} \begin{bmatrix} J_2 s^2 & 0 \\ 0 & M_3 s^2 \end{bmatrix} \begin{bmatrix} \Phi_2 \\ \Delta_3 \end{bmatrix}$$

The numerical subscripts are used to denote ports, while the algebraic subscripts r and t denote rotational and translational vertices, respectively.

The system graph is shown in Figure 10.2(b). It consists of two parts because the variables defined by the elements belong to two separate disciplines, rotation and translation. Note that the part corresponding to the rotational variables does not show terminal b since the driver only permits translational motion of point b, effectively pinning b_r to ground.

We choose elements 1, 2, and 3 as the elements of the forest, the union of the trees of the two parts of the system graph. Note that the across driver is selected to be part of the forest.

Using this forest as the basis for writing the fundamental cutset and circuit equations, one has

$$\begin{bmatrix} 1 & 0 & 0 & 0 & 0 & 0 & 1 \\ 0 & 1 & 0 & 1 & 0 & 1 & 0 \\ 0 & 0 & 1 & 0 & 1 & 0 & -1 \end{bmatrix} \begin{bmatrix} f_1 \\ \tau_2 \\ f_3 \\ \tau_4 \\ f_5 \\ \tau_6 \\ f_7 \end{bmatrix} = \mathbf{0} \qquad \textbf{(10.10a)}$$

$$\begin{bmatrix} 0 & -1 & 0 & 1 & 0 & 0 & 0 \\ 0 & 0 & -1 & 0 & 1 & 0 & 0 \\ 0 & -1 & 0 & 0 & 0 & 1 & 0 \\ -1 & 0 & 1 & 0 & 0 & 0 & 1 \end{bmatrix} \begin{bmatrix} \delta_1 \\ \varphi_2 \\ \delta_3 \\ \varphi_4 \\ \delta_5 \\ \varphi_6 \\ \delta_7 \end{bmatrix} = \mathbf{0} \qquad \textbf{(10.10b)}$$

The component equations can be written as a composite set of equations by writing a single matrix equation,

$$\begin{bmatrix} T_2 \\ F_3 \\ T_4 \\ F_5 \\ T_6 \\ F_7 \end{bmatrix} = \begin{bmatrix} J_2 s^2 & 0 & 0 & 0 & 0 & 0 \\ 0 & M_3 s^2 & 0 & 0 & 0 & 0 \\ 0 & 0 & k_4 & k_{45} & 0 & 0 \\ 0 & 0 & k_{45} & k_5 & 0 & 0 \\ 0 & 0 & 0 & 0 & k_6 & k_{67} \\ 0 & 0 & 0 & 0 & k_{67} & k_7 \end{bmatrix} \begin{bmatrix} \Phi_2 \\ \Delta_3 \\ \Phi_4 \\ \Delta_5 \\ \Phi_6 \\ \Delta_7 \end{bmatrix} \quad (10.11)$$

Notice that the terminal equations are all explicit in the through variable.

Upon inspection of the format of the respective equations, Equations 10.10 and 10.11, it is obvious that the component equations are amenable for substitution as a block into the cutset equations, provided the latter are partitioned as follows:

$$\begin{bmatrix} 1 \\ 0 \\ 0 \end{bmatrix} f_1 + \begin{bmatrix} 0 & 0 & 0 & 0 & 0 & 1 \\ 1 & 0 & 1 & 0 & 1 & 0 \\ 0 & 1 & 0 & 1 & 0 & -1 \end{bmatrix} \begin{bmatrix} \tau_2 \\ f_3 \\ \tau_4 \\ f_5 \\ \tau_6 \\ f_7 \end{bmatrix} = \mathbf{0} \quad (10.12)$$

The first column is separated from the cutset matrix. We then substitute Equations 10.11 into Equations 10.12,

$$\begin{bmatrix} 1 \\ 0 \\ 0 \end{bmatrix} F_1 + \begin{bmatrix} 0 & 0 & 0 & 0 & 0 & 1 \\ 1 & 0 & 1 & 0 & 1 & 0 \\ 0 & 1 & 0 & 1 & 0 & -1 \end{bmatrix} \begin{bmatrix} J_2 s^2 & 0 & 0 & 0 & 0 & 0 \\ 0 & M_3 s^2 & 0 & 0 & 0 & 0 \\ 0 & 0 & k_4 & k_{45} & 0 & 0 \\ 0 & 0 & k_{45} & k_5 & 0 & 0 \\ 0 & 0 & 0 & 0 & k_6 & k_{67} \\ 0 & 0 & 0 & 0 & k_{67} & k_7 \end{bmatrix}$$

$$\times \begin{bmatrix} \Phi_2 \\ \Delta_3 \\ \Phi_4 \\ \Delta_5 \\ \Phi_6 \\ \Delta_7 \end{bmatrix} = \mathbf{0} \quad (10.13)$$

If Equations 10.13 were multiplied out, there would be three equations involving seven unknowns. A reduction in the number or unknowns is necessary. Through the use of Equations 10.10b it is possible to express all the chord across variables in terms of all the branch across variables. The required relation obtained from the circuit equations 10.10b is

$$\begin{bmatrix} \Phi_4 \\ \Delta_5 \\ \Phi_6 \\ \Delta_7 \end{bmatrix} = \begin{bmatrix} 0 & 1 & 0 \\ 0 & 0 & 1 \\ 0 & 1 & 0 \\ 1 & 0 & -1 \end{bmatrix} \begin{bmatrix} \Delta_1 \\ \Phi_2 \\ \Delta_3 \end{bmatrix} \tag{10.14}$$

At this time, the merits of selecting the across driver as part of the forest are proven: δ_1 must be part of the set of variables on the right side of Equations 10.14—otherwise it would be difficult to include the specified variable in the final system model. With this substitution, the number of unknowns in Equations 10.13 is reduced to three, exactly equal to the number of equations.

To make the proposed substitution conformable for matrix operation, we augment 10.14 by adding the trivial relation

$$\begin{bmatrix} \Phi_2 \\ \Delta_3 \end{bmatrix} = \begin{bmatrix} 0 & 1 & 0 \\ 0 & 0 & 1 \end{bmatrix} \begin{bmatrix} \Delta_1 \\ \Phi_2 \\ \Delta_3 \end{bmatrix}$$

so that we obtain the following equations:

$$\begin{bmatrix} \Phi_2 \\ \Delta_3 \\ \Phi_4 \\ \Delta_5 \\ \Phi_6 \\ \Delta_7 \end{bmatrix} = \begin{bmatrix} 0 & 1 & 0 \\ 0 & 0 & 1 \\ 0 & 1 & 0 \\ 0 & 0 & 1 \\ 0 & 1 & 0 \\ 1 & 0 & -1 \end{bmatrix} \begin{bmatrix} \Delta_1 \\ \Phi_2 \\ \Delta_3 \end{bmatrix} \tag{10.15}$$

When Equations 10.15 are substituted into Equations 10.13, one has

$$\begin{bmatrix} 1 \\ 0 \\ 0 \end{bmatrix} F_1 + \overbrace{\begin{bmatrix} 0 & 0 & 0 & 0 & 0 & 1 \\ 1 & 0 & 1 & 0 & 1 & 0 \\ 0 & 1 & 0 & 1 & 0 & -1 \end{bmatrix}}^{\mathbf{C}} \overbrace{\begin{bmatrix} J_2 s^2 & 0 & 0 & 0 & 0 & 0 \\ 0 & M_3 s^2 & 0 & 0 & 0 & 0 \\ 0 & 0 & k_4 & k_{45} & 0 & 0 \\ 0 & 0 & k_{45} & k_5 & 0 & 0 \\ 0 & 0 & 0 & 0 & k_6 & k_{67} \\ 0 & 0 & 0 & 0 & k_{67} & k_7 \end{bmatrix}}^{\mathbf{W}}$$

$$\times \overbrace{\begin{bmatrix} 0 & 1 & 0 \\ 0 & 0 & 1 \\ 0 & 1 & 0 \\ 0 & 0 & 1 \\ 0 & 1 & 0 \\ 1 & 0 & -1 \end{bmatrix}}^{\mathbf{C}'} \begin{bmatrix} \Delta_1 \\ \Delta_3 \\ \Phi_4 \end{bmatrix} = \mathbf{0} \tag{10.16}$$

An inspection of the last equations verifies that there are three unknowns consisting of

$$F_1\ \Delta_3,\ \Phi_4$$

Recall that Δ_1 is specified.

Although the development of Equations 10.16 appears lengthy, involving the writing of a number of bulky matrices, a closer analysis of the development and the resulting equations will show the existence of a number of general properties that will greatly simplify the development of Equations 10.16.

Observe the following:

1. The triple matrix product is of the form

$$\mathbf{C} \quad \mathbf{W} \quad \mathbf{C}'$$

Knowledge of this fact will eliminate the writing of Equations 10.10b, 10.14, and 10.15.

2. The variables appearing to the right of the triple matrix product consist of only the branch across variables, numerically ordered identically to the order of the elements of the cutset equations.

3. The unknowns consist of the through variable associated with the specified across variable and the unspecified branch across variables.

These properties, shown to be true in the above example, will be derived for the general case in the next section.

Let us continue with the development of a set of simultaneous equations for the mechanical system. Upon multiplying Equations 10.16 out, one has

$$\begin{bmatrix} 1 \\ 0 \\ 0 \end{bmatrix} F_1 + \begin{bmatrix} k_7 & k_{67} & -k_7 \\ k_{67} & J_2 s^2 + k_{45} + k_6 & k_{45} - k_{67} \\ -k_7 & k_{45} - k_{67} & M_3 s^2 + k_5 + k_7 \end{bmatrix} \begin{bmatrix} \Delta_1 \\ \Phi_2 \\ \Delta_3 \end{bmatrix} = \mathbf{0} \tag{10.17}$$

Due to the structure of the matrix premultiplying F_1, the second and third Equations 10.17 do not involve F_1. This property is a direct consequence of the presence of the unit matrix in the cutset Equation 10.10a. Hence, these two equations may be solved separately to yield a solution for the unknown branch across variables in terms of the specified across variable, *i.e.*,

$$\begin{bmatrix} \Phi_2 \\ \Delta_3 \end{bmatrix} = -\begin{bmatrix} J_2 s^2 + k_{45} + k_6 & k_{45} - k_{67} \\ k_{45} - k_{67} & M_3 s^2 + k_5 + k_7 \end{bmatrix}^{-1} \begin{bmatrix} k_{67} \\ -k_7 \end{bmatrix} \Delta_1 \tag{10.18}$$

An inverse of order 2 is required, exactly equal to the number of unknown branch across variables.

10.4 Branch Equations—the General Structure

For systems having a system graph consisting of e elements, v vertices, and p parts, there are exactly (a) e terminal equations including n_x specified across drivers and n_y specified through drivers, (b) $e - v + p$ fundamental circuit equations, and (c) $v - p$ fundamental cutset equations. The equations constitute a set of two e independent statements regarding the component characteristics and component interconnections. These must be solved simultaneously to obtain a solution for any of the system variables not specified.

One procedure to obtain this objective will be presented here. It is a symbolic presentation of the branch formulation introduced in the previous section. We begin by classifying the system variables into four categories indicated by subscripts: (1) $\mathbf{X}_{b_1}$ specified across variables, $\mathbf{Y}_{b_1}$ covariables; (2) $\mathbf{X}_{b_2}$, $\mathbf{Y}_{b_2}$ component variables whose elements are in the forest; (3) $\mathbf{X}_{c_1}$, $\mathbf{Y}_{c_1}$ component variables whose elements are in the coforest; (4) $\mathbf{Y}_{c_2}$ specified through variables, $\mathbf{X}_{c_2}$ covariables. Hence,

$$\mathbf{X} = \begin{bmatrix} \mathbf{X}_{b_1} \\ \mathbf{X}_{b_2} \\ \mathbf{X}_{c_1} \\ \mathbf{X}_{c_2} \end{bmatrix} \quad \text{and} \quad \mathbf{Y} = \begin{bmatrix} \mathbf{Y}_{b_1} \\ \mathbf{Y}_{b_2} \\ \mathbf{Y}_{c_1} \\ \mathbf{Y}_{c_2} \end{bmatrix} \tag{10.19}$$

For branch formulation, the component equations must be expressed explicitly in the through variable. Thus, all multiterminal components must be expressible in terms of the short-circuit parameters; where this is not possible, the branch equations of a system containing such components cannot be formulated.

Let the component equations be given in the form

$$e - n_x - n_y \left\{ \begin{bmatrix} \mathbf{Y}_{b_2} \\ \mathbf{Y}_{c_1} \end{bmatrix} = \begin{bmatrix} \mathbf{W}_{11} & \mathbf{W}_{12} \\ \mathbf{W}_{21} & \mathbf{W}_{22} \end{bmatrix} \begin{bmatrix} \mathbf{X}_{b_2} \\ \mathbf{X}_{c_1} \end{bmatrix} \right. \tag{10.20}$$

Furthermore, the specified variables are

$$n_x\{\mathbf{X}_{b_1} = \mathbf{F}_x(t) \tag{10.21a}$$

$$n_y\{\mathbf{Y}_{c_2} = \mathbf{F}_y(t) \tag{10.21b}$$

Equations 10.20 and 10.21 comprise a total of e component equations.

The component equations are substituted into the cutset equations, which are written as

$$v - p \left\{ \begin{bmatrix} \mathbf{U} & \mathbf{0} & \mathscr{A}_{11} & \mathscr{A}_{12} \\ \mathbf{0} & \mathbf{U} & \mathscr{A}_{21} & \mathscr{A}_{22} \end{bmatrix} \begin{bmatrix} \mathbf{Y}_{b_1} \\ \mathbf{Y}_{b_2} \\ \mathbf{Y}_{c_1} \\ \mathbf{Y}_{c_2} \end{bmatrix} = \mathbf{0} \right. \tag{10.22}$$

To substitute the component equations into the cutset equations, the latter are partitioned as follows:

$$\begin{bmatrix} \mathbf{U} \\ \mathbf{0} \end{bmatrix} \mathbf{Y}_{b_1} + \begin{bmatrix} \mathbf{0} & \mathscr{A}_{11} \\ \mathbf{U} & \mathscr{A}_{21} \end{bmatrix} \begin{bmatrix} \mathbf{Y}_{b_2} \\ \mathbf{Y}_{b_1} \end{bmatrix} + \begin{bmatrix} \mathscr{A}_{12} \\ \mathscr{A}_{22} \end{bmatrix} \mathbf{Y}_{c_2} = \mathbf{0} \tag{10.23}$$

Upon substitution of Equations 10.20 and 10.21b into 10.21c, one has

$$\begin{bmatrix} \mathbf{U} \\ \mathbf{0} \end{bmatrix} \mathbf{Y}_{b_1} + \begin{bmatrix} \mathbf{0} & \mathscr{A}_{11} \\ \mathbf{U} & \mathscr{A}_{21} \end{bmatrix} \begin{bmatrix} \mathbf{W}_{11} & \mathbf{W}_{12} \\ \mathbf{W}_{21} & \mathbf{W}_{22} \end{bmatrix} \begin{bmatrix} \mathbf{X}_{b_2} \\ \mathbf{X}_{c_1} \end{bmatrix} + \begin{bmatrix} \mathscr{A}_{12} \\ \mathscr{A}_{22} \end{bmatrix} \mathbf{F}_y(t) = \mathbf{0} \tag{10.24}$$

Equations 10.24 represent a partial development of the branch equations. Involved are $v - p$ equations in terms of $e - n_y$ unknowns, which are

$$\mathbf{Y}_{b_1}, \qquad \mathbf{X}_{b_2}, \qquad \mathbf{X}_{c_1}$$

The number of unknowns may be reached by application of the circuit equations. They are given as

$$\begin{bmatrix} \mathbf{B}_{11} & \mathbf{B}_{12} & \mathbf{U} & \mathbf{0} \\ \mathbf{B}_{21} & \mathbf{B}_{22} & \mathbf{0} & \mathbf{U} \end{bmatrix} \begin{bmatrix} \mathbf{X}_{b_1} \\ \mathbf{X}_{b_2} \\ \mathbf{X}_{c_1} \\ \mathbf{X}_{c_2} \end{bmatrix} = \mathbf{0} \tag{10.25}$$

To generate the transformation

$$\begin{bmatrix} \mathbf{X}_{b_2} \\ \mathbf{X}_{c_1} \end{bmatrix} \longrightarrow \begin{bmatrix} \mathbf{X}_{b_1} \\ \mathbf{X}_{b_2} \end{bmatrix}$$

the top set of Equations 10.25 are rearranged to give

$$\mathbf{X}_{c_1} = -[\mathbf{B}_{11} \quad \mathbf{B}_{12}] \begin{bmatrix} \mathbf{X}_{b_1} \\ \mathbf{X}_{b_2} \end{bmatrix}$$

This set is augmented by the trivial relation

$$\mathbf{X}_{b_2} = [\mathbf{0} \quad \mathbf{U}] \begin{bmatrix} \mathbf{X}_{b_1} \\ \mathbf{X}_{b_2} \end{bmatrix}$$

to yield

$$\begin{bmatrix} \mathbf{X}_{b_2} \\ \mathbf{X}_{c_1} \end{bmatrix} = \begin{bmatrix} \mathbf{0} & \mathbf{U} \\ -\mathbf{B}_{11} & -\mathbf{B}_{12} \end{bmatrix} \begin{bmatrix} \mathbf{X}_{b_1} \\ \mathbf{X}_{b_2} \end{bmatrix} \tag{10.26}$$

Although Equations 10.26 may be substituted into Equations 10.24 and effect the desired reduction in the number of unknowns, we consider first the orthogonality relation between the cutset and circuit matrix,

$$\mathbf{B} \cdot \mathscr{A}' = \mathbf{0}$$

or in terms of the expanded form displayed by Equations 10.22 and 10.25,

$$\begin{bmatrix} \mathbf{B}_{11} & \mathbf{B}_{12} & \mathbf{U} & \mathbf{0} \\ \mathbf{B}_{21} & \mathbf{B}_{22} & \mathbf{0} & \mathbf{U} \end{bmatrix} \begin{bmatrix} \mathbf{U} & \mathbf{0} \\ \mathbf{0} & \mathbf{U} \\ \mathscr{A}'_{11} & \mathscr{A}'_{21} \\ \mathscr{A}'_{12} & \mathscr{A}'_{22} \end{bmatrix} = \mathbf{0} \tag{10.27}$$

Upon multiplication, one has

$$\begin{bmatrix} \mathbf{B}_{11} & \mathbf{B}_{12} \\ \mathbf{B}_{21} & \mathbf{B}_{22} \end{bmatrix} = -\begin{bmatrix} \mathscr{A}'_{11} & \mathscr{A}'_{21} \\ \mathscr{A}'_{12} & \mathscr{A}'_{22} \end{bmatrix} \tag{10.28}$$

And the following relationships between the submatrices may be stated

$$\left.\begin{aligned} \mathbf{B}_{11} &= -\mathscr{A}'_{11} \\ \mathbf{B}_{12} &= -\mathscr{A}'_{21} \\ \mathbf{B}_{21} &= -\mathscr{A}'_{12} \\ \mathbf{B}_{22} &= -\mathscr{A}'_{22} \end{aligned}\right] \tag{10.29}$$

With the use of these identities, we may rewrite Equations 10.26 as follows:

$$\begin{bmatrix} \mathbf{X}_{b_2} \\ \mathbf{X}_{c_1} \end{bmatrix} = \begin{bmatrix} \mathbf{0} & \mathbf{U} \\ \mathscr{A}'_{11} & \mathscr{A}'_{21} \end{bmatrix} \begin{bmatrix} \mathbf{X}_{b_1} \\ \mathbf{X}_{b_2} \end{bmatrix} \begin{bmatrix} \mathbf{0} & \mathscr{A}_{11} \\ \mathbf{U} & \mathscr{A}_{21} \end{bmatrix}' \begin{bmatrix} \mathbf{X}_{b_1} \\ \mathbf{X}_{b_2} \end{bmatrix} \tag{10.30}$$

This set of equations is substituted into 10.24, obtaining

$$\begin{bmatrix} \mathbf{U} \\ \mathbf{0} \end{bmatrix} \mathbf{Y}_{b_1} + \begin{bmatrix} \mathbf{0} & \mathscr{A}_{11} \\ \mathbf{U} & \mathscr{A}_{21} \end{bmatrix} \begin{bmatrix} \mathbf{W}_{11} & \mathbf{W}_{12} \\ \mathbf{W}_{21} & \mathbf{W}_{22} \end{bmatrix} \begin{bmatrix} \mathbf{0} & \mathscr{A}_{11} \\ \mathbf{U} & \mathscr{A}_{21} \end{bmatrix}' \begin{bmatrix} \mathbf{X}_{b_1} \\ \mathbf{X}_{b_2} \end{bmatrix} + \begin{bmatrix} \mathscr{A}_{12} \\ \mathscr{A}_{22} \end{bmatrix} \mathbf{F}_y(t) = \mathbf{0} \tag{10.31}$$

Since $\mathbf{X}_{b_1} = \mathbf{F}_x(t)$, the only unknown variables remaining in Equations 10.31 are

$$\mathbf{Y}_{b_1} \quad \text{and} \quad \mathbf{X}_{b_2}$$

Notice now that the bottom set of Equations 10.31 are independent of one set of unknowns, $\mathbf{Y}_{b_1}$. It is therefore possible to solve Equations 10.31 for $\mathbf{X}_{b_1}$ first using the bottom set of equations. For this purpose, we multiply the triple matrix product of Equations 10.31 and let it be represented symbolically such that Equations 10.31 are

$$\begin{bmatrix} \mathbf{U} \\ \mathbf{0} \end{bmatrix} \mathbf{Y}_{b_1} + \begin{bmatrix} \mathbf{D}_{11} & \mathbf{D}_{12} \\ \mathbf{D}_{21} & \mathbf{D}_{22} \end{bmatrix} \begin{bmatrix} \mathbf{F}_x(t) \\ \mathbf{X}_{b_2} \end{bmatrix} + \begin{bmatrix} \mathscr{A}_{12} \\ \mathscr{A}_{22} \end{bmatrix} \mathbf{F}_y(t) = \mathbf{0} \tag{10.32}$$

where

$$\begin{aligned} \mathbf{D}_{11} &= \mathscr{A}_{11}\mathbf{W}_{22}\mathscr{A}'_{11} \\ \mathbf{D}_{12} &= \mathscr{A}_{11}\mathbf{W}_{21} + \mathscr{A}_{11}\mathbf{W}_{22}\mathscr{A}'_{21} \\ \mathbf{D}_{21} &= \mathbf{W}_{12}\mathscr{A}'_{11} + \mathscr{A}_{21}\mathbf{W}_{22}\mathscr{A}'_{11} \\ \mathbf{D}_{22} &= \mathbf{W}_{11} + \mathscr{A}_{21}\mathbf{W}_{21} + \mathbf{W}_{12}\mathscr{A}'_{21} + \mathscr{A}_{21}\mathbf{W}_{22}\mathscr{A}'_{21} \end{aligned} \tag{10.33}$$

From the bottom Equation 10.33 we can solve for the unknown variables $\mathbf{X}_{b_2}$,

$$\mathbf{X}_{b_2} = -\mathbf{D}_{22}^{-1}\{\mathbf{D}_{21}\mathbf{F}_x(t) + \mathscr{A}_{22}\mathbf{F}_y(t)\} \tag{10.34}$$

The number of variables in the column vector is given by the number of all branch variables minus the number of specified branch variables, which is

$$v - p - n_x$$

This number represents the order of the square matrix $\mathbf{D}_{22}$ whose inverse has to be taken in the solution process. This number therefore represents the equation count for the system.

Several important properties will summarize the branch formulation procedure.

1. All component equations must be expressible explicitly in the through variable.

$$e - n_x - n_y \left\{ \begin{bmatrix} \mathbf{Y}_{b_2} \\ \mathbf{Y}_{c_1} \end{bmatrix} = \begin{bmatrix} \mathbf{W}_{11} & \mathbf{W}_{12} \\ \mathbf{W}_{21} & \mathbf{W}_{22} \end{bmatrix} \begin{bmatrix} \mathbf{X}_{b_2} \\ \mathbf{X}_{c_1} \end{bmatrix} \right. \tag{10.20}$$

2. The cutset equations are required. They serve as the only basis for the statement of component interconnections.

$$v - p \left\{ \begin{bmatrix} \mathbf{U} & \mathbf{0} & \mathscr{A}_{11} & \mathscr{A}_{12} \\ \mathbf{0} & \mathbf{U} & \mathscr{A}_{21} & \mathscr{A}_{22} \end{bmatrix} \right. \begin{bmatrix} \mathbf{Y}_{b_1} \\ \mathbf{Y}_{b_2} \\ \mathbf{Y}_{c_1} \\ \mathbf{Y}_{c_2} \end{bmatrix} = \mathbf{0} \tag{10.22}$$

3. The cutset equations are partitioned to separate the variables associated with the component equations from the variables associated with the drivers.

$$\begin{bmatrix} \mathbf{U} \\ \mathbf{0} \end{bmatrix} \mathbf{Y}_{b_1} + \begin{bmatrix} \mathbf{0} & \mathscr{A}_{11} \\ \mathbf{U} & \mathscr{A}_{21} \end{bmatrix} \begin{bmatrix} \mathbf{Y}_{b_2} \\ \mathbf{Y}_{c_1} \end{bmatrix} + \begin{bmatrix} \mathscr{A}_{12} \\ \mathscr{A}_{22} \end{bmatrix} \mathbf{Y}_{c_2} = \mathbf{0} \tag{10.23}$$

4. The component equations are substituted into the partitioned cutset equations and the transformation of variables is applied to reduce the number of unknowns.

$$\begin{bmatrix} \mathbf{U} \\ \mathbf{0} \end{bmatrix} \mathbf{Y}_{b_1} + \begin{bmatrix} \mathbf{0} & \mathscr{A}_{11} \\ \mathbf{U} & \mathscr{A}_{21} \end{bmatrix} \begin{bmatrix} \mathbf{W}_{11} & \mathbf{W}_{12} \\ \mathbf{W}_{21} & \mathbf{W}_{22} \end{bmatrix}$$

$$\times \begin{bmatrix} \mathbf{0} & \mathscr{A}_{11} \\ \mathbf{U} & \mathscr{A}_{21} \end{bmatrix}' \begin{bmatrix} \mathbf{X}_{b_1} \\ \mathbf{X}_{b_2} \end{bmatrix} + \begin{bmatrix} \mathscr{A}_{12} \\ \mathscr{A}_{22} \end{bmatrix} \mathbf{F}_y(t) = \mathbf{0} \tag{10.31}$$

There are exactly $v - p$ equations in $v - p$ unknowns.

5. The triple matrix product is formed and the bottom set of $v-p - n_x$ equations in $v - p - n_x$ unknowns may be solved.

$$\begin{bmatrix} \mathbf{U} \\ \mathbf{0} \end{bmatrix} \mathbf{Y}_{b_1} + \begin{bmatrix} \mathbf{D}_{11} & \mathbf{D}_{12} \\ \mathbf{D}_{21} & \mathbf{D}_{22} \end{bmatrix} \begin{bmatrix} \mathbf{F}_x(t) \\ \mathbf{X}_{b_2} \end{bmatrix} + \begin{bmatrix} \mathscr{A}_{12} \\ \mathscr{A}_{22} \end{bmatrix} \mathbf{F}_y(t) = \mathbf{0} \quad (10.32)$$

6. An inverse of order $v - p - n_x$ is required for the solution.

$$\mathbf{X}_{b_2} = -\mathbf{D}_{22}^{-1}\{\mathbf{D}_{21}\mathbf{F}_x(t) + \mathscr{A}_{22}\mathbf{F}_y(t)\} \quad (10.34)$$

Another example follows. Consider the system of Figure 10.3.

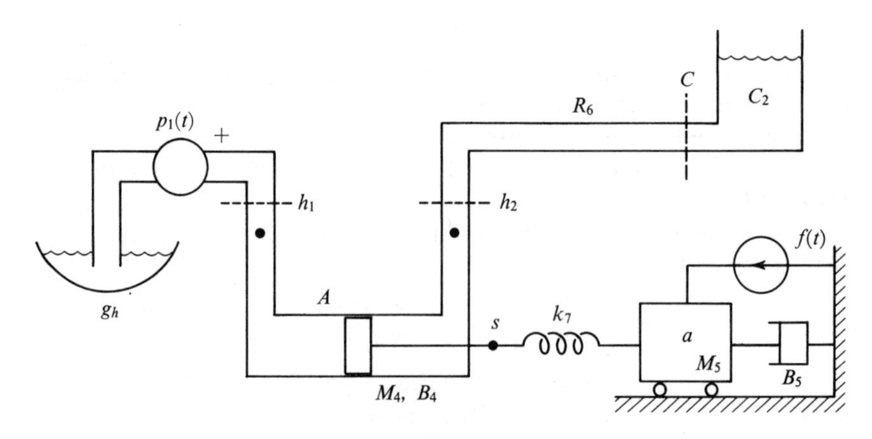

Fig. 10.3. *Hydraulic-mechanical system.*

To start this formulation problem, the system graph is developed. It is shown in Figure 10.4.

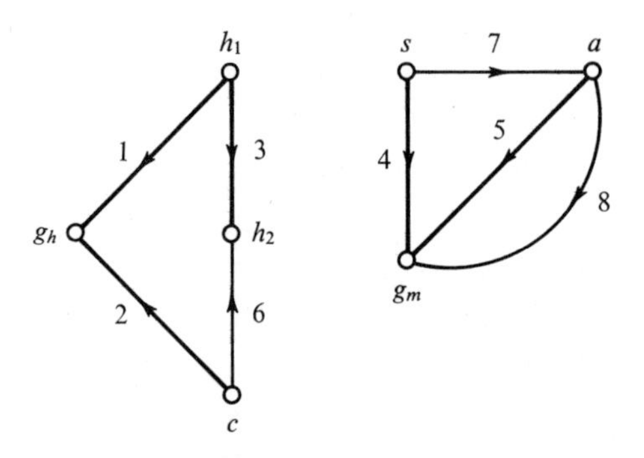

Fig. 10.4. *System graph of hydraulic-mechanical system.*

We number the elements of the graph so that they are arranged in numerical order according to the categorization detailed in Equations 10.19. We note that variable set b_1 corresponds to element 1; b_2 corresponds to elements 2, 3, 4, 5; c_1 corresponds to elements 6, 7; and c_2 corresponds to element 8. From the equation count

$$v - p - n_x = 7 - 2 - 1 = 4$$

it is determined that an inverse of order 4 will be required in the solutions of the resulting equations.

The component equations are

$$\begin{bmatrix} \dot{g}_2 \\ \dot{g}_3 \\ f_4 \\ f_5 \\ \dot{g}_6 \\ f_7 \end{bmatrix} = \begin{bmatrix} C_2 d/dt & 0 & 0 & 0 & 0 & 0 \\ 0 & 0 & Ad/dt & 0 & 0 & 0 \\ 0 & -A & Y_4 & 0 & 0 & 0 \\ 0 & 0 & 0 & Y_5 & 0 & 0 \\ 0 & 0 & 0 & 0 & 1/R_6 & 0 \\ 0 & 0 & 0 & 0 & 0 & k_7 \end{bmatrix} \begin{bmatrix} p_2 \\ p_3 \\ \delta_4 \\ \delta_5 \\ p_6 \\ \delta_7 \end{bmatrix} \qquad (10.35)$$

where

$$Y_4 = M_4 d^2/dt^2 + B_4 d/dt$$

and

$$Y_5 = M_5 d^2/dt^2 + B_5 d/dt$$

and the cutset equations are

$$\begin{bmatrix} 1 & 0 & 0 & 0 & 0 & -1 & 0 & 0 \\ 0 & 1 & 0 & 0 & 0 & 1 & 0 & 0 \\ 0 & 0 & 1 & 0 & 0 & 1 & 0 & 0 \\ 0 & 0 & 0 & 1 & 0 & 0 & 1 & 0 \\ 0 & 0 & 0 & 0 & 1 & 0 & -1 & 1 \end{bmatrix} \begin{bmatrix} \dot{g}_1 \\ \dot{g}_2 \\ \dot{g}_3 \\ f_4 \\ f_5 \\ \dot{g}_6 \\ f_7 \\ f_8 \end{bmatrix} = \mathbf{0} \qquad (10.36)$$

It is now possible to set up the equations involving the triple matrix product by properly partitioning the cutset matrix to separate the first and last columns which correspond to the drivers $p_1(t)$ and $f_8(t)$.

$$\begin{bmatrix} 1 \\ 0 \\ 0 \\ 0 \\ 0 \end{bmatrix} \dot{g}_1 + \begin{bmatrix} 0 & 0 & 0 & 0 & -1 & 0 \\ 1 & 0 & 0 & 0 & 1 & 0 \\ 0 & 1 & 0 & 0 & 1 & 0 \\ 0 & 0 & 1 & 0 & 0 & 1 \\ 0 & 0 & 0 & 1 & 0 & -1 \end{bmatrix} \begin{bmatrix} C_2 d/dt & 0 & 0 & 0 & 0 & 0 \\ 0 & 0 & Ad/dt & 0 & 0 & 0 \\ 0 & -A & Y_4 & 0 & 0 & 0 \\ 0 & 0 & 0 & Y_5 & 0 & 0 \\ 0 & 0 & 0 & 0 & 1/R_6 & 0 \\ 0 & 0 & 0 & 0 & 0 & k_7 \end{bmatrix}$$

$$\times \begin{bmatrix} 0 & 1 & 0 & 0 & 0 \\ 0 & 0 & 1 & 0 & 0 \\ 0 & 0 & 0 & 1 & 0 \\ 0 & 0 & 0 & 0 & 1 \\ -1 & 1 & 1 & 0 & 0 \\ 0 & 0 & 0 & 1 & -1 \end{bmatrix} \begin{bmatrix} p_1(t) \\ p_2 \\ p_3 \\ \delta_4 \\ \delta_5 \end{bmatrix} + \begin{bmatrix} 0 \\ 0 \\ 0 \\ 0 \\ 1 \end{bmatrix} f_8(t) = \mathbf{0} \qquad (10.37)$$

Upon multiplying the product out, we have

$$\begin{bmatrix} 1 \\ 0 \\ 0 \\ 0 \\ 0 \end{bmatrix} \dot{g}_1 + \begin{bmatrix} -1/R_6 & -1/R_6 & -1/R_6 & 0 & 0 \\ -1/R_6 & C_2 d/dt + 1/R_6 & 1/R_6 & 0 & 0 \\ -1/R_6 & 1/R_6 & 1/R_6 & A d/dt & 0 \\ 0 & 0 & -A & Y_4 + k_7 & -k_7 \\ 0 & 0 & 0 & -k_7 & Y_5 + k_7 \end{bmatrix} \begin{bmatrix} p_1(t) \\ p_2 \\ p_3 \\ \delta_4 \\ \delta_5 \end{bmatrix}$$

$$+ \begin{bmatrix} 0 \\ 0 \\ 0 \\ 0 \\ 1 \end{bmatrix} f_8(t) = \mathbf{0} \tag{10.38}$$

Equations 10.38 may now be solved by separating the bottom four equations involving p_2, p_3, δ_4, δ_5 as unknowns. As predicted, a fourth-order inverse is required. This inverse, however, is not obtainable when the equations are differential equations. The entire set must be transformed into the s-domain to facilitate a solution of the simultaneous equations. Since an inverse matrix containing differential operators as coefficients is invariably involved, it is generally good practice to formulate the entire process in the s-domain.

For initial conditions assumed to be zero, the solution is indicated by

$$\begin{bmatrix} P_2 \\ P_3 \\ \Delta_4 \\ \Delta_5 \end{bmatrix} = - \begin{bmatrix} C_2 s + 1/R_6 & 1/R_6 & 0 & 0 \\ 1/R_6 & 1/R_6 & As & 0 \\ 0 & -A & Y_4 + k_7 & -k_7 \\ 0 & 0 & -k_7 & Y_5 + k_7 \end{bmatrix}^{-1}$$

$$\left\{ \begin{bmatrix} -1/R_6 \\ -1/R_6 \\ 0 \\ 0 \end{bmatrix} P_1(s) + \begin{bmatrix} 0 \\ 0 \\ 0 \\ 1 \end{bmatrix} F_8(s) \right\} \tag{10.39}$$

The computational work involved in inverting the four $\times$ four matrix is considerable. One might wonder whether branch formulation in this example was the most suitable choice. As will be seen in the next section, another process, called chord formulation, will permit a simpler formulation requiring only a two $\times$ two inverse. This represents a considerable reduction in the amount of labor involved; it is therefore suggested that we postpone the solution of this system until later.

10.5 Chord Formulation—the General Structure

A number of important properties are associated with the formulation of a mathematical model in chord equations. As we have already seen in section 10.3, recognition of these properties will be of appreciable advantage in the application of this formulation procedure.

The structure of chord formulation is identical to that of branch formulation presented earlier. The elements of the graph and their associated variables are categorized exactly as before using the subscripts

$$\text{tree}\begin{cases} b_1 & \text{— specified across drivers} \\ b_2 & \left.\begin{matrix} \\ \\ \end{matrix}\right\} \text{component elements} \begin{cases}\text{branches}\\ \text{chords}\end{cases} \end{cases}$$

$$\text{co-tree}\begin{cases} c_1 & \\ c_2 & \text{— specified through drivers} \end{cases}$$

Recall that

$$\mathbf{X}_{b_1} = \mathbf{F}_x$$

and

$$\mathbf{Y}_{c_2} = \mathbf{F}_y$$

The terminal equations are given as

$$\begin{bmatrix} \mathbf{X}_{b_2} \\ \mathbf{X}_{c_1} \end{bmatrix} = \begin{bmatrix} \mathbf{Z}_{11} & \mathbf{Z}_{12} \\ \mathbf{Z}_{21} & \mathbf{Z}_{22} \end{bmatrix} \begin{bmatrix} \mathbf{Y}_{b_2} \\ \mathbf{Y}_{c_1} \end{bmatrix} \tag{10.40}$$

And the fundamental circuit equations are written as

$$\begin{bmatrix} \mathbf{B}_{11} & \mathbf{B}_{12} & \mathbf{U} & \mathbf{0} \\ \mathbf{B}_{21} & \mathbf{B}_{22} & \mathbf{0} & \mathbf{U} \end{bmatrix} \begin{bmatrix} \mathbf{X}_{b_1} \\ \mathbf{X}_{b_2} \\ \mathbf{X}_{c_1} \\ \mathbf{X}_{c_2} \end{bmatrix} = \mathbf{0} \tag{10.41}$$

which then are partitioned in the following manner to separate the variables associated with the specified drivers.

$$\begin{bmatrix} \mathbf{B}_{11} \\ \mathbf{B}_{21} \end{bmatrix} \mathbf{X}_{b_1} + \begin{bmatrix} \mathbf{B}_{12} & \mathbf{U} \\ \mathbf{B}_{22} & \mathbf{0} \end{bmatrix} \begin{bmatrix} \mathbf{X}_{b_2} \\ \mathbf{X}_{c_1} \end{bmatrix} + \begin{bmatrix} \mathbf{0} \\ \mathbf{U} \end{bmatrix} \mathbf{X}_{c_2} = \mathbf{0} \tag{10.42}$$

Upon substitution of the component equation into the last set, we have

$$\begin{bmatrix} \mathbf{B}_{11} \\ \mathbf{B}_{21} \end{bmatrix} \mathbf{F}_x + \begin{bmatrix} \mathbf{B}_{12} & \mathbf{U} \\ \mathbf{B}_{22} & \mathbf{0} \end{bmatrix} \begin{bmatrix} \mathbf{Z}_{11} & \mathbf{Z}_{12} \\ \mathbf{Z}_{21} & \mathbf{Z}_{22} \end{bmatrix} \begin{bmatrix} \mathbf{Y}_{b_2} \\ \mathbf{Y}_{c_1} \end{bmatrix} + \begin{bmatrix} \mathbf{0} \\ \mathbf{U} \end{bmatrix} \mathbf{X}_{c_2} = \mathbf{0} \tag{10.43}$$

Equations 10.43 are exactly $e - v + p$ equations (equal to the circuit equations of a graph of p parts) involving $e - n_x$ unknowns, which are

$$\mathbf{Y}_{b_2} \qquad \mathbf{Y}_{c_1} \qquad \mathbf{X}_{c_2}$$

Through application of the cutset equations, it is now possible to generate the transformation

$$\mathbf{Y}_{b_2} \longrightarrow \begin{bmatrix} \mathbf{Y}_{c_1} \\ \mathbf{Y}_{c_2} \end{bmatrix} = \begin{bmatrix} \mathbf{Y}_{c_1} \\ \mathbf{F}_y \end{bmatrix}$$

to effect a reduction in the unknowns. Let the cutset equations be given as

$$\begin{bmatrix} \mathbf{U} & \mathbf{0} & \mathscr{A}_{11} & \mathscr{A}_{12} \\ \mathbf{0} & \mathbf{U} & \mathscr{A}_{21} & \mathscr{A}_{22} \end{bmatrix} \begin{bmatrix} \mathbf{Y}_{b_1} \\ \mathbf{Y}_{b_2} \\ \mathbf{Y}_{c_1} \\ \mathbf{Y}_{c_2} \end{bmatrix} = \mathbf{0} \tag{10.44}$$

From the bottom set of this set of equations, one may write

$$\mathbf{Y}_{b_2} = -[\mathscr{A}_{21} \quad \mathscr{A}_{22}] \begin{bmatrix} \mathbf{Y}_{c_1} \\ \mathbf{Y}_{c_2} \end{bmatrix} = -[\mathscr{A}_{21} \quad \mathscr{A}_{22}] \begin{bmatrix} \mathbf{Y}_{c_1} \\ \mathbf{F}_y \end{bmatrix}$$

This set is augmented by the trivial relation

$$\mathbf{Y}_{c_1} = [\mathbf{U} \quad \mathbf{0}] \begin{bmatrix} \mathbf{Y}_{c_1} \\ \mathbf{F}_y \end{bmatrix}$$

so that

$$\begin{bmatrix} \mathbf{Y}_{b_2} \\ \mathbf{Y}_{c_1} \end{bmatrix} = \begin{bmatrix} -\mathscr{A}_{21} & -\mathscr{A}_{22} \\ \mathbf{U} & \mathbf{0} \end{bmatrix} \begin{bmatrix} \mathbf{Y}_{c_1} \\ \mathbf{F}_y \end{bmatrix}$$

Again, use is made of the orthogonality relation to show that

$$-\mathscr{A}_{21} = \mathbf{B}'_{12}$$

and

$$-\mathscr{A}_{22} = \mathbf{B}'_{22}$$

The desired transformation is finally given by

$$\begin{bmatrix} \mathbf{Y}_{b_2} \\ \mathbf{Y}_{c_1} \end{bmatrix} = \begin{bmatrix} \mathbf{B}'_{12} & \mathbf{B}'_{22} \\ \mathbf{U} & \mathbf{0} \end{bmatrix} \begin{bmatrix} \mathbf{Y}_{c_1} \\ F_y \end{bmatrix} = \begin{bmatrix} \mathbf{B}_{12} & \mathbf{U} \\ \mathbf{B}_{22} & \mathbf{0} \end{bmatrix} \begin{bmatrix} \mathbf{Y}_{c_1} \\ \mathbf{Y}_{c_2} \end{bmatrix} \tag{10.45}$$

Upon substitution of Equations 10.45 into 10.43, one has

$$\begin{bmatrix} \mathbf{B}_{11} \\ \mathbf{B}_{21} \end{bmatrix} \mathbf{F}_x + \begin{bmatrix} \mathbf{B}_{12} & \mathbf{U} \\ \mathbf{B}_{22} & \mathbf{0} \end{bmatrix} \begin{bmatrix} \mathbf{Z}_{11} & \mathbf{Z}_{12} \\ \mathbf{Z}_{21} & \mathbf{Z}_{22} \end{bmatrix} \begin{bmatrix} \mathbf{B}_{12} & \mathbf{U} \\ \mathbf{B}_{22} & \mathbf{0} \end{bmatrix}' \begin{bmatrix} \mathbf{Y}_{c_1} \\ \mathbf{Y}_{c_2} \end{bmatrix} + \begin{bmatrix} \mathbf{0} \\ \mathbf{U} \end{bmatrix} \mathbf{X}_{c_2} = \mathbf{0} \tag{10.46}$$

Equation 10.46 reveals the triple matrix product involving the component matrix flanked by a submatrix of the circuit matrix and its transpose. If we let the result of the triple product be represented symbolically, then Equations 10.46 yield

$$\begin{bmatrix} \mathbf{B}_{11} \\ \mathbf{B}_{21} \end{bmatrix} \mathbf{F}_x + \begin{bmatrix} \mathbf{N}_{11} & \mathbf{N}_{12} \\ \mathbf{N}_{21} & \mathbf{N}_{22} \end{bmatrix} \begin{bmatrix} \mathbf{Y}_{c_1} \\ \mathbf{F}_y \end{bmatrix} + \begin{bmatrix} \mathbf{0} \\ \mathbf{U} \end{bmatrix} \mathbf{X}_{c_2} = \mathbf{0} \tag{10.47}$$

where the number of unknowns totals $e - v + p$, exactly equal to the number of equations. It is left as an exercise to relate the N-matrix to the triple product.

The solution of these unknowns is obtained in two steps. First, the top set of equations is taken to yield

$$\mathbf{Y}_{c_1} = -\mathbf{N}_{11}^{-1}\{\mathbf{B}_{11}\mathbf{F}_x + \mathbf{N}_{12}\mathbf{F}_y\} \tag{10.48}$$

This partial solution is a direct consequence of the manner in which the fundamental circuit equations are written. Through the zero-matrix multiplying $\mathbf{X}_{c_2}$ in the top set, it is possible to solve first for

$$e - v + p - n_y$$

unknowns. And the order of the required inverse is given by the same number. Second, the bottom set of equations yields

$$\mathbf{X}_{c_2} = -\mathbf{B}_{21}\mathbf{F}_x - \mathbf{N}_{21}\mathbf{Y}_{c_1} - \mathbf{N}_{22}\mathbf{F}_y$$

and upon using the result of Equation 10.48,

$$\mathbf{X}_{c_2} = \{\mathbf{N}_{21}\mathbf{N}_{11}^{-1}\mathbf{B}_{11} - \mathbf{B}_{21}\}\mathbf{F}_x + \{\mathbf{N}_{21}\mathbf{N}_{11}^{-1}\mathbf{N}_{12} - \mathbf{N}_{22}\}\mathbf{F}_y \tag{10.49}$$

In conclusion, the chord formulation can be summarized by listing several important properties.

1. All component equations must be expressible explicitly in the across variable.

$$\begin{bmatrix} \mathbf{X}_{b_2} \\ \mathbf{X}_{c_1} \end{bmatrix} = \begin{bmatrix} \mathbf{Z}_{11} & \mathbf{Z}_{12} \\ \mathbf{Z}_{21} & \mathbf{Z}_{22} \end{bmatrix} \begin{bmatrix} \mathbf{Y}_{b_2} \\ \mathbf{Y}_{c_1} \end{bmatrix} \tag{10.40}$$

2. The circuit equations are required. They serve as the only basis for the statement of component interconnections. They are written in partitioned form.

$$\begin{bmatrix} \mathbf{B}_{11} \\ \mathbf{B}_{21} \end{bmatrix} \mathbf{X}_{b_1} + \begin{bmatrix} \mathbf{B}_{12} & \mathbf{U} \\ \mathbf{B}_{22} & \mathbf{0} \end{bmatrix} \begin{bmatrix} \mathbf{X}_{b_2} \\ \mathbf{X}_{c_1} \end{bmatrix} + \begin{bmatrix} \mathbf{0} \\ \mathbf{U} \end{bmatrix} \mathbf{X}_{c_2} = \mathbf{0} \tag{10.42}$$

3. The component equations are substituted into the partitioned circuit equations. The transformation of variables is applied to reduce the number of unknowns.

$$\begin{bmatrix} \mathbf{B}_{11} \\ \mathbf{B}_{21} \end{bmatrix} \mathbf{F}_x + \begin{bmatrix} \mathbf{B}_{12} & \mathbf{U} \\ \mathbf{B}_{22} & \mathbf{0} \end{bmatrix} \begin{bmatrix} \mathbf{Z}_{11} & \mathbf{Z}_{12} \\ \mathbf{Z}_{21} & \mathbf{Z}_{22} \end{bmatrix} \begin{bmatrix} \mathbf{B}_{12} & \mathbf{U} \\ \mathbf{B}_{22} & \mathbf{0} \end{bmatrix}' \begin{bmatrix} \mathbf{Y}_{c_1} \\ \mathbf{F}_x \end{bmatrix} + \begin{bmatrix} \mathbf{0} \\ \mathbf{U} \end{bmatrix} \mathbf{X}_{c_2} = \mathbf{0} \tag{10.46}$$

There are exactly $e - v + p$ equations in $e - v + p$ unknowns.

4. The triple matrix product is formed and the top set of $e - v + p - n_y$ equations in $e - v + p - n_y$ unknowns may be solved.

$$\begin{bmatrix} \mathbf{B}_{11} \\ \mathbf{B}_{21} \end{bmatrix} \mathbf{F}_x + \begin{bmatrix} \mathbf{N}_{11} & \mathbf{N}_{12} \\ \mathbf{N}_{21} & \mathbf{N}_{22} \end{bmatrix} \begin{bmatrix} \mathbf{Y}_{c_1} \\ \mathbf{F}_y \end{bmatrix} + \begin{bmatrix} \mathbf{0} \\ \mathbf{U} \end{bmatrix} \mathbf{X}_{c_2} = \mathbf{0} \tag{10.47}$$

5. An inverse of order $e - v + p - n_y$ is required for the solution.

$$\mathbf{Y}_{c_1} = -\mathbf{N}_{11}^{-1}\{\mathbf{B}_{11}\mathbf{F}_x + \mathbf{N}_{12}\mathbf{F}_y\} \tag{10.48}$$

To illustrate the above general representation, let us continue with the development of the mathematical model for the system of Figure 10.3 in terms of the chord equations. The equations count is

$$e - v + p - n_y = 8 - 7 + 2 - 1 = 2$$

Hence, an inverse of order 2 will be required in the solution. For chord formulation, the component equations are given explicitly in the across variable. Equations 10.35 list the component equations in terms of the through variables. To list the same equations in terms of the across variables requires an s-domain representation of the component characteristics. Thus,

$$\begin{bmatrix} P_2 \\ P_3 \\ \Delta_4 \\ \Delta_5 \\ P_6 \\ \Delta_7 \end{bmatrix} = \begin{bmatrix} 1/C_2 s & 0 & 0 & 0 & 0 & 0 \\ 0 & Z_3 & -1/A & 0 & 0 & 0 \\ 0 & -1/As & 0 & 0 & 0 & 0 \\ 0 & 0 & 0 & Z_5 & 0 & 0 \\ 0 & 0 & 0 & 0 & R_6 & 0 \\ 0 & 0 & 0 & 0 & 0 & 1/k_7 \end{bmatrix} \begin{bmatrix} \dot{G}_2 \\ \dot{G}_3 \\ F_4 \\ F_5 \\ \dot{G}_6 \\ F_7 \end{bmatrix} \tag{10.50}$$

where

$$Z_3 = \frac{1}{A^2}(M_3 s^2 + B_3 s)$$

and

$$Z_5 = \frac{1}{M_5 s^2 + B_5 s}$$

The circuit equations are

$$\left[\begin{array}{ccccc:ccc} 1 & -1 & -1 & 0 & 0 & 1 & 0 & 0 \\ 0 & 0 & 0 & -1 & 1 & 0 & 1 & 0 \\ 0 & 0 & 0 & 0 & -1 & 0 & 0 & 1 \end{array}\right] \begin{bmatrix} P_1 \\ P_2 \\ P_3 \\ \Delta_4 \\ \Delta_5 \\ P_6 \\ \Delta_7 \\ \Delta_8 \end{bmatrix} = \mathbf{0} \tag{10.51}$$

With Equations 10.50 and 10.51 available, it is now possible to prepare the triple matrix product.

$$\begin{bmatrix} 1 \\ 0 \\ 0 \end{bmatrix} P_1 + \begin{bmatrix} -1 & -1 & 0 & 0 & 1 & 0 \\ 0 & 0 & -1 & 1 & 0 & 1 \\ 0 & 0 & 0 & -1 & 0 & 0 \end{bmatrix} \times$$

$$\begin{bmatrix} 1/C_2s & 0 & 0 & 0 & 0 & 0 \\ 0 & Z_3 & -1/A & 0 & 0 & 0 \\ 0 & -1/As & 0 & 0 & 0 & 0 \\ 0 & 0 & 0 & Z_5 & 0 & 0 \\ 0 & 0 & 0 & 0 & R_6 & 0 \\ 0 & 0 & 0 & 0 & 0 & 1/k_7 \end{bmatrix} \begin{bmatrix} -1 & 0 & 0 \\ -1 & 0 & 0 \\ 0 & -1 & 0 \\ 0 & 1 & -1 \\ 1 & 0 & 0 \\ 0 & 1 & 0 \end{bmatrix} \times$$

$$\begin{bmatrix} \dot{G}_6 \\ F_7 \\ F_8 \end{bmatrix} + \begin{bmatrix} 0 \\ 0 \\ 1 \end{bmatrix} \Delta_8 = \mathbf{0} \tag{10.52}$$

The multiplication of this triple product yields

$$\begin{bmatrix} 1 \\ 0 \\ 0 \end{bmatrix} P_1 + \begin{bmatrix} 1/C_2s + Z_3 + R_6 & -1/A & 0 \\ -1/As & Z_5 + 1/k_7 & -Z_5 \\ 0 & -Z_5 & Z_5 \end{bmatrix} \begin{bmatrix} \dot{G}_6 \\ F_7 \\ F_8 \end{bmatrix} + \begin{bmatrix} 0 \\ 0 \\ 1 \end{bmatrix} \Delta_8 = \mathbf{0} \tag{10.53}$$

Equations 10.53 may be solved in two parts by separating the top two equations involving the unknown chord variables $\dot{G}_6$ and F_7. We have

$$\begin{bmatrix} \dot{G}_6 \\ F_7 \end{bmatrix} = -\begin{bmatrix} 1/C_2s + Z_3 + R_6 & -1/A \\ -1/As & Z_5 + 1/k_7 \end{bmatrix}^{-1} \begin{bmatrix} 1 & 0 \\ 0 & -Z_5 \end{bmatrix} \begin{bmatrix} P_1 \\ F_8 \end{bmatrix} \tag{10.54}$$

As predicted, only a two × two inverse is required, representing a considerable reduction in the amount of work involved in obtaining a solution to the problem that was started on a branch formulation basis.

10.6 Further Examples in Branch and Chord Formulation

This section will explore further the branch and chord formulation procedures in deriving mathematical models for systems. Although the two procedures were introduced for the specific purpose of formulating equations for systems involving multiterminal components, we must not overlook their potential in dealing with systems made up entirely of two-terminal components. As the ensuing discussion will demonstrate, definite benefits can be derived under conditions of certain problem objectives by employing branch or chord formulation instead of mesh or node formulation techniques. Perhaps the greatest advantage that may be realized is the freedom to choose system variables in terms of which a formulation is desired. For example, if a problem is formulated in terms of node equations, the variables of the equations consist of the $v - 1$ node variables, all of which are uniquely specified by the graph once the reference node is selected. On the other hand, when the same problem is formulated in terms of branch equations, a variety of sets of branch variables may be utilized in the equations depending on the choice of the tree. This greater flexibility, of course, is obtained only at the cost of additional complexity in the formulation process. The examples presented in this section serve to seek out the advantages of using one formulation technique over another.

Example 10.1 Consider the mechanical system of Figure 10.5. We wish to calculate the transient response in the shaft displacements φ_1 and φ_2 and the final velocity φ_3, when the applied torque is suddenly applied with constant magnitude. The flywheel is initially at rest.

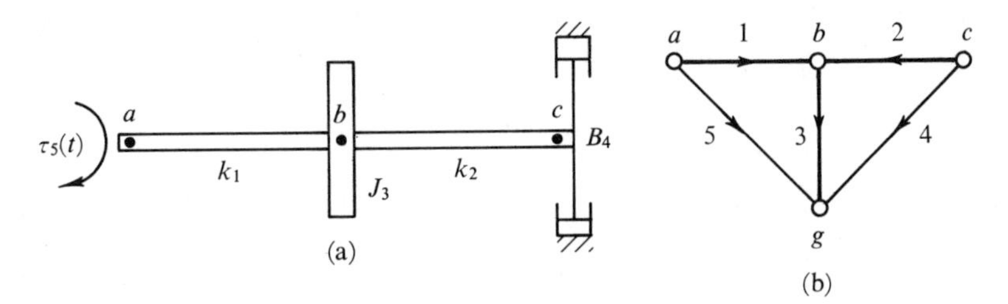

Fig. 10.5. *Mechanical system:* (a) *schematic;* (b) *system graph.*

The statement of the problem requires the calculation of three across variables. Hence, our first choice of formulation process would be either node or branch formulation. In node formulation, the resulting equations would be expressed in terms of the node across variables, $\varphi_a, \varphi_b, \varphi_c$, of which only one, φ_b, corresponds to the required information. On the other hand, through branch formulation, using elements 1, 2, and 3 as the tree, the desired information will be available immediately upon solution of the simultaneous equations. The equation count in either case is

$$v - 1 - n_x = 4 - 1 - 0 = 3$$

If mesh or chord formulation is used, we would benefit from an appreciable reduction in the equation count,

$$e - v + 1 - n_y = 5 - 4 + 1 - 1 = 1$$

However, mesh formulation would yield a solution in terms of the mesh torque defined for the $2-3-4$ window, while chord formulation would involve τ_4 as the chord variable. This discussion may be summarized as follows:

Formulation	Variable	Equation count
1. Branch	$\varphi_1, \varphi_2, \varphi_3$	3
2. Node	$\varphi_a, \varphi_b, \varphi_c$	3
3. Chord	τ_4	1
4. Mesh	τ_b	1

In view of the objective of this section, let us investigate all four approaches.

1. Branch formulation. The cutset equations are

$$\begin{bmatrix} 1 & 0 & 0 & 0 & -1 \\ 0 & 1 & 0 & 1 & 0 \\ 0 & 0 & 1 & 1 & -1 \end{bmatrix} \begin{bmatrix} T_1 \\ T_2 \\ T_3 \\ T_4 \\ T_5 \end{bmatrix} = \mathbf{0} \tag{10.55}$$

We partition these equations to separate T_5 and form the triple matrix product by substituting the terminal equations, yielding

$$\begin{bmatrix} 1 & 0 & 0 & 0 \\ 0 & 1 & 0 & 1 \\ 0 & 0 & 1 & 1 \end{bmatrix} \begin{bmatrix} k_1 & 0 & 0 & 0 \\ 0 & k_2 & 0 & 0 \\ 0 & 0 & J_3s^2 & 0 \\ 0 & 0 & 0 & B_4s \end{bmatrix} \begin{bmatrix} 1 & 0 & 0 \\ 0 & 1 & 0 \\ 0 & 0 & 1 \\ 0 & 1 & 1 \end{bmatrix} \begin{bmatrix} \Phi_1 \\ \Phi_2 \\ \Phi_3 \end{bmatrix} = \begin{bmatrix} 1 \\ 0 \\ 1 \end{bmatrix} T_5$$

or*

$$\begin{bmatrix} k_1 & 0 & 0 \\ 0 & k_2 + B_4s & B_4s \\ 0 & B_4s & J_3s^2 + B_4s \end{bmatrix} \begin{bmatrix} \Phi_1 \\ \Phi_2 \\ \Phi_3 \end{bmatrix} = \begin{bmatrix} 1 \\ 0 \\ 1 \end{bmatrix} T_5 \tag{10.56}$$

Although the equation count indicated a three × three inverse, we note that only a two × two inverse will be required. (The first equation may be solved independently of the other two.) This is an unusual coincidence. Thus,

---

* When the coefficient matrix of the component equations is diagonal (for two-terminal components only), the triple matrix product may be performed in one step. Notice that the product of the first two matrices results in a matrix of the same order and structure as the first matrix,

$$\begin{bmatrix} k_1 & 0 & 0 & 0 \\ 0 & k_2 & 0 & B_4s \\ 0 & 0 & J_3s^2 & B_4s \end{bmatrix} \Longrightarrow \begin{array}{c} \begin{matrix} k_1 & k_2 & J_3s^2 & B_4s \end{matrix} \\ \begin{bmatrix} 1 & 0 & 0 & 0 \\ 0 & 1 & 0 & 1 \\ 0 & 0 & 1 & 1 \end{bmatrix} \end{array}$$

If we record this by writing the products shown in the matrix to the right, then the remaining product consists of multiplying the first matrix into its transpose, with appropriate weighting for every nonzero term by the coefficients of the component matrix. Since the columns of the third matrix are identical to the rows of the first matrix, the required multiplication simply involves the multiplication of the rows of the first matrix into themselves with the appropriate weighting by the component coefficients. For instance, the (2, 2) coefficient is obtained by multiplying the second row into itself: there are two nonzero terms multiplied by k_2 and B_4s, respectively; hence the term is $k_2 + B_4s$. The (3, 2) coefficient is formed by the product of the third row into the second row, etc.

$$\Phi_1 = \frac{1}{k_1} T_5 \tag{10.57a}$$

and

$$\begin{bmatrix} \Phi_2 \\ \Phi_3 \end{bmatrix} = \frac{1}{\Delta(s)} \begin{bmatrix} +B_4 s \\ (k_2 + B_4 s) \end{bmatrix} T_5$$

where

$$\Delta(s) = k_2 J_3 s^2 + B_4 s(k_2 + J_3 s^2)$$

so that

$$\Phi_2 = \frac{B_4}{k_2 B_4 + k_2 J_3 s + B_4 J_3 s^2} T_5 \tag{10.57b}$$

and

$$\dot{\Phi}_3 (=) s\Phi_3 = \frac{(k_2 + B_4 s)}{k_2 B_4 + k_2 J_3 s + B_4 J_3 s^2} T_5 \tag{10.57c}$$

We will return to the solution of Equations 10.57 later.

2. Node formulation. The node equations are

$$\begin{bmatrix} k_1 & -k_1 & 0 \\ -k_1 & k_1 + k_2 + J_3 s^2 & -k_2 \\ 0 & -k_2 & k_2 + B_4 s \end{bmatrix} \begin{bmatrix} \Phi_a \\ \Phi_b \\ \Phi_c \end{bmatrix} = \begin{bmatrix} T_5 \\ 0 \\ 0 \end{bmatrix} \tag{10.58}$$

We see that a three $\times$ three inverse is required, as predicted by the equation count.

3. Chord formulation. The circuit equations are

$$\begin{bmatrix} 0 & -1 & -1 & 1 & 0 \\ 1 & 0 & 1 & 0 & 1 \end{bmatrix} \begin{bmatrix} \Phi_1 \\ \Phi_2 \\ \Phi_3 \\ \Phi_4 \\ \Phi_5 \end{bmatrix} = \mathbf{0}$$

Next, we partition these equations; to use the algorithm for multiplying the triple matrix product, we record the coefficients of the component matrix,

$$\begin{matrix} \frac{1}{k_1} & \frac{1}{k_2} & \frac{1}{J_3 s^2} & \frac{1}{B_4 s} \end{matrix}$$
$$\begin{bmatrix} 0 & -1 & -1 & 1 \\ 1 & 0 & 1 & 0 \end{bmatrix} \begin{bmatrix} \Phi_1 \\ \Phi_2 \\ \Phi_3 \\ \Phi_4 \end{bmatrix} + \begin{bmatrix} 0 \\ 1 \end{bmatrix} \Phi_5 = \mathbf{0}$$

so that the result is

$$\begin{bmatrix} \frac{1}{k_2} + \frac{1}{J_3 s^2} + \frac{1}{B_4 s} & -\frac{1}{J_3 s^2} \\ -\frac{1}{J_3 s^2} & \frac{1}{k_1} + \frac{1}{J_3 s^2} \end{bmatrix} \begin{bmatrix} T_4 \\ T_5 \end{bmatrix} + \begin{bmatrix} 0 \\ 1 \end{bmatrix} \Phi_5 = 0 \tag{10.59}$$

Solving for T_4, we obtain

$$T_4 = \frac{k_2 B_4}{k_2 B_4 + k_2 J_3 s + B_4 J_3 s^2} T_5$$

With T_4 known, we solve for the desired quantities. Thus,

$$\Phi_1 = \frac{1}{k_1} T_1 = \frac{1}{k_1} T_5 \tag{10.60a}$$

$$\Phi_2 = \frac{1}{k_2} T_2 = -\frac{1}{k_2} T_4 \tag{10.60b}$$

$$= \frac{B_4}{k_2 B_4 + k_2 J_3 s + B_4 J_3 s^2} T_5$$

$$\dot{\Phi}_3 = \frac{1}{J_3 s} T_3$$

$$= \frac{1}{J_3 s}[T_5 - T_4]$$

$$= \frac{k_2 + B_4 s}{k_2 B_4 + k_2 J_3 s + B_4 J_3 s^2} T_5 \tag{10.60c}$$

These last three equations are identical to the solution obtained through branch formulation.

4. Mesh formulation. The mesh equations are

$$\begin{bmatrix} \dfrac{1}{k_1} + \dfrac{1}{J_3 s^2} & -\dfrac{1}{J_3 s^2} \\ -\dfrac{1}{J_3 s^2} & \dfrac{1}{k_2} + \dfrac{1}{B_4 s} + \dfrac{1}{J_3 s^2} \end{bmatrix} \begin{bmatrix} T_a \\ T_b \end{bmatrix} = \begin{bmatrix} -\Phi_5 \\ 0 \end{bmatrix} \tag{10.61}$$

where $T_a = T_5$. A comparison of the mesh equations with the chord equations reveals that they are identical, due to the fact that

$$T_4 \equiv T_b$$

Of the four formulation procedures investigated in this example, one can readily agree that the mesh equations will yield a solution in a more effortless manner than either branch or chord equations. On the other hand, branch equations will yield the desired solution more directly. Of the four approaches, node formulation is probably the least desirable due to the large inverse to be taken. Consider now a numerical solution if the following values are prescribed:

$$\tau_5(t) = u(t)$$

(step function),

$$k_1 = 5, \qquad k_2 = 3, \qquad J_3 = 10, \qquad B_4 = 5$$

With these values substituted into Equations 10.60, we get

$$\Phi_1 = \frac{1}{5s} \tag{10.62a}$$

$$\Phi_2 = \frac{5}{s(15 + 30s + 50s^2)} \tag{10.62b}$$

$$\dot{\Phi}_3 = \frac{3 + 5s}{s(15 + 30s + 50s^2)} \tag{10.62c}$$

From these expressions, the desired s-domain results are obtained.

a. Displacement of shaft k_1. The transformed expression for φ_1 is readily inverted with the result

$$\varphi_1(t) = 0.2$$

b. Displacement of shaft k_2. From Equation 10.62b we determine a partial fraction expansion. To make the coefficient of s^2 unity we divide by 50 and obtain the partial fraction expansion

$$\Phi_2 = \frac{0.1}{s(s^2 + 0.6s + 0.3)} = \frac{k_1}{s} + \frac{k_2}{s + 0.3 - j0.447} + \frac{k_2^*}{s + 0.3 + j0.447}$$

We evaluate the expansion coefficients

$$k_1 = s\Phi_2]_{s=0} = 0.33$$

$$k_2 = (s + 0.3 - j0.447)\Phi_2]_{s=-0.3+j0.447} = \frac{0.1}{(-0.3 + j0.447)2j(0.447)}$$

In order to conform with the procedures of Appendix B, we put k_2 into polar coordinates.

$$k_2 = \frac{0.1}{(0.548 \measuredangle 123.9°)2j(0.447)} = \frac{0.408}{2j} \measuredangle -123.9°$$

According to Table B. 2, solution is

$$\varphi_2(t) = 0.33 + 0.408e^{-0.3t} \sin (0.447t - 123.9°)$$

In comparing the solutions for the two shaft displacements, we note that φ_1 is constant while φ_2 has a transient, a fact attributable to the manner in which the shaft k_1 merely serves to transmit the constant torque $\tau_5(t)$.

c. Final velocity of flywheel J_3. By application of the final value theorem, we have

$$\lim_{t \to \infty} \dot{\varphi}_3(t) = \lim_{s \to 0} s\dot{\Phi}_3(s)$$
$$= \lim_{s \to 0} \frac{(3 + 5s)}{(15 + 30s + 50s^2)}$$
$$= 1/5$$

If this result had been carried out in algebraic notation, we would find that

$$\dot{\varphi}_3(t)|_{ss} = 1/B_4$$

Example 10.2. Investigate the selection of a suitable formulation process for the system shown in Figure 10.6.

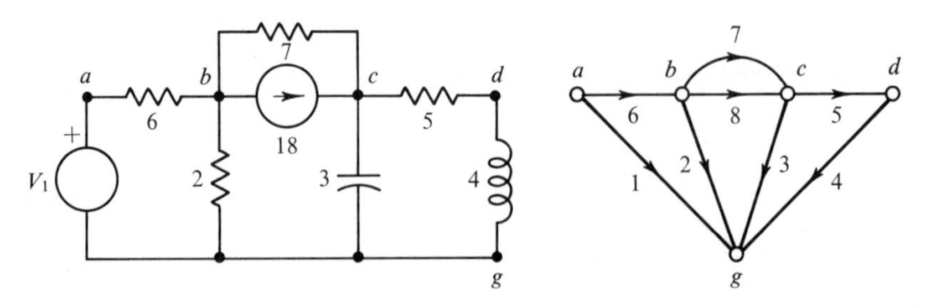

Fig. 10.6. *Electrical network and system graph.*

The system is composed entirely of two-terminal components. The equation count for node formulation is

$$v - 1 - n_x = 3$$

There are four node equations, only three of which have to be solved simultaneously, because the across driver is identical to a node variable. For mesh formulation,

$$e - v + 1 - n_y = 4$$

There are four mesh equations; because the through driver cannot be identified as a mesh variable, the equation count may not be reduced.

For branch formulation,

$$v - 1 - n_x = 3$$

With the tree selected as shown in Figure 10.6, the branch equation model will consist of four equations: the three equations involving v_2, v_3, and v_4 may be solved simultaneously as a block. Thus, branch formulation is identical to node formulation in complexity of resulting model.

For chord formulation,

$$e - v + 1 - n_y = 3$$

The chord equation model will consist of four equations; the three equations involving i_5, i_6, and i_7 may be solved separately as a block. Chord formulation thus offers a more efficient procedure than mesh formulation in this example. The gain that is realized is directly attributable to the fact that a through driver is always selected as an element of the co-tree.

10.7 Terminal Representations of Systems Containing Multiterminal Components

Branch and chord formulation procedures may be effectively employed in the general problem of deriving terminal representations of systems including multiterminal components. The approach is merely an extension of the more specific techniques of mesh and node formulation as applied to the equivalent representation of systems of two-terminal components. As in the procedure outlined in Section 8.7, we apply drivers to the system which is to be represented by an equivalent representation in a one-to-one correspondence with the desired terminal graph. Where possible, the equation count should determine the formulation procedure; frequently, however, the choice depends on the form of the component equations. When branch formulation is followed, the drivers are selected as across drivers and the resulting model is expressed in terms of short-circuit parameters; in chord formulation through drivers are selected with a resulting open-circuit parameter model. Two examples will illustrate the procedure.

Example 10.3. Derive a terminal representation for the electrical network shown in Figure 10.7(a) according to the terminal graph of Figure 10.7(b). The system graph with the augmenting drivers is shown in Figure 10.8.

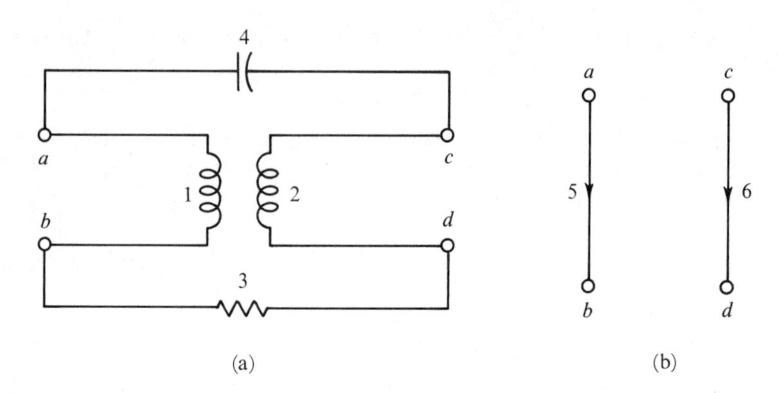

Fig. 10.7. *Electrical network:* (a) *schematic;* (b) *terminal graph of equivalent representation.*

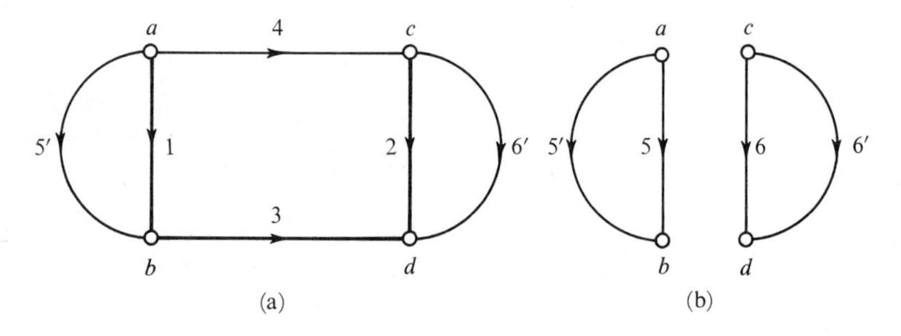

Fig. 10.8. *System graph:* (a) *system with drivers;* (b) *terminal graph with drivers.*

In selecting the appropriate formulation procedure, we consider first the form of the component equations. Since the transformer is most conveniently modeled as an open-circuit parameter model,

$$\begin{bmatrix} V_1 \\ V_2 \end{bmatrix} = \begin{bmatrix} Z_1 & Z_{12} \\ Z_{12} & Z_2 \end{bmatrix} \begin{bmatrix} I_1 \\ I_2 \end{bmatrix}$$

where

$$Z_1 = R_1 + L_1 s, \qquad Z_2 = R_2 + L_2 s, \qquad Z_{12} = Ms$$

the formulation procedure is automatically determined as chord formulation. In any event, both formulation procedures have the same equation count.

Chord formulation:

$$e - v + 1 - n_y = 1$$
$$(n_y = 2, \qquad n_x = 0)$$

Branch formulation:

$$v - 1 - n_x = 1$$
$$(n_x = 2, \qquad n_y = 0)$$

On the basis of this decision, the tree is selected as shown to include the drivers in the co-tree.

The fundamental circuit equations are

$$\begin{bmatrix} -1 & 1 & -1 & 1 & 0 & 0 \\ -1 & 0 & 0 & 0 & 1 & 0 \\ 0 & -1 & 0 & 0 & 0 & 1 \end{bmatrix} \begin{bmatrix} V_1 \\ V_2 \\ V_3 \\ \hdashline V_4 \\ V_5' \\ V_6' \end{bmatrix} = 0 \tag{10.63}$$

Substituting the component equations and setting up the triple matrix product yields

$$\begin{bmatrix} -1 & 1 & -1 & 1 \\ -1 & 0 & 0 & 0 \\ 0 & -1 & 0 & 0 \end{bmatrix} \begin{bmatrix} Z_1 & Z_{12} & 0 & 0 \\ Z_{12} & Z_2 & 0 & 0 \\ 0 & 0 & R_3 & 0 \\ 0 & 0 & 0 & 1/C_4 s \end{bmatrix} \begin{bmatrix} -1 & -1 & 0 \\ 1 & 0 & -1 \\ -1 & 0 & -0 \\ 1 & 0 & 0 \end{bmatrix} \begin{bmatrix} I_4 \\ I_5' \\ I_6' \end{bmatrix}$$
$$+ \begin{bmatrix} 0 & 0 \\ 1 & 0 \\ 0 & 1 \end{bmatrix} \begin{bmatrix} V_{5'} \\ V_{6'} \end{bmatrix} = 0$$

or

$$\begin{bmatrix} Z_1 + Z_2 - 2Z_{12} + R_3 + 1/C_4 s & Z_1 - Z_{12} & -Z_2 + Z_{12} \\ Z_1 - Z_{12} & Z_1 & Z_{12} \\ -Z_2 + Z_{12} & Z_{12} & Z_2 \end{bmatrix} \begin{bmatrix} I_4 \\ I_5' \\ I_6' \end{bmatrix}$$
$$+ \begin{bmatrix} 0 \\ V_5' \\ V_6' \end{bmatrix} = 0 \tag{10.64}$$

Equations 10.64 are three chord equations of which the top equation will have to be eliminated to generate the desired terminal representation. If we partition the equations at the first row and first column and indicate this in symbolic form

$$\begin{bmatrix} \mathbf{Z}_1 & \mathbf{Z}_{12} \\ \mathbf{Z}_{21} & \mathbf{Z}_2 \end{bmatrix} \begin{bmatrix} \mathbf{I}_{c_1} \\ \mathbf{I}_{c_2} \end{bmatrix} + \begin{bmatrix} 0 \\ \mathbf{V}_{c_2} \end{bmatrix} = 0 \tag{10.65}$$

we find that the remainder of this problem follows exactly the procedures outlined in Section 10.5.

$$\mathbf{V}_{c_2} + \{\mathbf{Z}_2 - \mathbf{Z}_{21} Z^{-1} \mathbf{Z}_{12}\} \mathbf{I}_{c_2} = 0 \tag{10.66}$$

And since from the graph of Figure 10.8

$$\mathbf{V}_{c2} = \mathbf{V}_t \quad \text{and} \quad \mathbf{I}_{c2} = -\mathbf{I}_t$$

$$\mathbf{V}_t = \{Z_2 - Z_{21}Z_1^{-1}Z_{12}\}\,\mathbf{I}_t \tag{10.67}$$

where, as before, the subscript t denotes terminal variable.

Applying the symbolic solution (Equation 10.67) to Equations 10.64 yields the desired terminal equations.

$$\begin{bmatrix} V_5 \\ V_6 \end{bmatrix} = \left\{ \begin{bmatrix} Z_1 & Z_{12} \\ Z_{12} & Z_2 \end{bmatrix} - \begin{bmatrix} Z_1 - Z_{12} \\ Z_{12} - Z_2 \end{bmatrix} \frac{[Z_1 - Z_{12} \quad Z_{12} - Z_2]}{Z(s)} \right\} \begin{bmatrix} I_5 \\ I_6 \end{bmatrix}$$

or

$$\begin{bmatrix} V_5 \\ V_6 \end{bmatrix} = \begin{bmatrix} Z_1 - (Z_1 - Z_{12})^2/Z(s) & Z_{12} - (Z_1 - Z_{12})(Z_{12} - Z_2)/Z(s) \\ Z_{12} - (Z_{12} - Z_2)(Z_1 - Z_{12})/Z(s) & Z_2 - (Z_2 - Z_{12})^2/Z(s) \end{bmatrix} \begin{bmatrix} I_5 \\ I_6 \end{bmatrix} \tag{10.68}$$

where

$$Z(s) = Z_1 + Z_2 - 2Z_{12} + R_3 + 1/C_4 s$$
$$Z_1 = R_1 + L_1 s$$
$$Z_2 = R_2 + L_2 s$$
$$Z_{12} = Ms$$

This result is by no means simple.

10.8 Terminal Graph Transformations

The technique of deriving equivalent mathematical models of systems containing multiterminal components may be employed to great advantage in altering the existing terminal representation of the multiterminal components. Consider, for instance, the five-terminal component symbolically shown in Figure 10.9(a). The terminal graph of this

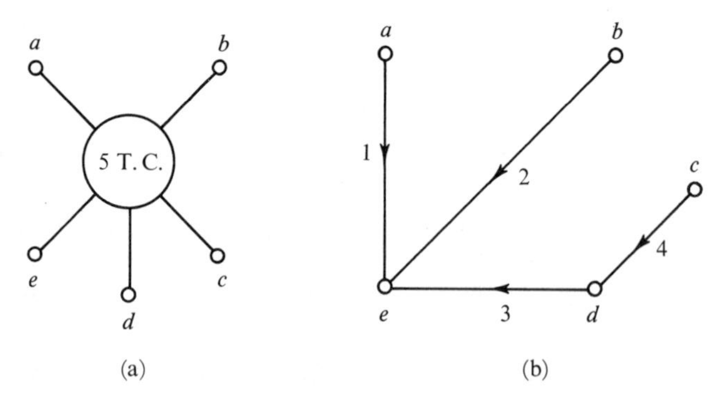

Fig. 10.9. *Five-terminal component and terminal graph.*

component may contain a maximum of $v - 1$ elements or four. Let the terminal graph for this component be constructed as shown in Figure

10.9(b). Suppose some application would make a terminal representation associated with a different terminal graph more desirable. Then it is possible to generate the new terminal equations through direct application of branch or chord formulation procedures. For instance, let it be required to determine the terminal equations of the five-terminal component associated with the terminal graph of Figure 10.10. Then the application of a set of drivers to the original terminal graph in a one-to-one correspondence with the new terminal graph as shown in Figure 10.10 will permit the development of a new set of equations as

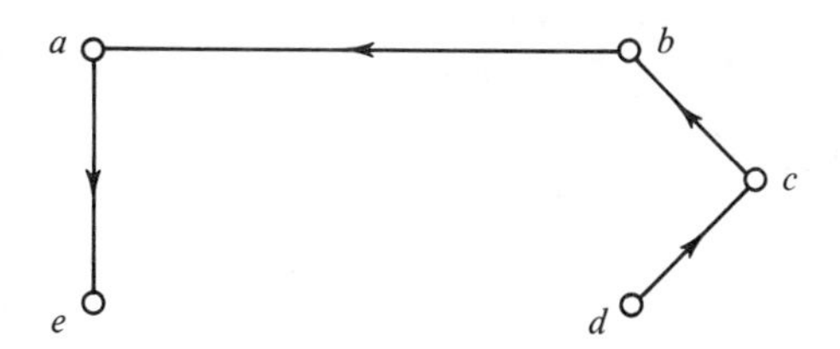

Fig. 10.10. *Alternate terminal graph.*

either branch equations or chord equations, depending upon whether the old terminal equations are expressed in terms of the short-circuit or open-circuit parameters, respectively. Since in either case the set of drivers constitutes a complete tree, or co-tree, the equation count is zero, and the desired result is obtained when the triple matrix product is multiplied out. We refer to this process as a terminal graph transformation. Example 10.4 illustrates such a transformation.

Example 10.4. Consider the terminal representation of the rotational dashpot as given by Equations 8.44, *i.e.*,

$$\begin{bmatrix} T_1 \\ T_2 \end{bmatrix} = \begin{bmatrix} J_1 s + B_{12} & -B_{12} \\ -B_{12} & J_2 s + B_{12} \end{bmatrix} \begin{bmatrix} \dot{\Phi}_1 \\ \dot{\Phi}_2 \end{bmatrix}$$

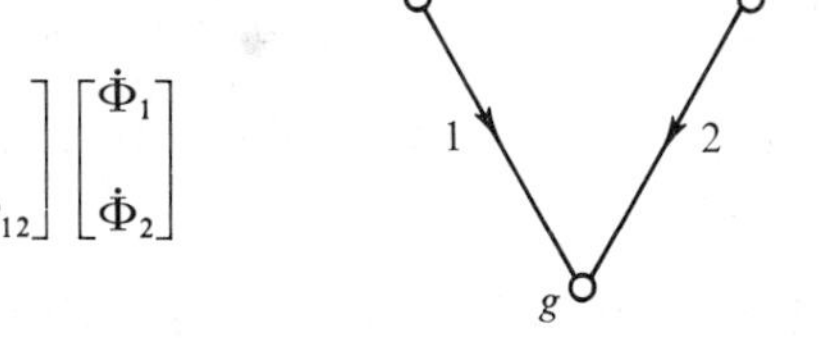

Through a graph transformation, verify Equations 8.45, which are associated with the terminal graph shown in Figure 10.11(a). Figure 10.11(b) shows the original terminal graph with appropriate drivers applied. Since the terminal equations of the dashpot are given in the through variable, we select the drivers as across drivers so that branch formulation may be followed. Thus, the tree of the graph of Figure 10.11(b) is selected containing elements 1′ and 3′.

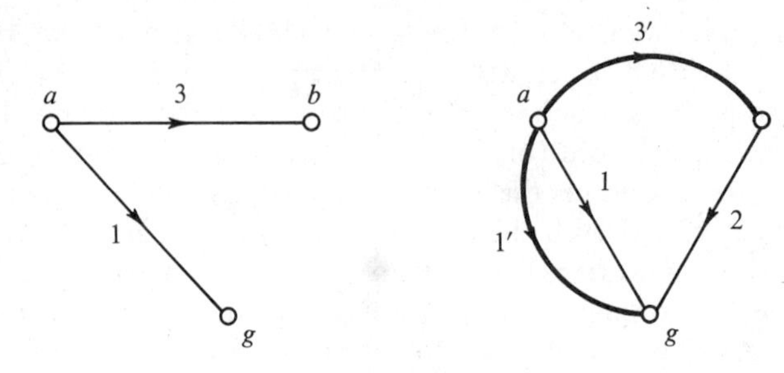

Fig. 10.11. (a) *Transformed terminal graph;* (b) *original terminal graph and drivers.*

The cutset equations are

$$\begin{bmatrix} 1 & 0 & 1 & 1 \\ 0 & 1 & 0 & -1 \end{bmatrix} \begin{bmatrix} T_{1'} \\ T_{3'} \\ T_1 \\ T_2 \end{bmatrix} = \mathbf{0}$$

The equations are partitioned and the component equations substituted,

$$\begin{bmatrix} 1 & 0 \\ 0 & 1 \end{bmatrix} \begin{bmatrix} T_{1'} \\ T_{3'} \end{bmatrix} + \begin{bmatrix} 1 & 1 \\ 0 & -1 \end{bmatrix} \begin{bmatrix} J_1 s + B_{12} & -B_{12} \\ -B_{12} & J_2 s + B_{12} \end{bmatrix} \begin{bmatrix} 1 & 0 \\ 1 & -1 \end{bmatrix} \begin{bmatrix} \dot{\Phi}_1{}' \\ \dot{\Phi}_3{}' \end{bmatrix}$$

or

$$\begin{bmatrix} T_{1'} \\ T_{3'} \end{bmatrix} + \begin{bmatrix} (J_1 + J_2)s & -J_2 s \\ -J_2 s & J_2 s + B_{12} \end{bmatrix} \begin{bmatrix} \dot{\Phi}_1{}' \\ \dot{\Phi}_3{}' \end{bmatrix} = \mathbf{0}$$

And, finally,

$$\begin{bmatrix} T_1 \\ T_3 \end{bmatrix} = \begin{bmatrix} (J_1 + J_2)s & -J_2 s \\ -J_2 s & J_2 s + B_{12} \end{bmatrix} \begin{bmatrix} \dot{\Phi}_1 \\ \dot{\Phi}_3 \end{bmatrix}$$

These last equations are identical to Equations 8.45.

Terminal graph transformations represent an effective means for obtaining terminal representations that may be difficult to derive in terms of one set of terminal variables, yet easily realizable in terms of another set of terminal variables. The rotational dashpot is an example. The vacuum tube and transistor, both of which belong to an important class of multiterminal electrical components, provide further evidence of the importance of such terminal graph representations.

10.9 Branch-Chord Formulation

In Chapter 8, a class of multiterminal components called ideal transducers are discussed. Some components whose equations are derived in Chapter 8 are

1. ideal transformer,
2. ideal hydraulic transformer,

3. ideal gear box,
4. ideal mechanical lever,
5. ideal shaft and pulley,
6. ideal dynamometer.

The terminal equations of these components are always written in either the h-parameter or g-parameter format, and the matrix is always skew-symmetric. In this form, the terminal equations can be written neither in the open-circuit nor short-circuit form, and branch or chord formulation cannot be used directly.

To prepare for the possibility of this event, a hybrid formulation procedure, called branch-chord formulation will be introduced. This formulation technique is based upon the same principles as branch or chord formulation, that is, the gradual reduction of two e simultaneous equations, which serve as mathematical statements of the component characteristics and their interconnection, to a set of nonreducible simultaneous equations. The technique which will be presented has evolved as one that is both efficient and fairly simple to use. It is considered most expedient to develop it in symbolic form first.

Criterion for Branch-Chord Formulation

To apply branch-chord formulation successfully, the following requirements must be satisfied.

A forest must be chosen such that the component equations can be written in the form

$$\begin{bmatrix} \mathbf{X}_{b_2} \\ \mathbf{Y}_{c_1} \end{bmatrix} = \begin{bmatrix} \mathbf{H}_{11} & \mathbf{H}_{12} \\ \mathbf{H}_{21} & \mathbf{H}_{22} \end{bmatrix} \begin{bmatrix} \mathbf{Y}_{b_2} \\ \mathbf{X}_{c_1} \end{bmatrix} \tag{10.69}$$

Consider now a formulation problem where the above criterion is satisfied. In addition to Equations 10.69 we assume that the drivers are specified

$$\left.\begin{aligned} \mathbf{X}_{b_1} &= \mathbf{F}_x \\ \mathbf{Y}_{c_2} &= \mathbf{F}_y \end{aligned}\right] \tag{10.70}$$

The formulation procedure is oriented to develop a set of simultaneous equations involving the unspecified branch across variables $\mathbf{X}_{b_2}$ and the unspecified chord through variables $\mathbf{Y}_{c_1}$ as unknowns. Consistent with this objective, let us develop a transformation to change the variables on the right side of Equations 10.69 from

$$\begin{bmatrix} \mathbf{Y}_{b2} \\ \mathbf{X}_{c_1} \end{bmatrix} \quad \text{to} \quad \begin{bmatrix} \mathbf{X}_{b_1} \\ \mathbf{X}_{b_2} \\ \mathbf{Y}_{c_1} \\ \mathbf{Y}_{c_2} \end{bmatrix}$$

using the cutset and circuit equations. If the latter are written as

$$\begin{bmatrix} \mathbf{U} & \mathbf{0} & \mathscr{A}_{11} & \mathscr{A}_{12} \\ \mathbf{0} & \mathbf{U} & \mathscr{A}_{21} & \mathscr{A}_{22} \end{bmatrix} \begin{bmatrix} \mathbf{Y}_{b_1} \\ \mathbf{Y}_{b_2} \\ \mathbf{Y}_{c_1} \\ \mathbf{Y}_{c_2} \end{bmatrix} = \mathbf{0} \tag{10.71}$$

and

$$\begin{bmatrix} \mathbf{B}_{11} & \mathbf{B}_{12} & \mathbf{U} & \mathbf{0} \\ \mathbf{B}_{21} & \mathbf{B}_{22} & \mathbf{0} & \mathbf{U} \end{bmatrix} \begin{bmatrix} \mathbf{X}_{b_1} \\ \mathbf{X}_{b_2} \\ \mathbf{X}_{c_1} \\ \mathbf{X}_{c_2} \end{bmatrix} = \mathbf{0} \tag{10.72}$$

we obtain the desired transformation as

$$\begin{bmatrix} \mathbf{Y}_{b_2} \\ \mathbf{X}_{c_1} \end{bmatrix} = \begin{bmatrix} \mathbf{0} & -\mathscr{A}_{21} \\ -\mathbf{B}_{12} & \mathbf{0} \end{bmatrix} \begin{bmatrix} \mathbf{X}_{b_2} \\ \mathbf{Y}_{c_1} \end{bmatrix} + \begin{bmatrix} \mathbf{0} & -\mathscr{A}_{22} \\ -\mathbf{B}_{11} & \mathbf{0} \end{bmatrix} \begin{bmatrix} \mathbf{X}_{b_1} \\ \mathbf{Y}_{c_2} \end{bmatrix} \tag{10.73}$$

When Equations 10.73 are substituted into Equations 10.69 and terms are collected, one has

$$\begin{bmatrix} \mathbf{U} + \mathbf{H}_{12}\mathbf{B}_{12} & \mathbf{H}_{11}\mathscr{A}_{21} \\ \mathbf{H}_{22}\mathbf{B}_{12} & \mathbf{U} + \mathbf{H}_{21}\mathscr{A}_{21} \end{bmatrix} \begin{bmatrix} \mathbf{X}_{b_2} \\ \mathbf{Y}_{c_1} \end{bmatrix} = \begin{bmatrix} -\mathbf{H}_{12}\mathbf{B}_{11} & -\mathbf{H}_{11}\mathscr{A}_{22} \\ -\mathbf{H}_{22}\mathbf{B}_{11} & -\mathbf{H}_{21}\mathscr{A}_{22} \end{bmatrix} \begin{bmatrix} \mathbf{F}_x \\ \mathbf{F}_y \end{bmatrix} \tag{10.74}$$

Equations 10.74 constitute a set of $e - n_x - n_y$ equations which must be solved simultaneously. A solution is possible only when the inverse of the matrix on the left side exists, *i.e.*,

$$\det \begin{bmatrix} \mathbf{U} + \mathbf{H}_{12}\mathbf{B}_{12} & \mathbf{H}_{11}\mathscr{A}_{21} \\ \mathbf{H}_{22}\mathbf{B}_{12} & \mathbf{U} + \mathbf{H}_{21}\mathscr{A}_{21} \end{bmatrix} = 0 \tag{10.75}$$

As the existence of this inverse is subject to the values of the coefficients of the component equations, Equation 10.75 may frequently be used as a condition for the existence of a solution. When Equation 10.75 is satisfied, the solution is symbolically indicated as

$$\begin{bmatrix} \mathbf{X}_{b_2} \\ \mathbf{Y}_{c_1} \end{bmatrix} = \begin{bmatrix} \mathbf{E}_{11} & \mathbf{E}_{12} \\ \mathbf{E}_{21} & \mathbf{E}_{22} \end{bmatrix} \begin{bmatrix} \mathbf{F}_x \\ \mathbf{F}_y \end{bmatrix} \tag{10.76}$$

In terms of the system variables available through the solutions, all other variables may be determined. If, for instance, the co-variables of the drivers are to be calculated, we have from the cutset and circuit equation not previously used

$$\begin{bmatrix} \mathbf{Y}_{b_1} \\ \mathbf{X}_{c_2} \end{bmatrix} = \begin{bmatrix} \mathbf{0} & -\mathscr{A}_{11} \\ -\mathbf{B}_{22} & \mathbf{0} \end{bmatrix} \begin{bmatrix} \mathbf{X}_{b_2} \\ \mathbf{Y}_{c_1} \end{bmatrix} + \begin{bmatrix} \mathbf{0} & -\mathscr{A}_{12} \\ -\mathbf{B}_{21} & \mathbf{0} \end{bmatrix} \begin{bmatrix} \mathbf{F}_x \\ \mathbf{F}_y \end{bmatrix} \tag{10.77}$$

When the solution (Equation 10.76) is substituted into Equations 10.77, we have

$$\begin{bmatrix} \mathbf{Y}_{b_1} \\ \mathbf{X}_{c_2} \end{bmatrix} = \left[\begin{array}{c:c} -\mathscr{A}_{11}\mathbf{E}_{21} & \mathscr{A}_{11}\mathbf{E}_{22} - \mathscr{A}_{12} \\ -\mathbf{B}_{22}\mathbf{E}_{11} - \mathbf{B}_{21} & -\mathbf{B}_{22}\mathbf{E}_{12} \end{array}\right] \begin{bmatrix} \mathbf{F}_x \\ \mathbf{F}_y \end{bmatrix} \tag{10.78}$$

The procedure leading to Equations 10.78 may be effectively utilized in finding an equivalent terminal representation for a system containing hybrid components.

Although the technique developed above is straightforward and the formulation criterion is readily met in almost all circumstances, a successful application is usually greatly impeded by having to determine an inverse of sizable order. Therefore, every effort should be made to avoid branch-chord formulation.

Example 10.5. Consider the linkage system Figure 10.12. It is to be included as a component in a larger system. For that purpose, it is necessary to derive a terminal representation according to the terminal graph of Figure 10.12(b), retaining terminals *a* and *b*, and of course *g*. To present the characteristics

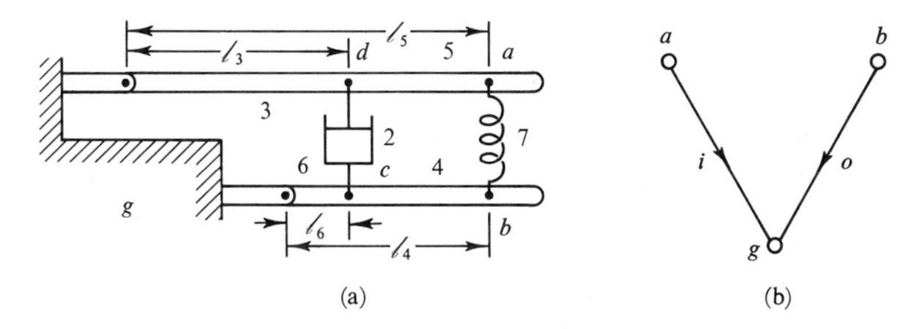

Fig. 10.12. *Linkage system:* (a) *schematic;* (b) *equivalent terminal graph.*

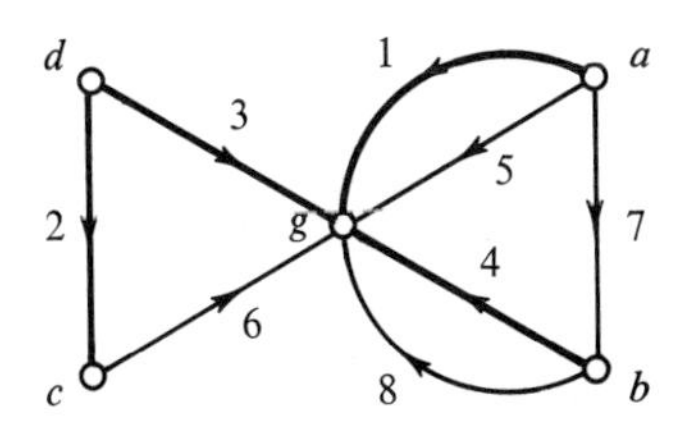

Fig. 10.13. *System graph of linkage with applied drivers.*

of this linkage in a simple manner, the two levers should be modeled as ideal transducers, thus neglecting all physical properties except the lever ratios.

The system graph of the linkage and the two drivers is shown in Figure 10.13. The drivers, represented by elements 1 and 8, are provided in correspondence with the desired terminal graph.

If we wish to represent the equivalent model in terms of the hybrid parameters, that is in the form

$$\begin{bmatrix} F_{\text{in}} \\ \Delta_{\text{out}} \end{bmatrix} = \begin{bmatrix} \quad & \quad \\ \quad & \quad \end{bmatrix} \begin{bmatrix} \Delta_{\text{in}} \\ F_{\text{out}} \end{bmatrix}$$

then it becomes necessary to select elements 1 and 8 as across and through drivers, respectively. In accordance with the branch-chord formulation criterion, we have then two choices for the tree: Tree 1, elements 1, 2, 3, 4; Tree 2, elements 1, 3, 6, 7. In either case, it is possible write the component equations in a form satisfying the criterion.

The component equations corresponding to the first choice are

$$\begin{matrix} \text{branches} \left\{ \begin{matrix} \\ \\ \\ \end{matrix} \right. \\ \\ \text{chords} \left\{ \begin{matrix} \\ \\ \\ \end{matrix} \right. \end{matrix} \begin{bmatrix} \Delta_2 \\ \Delta_3 \\ \Delta_4 \\ F_5 \\ F_6 \\ F_7 \end{bmatrix} = \begin{bmatrix} \dfrac{1}{B_2 s} & 0 & 0 & 0 & 0 & 0 \\ 0 & 0 & 0 & N_{35} & 0 & 0 \\ 0 & 0 & 0 & 0 & N_{46} & 0 \\ 0 & -N_{35} & 0 & 0 & 0 & 0 \\ 0 & 0 & -N_{46} & 0 & 0 & 0 \\ 0 & 0 & 0 & 0 & 0 & k_7 \end{bmatrix} \begin{bmatrix} F_2 \\ F_3 \\ F_4 \\ \Delta_5 \\ \Delta_6 \\ \Delta_7 \end{bmatrix} \tag{10.79}$$

where $N_{35} = l_3/l_5$ and $N_{46} = l_4/l_6$.

We now replace the branch through variables and the chord across variables by the branch across variables and chord through variables, respectively, by use of the cutset and circuit equations. We set the equations up in the from

$$\begin{bmatrix} F_2 \\ F_3 \\ F_4 \\ \Delta_5 \\ \Delta_6 \\ \Delta_7 \end{bmatrix} = \left[\begin{array}{ccc|ccc} & & & 0 & 1 & 0 \\ & \bigcirc & & 0 & -1 & 0 \\ & & & 0 & 0 & 1 \\ \hline 0 & 0 & 0 & & & \\ -1 & 1 & 0 & & \bigcirc & \\ 0 & 0 & -1 & & & \end{array} \right] \begin{bmatrix} \Delta_2 \\ \Delta_3 \\ \Delta_4 \\ F_5 \\ F_6 \\ F_7 \end{bmatrix} + \begin{bmatrix} 0 & 0 \\ 0 & 0 \\ 0 & -1 \\ 1 & 0 \\ 0 & 1 \\ 1 & 0 \end{bmatrix} \begin{bmatrix} \Delta_1 \\ F_8 \end{bmatrix} \tag{10.80}$$

This may be readily accomplished by rewriting the cutset and circuit equations, or directly from the graph. In the latter case, we only look for cutsets 2, 3, and 4, and circuits 5, 6, and 7.

We can now substitute Equations 10.80 into 10.79, with the result

$$\begin{bmatrix} \Delta_2 \\ \Delta_3 \\ \Delta_4 \\ F_5 \\ F_6 \\ F_7 \end{bmatrix} = \begin{bmatrix} 0 & 0 & 0 & 0 & \dfrac{1}{B_2 s} & 0 \\ 0 & 0 & 0 & 0 & 0 & 0 \\ -N_{46} & N_{46} & 0 & 0 & 0 & 0 \\ 0 & 0 & 0 & 0 & N_{35} & 0 \\ 0 & 0 & 0 & 0 & 0 & -N_{46} \\ 0 & 0 & -k_7 & 0 & 0 & 0 \end{bmatrix} \begin{bmatrix} \Delta_2 \\ \Delta_3 \\ \Delta_4 \\ F_5 \\ F_6 \\ F_7 \end{bmatrix} + \begin{bmatrix} 0 & 0 \\ N_{35} & 0 \\ 0 & 0 \\ 0 & 0 \\ 0 & N_{46} \\ k_7 & 0 \end{bmatrix} \begin{bmatrix} \Delta_1 \\ F_8 \end{bmatrix} \tag{10.81}$$

This is a relation between six unknown system variables and the two specified drivers. We now collect terms and solve for the six unknowns.

$$\begin{bmatrix} 1 & 0 & 0 & 0 & -\dfrac{1}{B_2 s} & 0 \\ 0 & 1 & 0 & 0 & 0 & 0 \\ N_{46} & -N_{46} & 1 & 0 & 0 & 0 \\ 0 & 0 & 0 & 1 & -N_{35} & 0 \\ 0 & 0 & 0 & 0 & 1 & N_{46} \\ 0 & 0 & k_7 & 0 & 0 & 1 \end{bmatrix} \begin{bmatrix} \Delta_2 \\ \Delta_3 \\ \Delta_4 \\ F_5 \\ F_6 \\ F_7 \end{bmatrix} = \begin{bmatrix} 0 & 0 \\ N_{35} & 0 \\ 0 & 0 \\ 0 & 0 \\ 0 & N_{46} \\ k_7 & 0 \end{bmatrix} \begin{bmatrix} F_8 \\ \Delta_1 \end{bmatrix} \tag{10.82}$$

A solution for the six system variables will exist if the six $\times$ six matrix on the left side has an inverse. The existence of the inverse may be checked either by evaluating the determinant or by determining the rank of the matrix. The latter approach will yield a triangular matrix. It is then a simple extension to generate a full unit matrix on the left side. Through elementary row operations, carried out on both sides of the equation, we find the triangular matrix

$$\begin{bmatrix} 1 & 0 & 0 & 0 & -\dfrac{1}{B_2 s} & 0 \\ 0 & 1 & 0 & 0 & 0 & 0 \\ 0 & 0 & 1 & 0 & \dfrac{N_{46}}{B_2 s} & 0 \\ 0 & 0 & 0 & 1 & -N_{35} & 0 \\ 0 & 0 & 0 & 0 & 1 & N_{46} \\ 0 & 0 & 0 & 0 & 0 & 1 \end{bmatrix} \begin{bmatrix} \Delta_2 \\ \Delta_3 \\ \Delta_4 \\ F_5 \\ F_6 \\ F_7 \end{bmatrix}$$

$$= \begin{bmatrix} 0 & 0 \\ N_{35} & 0 \\ N_{46}N_{35} & 0 \\ 0 & 0 \\ 0 & N_{46} \\ \dfrac{B_2 s k_7 (1 - N_{46}N_{35}) s}{B_2 s + N_{46}^2 k_7} & \dfrac{k_7 N_{46}^2}{B_2 s k_7 N_{46}^2} \end{bmatrix} \begin{bmatrix} \Delta_1 \\ F_8 \end{bmatrix} \tag{10.83}$$

Indeed, the rank is maximum and the inverse exists. Continuing with the solution, we may either solve the system of equations one variable at a time, starting with the bottom equation, or generate a complete unit matrix on the left side by continuing to apply row operations. In either case, the solution is given by

$$\begin{bmatrix} \Delta_2 \\ \Delta_3 \\ \Delta_4 \\ F_5 \\ F_6 \\ F_7 \end{bmatrix} = \frac{1}{D} \begin{bmatrix} -N_{46}k_7(1 - N_{46}N_{35}) & N_{46} \\ DN_{35} & 0 \\ N_{46}^2 k_7\left(1 + N_{35}/N_{46}\dfrac{B_2 s}{k_7}\right) & -N_{46}^2 \\ -N_{35}N_{46}(1 - N_{35}N_{46}) B_2 k_7 s & N_{35}N_{46}B_2 s \\ -N_{46} + B_2 k_7 (1 - N_{46}N_{35}) s & N_{46}B_2 s \\ B_2 k_7 (1 - N_{35}N_{46}) s & k_7 N_{46}^2 \end{bmatrix} \begin{bmatrix} \Delta_1 \\ F_8 \end{bmatrix} \tag{10.84}$$

where $D = N_{46}^2 k_7 + B_2 s$.

To complete this problem, it is necessary to substitute Equations 10.84 into

$$\begin{bmatrix} F_1 \\ \Delta_8 \end{bmatrix} \begin{bmatrix} 0 & 0 & 0 & -1 & 0 & -1 \\ 0 & 0 & -1 & 0 & 0 & 0 \end{bmatrix} \begin{bmatrix} \Delta_2 \\ \Delta_3 \\ \Delta_4 \\ F_5 \\ F_6 \\ F_7 \end{bmatrix} + \begin{bmatrix} 0 & 0 \\ 0 & 0 \end{bmatrix} \begin{bmatrix} \Delta_1 \\ F_8 \end{bmatrix}$$

with the result

$$\begin{bmatrix} F_1 \\ \Delta_8 \end{bmatrix} \begin{bmatrix} -H_{11}(s) & H_{12}(s) \\ H_{21}(s) & -H_{22}(s) \end{bmatrix} \begin{bmatrix} \Delta_1 \\ F_8 \end{bmatrix} \tag{10.85}$$

Since

$$\begin{bmatrix} F_1 \\ F_8 \end{bmatrix} = - \begin{bmatrix} F_i \\ F_o \end{bmatrix} \qquad \begin{bmatrix} \Delta_1 \\ \Delta_8 \end{bmatrix} = \begin{bmatrix} \Delta_i \\ \Delta_o \end{bmatrix}$$

we finally obtain

$$\begin{bmatrix} F_i \\ \Delta_o \end{bmatrix} \begin{bmatrix} H_{11}(s) & H_{12}(s) \\ H_{21}(s) & H_{22}(s) \end{bmatrix} \begin{bmatrix} \Delta_i \\ F_o \end{bmatrix} \tag{10.86}$$

where

$$H_{11}(s) = \frac{(1 - N_{35}N_{46})^2 B_2 s}{N_{46}^2(1 + \tau_2 s)}$$

$$H_{12}(s) = \frac{1 + \tau_1 s}{1 + \tau_2 s}$$

$$H_{21}(s) = H_{12}(s)$$

$$H_{22}(s) = \frac{1/k_7}{1 + \tau_2 s}$$

and

$$\tau_1 = \frac{N_{35}}{N_{46}} \frac{B_2}{k_7}$$

$$\tau_2 = \frac{1}{N_{46}^2} \frac{B_2}{k_7}$$

It is helpful to consider a simulated application of this lever linkage in achieving an intuitive understanding of its characteristics. Suppose the following conditions are specified:

$$F_o = 0$$

(open circuit—no load),

$$\Delta_i = 1/s$$

(step input).

Then determine $\delta_o(t)$. From Equations 10.86 we have

$$\Delta_o = H_{21}(s)\Delta_i$$
$$= \frac{1 + \tau_1 s}{1 + \tau_2 s}\frac{1}{s} \tag{10.87}$$

Since the transfer function contains one pole, the time response will be exponential with time constant τ_2. If the initial and final values are determined, we may sketch out the total response. Initial value:

$$\delta_o(0) = \lim_{s\to\infty} s\Delta_o(s) = \tau_1/\tau_2 = N_{35}N_{46}$$

Final value:

$$\delta_o(\infty) = \lim_{s\to 0} s\Delta_o(s) = 1$$

Consider now a likely choice of numerical values for the lever arm ratios. Recall that

$$N_{35} = l_3/l_5 \qquad \text{and} \qquad N_{46} = l_4/l_6$$

so that $N_{35}N_{46} = l_3l_4/l_5l_6$. From Figure 10.13 we conclude that $N_{35}N_{46}$ can be made very much larger than unity by a suitable choice of l_6. Hence, the transient response of Figure 10.14.

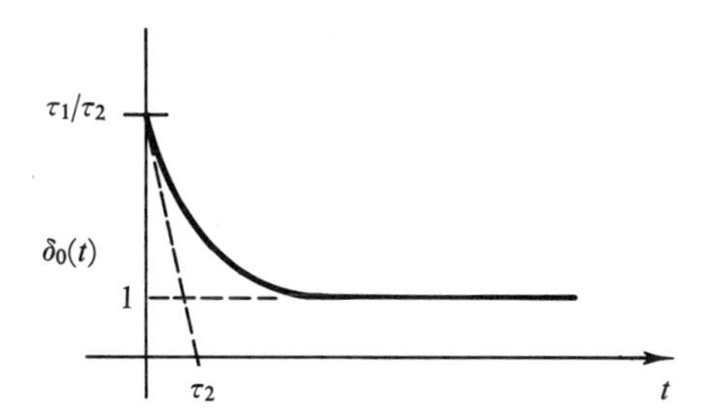

Fig. 10.14. *Transient response of system of Figure 10.12.*

The dashpot acts like a stiff connection at the beginning of the transient, while the spring maintains constant displacement at the end of the transient.

As another illustration of the branch-chord formulation procedure, consider the free lever shown in Figure 10.15 whose terminal representation is given by Equation 10.88. It is proposed that a new terminal representation be derived according to the terminal graph of Figure 10.16(b).

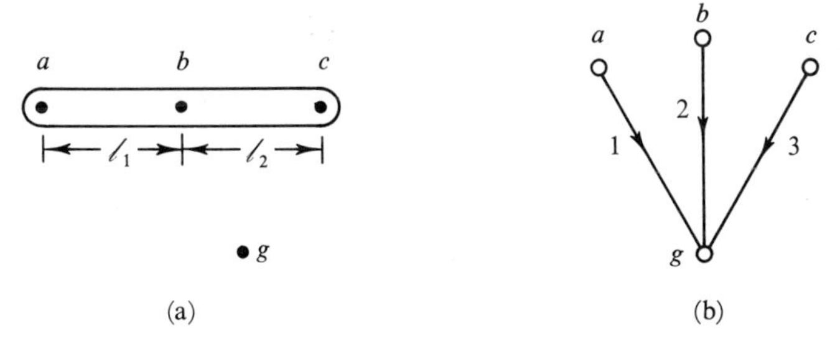

Fig. 10.15. *Free lever:* (a) *schematic;* (b) *terminal graph.*

$$\begin{bmatrix} \delta_1 \\ f_2 \\ f_3 \end{bmatrix} = \begin{bmatrix} 0 & N_{12} & -N_{13} \\ -N_{12} & 0 & 0 \\ N_{13} & 0 & 0 \end{bmatrix} \begin{bmatrix} F_1 \\ \delta_2 \\ \delta_3 \end{bmatrix} \tag{10.88}$$

where

$$N_{12} = \frac{l_1 + l_2}{l_2} \qquad N_{13} = l_1/l_2$$

For this purpose, two drivers are applied to the original terminal graph, as shown in Figure 10.16(a). On account of the terminal equations of the lever, the tree is selected such that the elements of the terminal graph of the lever

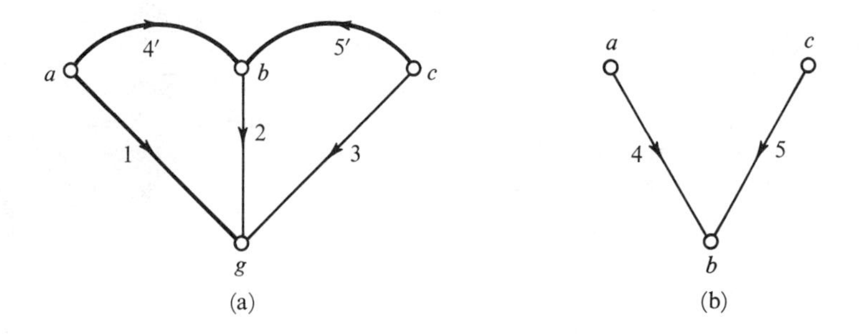

Fig. 10.16. *Alternate free lever terminal graph.*

are 1—branch; 2,3—chords. This is required to satisfy the criterion for branch-chord formulation. By necessity, the applied drivers are across variables. No choice is possible. In proceeding with the formulation, we start with the component equations

$$\begin{bmatrix} \delta_1 \\ f_2 \\ f_3 \end{bmatrix} = \begin{bmatrix} 0 & N_{12} & -N_{13} \\ -N_{12} & 0 & 0 \\ N_{13} & 0 & 0 \end{bmatrix} \begin{bmatrix} f_1 \\ \delta_2 \\ \delta_3 \end{bmatrix}$$

and by substitution of suitable selected cutset and circuit equations, eliminate the variables on the right side to obtain

$$\begin{bmatrix} 1 - N_{12} + N_{13} & 0 & 0 \\ 0 & 1 - N_{12} & -N_{12} \\ 0 & N_{13} & 1 + N_{13} \end{bmatrix} \begin{bmatrix} \delta_1 \\ f_2 \\ f_3 \end{bmatrix} = \begin{bmatrix} -N_{12} + N_{13} & -N_{13} \\ 0 & 0 \\ 0 & 0 \end{bmatrix} \begin{bmatrix} \delta_{4'} \\ \delta_{5'} \end{bmatrix} \tag{10.89}$$

A solution for the variables on the left side of Equations 10.89 is required in order to obtain the desired terminal representation. To investigate the existence of this solution, we examine the determinant of the matrix on the left side. It is

$$\det = (1 - N_{12} + N_{13})^2 = 0$$

Upon substitution of the values of N_{12} and N_{13}, the determinant is shown to vanish. Hence, the proposed terminal representation is not obtainable through branch-chord formulation. This result is corroborated by the fact that the necessary choice of drivers, across variables, would have resulted in a set of terminal equations of the form

$$\begin{bmatrix} f_4 \\ f_5 \end{bmatrix} \begin{bmatrix} \quad & \quad \\ \quad & \quad \end{bmatrix} \begin{bmatrix} \delta_4 \\ \delta_5 \end{bmatrix}$$

which is not possible for a lever treated as an ideal transducer.

10.10 State Equations of Systems with Multiterminal Components

We have consider three general methods of formulating and solving system equations called the chord, branch, and branch-chord methods. These methods are generalizations of the loop and node equation methods. A fourth method is the formulation of the state variable equations from the system graph. If multiterminal components are present in the system, the choice of state variables and the selection of an appropriate graph tree (or forest) becomes important.

In Chapter 6 a systematic procedure is developed for the selection of state variables and the best tree in simple systems. In the examples to follow, reasons for additional restrictions are presented. As an illustration of some of the problem areas, consider the example in Figure 10.17.

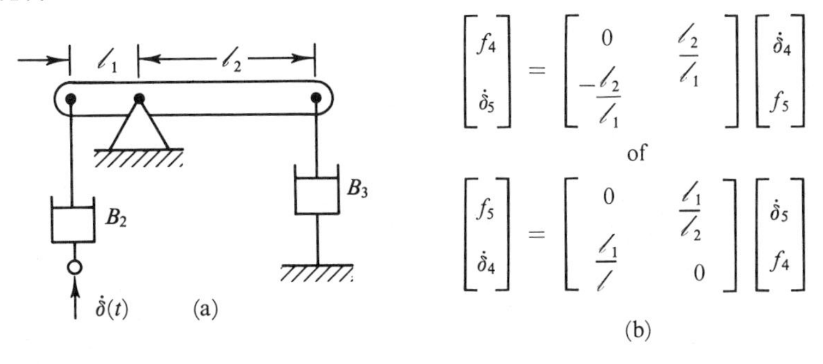

Fig. 10.17. (a) *Mechanical lever system;* (b) *lever equations.*

Assuming an ideal lever, let us draw a system graph and consider all possible trees. These are illustrated in Figure 10.18. Sincc the velocity source $\dot{\delta}(t)$ must be a branch, either the dashpot B_1 or the left side of the lever must be a branch to complete a tree. On the right side of the lever either the dashpot B_2 or the lever element 5 must be a branch. This system has no energy storage elements and therefore has no time-dependent state equations. However, let us consider the output to be

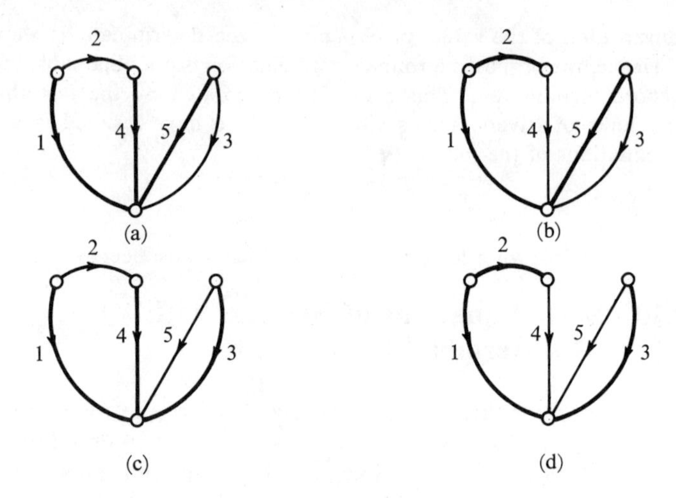

Fig. 10.18. *Possible trees for system of Figure 10.17.*

the velocity of dashpot B_3 and attempt to find the solution using the cutset and circuit equations from Figure 10.18(a).

$$\dot{\delta}_3 = \dot{\delta}_5 = -\frac{l_2}{l_1}\dot{\delta}_4$$

Element 4 does not define a fundamental circuit, therefore we should consider a different tree with element 4 a chord. This is the case in Figure 10.18(b). Then using the cutset and fundamental circuit equations of this graph we have

$$\dot{\delta}_4 = \dot{\delta}_1 - \dot{\delta}_2 = \dot{\delta}_1 - \frac{1}{B_2}f_2 = \dot{\delta}_1 - \frac{1}{B_2}f_4 = \dot{\delta}_1 - \frac{1}{B_2}\frac{l_2}{l_1}f_5$$
$$= \dot{\delta}_1 + \frac{1}{B_2}\frac{l_2}{l_1}f_3 = \dot{\delta}_1 + \frac{1}{B_2}\frac{l_2}{l_1}B_3\dot{\delta}_3$$

Finally,

$$\dot{\delta}_3\left[1 + \frac{B_3}{B_2}\left(\frac{l_2}{l_1}\right)^2\right] = -\frac{l_2}{l_1}\dot{\delta}_1 \tag{10.90}$$

is the solution equation. Using the graph of Figure 10.18(c), our first equation cannot be written for $\dot{\delta}_3$ using a fundamental circuit. However, we may write

$$\dot{\delta}_3 = \frac{1}{B_3}f_3 = -\frac{1}{B_3}\left(\frac{l_1}{l_2}\right)f_4 = -\frac{1}{B_3}\frac{l_1}{l_2}f_2$$
$$= -\frac{1}{B_3}\frac{l_1}{l_2}B_2\dot{\delta}_2 = -\frac{B_2}{B_2}\frac{l_1}{l_2}(\dot{\delta}_1 - \dot{\delta}_4) = -\frac{B_2}{B_3}\frac{l_1}{l_2}\left(\dot{\delta}_1 + \frac{l_1}{l_2}\dot{\delta}_3\right)$$

Therefore,

$$\dot{\delta}_3\left[1 + \frac{B_2}{B_3}\left(\frac{l_1}{l_2}\right)^2\right] = -\frac{B_2}{B_3}\frac{l_1}{l_2}\dot{\delta}_1 \tag{10.91}$$

and is another form of the solution Equation 10.90. Using the graph of Figure 10.18(d) we write

$$\dot{\delta}_3 = \frac{1}{B_3}f_3 = \frac{1}{B_3}f_5 = -\frac{1}{B_3}\frac{l_1}{l_2}f_4$$

As this point we note that there is no cutset equation defined for element 4 and a straightforward solution cannot be found.

We have assumed that fundamental cutset and circuit equations must be used to write equations. These fundamental equations, of course, are not the only ones which can be used for a system solution, but state equations which are written using the fundamental equations always give a unique and easy-to-use procedure. A conclusion can be generalized from this example: To write the state equations from the system graph of a system which contains ideal n-port components, it is necessary to choose a tree such that some parts of the subgraph representing a component are branches and the rest are chords. For a two-port component, one element must be a branch, the other a chord.

To illustrate the assignment of branches and chords for a system containing an ideal four-port component, let us consider an example.

Example 10.6. The four-port free lever illustrated in Figure 10.19(a) is an example of an ideal n-port component. The system graph is shown in Figure 10.19(b) and the component equations are written in part (c) of the figure. If this form were the only way the equations could be written, elements 5 and 6 must be branches and elements 7 and 8 must be chords. In general terms, elements whose across variables are on the left side of the component equations must be branches and elements whose through variables are on the left side must be chords. In this example, however, the matrix of the equations has an inverse, therefore we may also write

$$\begin{bmatrix} f_5 \\ f_6 \\ \dot{\delta}_7 \\ \dot{\varphi}_8 \end{bmatrix} = \begin{bmatrix} 0 & 0 & \dfrac{-l_2}{l_1 + l_2} & \dfrac{1}{l_1 + l_2} \\ 0 & 0 & \dfrac{-l_1}{l_1 + l_2} & \dfrac{-1}{l_1 + l_2} \\ \dfrac{l_2}{l_1 + l_2} & \dfrac{l_1}{l_1 + l_2} & 0 & 0 \\ \dfrac{-1}{l_1 + l_2} & \dfrac{1}{l_1 + l_2} & 0 & 0 \end{bmatrix} \begin{bmatrix} \dot{\delta}_5 \\ \dot{\delta}_6 \\ f_7 \\ \tau_8 \end{bmatrix} \tag{10.92}$$

and the fifth and sixth elements would be made chords, etc. It may be shown that these two forms of the lever equations are the only existing forms; hence, there exist only the two chord-branch arrangements of the lever subgraph.

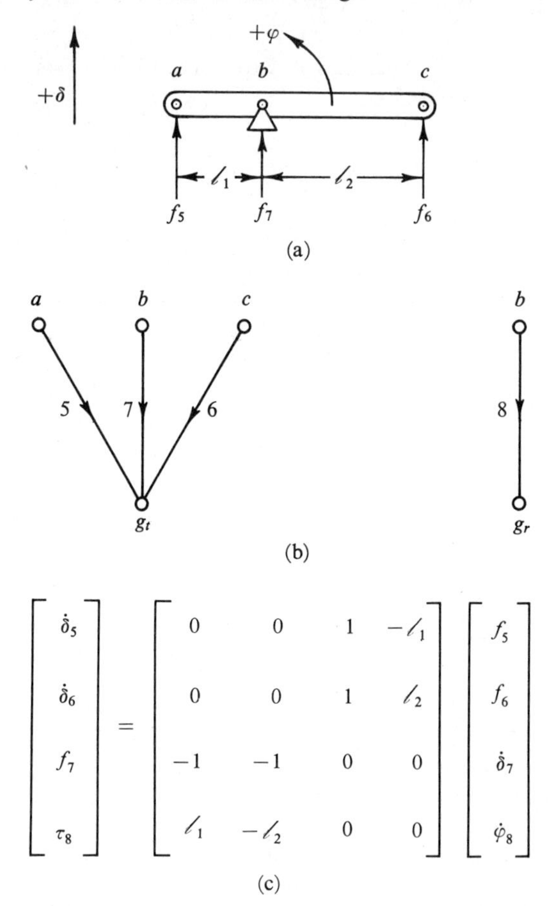

$$\begin{bmatrix} \dot{\delta}_5 \\ \dot{\delta}_6 \\ f_7 \\ \tau_8 \end{bmatrix} = \begin{bmatrix} 0 & 0 & 1 & -l_1 \\ 0 & 0 & 1 & l_2 \\ -1 & -1 & 0 & 0 \\ l_1 & -l_2 & 0 & 0 \end{bmatrix} \begin{bmatrix} f_5 \\ f_6 \\ \dot{\delta}_7 \\ \dot{\varphi}_8 \end{bmatrix}$$

Fig. 10.19. (a) *Free ideal level;* (b) *system graph;* (c) *system equations.*

As an illustration of the formulation of the state equations of a system containing the free lever, consider Figure 10.20. Using the procedures developed in Chapter 6, we form a forest of elements 1, 2, 5, and 6. Elements 1 and 2 are branches because they represent mass and inertia components. Element 3 should be a chord because it represents a spring. Elements 5 and 6 can be either branches or chords. It they are chosen as branches, then elements 7 and 8 must be chords if the lever is ideal. As can be seen, all the desired conditions on chords and branches can be met and we may write the state equations using the cutset and circuit equations as follows:

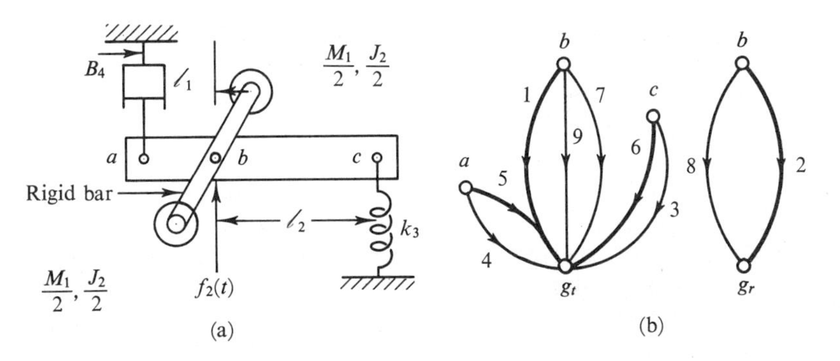

Fig. 10.20. (a) *Mechanical system;* (b) *system graph.*

$$
\begin{aligned}
M_1\ddot{\delta}_1 &= f_1 = -f_9 - f_7 \\
J_2\ddot{\varphi}_2 &= +\tau_2 = -\tau_8 \\
\frac{1}{k_3}\dot{f}_3 &= \dot{\delta}_3 = \dot{\delta}_6
\end{aligned} \tag{10.93}
$$

From the lever equations of Figure 10.19(c) and the cutset and circuit equations,

$$
\begin{aligned}
f_7 &= -f_5 - f_6 = f_4 + f_3 \\
\tau_8 &= l_1 f_5 - l_2 f_6 = -l_1 f_4 + l_2 f_3 \\
\dot{\delta}_6 &= \dot{\delta}_7 + l_2\dot{\varphi}_8 = \dot{\delta}_1 + l_2\dot{\varphi}_2
\end{aligned} \tag{10.94}
$$

Then

$$
f_4 = B_4\dot{\delta}_4 = B_4\dot{\delta}_5 = B_4(\dot{\delta}_7 - l_1\dot{\varphi}_8) = B_4(\dot{\delta}_1 - l_1\dot{\varphi}_2) \tag{10.95}
$$

Finally,

$$
\begin{bmatrix} \ddot{\delta}_1 \\ \ddot{\varphi}_2 \\ \dot{f}_3 \end{bmatrix} = \begin{bmatrix} \dfrac{B_4}{M_1} & \dfrac{l_1 B_4}{M_1} & -\dfrac{1}{M_1} \\ \dfrac{l_1 B_4}{J_2} & -\dfrac{l_1^2 B_4}{J_2} & -\dfrac{l_2}{J_2} \\ k_3 & l_2 k_3 & 0 \end{bmatrix} \begin{bmatrix} \dot{\delta}_1 \\ \dot{\varphi}_2 \\ f_3 \end{bmatrix} + \begin{bmatrix} -\dfrac{1}{M_1} \\ 0 \\ 0 \end{bmatrix} f_9(t) \tag{10.96}
$$

Suppose component B_4, the dashpot, in the system of Figure 10.20 were replaced by a mass component. In writing the state equations of this new system we would expect to include the equation

$$
M_4\ddot{\delta}_4 = f_4 \tag{10.97}
$$

and element 4 of the system graph would be a branch. However, we may not make both elements 4 and 5 branches because this violates the requirements of a system tree. For cases of this nature we classify component 4 as an excess component. Element 4 is made a chord and the state equations do not include Equation 10.97.

This system formulation implies that there is a priority schedule in the assignment of branches and chords in the system graph. The priorities are listed below, in order.

1. All across sources must be branches and all through sources must be chords.

2. Certain elements of n-port ideal components must be branches and the rest chords depending on the existing ways of writing the component equations. Specifically, graph elements associated with across variables on the left side of the component equations are branches and through variable elements are chords.

3. All differentiating-type components should be branches and all integrating-type components should be chords.

4. The assignment of branches and chords to dissipative elements is such that a tree (or forest) of the system graph is complete.

There can be no conflict between statements 1 and 2, but there may be conflicts between 1 and 3 or 2 and 3. If so, the conflicting components are excess components.

10.11 Excess Components

In the assignment of branches and chords for a system graph, it is essential that the branches form a tree (or forest) subgraph. If the tree contains *every* differentiating-type element in the system, such a tree is a *proper tree*. If there are excess differentiating elements, the resulting tree is a *modified proper tree*. Trivial examples of excess differentiating elements are illustrated in Figure 10.21. In part (a), the voltage source

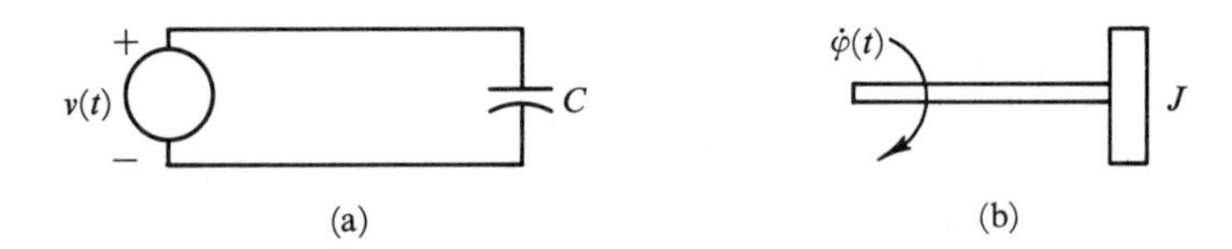

Fig. 10.21. (a) *Excess capacitance;* (b) *excess inertia.*

is an across source and specified. The capacitance voltage is normally a state variable but is specified in this example. A similar argument applies to part (b) where $\dot{\varphi}(t)$ is a specified angular velocity.

Similarly, not all integrating components can be assigned chords in the system graph. The integrating components which must be made branches to complete a tree are excess, and a modified proper tree includes these elements as branches. In addition, no state equations can be written for the excess integrating elements. A trivial example is shown

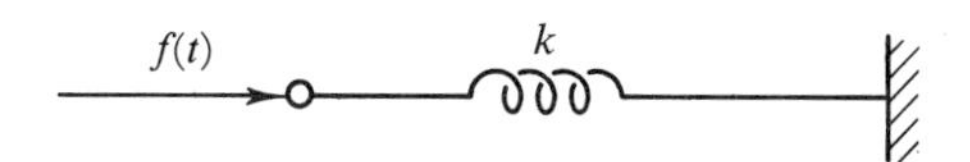

Fig. 10.22. *Excess spring.*

in Figure 10.22. The spring force is the state variable but the force is specified. The following example is an electrical network with both an excess inductor and an excess capacitor.

Example 10.7. In the network of Figure 10.23(a), element 1 must be a

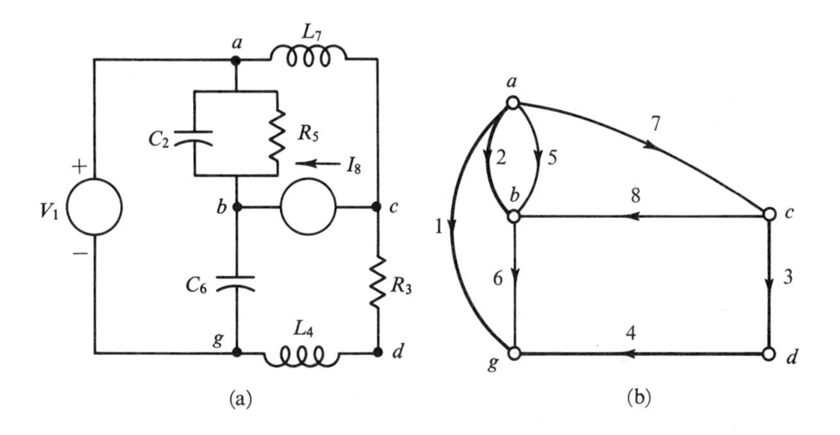

Fig. 10.23. (a) *Electrical network;* (b) *system graph.*

branch and element 8 a chord because they are an across and through source, respectively. Either capacitance C_2 or C_6 must be a chord to avoid a loop of branches, and either inductor L_4 or L_7 must be a branch to obtain a complete tree. In Figure 10.23(b), C_6 and L_4 are assumed to be the excess components. The state equations are (using cutset, circuit, and component equations)

$$\begin{aligned} C_2\dot{v}_2 &= i_2 = i_6 - i_5 - I_8 = C_6\dot{v}_6 - G_5v_5 - I_8 \\ L_7\dot{i}_7 &= v_7 = v_3 - v_4 = - R_3i_3 - L_4\dot{i}_4 + V_1 \end{aligned} \tag{10.98}$$

The right sides of Equations 10.98 contain the derivatives of variables and are not suitable for the state equations in this form. A new set of state variables will be defined. Let

$$\begin{aligned} \dot{x}_1 &= C_2\dot{v}_2 - C_6\dot{v}_6 = C_2\dot{v}_2 - C_6(\dot{V}_1 - \dot{v}_2) = (C_2 + C_6)\dot{v}_2 - C_6\dot{V}_1 \\ \dot{x}_2 &= L_7\dot{i}_7 + L_4\dot{i}_4 = L_7\dot{i}_7 + L_4(\dot{i}_7 - \dot{I}_8) = (L_7 + L_4)\dot{i}_7 - L_4\dot{I}_8 \end{aligned} \tag{10.99}$$

In addition, we need v_5 and i_3

$$\begin{aligned} v_5 &= v_2 \\ i_3 &= i_7 - I_8 \end{aligned}$$

From Equations 10.99,

$$i_7 = \frac{x_2}{L_7 + L_4} + \frac{L_4}{L_7 + L_4} I_8$$
$$v_2 = \frac{x_1}{C_2 + C_6} + \frac{C_6}{C_2 + C_6} V_1 \tag{10.100}$$

Finally,

$$\begin{bmatrix} \dot{x}_1 \\ \dot{x}_2 \end{bmatrix} = \begin{bmatrix} \dfrac{G_5}{C_2 + C_6} & 0 \\ 0 & \dfrac{-R_3}{L_7 + L_4} \end{bmatrix} \begin{bmatrix} x_1 \\ x_2 \end{bmatrix} + \begin{bmatrix} -\dfrac{C_6 G_5}{C_2 + C_6} & -1 \\ 1 & \dfrac{L_7 R_3}{L_7 + L_4} \end{bmatrix} \begin{bmatrix} V_1 \\ I_8 \end{bmatrix} \tag{10.101}$$

As another example of excess components, consider again the mechanical system of Figure 10.20.

Example 10.8. For the system of Figure 10.20, replace the component B_4 with a mass, M_4, and write the state equations. For this case, we write the equations for M_4 as

$$f_4 = M_4 \ddot{\delta}_4 = M_4(\ddot{\delta}_7 - l_1 \ddot{\varphi}_8) = M_4(\ddot{\delta}_1 - l_1 \ddot{\varphi}_2) \tag{10.102}$$

The state equations may not be written directly because the matrix will contain derivatives of the original state variables. However, define the new state variables

$$\dot{x}_1 = M_1 \ddot{\delta}_1 + f_4 = (M_1 + M_4)\ddot{\delta}_1 - M_4 l_1 \ddot{\varphi}_2$$
$$\dot{x}_2 = J_2 \ddot{\varphi}_2 - l_1 f_4 = (J_2 + l_1^2 M_4)\ddot{\varphi}_2 - M_4 l_1 \ddot{\delta}_1$$
$$\dot{x}_3 = \frac{1}{k_3}\dot{f}_3 \tag{10.103}$$

After integrating Equations 10.103 we may solve for $\dot{\delta}_1$, $\dot{\varphi}_2$, and f_3 explicitly in terms of x_1, x_2, and x_3, that is

$$\begin{bmatrix} M_1 + M_4 & -M_4 l_1 \\ -M_4 l_1 & J_2 + l_1^2 M_4 \end{bmatrix} \begin{bmatrix} \dot{\delta}_1 \\ \dot{\varphi}_2 \end{bmatrix} = \begin{bmatrix} x_1 \\ x_2 \end{bmatrix}$$
$$\begin{bmatrix} \dot{\delta}_1 \\ \dot{\varphi}_2 \end{bmatrix} = \frac{\begin{bmatrix} J_2 + l_1^2 M_4 & M_4 l_1 \\ M_4 l_1 & M_1 + M_4 \end{bmatrix} \begin{bmatrix} x_1 \\ x_2 \end{bmatrix}}{J_2(M_1 + M_4) + l_1^2 M_1 M_4}$$
$$f_3 = k_3 x_3 \tag{10.104}$$

Rewriting Equations 10.93 combined with Equations 10.94, we have

$$M_1 \ddot{\delta}_1 = -f_9 - f_4 - f_3$$
$$J_2 \ddot{\varphi}_2 = l_1 f_4 - l_2 f_3$$
$$\frac{1}{k_3}\dot{f}_3 = \dot{\delta}_6 \tag{10.105}$$

Then from equations 10.103, 10.104, and 10.105,

$$\dot{x}_1 = M_1 \ddot{\delta}_1 + f_4 = -f_9 - f_3 = -f_9 - k_3 x_3$$
$$\dot{x}_2 = J_2 \ddot{\varphi}_2 - l_1 f_4 = -l_2 f_3 = -l_2 k_3 x_3$$
$$\dot{x}_3 = \dot{\delta}_6 = \dot{\delta}_1 + l_2 \dot{\varphi}_2$$
$$= \frac{J_2 + l_1^2 M_4}{D} x_1 + \frac{M_4 l_1}{D} x_2 + \frac{M_4 l_1 l_2}{D} x_1 + \frac{l_2(M_1 + M_4)}{D} x_2 \tag{10.106}$$

where

$$D = J_2(M_1 + M_4) + l_1^2 M_1 M_4$$

Finally,

$$\begin{bmatrix} \dot{x}_1 \\ \dot{x}_2 \\ \dot{x}_3 \end{bmatrix} = \begin{bmatrix} 0 & 0 & -k_3 \\ 0 & 0 & -l_2 k_3 \\ \dfrac{J_2 + l_1^2 M_4 + M_4 l_1 l_2}{D} & \dfrac{M_4 l_1 + l_2(M_1 + M_4)}{D} & 0 \end{bmatrix} \begin{bmatrix} x_1 \\ x_2 \\ x_3 \end{bmatrix} + \begin{bmatrix} -1 \\ 0 \\ 0 \end{bmatrix} f_9(t) \tag{10.107}$$

10.12 Nonlinear and Time-Varying Systems—Alternate State Variables

In many problems, the system variables which have been normally assigned as state variables cannot be used for various reasons. One reason is illustrated in Examples 10.7 and 10.8, where excess components are involved. Other reasons are considered in this section.

State variables can be any of the following: (1) the across variable of differentiating components, (2) the through variable of integrating components, (3) variables proportional to either (1) or (2), (4) any linear combination of (1) or (2). In some instances a state variable other than (1) or (2) may be desired, for example, the displacement of a mechanical spring rather than the spring force. For a linear spring we have the defining equation

$$f = k\delta$$

and the two state variables are proportionally related.

In certain time-varying and nonlinear problems, the normal state variables cannot be used. If a mechanical spring, for example, is nonlinear, then we may write

$$f = k(\delta) \tag{10.108}$$

where $k(\delta)$ is a functional relationship of f to δ. Figure 10.24 illustrates a $k(\delta)$.

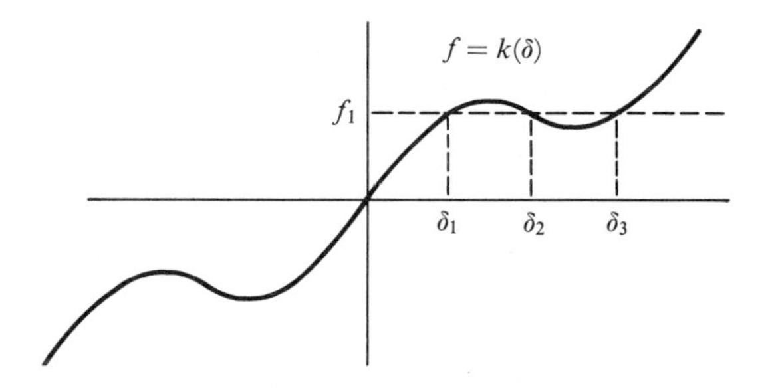

Fig. 10.24. *Mechanical spring characteristic.*

If we attempt to write the state equation of this component we have

$$\dot{f} = \frac{d}{dt}[k(\delta)] = k'(\delta)\frac{d\delta}{dt} \tag{10.109}$$

where

$$k'(\delta) = \frac{d[k(\delta)]}{d\delta}$$

Normally, $d\delta/dt = \dot{\delta}$ is related to other state variables, but δ itself is not. To express δ as a state variable we need to write $\delta = k^{-1}(f)$ where k^{-1} symbolized the inverse of $k(\delta)$. For the spring of Figure 10.24, a unique inverse does not exist because for the value $f = f_1$, for example, the displacement may assume the three values δ_1, δ_2, or δ_3. This problem is avoided if the spring displacement is the state variable; then the state equation for the spring is simply

$$\dot{\delta} = \dot{\delta} \tag{10.110}$$

where $\dot{\delta}$ is related to other state variables.

Example 10.9. In Figure 10.25, let both the spring and damper be nonlinear, and let the state variables be (1) the momentum, p_1 of M_1 ($M_1\dot{\delta}_1 = p_1$); (2) the displacement of k_3 or δ_3. The state equations are

$$\dot{\delta}_3 = \dot{\delta}_1 = \frac{1}{M_1} p_1$$

$$\dot{p}_1 = f_1 = -f_2 - f_3 = -B(\dot{\delta}_2) - k_3(\delta_3) = -B_2\left(\frac{p_1}{M_1}\right) - k_3(\delta_3) \tag{10.111}$$

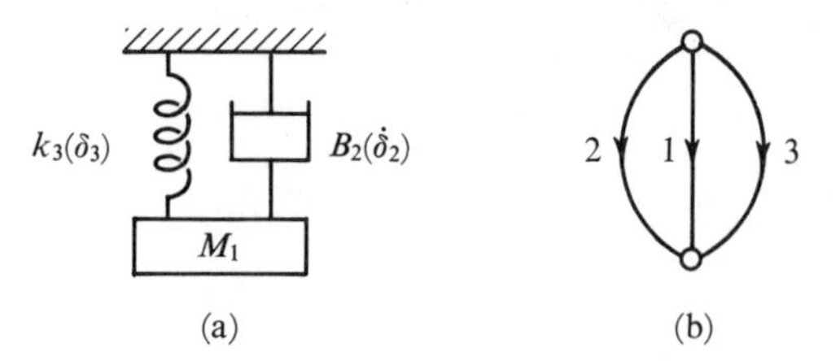

Fig. 10.25. (a) *Nonlinear mechanical system;* (b) *system graph.*

Because of the nonlinearities, these equations are written in the general format

$$\begin{bmatrix} \dot{x}_1 \\ \dot{x}_2 \end{bmatrix} \begin{bmatrix} f_1(x_1, x_2) \\ f_2(x_1, x_2) \end{bmatrix} \tag{10.112}$$

where

$$x_1 = \delta_3$$
$$x_2 = p_1$$

$$f_1(x_1, x_2) = \frac{1}{M_1} p_1$$

$$f_2(x_1, x_2) = -B_2\left(\frac{p_1}{M_1}\right) - k_3(\delta_3)$$

In Example 10.9, the momentum of the mass instead of the velocity of the mass is used as the state variable for the following reason: Suppose the mass is time varying—then the fundamental equation for the force on the mass is

$$f = \dot{p} = \frac{d}{dt}(M\dot{\delta}) = M\ddot{\delta} + \dot{m}\dot{\delta} \neq M\ddot{\delta} \tag{10.113}$$

Using momentum as the state variable of the mass allows us to take the time-varying mass into account. An example which involves a time-varying inertia follows.

Example 10.10. In Figure 10.26, the mass on the end of a pendulum is free to translate only along the pendulum bar. We wish to write the state equations for this system.

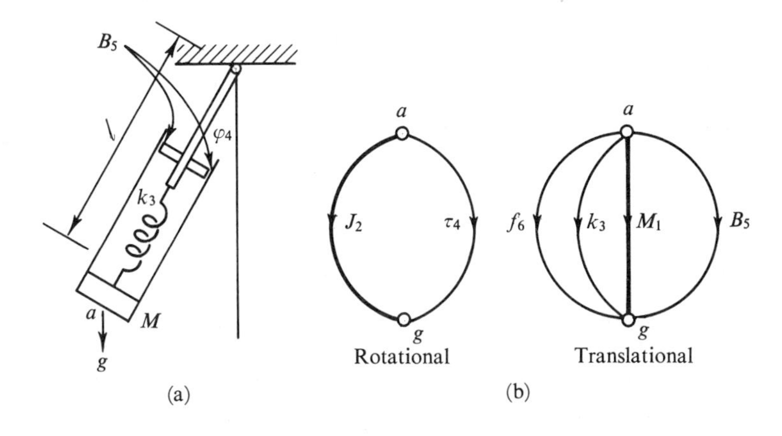

Fig. 10.26. (a) *Pendulum;* (b) *system graph.*

If the pendulum is assumed to be simple, then the inertia about the pivot point is

$$J_2 = M_1 l^2 \tag{10.114}$$

where J_2 is variable.

$$\tau_2 = \frac{d}{dt}(J_2\dot{\varphi}_2) = \frac{dh_2}{dt} \tag{10.115}$$

The torque τ_4 is produced by the mass weight when φ_4 is nonzero. This element is a nonlinear spring element and its equation is

$$\tau_4 = M_1 gl \sin \varphi_4 \tag{10.116}$$

The force f_6 along the pendulum length is also caused by the mass weight

$$f_6 = M_1 g \cos \varphi_4 \tag{10.117}$$

where g is gravity acceleration. The state variables are

1. p_1, the momentum of M_1,
2. h_2, the angular momentum of J_2,
3. δ_3, the displacement of the spring from an unforced position,
4. φ_4, the pendulum angle.

The state equations are

$$\begin{aligned}
\dot{p}_1 &= f_1 = f_6 - f_3 - f_5 = M_1 g \cos \varphi_4 - k_3\delta_3 - \frac{B_5}{M_1} p_1 \\
\dot{h}_2 &= \tau_2 = -\tau_4 = -M_1 g \sin \varphi_4 \\
\dot{\delta}_3 &= \dot{\delta}_1 = \frac{1}{M_1} p_1 \\
\dot{\varphi}_4 &= \dot{\varphi}_2 = \frac{1}{J_2} h_2 = \frac{1}{M_1 l^2} h_2
\end{aligned} \tag{10.118}$$

We have defined l as the total length of the pendulum, therefore, $l = l_0 + \delta_3$ where l_0 is the unforced length. The state equations in terms only of state variables are

$$\begin{aligned}
\dot{p}_1 &= M_1 g \cos \varphi_4 - k_3\delta_3 - \frac{B_5}{M_1} p_1 \\
\dot{h}_2 &= -M_1 g (l_0 + \delta_3) \sin \varphi_4 \\
\dot{\delta}_3 &= \frac{1}{M_1} p_1 \\
\dot{\varphi}_4 &= \frac{1}{M_1 (l_0 + \delta_3)^2} h_2
\end{aligned} \tag{10.119}$$

The systems of Examples 10.9 and 10.10 illustrate the potential of the state equation technique for nonlinear systems. Futher, they illustrate the need to use an alternate set of state variables. These equations, of course, cannot easily be solved analytically and would require a computer solution.

Although we have considered only mechanical systems, similar problems with the normal state variables arise in electrical systems which have nonlinear or time-varying inductances or capacitances. A useful set of alternate state variables for inductors and capacitors are (1) flux linkage, λ, of inductors ($\lambda = Li$); (2) charge, q, of capacitors, ($q = Cv$).

The next example illustrates the use of the flux linkage and charge for state variables.

Example 10.11. In the electrical network of Figure 10.27(a), R_5 is a diode and its equation may be written as

$$v_5 = R_5(i_5) \tag{10.120}$$

and a typical plot of v_5 versus i_5 is illustrated in Figure 10.28(a). C_2 is a varactor whose capacitance is a function of the capacitance charge; that is, $C_2 = C_2(q_2)$. A typical plot of C_2 is shown in Figure 10.28(b). The transformer is assumed to be nonlinear and its equations are written generally as

$$\begin{bmatrix} i_7 \\ i_8 \end{bmatrix} = \begin{bmatrix} \Gamma_7(\lambda_7, \lambda_8) \\ \Gamma_8(\lambda_7, \lambda_8) \end{bmatrix} \tag{10.121}$$

and if we assume that these equations have no inverse, that is, that

$$\begin{bmatrix} \lambda_7 \\ \lambda_8 \end{bmatrix} = \begin{bmatrix} L_7(i_7, i_8) \\ L_8(i_7, i_8) \end{bmatrix}$$

does not exist, then we may use the system graph of Figure 10.27(b). Elements 7 and 8 are chords for the integrating transformer component and element 2 is a branch representing the capacitor.

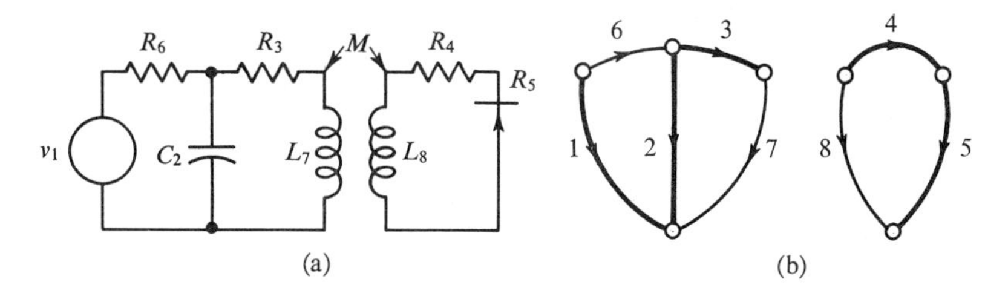

Fig. 10.27. (a) *Nonlinear electrical system;* (b) *system graph.*

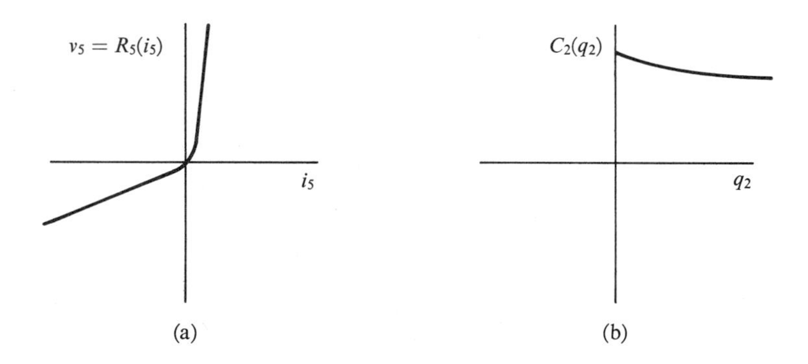

Fig. 10.28. (a) *Diode characteristics;* (b) *varactor characteristics.*

The state equations are easily written using the cutset and circuit equations as

$$\begin{aligned} \dot{q}_2 = i_2 = i_6 - i_7 &= G_6 v_6 - \Gamma_7(\lambda_7, \lambda_8) \\ &= G_6 V_1 - \frac{G_6 q_2}{C_2(q_2)} - \Gamma_7(\lambda_7, \lambda_8) \end{aligned}$$

$$\dot{\lambda}_7 = v_7 = v_2 - v_3 = \frac{q_2}{C_2(q_2)} - R_3\Gamma_7(\lambda_7, \lambda_8)$$
$$\dot{\lambda}_8 = v_8 = v_4 + v_5 = -R_4\Gamma_8(\lambda_7, \lambda_8) - R_5[\Gamma_8(\lambda_7, \lambda_8)] \quad (10.122)$$

Writing these equations in the standard matrix format, we have

$$\dot{\mathbf{x}} = \begin{bmatrix} \dot{q}_2 \\ \dot{\lambda}_7 \\ \dot{\lambda}_8 \end{bmatrix} = \mathbf{f}(\mathbf{x}, V_1)$$

$$= \begin{bmatrix} \dfrac{-G_6 q_2}{C_2(q_2)} - \Gamma_7(\lambda_7, \lambda_8) + G_6 V_1 \\ \dfrac{q_2}{C_2(q_2)} - R_3\Gamma_7(\lambda_7, \lambda_8) \\ -R_4\Gamma_8(\lambda_7, \lambda_8) - R_5[\Gamma_8(\lambda_7, \lambda_8)] \end{bmatrix} \quad (10.123)$$

where Γ_7 and Γ_8 are functions of λ_7 and λ_8, and $R_5[\Gamma_8]$ is a function of Γ_8. A solution of this system obviously requires a computer.

ADDITIONAL READINGS

Harman, W. W., and D. W. Lytle, *Electrical and Mechanical Networks*, New York: McGraw-Hill Book Co., 1962.

Huelsman, L., *Circuits, Matrices, and Linear Vector Spaces*, New York: McGraw-Hill Book Co., 1963.

Koenig, Herman E., and William A. Blackwell, *Electromechanical System Theory*, New York: McGraw-Hill Book Co., 1961.

Koenig, Herman E., Y. Tokad, and H. K. Kesavan, *Discrete Physical Systems*, New York: McGraw-Hill Book Co., 1966.

Kuo, Benjamin C., *Linear Networks and Systems*, New York: McGraw-Hill Book Co., 1967.

Schwarz, R. J., and B. Friedland, *Linear Systems*, New York: McGraw-Hill Book Co., 1965.

Seshu, S., and M. B. Reed, *Linear Graphs and Electrical Networks*, Reading, Mass.: Addison-Wesley Publishing Co., Inc., 1961.

Timothy and Bona, *State Space Analysis—An Introduction*, New York: McGraw-Hill Book Co., 1967.

Van Valkenburg, M. E., *Network Analysis*, 2nd ed., Englewood Cliffs, New Jersey: Prentice-Hall, Inc., 1964.

Zadeh, L. A., and C. A. Desoer, *Linear System Theory*, New York: McGraw-Hill Book Co., 1963.

PROBLEMS

10.1. For the system in Figure P 10.1 formulate a mathematical model and solve the system for the conditions specified.

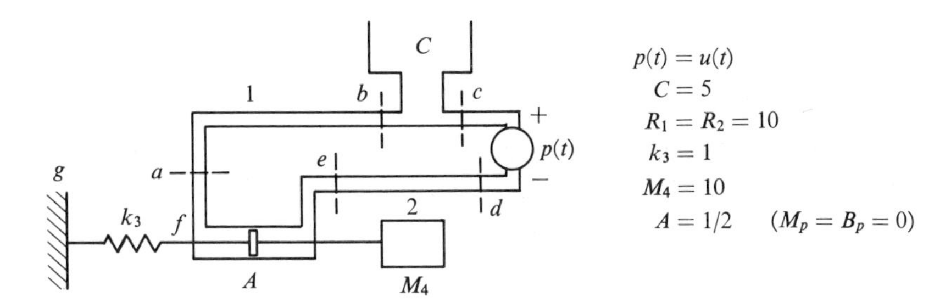

Fig. P 10.1. *Hydromechanical system.*

a) Calculate the transient in the spring displacement.
b) Develop a steady-state relation between the spring displacement and the pressure on the capacitor when $p(t) = 0$.

10.2. Calculate the transfer functions relating V_R to V_1 and I_6 in Figure P 10.2. How many poles do the transfer functions have?

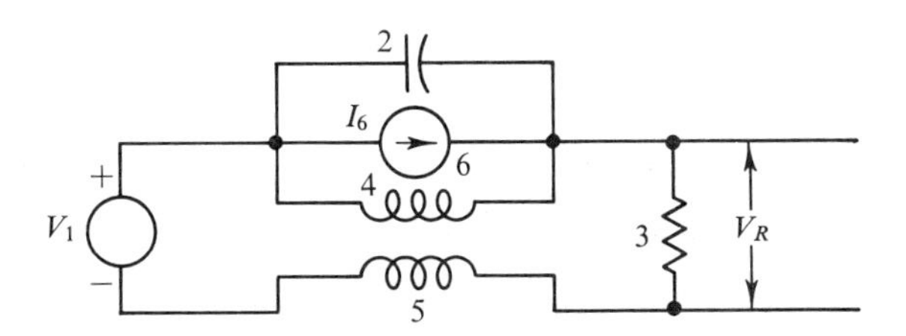

Fig. P 10.2. *Electrical circuit.*

10.3. What would you do in the above problem if the transformer is treated as an ideal transducer?

10.4. Using either branch or chord formulation, determine a transfer function relating δ_5 to $\delta(t)$ in Figure P 10.4.

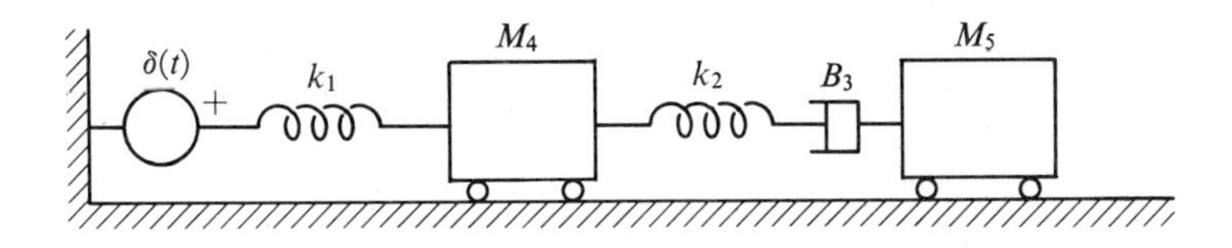

Fig. P 10.4. *Mechanical system.*

10.5. For the electrical network of Figure P 10.5 solve for the transfer function $V_b = G_{ba}(s)V_a$.

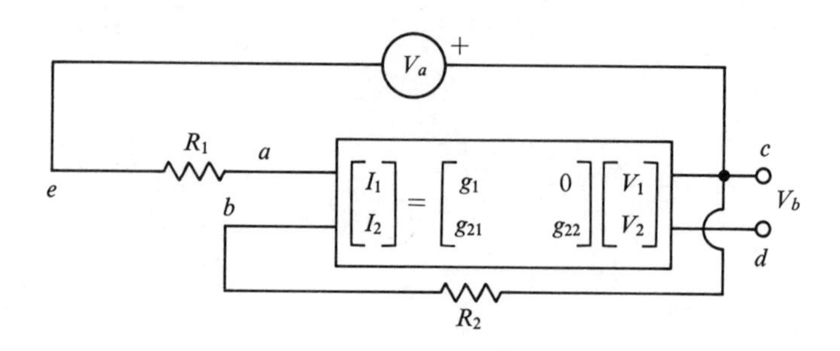

Fig. P 10.5. *Electrical network.*

10.6 a) Derive a terminal representation for the lever system of Figure P 10.6 such that

$$\begin{bmatrix} f_i \\ \delta_o \end{bmatrix} = \begin{bmatrix} & \\ & \end{bmatrix} \begin{bmatrix} \delta_i \\ f_o \end{bmatrix}$$

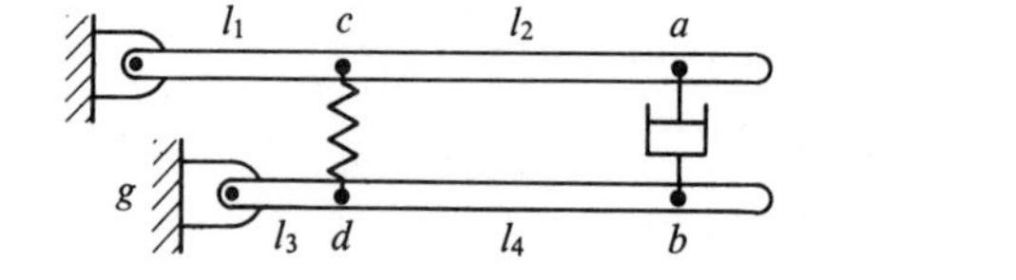

Fig. P 10.6. *Lever system.*

b) Let $\delta_i(t) = u(t)$; find $\delta_o(t)$; and plot.

10.7. Derive a terminal representation for the "flexible" lever of Figure P 10.7 in the form

$$\begin{bmatrix} f_1 \\ f_2 \end{bmatrix} = \begin{bmatrix} & \\ & \end{bmatrix} \begin{bmatrix} \delta_1 \\ \delta_2 \end{bmatrix}$$

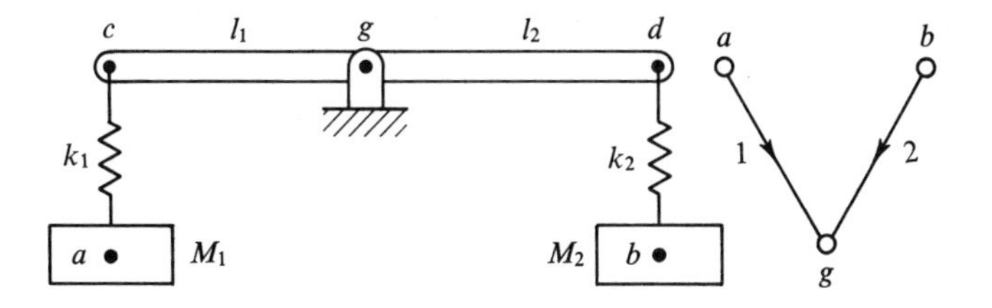

Fig. P 10.7. *Flexible lever.*

Is the component symmetric when $M_1 = M_2$, $k_1 = k_2$, $l_1 = l_2$?

10.8. Let $v_i(t) = \sin \omega t$. Calculate the frequency response of the voltage across the resistor in Figure P 10.8.

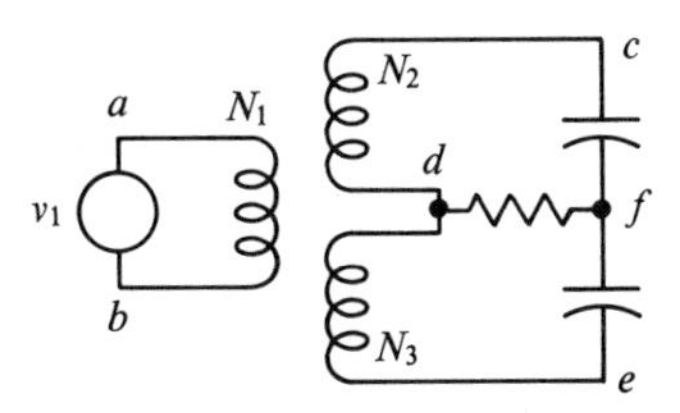

Fig. P 10.8. *An electrical system.*

10.9. The three-terminal component of Figure P 10.9 is a linear model of a vacuum triode. Its terminal equations are given as

$$\begin{bmatrix} i_2 \\ v_3 \end{bmatrix} = \begin{bmatrix} 0 & 0 \\ -\mu & r_p \end{bmatrix} \begin{bmatrix} v_2 \\ i_2 \end{bmatrix}$$

μ = amplification factor, r_p = plate resistance.

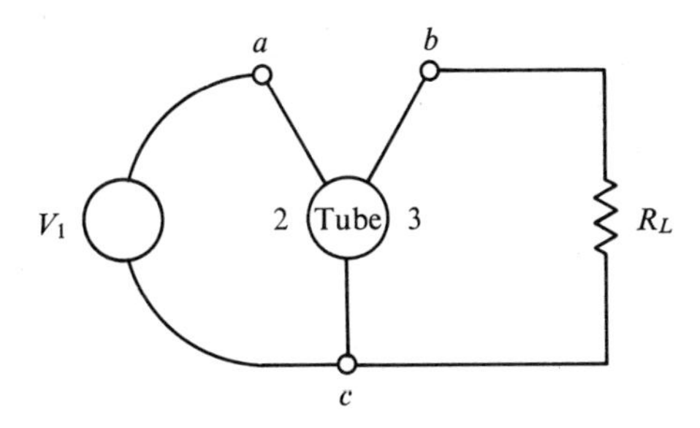

Fig. P 10.9. *Vacuum tube model.*

The electrical network shows the triode employed as an amplifier. Calculate V_{R_L}/V_1; this represents the gain for the tube.

10.10. a) Explain why, in the network of Figure P 10.10, it is improper to assign v_c, i_3, and i_4 as state variables. Define a set of state variables **x** and write a set of independent state equations in normal form.

b) Write the output equation in the form of $\mathbf{c} = \mathbf{Cx} + \mathbf{Dr}$ where

$$\mathbf{x} = \begin{bmatrix} v_c \\ i_3 \\ i_4 \end{bmatrix} \quad \text{and} \quad \mathbf{r} = \begin{bmatrix} v_g \\ i_g \end{bmatrix}$$

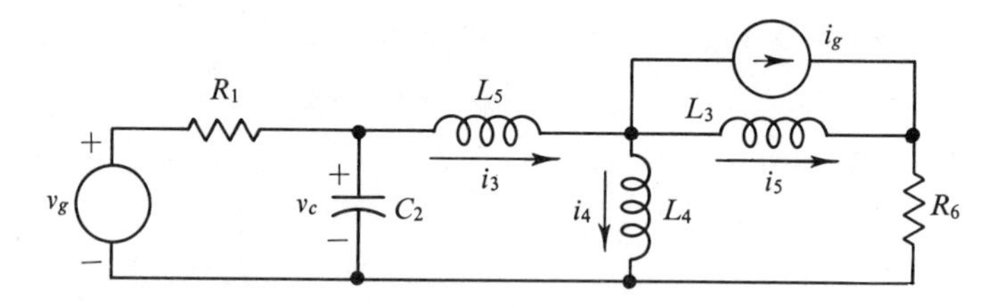

Fig. P 10.10. *An electrical network.*

10.11. Develop the transfer function of output/input for the translational accelerometer sketched in Figure P 10.11 by first finding a system solution using the branch or chord method.

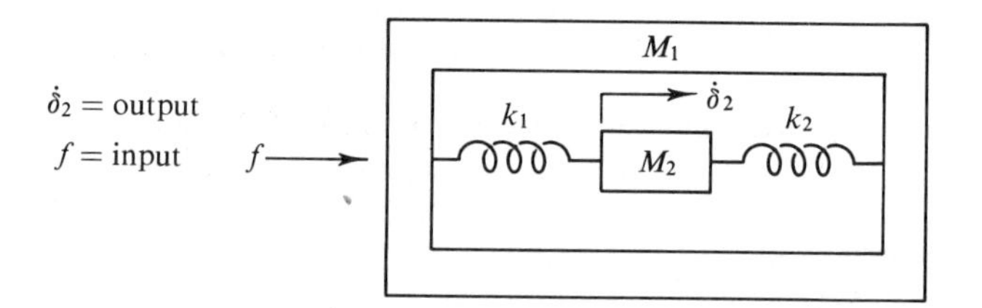

Fig. P 10.11. *Accelerometer.*

10.12. In the transistor amplifier sketched in Figure P 10.12, find the equivalent two-port terminal representation of input and output. Use the branch method and simplify the problem as much as possible first by combining series and parallel impedances.

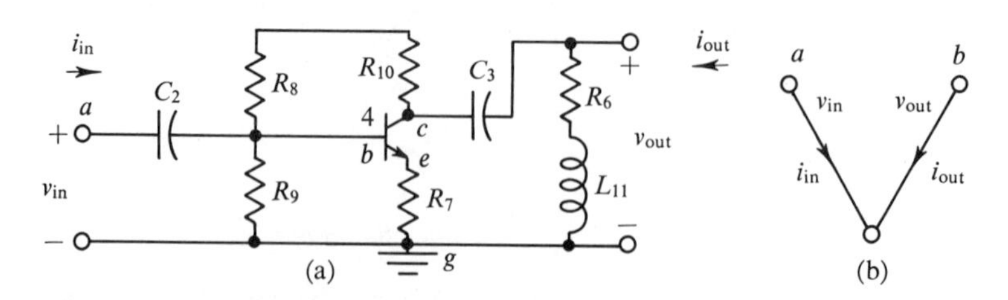

Fig. P 10.12. (a) *Amplifier;* (b) *two-part terminal graph.*

The transistor terminal graph and equations are

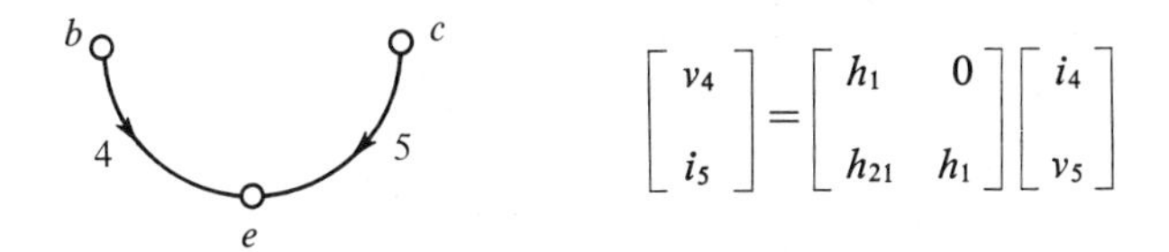

$$\begin{bmatrix} v_4 \\ i_5 \end{bmatrix} = \begin{bmatrix} h_1 & 0 \\ h_{21} & h_1 \end{bmatrix} \begin{bmatrix} i_4 \\ v_5 \end{bmatrix}$$

10.13. In the triode equivalent circuit sketched in Figure P 10.13, find the response of the load voltage v_L to a step change of input voltage v_g. Use node equations.

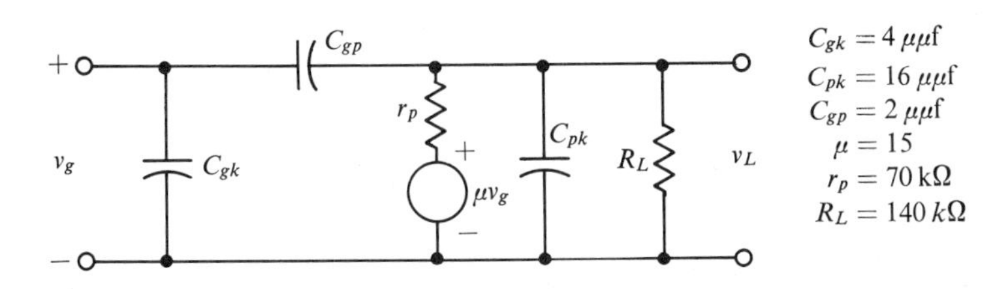

Fig. P 10.13. *Equivalent vacuum tube circuit.*

10.14. a) Draw a system graph of the mechanical system sketched in Figure P 10.14.

b) Simplify by combining components in parallel and draw a new system graph.

c) If $\dot{\delta}$ is a velocity source and f is a force source, find the velocity of m_1 in terms of $\dot{\delta}$ and f in the s-domain.

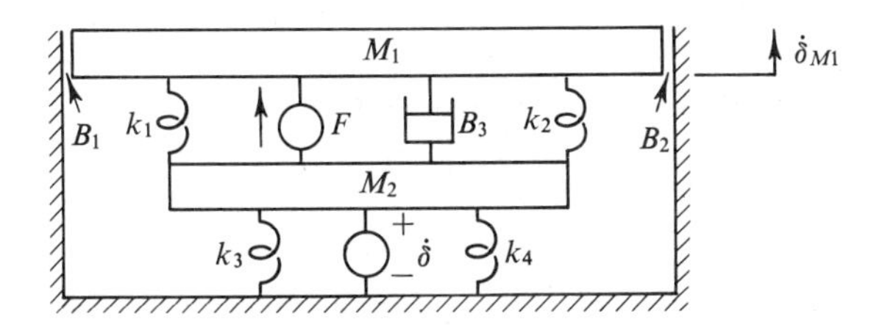

Fig. P 10.14. *A mechanical system.*

10.15. For the system of Figure P 10.15, write a set of state equations. Find a solution in the s-domain for the velocity of M_1. What is the impedance, in the s-domain, seen by the force source?

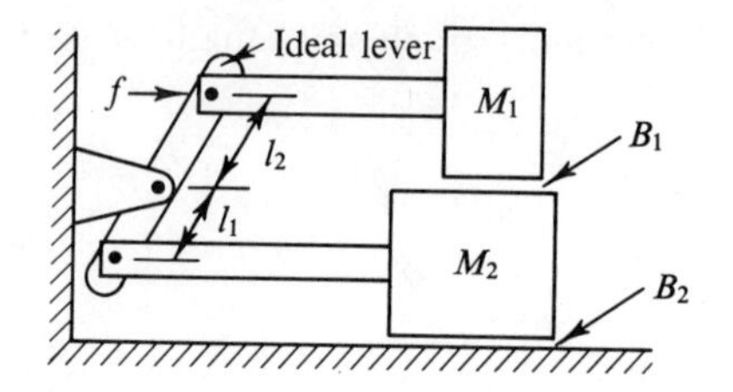

Fig. P 10.15. *Mechanical system.*

10.16. Find a set of equations in matrix form that models the system shown in Figure P 10.16 by using either the chord or branch method of analysis.

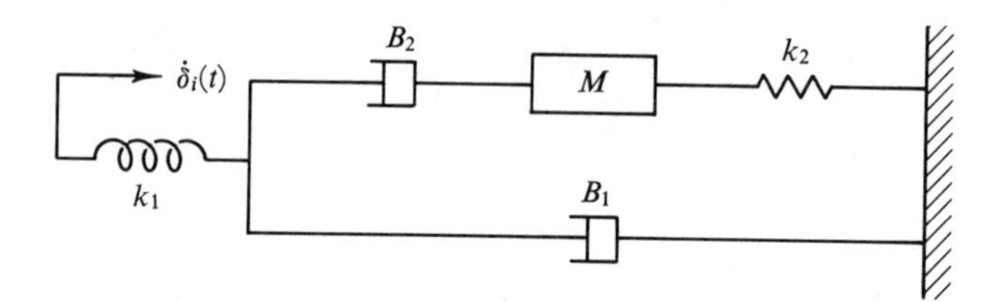

Fig. P 10.16. *A mechanical system.*

10.17. If, in Problem 10.16, the velocity of the mass is the system output, find the output-to-input transfer function.

10.18. Derive a set of state equations for the simple pendulum using the angular momentum of the pendulum mass and the deflection angle as state variables.

10.19. For the oscillator circuit of Figure P 10.19(a) the common cathode terminal equations of the triode are shown in Figure 10.19(b)

a) Draw a system graph.
b) Derive a set of state equations.

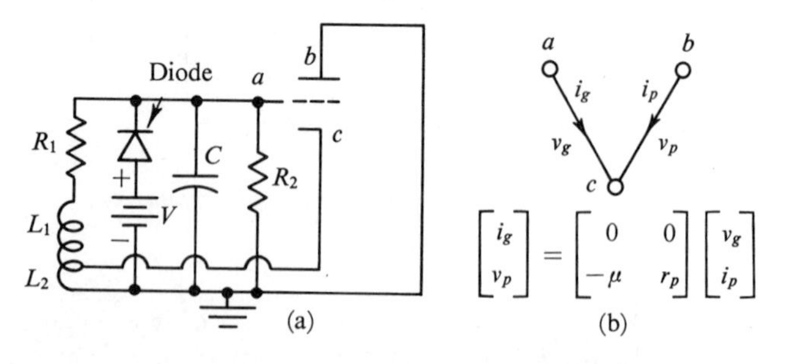

Fig. P 10.19. (a) *Oscillator circuit;* (b) *triode equations.*

10.20. A spinning gyroscope rotor shown in Figure P 10.20 can be considered a four-terminal component whose equations are

$$\begin{bmatrix} \tau_x \\ \tau_y \end{bmatrix} = \begin{bmatrix} I\frac{d}{dt} & J\dot{\varphi}_z \\ -J\dot{\varphi}_z & I\frac{d}{dt} \end{bmatrix} \begin{bmatrix} \dot{\varphi}_x \\ \dot{\varphi}_y \end{bmatrix}$$

where I = moment of inertia about the x or y axis and J = moment of inertia about the z axis

a) Find the transfer functions

$$\frac{\dot{\Phi}_x}{\mathrm{T}_x}(s) \quad \text{and} \quad \frac{\dot{\Phi}_y}{\mathrm{T}_x}(s)$$

if $\dot{\varphi}_z$ = a constant.

b) Let $\tau_y(t) = 0$ and $\tau_x(t)$ be a unit step function. Find the drift rates $\dot{\varphi}_x(t)$ and $\dot{\varphi}_y(t)$ for $t > 0$.

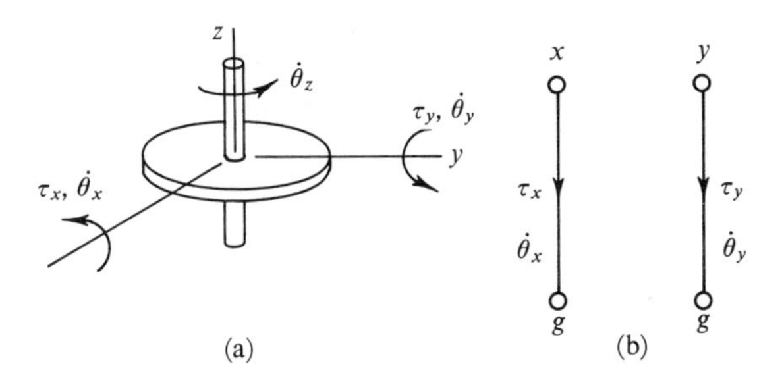

Fig. P 10.20. (a) *Gyroscope;* (b) *system graph.*

10.21. If the z-axis of the gyroscope of Problem 10.20 is constrained by equal springs about the x and y axes, derive a set of state equations for the system if the inputs are angular velocities about the x and y axes and the outputs are the spring displacements.

Analysis of Large-Scale Systems

11

The preceding chapters present general procedures for the formulation and solution of a variety of linear systems. To be useful, the mathematical model developed during the formulation stage has to be an acceptable representation of the physical characteristics of the system; at the same time, it must be amenable to solution.

Formulation techniques such as mesh, node, state variable, branch, and chord formulation are successful in a broad range of problems, and they are usually conveniently applied. However, it has become evident that as the order of the system gets large, increasing difficulty is encountered with the large bulk of equations required during the formulation process. In this chapter alternate approaches, particularly designed for the analysis of large-scale systems, will be investigated.

Consistent with these considerations, there are two feasible processes of formulation: (a) s-domain models and (b) state models. These approaches are well established, both in the methods of developing the equation and in the ensuing solution process. While the s-domain approach is limited to systems which can be represented by linear or piecewise linear equations only, the state variable approach is open to both linear and general nonlinear equations. Analytical solution methods are available for the processing of linear mathematical models, while usually only computers are capable of processing nonlinear models.

One of the most effective ways to reduce the complexity of formulating large scale systems is the breakdown of the large system into smaller subassemblies, each one of which is modeled as a multiterminal component. The overall systems model may then be obtained by the subsequent recombination of the subassemblies. The derivation of equations representative of subassemblies was studied in Chapters 8 and 10. Let us consider now the techniques of combining multiterminal components. Basic to this approach are a number of interconnection patterns which frequently occur. Although our main interest lies in procedures relating to two-port components, we will see by employment of appropriately chosen examples that extensions to other components are readily made.

In the study of component interconnections we distinguish between these four modes:

1. Parallel
2. Series
3. Cascade
4. Series-Parallel

11.1 Parallel Connection of Two-Ports

A parallel connection of two components is shown schematically in Figure 11.1. The terminals of A are connected in a one-to-one correspondence to the terminals of component B. From the system graph of Figure 11.2 we write the following equations relating the variables

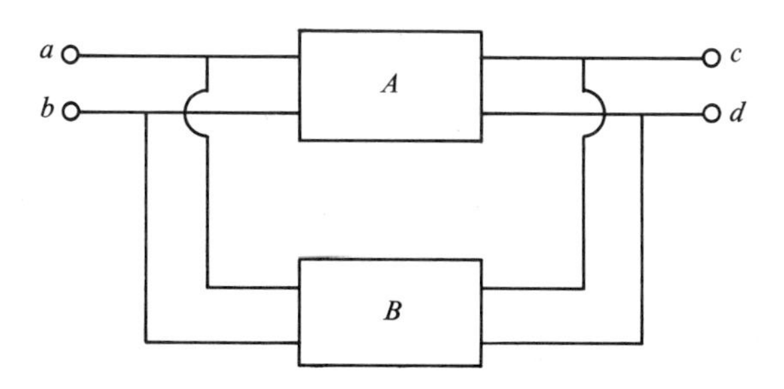

Fig. 11.1. *Parallel connection.*

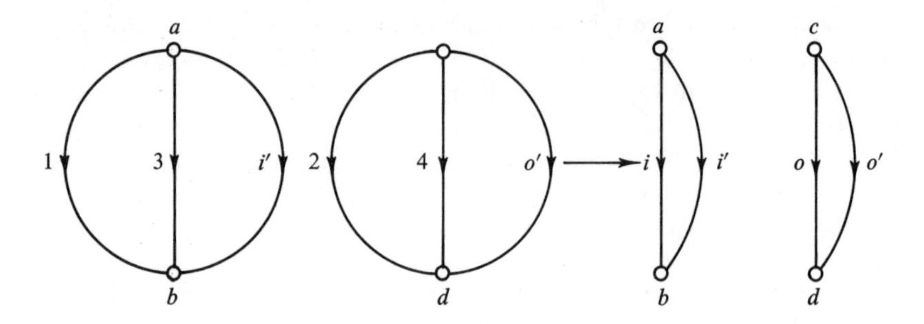

Fig. 11.2. (a) *System graph of interconnection components with augmented drivers;* (b) *equivalent terminal graph.*

of the combined representation to the terminal variables of the two components:

$$\left. \begin{aligned} y_i &= -y_i' = y_1 + y_3 \\ y_o &= -y_o' = y_2 + y_4 \end{aligned} \right\} \tag{11.1}$$

and

$$\left. \begin{aligned} x_i &= x_1 = x_3 \\ x_o &= x_2 = x_4 \end{aligned} \right\} \tag{11.2}$$

Equations 11.1 indicate that the through variables of the components are added, while Equations 11.2 indicate equality between the across variables. To perform the algebraic operations indicated by these equations, it is required that the component equations be available in terms of short-circuit parameters. Therefore, for component A,

$$\begin{bmatrix} y_1 \\ y_2 \end{bmatrix} = \begin{bmatrix} w_1 & w_{12} \\ w_{21} & w_2 \end{bmatrix} \begin{bmatrix} x_1 \\ x_2 \end{bmatrix} \tag{11.3}$$

For component B,

$$\begin{bmatrix} y_3 \\ y_4 \end{bmatrix} = \begin{bmatrix} w_3 & w_{34} \\ w_{43} & w_4 \end{bmatrix} \begin{bmatrix} x_3 \\ x_4 \end{bmatrix} \tag{11.4}$$

We now substitute the component equations into Equations 11.1,

$$\begin{bmatrix} y_i' \\ y_o' \end{bmatrix} = -\begin{bmatrix} w_1 & w_3 & w_{12} & w_{34} \\ w_{21} & w_{43} & w_2 & w_4 \end{bmatrix} \begin{bmatrix} x_1 \\ x_3 \\ x_2 \\ x_4 \end{bmatrix}$$

Using Equations 11.2 and the relation between the augmenting drivers and final terminal variables yields the final equations.

$$\begin{bmatrix} y_i \\ y_o \end{bmatrix} = \begin{bmatrix} w_1 + w_3 & w_{12} + w_{34} \\ w_{21} + w_{43} & w_2 + w_4 \end{bmatrix} \begin{bmatrix} x_i \\ x_o \end{bmatrix} \tag{11.5}$$

It is readily recognized that a parallel combination requires the addition of the admittance matrices of the individual components.

Example 11.1. Combine the two components of Figure 11.3 by means of a parallel combination.

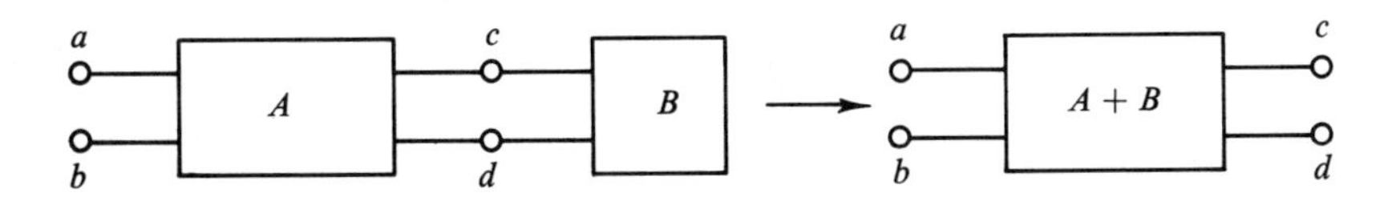

Fig. 11.3. *Paralleling of a two-port with a one-port component.*

Although component B is only a one-port, it may be viewed as a two-port. Let the component equation of B be

$$y_b = wx_b$$

To convert B into a two-port component we add two blank terminals as shown in Figure 11.4.

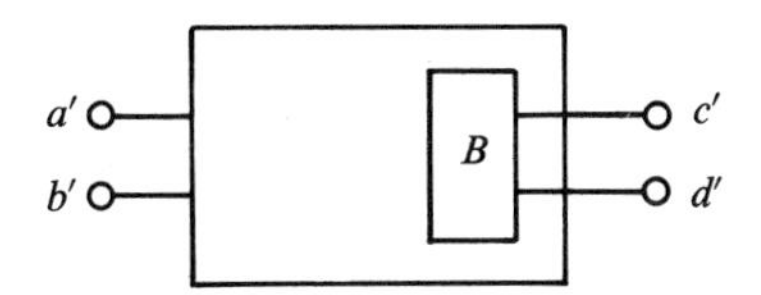

Fig. 11.4. *A one-port viewed as a two-port.*

The corresponding terminal equations are readily established as

$$\begin{bmatrix} y_3 \\ y_4 \end{bmatrix} = \begin{bmatrix} 0 & 0 \\ 0 & w \end{bmatrix} \begin{bmatrix} x_3 \\ x_4 \end{bmatrix}$$

If the component equations for A are as given by Equation 11.3, then the parallel combination of A and B yields

$$\begin{bmatrix} y_i \\ y_o \end{bmatrix} = \begin{bmatrix} w_1 & w_{12} \\ w_{21} & w_2 + w \end{bmatrix} \begin{bmatrix} x_i \\ x_o \end{bmatrix}$$

Example 11.2. Consider the connection of a mechanical load characterized by

$$\tau_L = \left(B_L + J_L \frac{d}{dt}\right)\dot{\varphi}_L$$

to an electromechanical transducer characterized by

$$\begin{bmatrix} v_a \\ \tau_m \end{bmatrix} = \begin{bmatrix} R_a + L_a \frac{d}{dt} & k_m \\ -k_m & B_m + J_m \frac{d}{dt} \end{bmatrix} \begin{bmatrix} i_a \\ \dot{\varphi}_m \end{bmatrix}$$

according to the schematic of Figure 11.5. In order to utilize the above pro-

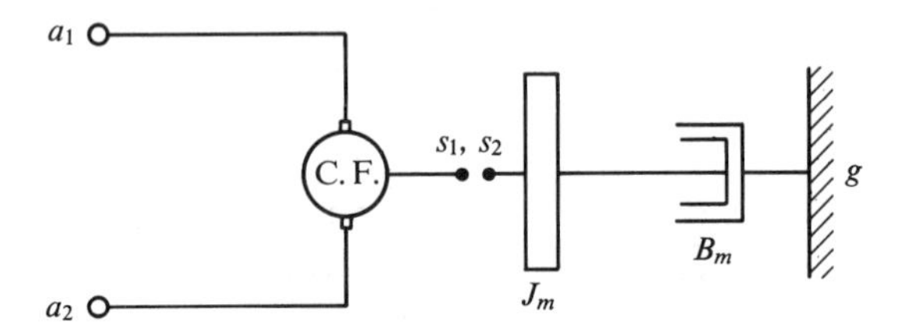

Fig. 11.5. *Electromechanical transducer connected to a load.*

cedures, we would expand the load into a two-port, invert the top equation of the transducer to put it into short-circuit form, and add the resulting matrices. However, since the entries of the first matrix are all zero except for the (2, 2) entry, there is no need to reformulate the transducer equations. We may proceed immediately with the present equations and obtain

$$\begin{bmatrix} v_i \\ \tau_0 \end{bmatrix} = \begin{bmatrix} R_a + L_a \frac{d}{dt}n & k_m \\ -k_m & B_m + B_L + (J_m + J_L)\frac{d}{dt} \end{bmatrix} \begin{bmatrix} i_i \\ \dot{\varphi}_o \end{bmatrix}$$

11.2 Series Connection of Two-Ports

Figure 11.6 shows the schematic of a series connection of two two-port components. It is the objective here to derive an equivalent representation according to the terminal graph of Figure 11.7. The derivation is identical in principle except for the fact that the roles of the across and through variables are interchanged. From the system graph of Figure 11.7 we have

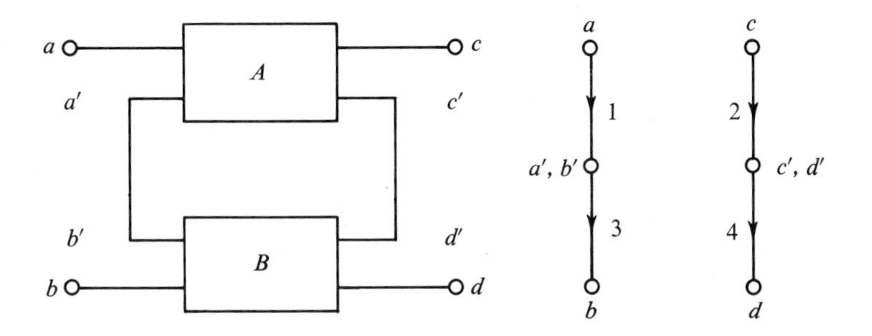

Fig. 11.6. *Series connection of two-ports.*

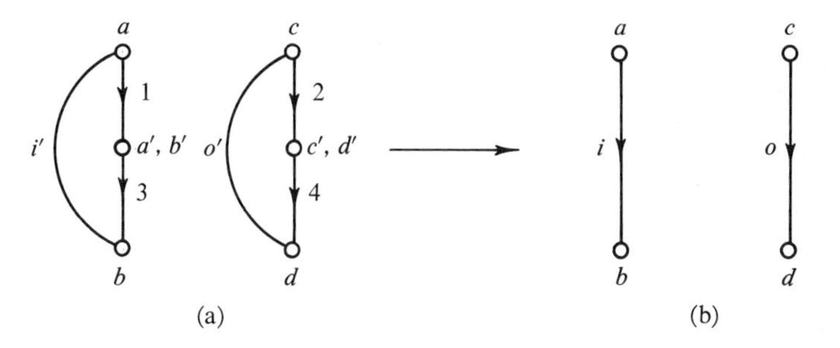

Fig. 11.7. (a) *System graph of series connection with augmenting drivers;* (b) *resultant terminal graph.*

$$\begin{aligned} x_i &= x_i' = x_1 + x_3 \\ x_o &= x_o' = x_2 + x_4 \end{aligned} \tag{11.6}$$

also

$$\begin{aligned} y_i &= -y_i' = y_1 = y_3 \\ y_o &= -y_o' = y_2 = y_4 \end{aligned} \tag{11.7}$$

Since Equations 11.6 require a summation of across variables, we write the terminal equations for the two components in terms of the open-circuit parameters. Component A:

$$\begin{bmatrix} x_1 \\ x_2 \end{bmatrix} \begin{bmatrix} z_1 & z_{12} \\ z_{21} & z_2 \end{bmatrix} \begin{bmatrix} y_1 \\ y_2 \end{bmatrix} \tag{11.8}$$

Component B:

$$\begin{bmatrix} x_3 \\ x_4 \end{bmatrix} = \begin{bmatrix} z_3 & z_{34} \\ z_{43} & z_4 \end{bmatrix} \begin{bmatrix} y_3 \\ y_4 \end{bmatrix} \tag{11.9}$$

We substitute Equations 11.8 and 11.9 into Equations 11.6 and, using Equations 11.7, obtain

$$\begin{bmatrix} x_i \\ x_o \end{bmatrix} = \begin{bmatrix} z_1 + z_3 & z_{12} + z_{34} \\ z_{21} + z_{43} & z_2 + z_4 \end{bmatrix} \begin{bmatrix} y_i \\ y_o \end{bmatrix} \quad \textbf{(11.10)}$$

Thus a series combination is obtained by the summation of the impedance matrices.

Example 11.3. Figure 11.8 shows two vacuum tubes connected in series. Let the small-signal approximations of the components be given as

$$\begin{bmatrix} i_1 \\ v_2 \end{bmatrix} = \begin{bmatrix} 0 & 0 \\ -\mu & r_p \end{bmatrix} \begin{bmatrix} v_1 \\ i_2 \end{bmatrix}$$

and

$$\begin{bmatrix} i_3 \\ v_4 \end{bmatrix} = \begin{bmatrix} 0 & 0 \\ -\mu & r_p \end{bmatrix} \begin{bmatrix} v_3 \\ i_4 \end{bmatrix}$$

Although the form of the equations is not the open-circuit parameter form, we may still apply the rule of adding the respective matrices in order to form the desired equivalent combination because all input currents are zero. The result, therefore, is

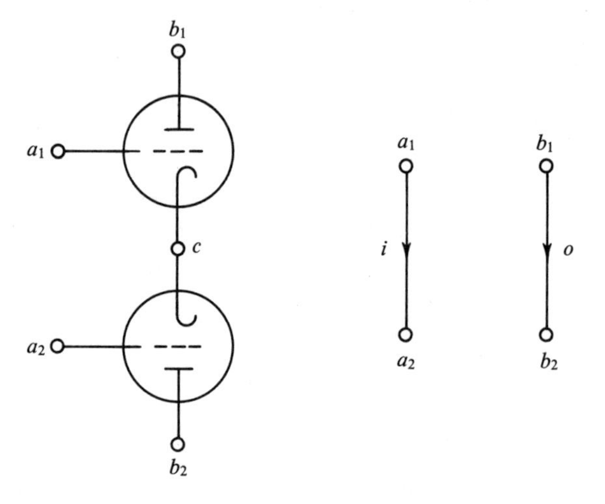

Fig. 11.8. *Series connected vacuum tubes and equivalent terminal graph.*

$$\begin{bmatrix} i_i \\ v_o \end{bmatrix} = \begin{bmatrix} 0 & 0 \\ -2\mu & 2r_p \end{bmatrix} \begin{bmatrix} v_i \\ i_o \end{bmatrix}$$

11.3 Cascade Connection of Components

Two two-port components are said to be connected in cascade if they are connected as shown in Figure 11.9. It is our objective to combine the terminal equations of the two components so that a new two-port

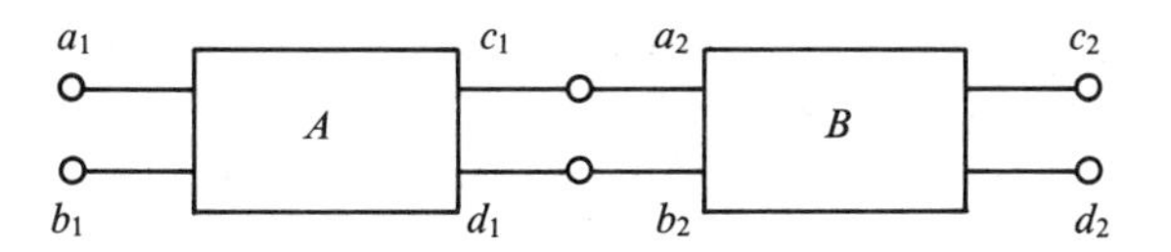

Fig. 11.9. *Cascade connection of components.*

component is formed retaining terminals a_1-b_1 and c_2-d_2. The interconnection of the components imposes the constraints

$$x_2 - x_3 = 0 \tag{11.11a}$$

and

$$y_2 + y_3 = 0 \tag{11.11b}$$

where the subscripts 2 and 3 denote the output port of component A and the input port of component B, respectively. We will investigate procedures which will apply to both s-domain and state equation models.

Cascading of s-Domain Models

If the s-domain models are available in a form such that the second equation of the first component and the first equation of the second component are explicit in either an across variable or a through variable, then Equations 11.11 may be conveniently applied. When these conditions are met, the cascading process is straightforward. The following component models illustrate the procedure. Component A:

$$\begin{bmatrix} X_1 \\ Y_2 \end{bmatrix} = \begin{bmatrix} H_1 & H_{12} \\ H_{21} & H_2 \end{bmatrix} \begin{bmatrix} Y_1 \\ X_2 \end{bmatrix} \tag{11.12}$$

Component B:

$$\begin{bmatrix} Y_3 \\ Y_4 \end{bmatrix} = \begin{bmatrix} W_{33} & W_{34} \\ W_{43} & W_{44} \end{bmatrix} \begin{bmatrix} X_3 \\ X_4 \end{bmatrix} \tag{11.13}$$

Using Equations 11.11b, we have

$$Y_2 + Y_3 = H_{21}Y_1 + H_2X_2 + W_{33}X_3 + W_{34}X_4 = 0$$

Using Equation 11.11a, this equation simplifies to

$$0 = H_{21}Y_1 + (H_2 + W_{33})X_2 + Y_{34}X_4$$

Solving for X_2,

$$X_2 = X_3 = -\frac{1}{H_2 + W_{33}}(H_{21}Y_1 + W_{34}X_4) \tag{11.14}$$

Notice that X_2 and X_3 are equal in this process, and in Equation 11.14 are only a function of Y_1 and X_4, which will be part of the set of terminal variables of the equivalent representation. Substituting Equation 11.14 into the top equation of Equations 11.12 and the bottom equation of Equations 11.13 yields

$$X_1 = H_1 Y_1 + H_{12}\left(-\frac{H_{21}}{H_2 + W_{33}} Y_1 - \frac{W_{34}}{H_2 + W_{33}} X_4\right)$$

and

$$Y_4 = W_{43}\left(-\frac{H_{21}}{H_2 + W_{33}} Y_1 - \frac{W_{34}}{H_2 + W_{33}} X_4\right) + W_{44} X_4$$

This we simplify and write in matrix form:

$$\begin{bmatrix} X_1 \\ Y_4 \end{bmatrix} = \begin{bmatrix} H_1 - \dfrac{H_{12} H_{12}}{H_2 + W_{33}} & -\dfrac{H_{12} W_{34}}{H_2 + W_{33}} \\ -\dfrac{H_{21} W_{43}}{H_2 + W_{33}} & Y_{44} - \dfrac{W_{34} W_{43}}{H_2 + W_{33}} \end{bmatrix} \begin{bmatrix} Y_1 \\ X_4 \end{bmatrix} \qquad \textbf{(11.15)}$$

This procedure applies equally to all other forms of component models, that is, open-circuit, short-circuit, and hybrid parameter, provided that the constraint Equations 11.11 may be applied to the second and third of the component equations.

Example 11.4. Two dc machines are connected as shown in Figure 11.10. One is operated as an electromechanical amplifier, while the second is used as a transducer, such that their armature windings are connected back-to-back. This subassembly is used very frequently as a speed control system, and is called a Ward-Leonard system.

The component equations are obtained from Equations 8.137 and 8.138, given here as s-domain models.

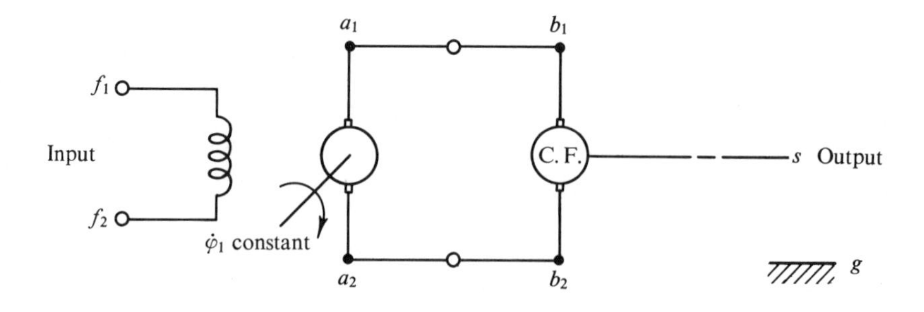

Fig. 11.10. *Ward-Leonard system.*

First machine:

$$\begin{bmatrix} V_f \\ V_a \end{bmatrix} = \begin{bmatrix} R_f + L_f s & 0 \\ k_{mg}\dot{\Phi}_1 & R_a + L_a s \end{bmatrix} \begin{bmatrix} I_f \\ I_a \end{bmatrix}$$

Second machine:

$$\begin{bmatrix} V_b \\ \tau_m \end{bmatrix} = \begin{bmatrix} R_b + L_b s & k_{mg} I_{f_2} \\ -k_{mg} I_{f_2} & B + Js \end{bmatrix} \begin{bmatrix} I_b \\ \dot{\Phi}_m \end{bmatrix}$$

For simplicity, we assume the machines to be identical.

The armature voltage and currents are related by

$$V_a - V_b = 0$$

and

$$I_a = -I_b$$

Therefore

$$0 = k_{mg}\dot{\Phi}_1 I_f + 2(R + Ls) I_a - k_{mg} I_{f_2} \dot{\Phi}_m$$

from which

$$I_a = -I_b = \frac{1}{Z(s)}(-k_{mg}\dot{\Phi}_1 I_f + k_{mg} I_{f_2} \dot{\Phi}_m)$$

where

$$Z(s) = 2(R + Ls)$$

Combining the last expression with the component equations yields

$$\begin{bmatrix} V_f \\ \tau_m \end{bmatrix} = \begin{bmatrix} R_f + L_f s & 0 \\ -\dfrac{k_{mg}^2 I_{f_2} \dot{\Phi}_1}{Z(s)} & Js + B + \dfrac{k_{mg}^2 I^2{}_{f2}}{Z(s)} \end{bmatrix} \begin{bmatrix} I_f \\ \dot{\Phi}_m \end{bmatrix}$$

Example 11.5. Derive the characteristics of a hydraulic transformer by viewing it as a cascade combination of two components as indicated schematically in Figure 11.11.

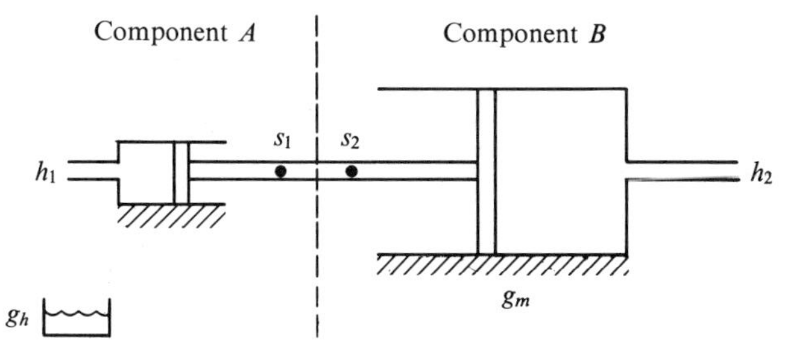

Fig. 11.11. *The hydraulic transformer as a cascade combination.*

The component models follow. Component A:

$$\begin{bmatrix} \dot{G}_1 \\ F_2 \end{bmatrix} = \begin{bmatrix} 0 & A_1 \\ -A_1 & M_1 s + B \end{bmatrix} \begin{bmatrix} P_1 \\ \dot{\Delta}_2 \end{bmatrix}$$

Component B:

$$\begin{bmatrix} F_3 \\ \dot{G}_4 \end{bmatrix} = \begin{bmatrix} M_2 s + B_2 & +A_2 \\ -A_2 & 0 \end{bmatrix} \begin{bmatrix} \dot{\Delta}_3 \\ P_4 \end{bmatrix}$$

Notice that B is the left-hand version of A.

We have

$$F_2 + F_3 = 0 \qquad \text{and} \qquad \dot{\Delta}_2 = \dot{\Delta}_3$$

Therefore

$$0 = -A_1 P_1 + [(M_1 + M_2)s + B_1 + B_2]\dot{\Delta}_2 + A_2 P_4$$

or

$$\dot{\Delta}_2 = \frac{1}{Y(s)}(A_1 P_1 - A_2 P_4)$$

Finally,

$$\begin{bmatrix} \dot{G}_1 \\ \dot{G}_4 \end{bmatrix} = \begin{bmatrix} A_1^2/Y(s) & -A_1 A_2/Y(s) \\ -A_1 A_2/Y(s) & A_2^2/Y(s) \end{bmatrix} \begin{bmatrix} P_1 \\ P_4 \end{bmatrix}$$

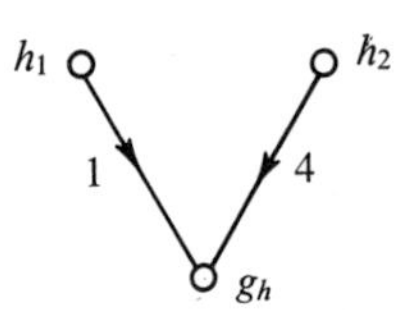

or in hybrid parameter form,

$$\begin{bmatrix} \dot{G}_1 \\ P_4 \end{bmatrix} \begin{bmatrix} 0 & -A_1/A_2 \\ A_1/A_2 & Y(s)/A_2^2 \end{bmatrix} \begin{bmatrix} P_1 \\ \dot{G}_4 \end{bmatrix}$$

where

$$Y(s) = (M_1 + M_2)s + B_1 + B_2$$

The reader should verify that these equations agree with Equations 8.59 through 8.61.

It is appropriate to consider three special cases in cascade connections because of their frequent occurrence.

1. Cascading of two unilateral components. Let the component equations be given as follows. Component A:

$$\begin{bmatrix} Y_1 \\ X_2 \end{bmatrix} = \begin{bmatrix} G_1 & 0 \\ G_{21} & G_2 \end{bmatrix} \begin{bmatrix} X_1 \\ Y_2 \end{bmatrix} \tag{11.16}$$

Component B:

$$\begin{bmatrix} Y_3 \\ X_4 \end{bmatrix} = \begin{bmatrix} G_3 & 0 \\ G_{43} & G_4 \end{bmatrix} \begin{bmatrix} X_3 \\ Y_4 \end{bmatrix} \tag{11.17}$$

The zero in the (1, 2) position of the matrices is characteristic of unilateral components. The equivalent system characteristics are easily derived and are

$$\begin{bmatrix} Y_1 \\ X_4 \end{bmatrix} = \begin{bmatrix} G_1 & 0 \\ \dfrac{G_{43}G_{21}}{1 + G_2G_3} & G_4 \end{bmatrix} \begin{bmatrix} X_1 \\ Y_4 \end{bmatrix} \tag{11.18}$$

2. Cascading of two ideal unilateral components. Let the components be described by the equations

$$\begin{bmatrix} Y_1 \\ X_2 \end{bmatrix} = \begin{bmatrix} 0 & 0 \\ G_{21} & G_2 \end{bmatrix} \begin{bmatrix} X_1 \\ Y_2 \end{bmatrix} \tag{11.19}$$

$$\begin{bmatrix} Y_3 \\ X_4 \end{bmatrix} = \begin{bmatrix} 0 & 0 \\ G_{43} & G_4 \end{bmatrix} \begin{bmatrix} X_3 \\ Y_4 \end{bmatrix} \tag{11.20}$$

By use of Equation 11.18 we obtain immediately

$$\begin{bmatrix} Y_1 \\ X_4 \end{bmatrix} = \begin{bmatrix} 0 & 0 \\ G_{21}G_{43} & G_4 \end{bmatrix} \begin{bmatrix} X_1 \\ Y_4 \end{bmatrix} \tag{11.21}$$

The functions G_{21} and G_{43} represent the transfer functions of the ideal unilateral components. Under no-load conditions they completely characterize input-output relations. Since the two components do not load one another, Equations 11.21 show the product of the two transfer functions when they are connected in cascade. This is a simple result; it is of considerable consequence in the analysis of control systems.

3. Cascading of any two-port with an ideal transducer. An ideal transducer is characterized by the model

$$\begin{bmatrix} Y_3 \\ X_4 \end{bmatrix} = \begin{bmatrix} 0 & -G_{34} \\ G_{34} & 0 \end{bmatrix} \begin{bmatrix} X_3 \\ Y_4 \end{bmatrix} \tag{11.22}$$

It is connected to another two-port component with the equations

$$\begin{bmatrix} Y_1 \\ X_2 \end{bmatrix} = \begin{bmatrix} G_1 & G_{12} \\ G_{21} & G_2 \end{bmatrix} \begin{bmatrix} X_1 \\ Y_2 \end{bmatrix} \tag{11.23}$$

The two components are connected as usual such that

$$X_2 = X_3 \tag{11.24}$$

and

$$Y_2 + Y_3 = 0 \tag{11.25}$$

We proceed as follows. From Equation 11.22 we have

$$Y_3 = -G_{34} Y_4$$

and

$$X_3 = 1/G_{34}X_4$$

Using Equation 11.24 and 11.25,

$$Y_2 = -Y_3 = G_{34} Y_4$$

and

$$X_2 = X_3 = 1/G_{34}X_4$$

and substituting into Equation 11.23 yields

$$\begin{bmatrix} Y_1 \\ 1/G_{34}X_4 \end{bmatrix} = \begin{bmatrix} G_1 & G_{12} \\ G_{21} & G_2 \end{bmatrix} \begin{bmatrix} X_1 \\ H_{34}Y_4 \end{bmatrix}$$

This simplifies to

$$\begin{bmatrix} Y_1 \\ X_4 \end{bmatrix} = \begin{bmatrix} G_1 & G_{34}G_{12} \\ G_{34}G_{21} & G_{34}^2 G_2 \end{bmatrix} \begin{bmatrix} X_1 \\ X_4 \end{bmatrix} \tag{11.26}$$

Example 11.6. Derive the terminal equation of the subassembly shown schematically in Figure 11.12 showing a hydraulic motor connected to a gear box.

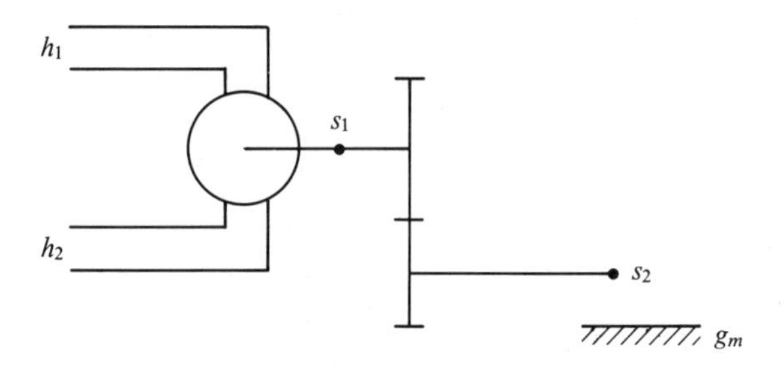

Fig. 11.12. *Hydraulic motor and gearbox.*

We will treat the gear box as an ideal transducer. The terminal equations of the motor are

$$\begin{bmatrix} \dot{G}_1 \\ T_2 \end{bmatrix} = \begin{bmatrix} 0 & V \\ -V & J_m s + B_m \end{bmatrix} \begin{bmatrix} P_1 \\ \dot{\Phi}_2 \end{bmatrix}$$

h_1, 1, h_2; s_1, 2, g_m

where V is volumetric displacement of the motor. For the gearbox we have

$$\begin{bmatrix} T_3 \\ \dot{\Phi}_4 \end{bmatrix} = \begin{bmatrix} 0 & -n \\ n & 0 \end{bmatrix} \begin{bmatrix} \dot{\Phi}_3 \\ T_4 \end{bmatrix}$$

s_1, s_2, 3, 4, g_m

Substituting the last equations into the former by the methods of Equations 11.24 through 11.26, we obtain

$$\begin{bmatrix} \dot{G}_1 \\ nT_4 \end{bmatrix} = \begin{bmatrix} 0 & V \\ -V & J_m s + B_m \end{bmatrix} \begin{bmatrix} P_1 \\ \frac{1}{n}\dot{\Phi}_4 \end{bmatrix}$$

or

$$\begin{bmatrix} G_1 \\ T_4 \end{bmatrix} = \begin{bmatrix} 0 & \frac{1}{n}V \\ -\frac{1}{n}V & \frac{1}{n^2}(J_m s + B_m) \end{bmatrix} \begin{bmatrix} P_1 \\ \dot{\Phi}_4 \end{bmatrix}$$

11.4 Series-Parallel Connection of Two-Ports

A series-parallel connection of two two-ports is described by Figure 11.13. It shows that the components are connected in series on one side and in parallel on the other. It is possible to connect components A and B, which are oriented with respect to input and output ports as shown in Figure 11.14. The first part shows both components in " feedforward " connection, while the second part shows A in feed-forward and B in " feedback " connection.

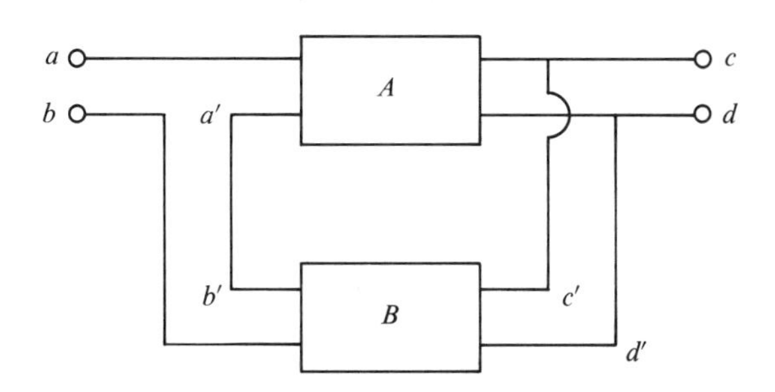

Fig. 11.13. *Series-parallel connection.*

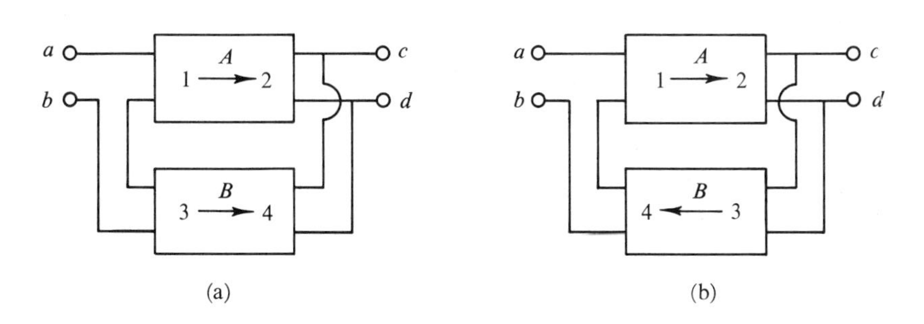

Fig. 11.14. *Series-parallel connections with* (a) *B in feedforward and* (b) *B in feedback connection.*

The equations for the feedback connection will be developed, and the investigation of the other case left to the reader.

As in the previous developments, we rely on the system graph corresponding to the connection of Figure 11.14(b) to guide us in the development. It is shown in Figure 11.15. Augmenting drivers corresponding to elements i' and o' are provided to derive the equivalent representation. From the system graph we have the equations

$$X_i = X_{i'} = X_1 + X_4 \tag{11.27}$$

$$Y_i = -Y_{i'} = Y_1 = Y_4 \tag{11.28}$$

and

$$Y_o = -Y_{o'} = Y_2 + Y_3 \tag{11.29}$$

$$X_o = X_{o'} = X_2 = X_3 \tag{11.30}$$

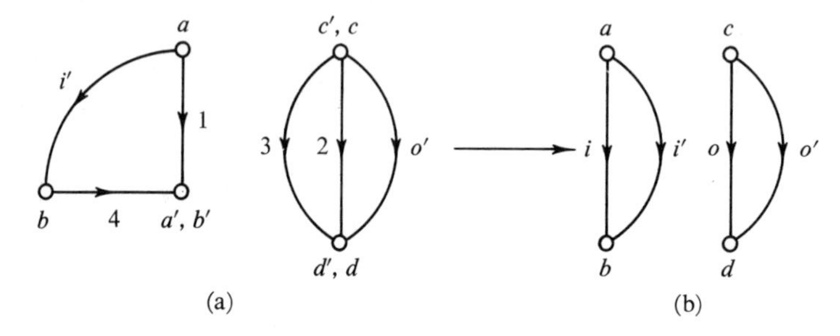

Fig. 11.15. (a) *System graph of series-parallel connection with augmenting drivers;* (b) *terminal graph of equivalent representation.*

In consideration of the relations specified by Equations 11.27 and 11.29, the terminal equations of components A and B should be written in the following form. Component A (h-parameters):

$$\begin{bmatrix} X_1 \\ Y_2 \end{bmatrix} = \begin{bmatrix} H_1 & H_{12} \\ H_{21} & H_2 \end{bmatrix} \begin{bmatrix} Y_1 \\ X_2 \end{bmatrix} \tag{11.31}$$

Component B:

$$\begin{bmatrix} X_4 \\ Y_3 \end{bmatrix} = \begin{bmatrix} G_4 & G_{43} \\ G_{34} & G_3 \end{bmatrix} \begin{bmatrix} Y_4 \\ X_3 \end{bmatrix} \tag{11.32}$$

It is then easily seen that the terminal equations of the equivalent representation are

$$\begin{bmatrix} X_i \\ Y_o \end{bmatrix} = \begin{bmatrix} H_1 + G_4 & H_{12} + G_{43} \\ H_{21} + G_{34} & H_2 + G_3 \end{bmatrix} \begin{bmatrix} Y_i \\ X_o \end{bmatrix}$$

Thus a simple expression results for series-parallel connection: the *h*-parameter of component *A* add to the *g*-parameters of component *B*. Several examples will illustrate this result.

Example 11.7. Consider the schematic of a feedback system in Figure 11.16. A Ward-Leonard system is connected to a tachometer. The output shaft of the Ward-Leonard is connected in parallel to the shaft of the tachometer, while the input field is connected in series to the output of the tachometer.

The Ward-Leonard system is described by the results obtained from Example 11.4.

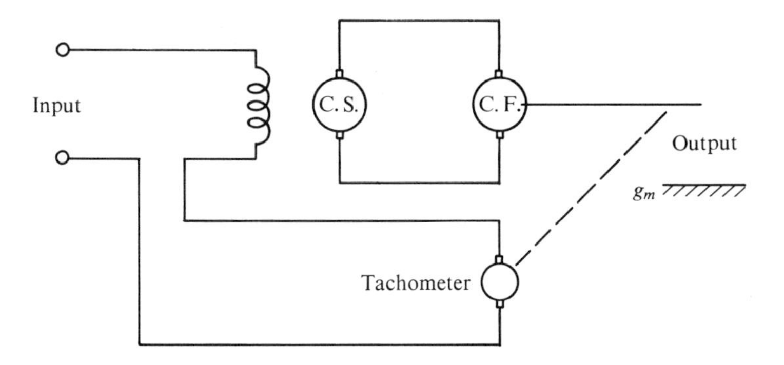

Fig. 11.16. *Ward-Leonard feedback control system.*

$$\begin{bmatrix} V_1 \\ T_2 \end{bmatrix} = \begin{bmatrix} R_f + L_f s & 0 \\ -\dfrac{k_{mg} I_{f2} \dot{\Phi}_1}{Z(s)} & Js + B + \dfrac{k_{mg}^2 I_{f2}^2}{Z(s)} \end{bmatrix} \begin{bmatrix} I_1 \\ \dot{\Phi}_2 \end{bmatrix}$$

For the tachometer we have

$$\begin{bmatrix} V_4 \\ T_3 \end{bmatrix} = \begin{bmatrix} R_t + L_t s & -k_t \\ +k_t & 0 \end{bmatrix} \begin{bmatrix} I_4 \\ \dot{\Phi}_3 \end{bmatrix}$$

where k_t is the tachometer constant for constant field, and the assumption is made that the mechanical constants are negligible.

By Equation 11.33, the combination results in

$$\begin{bmatrix} V_i \\ T_o \end{bmatrix} = \begin{bmatrix} R_f + R_t + (L_f + L_t)s & -k_t \\ k_t - \dfrac{k_{mg} I_{f2} \dot{\Phi}_1}{Z(s)} & Js + B + \dfrac{k_{mg}^2 I_{f2}^2}{Z(s)} \end{bmatrix} \begin{bmatrix} I_i \\ \dot{\Phi}_o \end{bmatrix}$$

Although the control system as defined by Figure 11.16 is theoretically possible, there exists a practical problem of matching the physical size of the field winding of the Ward-Leonard system to the armature winding of the tachometer. Since the tachometer is an instrument-size dc machine, it is incompatible to form a series circuit with the field winding. To overcome this problem one introduces an amplifier whose input is in series with the tachometer and whose output is cascaded to the field winding. Such a system will be presented later.

Example 11.8. Determine a two-port representation for the feedback amplifier shown in Figure 11.17. The system may be viewed as a series-parallel connection if one considers the amplifier the feedforward component and the *R-C* network (shown encircled by a dashed line) the feedback component.

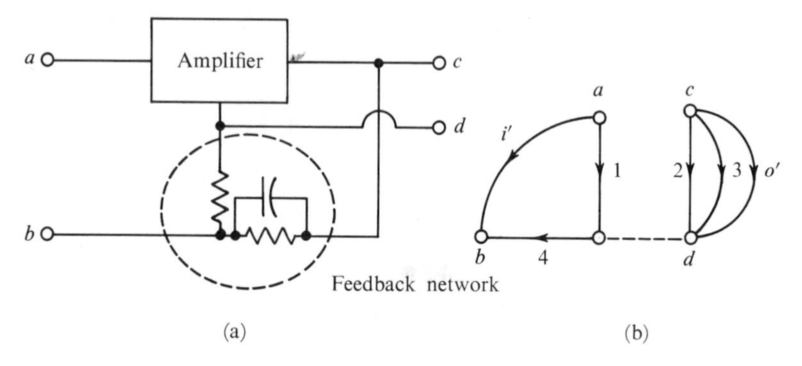

Fig. 11.17. *Feedback amplifier:* (a) *schematic;* (b) *system graph.*

The terminal equations are as follows. The amplifier:

$$\begin{bmatrix} I_1 \\ I_2 \end{bmatrix} = \begin{bmatrix} 0 & 0 \\ W_{21} & W_2 \end{bmatrix} \begin{bmatrix} V_1 \\ V_2 \end{bmatrix}$$

The *R-C* network:

$$\begin{bmatrix} V_4 \\ I_3 \end{bmatrix} = \begin{bmatrix} G_4 & G_{43} \\ G_{34} & G_3 \end{bmatrix} \begin{bmatrix} I_4 \\ V_3 \end{bmatrix}$$

Although the amplifier cannot be represented in terms of h-parameters due to the zeros in the top row, we may proceed nevertheless to follow the basic outline of series-parallel connections. We start by performing the parallel connection

$$\begin{aligned} I_o &= I_2 + I_3 \\ &= W_{21}V_1 + W_2V_o + G_{34}I_4 + G_3V_o \\ &= W_{21}V_1 + (W_2 + G_3)V_o + G_{34}I_4 \end{aligned}$$

but $I_4 = 0$ since the amplifier input current is zero. Therefore

$$I_o = W_{21}V_1 + (W_2 + G_3)V_o$$

From the series combination we have

$$V_i = V_1 + V_4$$

or

$$\begin{aligned} V_1 &= V_i - V_4 \\ &= V_i - G_4 I_4 - G_{43} V_o \\ &= V_i - G_{43} V_o \end{aligned}$$

since $I_4 = 0$. Combining this with the expression for I_0,

$$I_o = W_{21}(V_i - G_{43}V_o) + (W_2 + G_3)V_o$$

When we add the fact that $I_o = 0$ we may write this result in terms of a matrix, giving us the desired two-port representation.

$$\begin{bmatrix} I_i \\ I_o \end{bmatrix} = \begin{bmatrix} 0 & 0 \\ W_{21} & W_2 + G_3 - W_{21}G_{43} \end{bmatrix} \begin{bmatrix} V_i \\ V_o \end{bmatrix}$$

The transfer function of the feedback amplifier is

$$\left. \frac{V_o}{V_i} \right|_{I_o=0} = \frac{-W_{21}}{W_2 + G_3 - W_{21}G_{43}}$$

Now consider an extension of this development to cover series-parallel connections of three-port components. It will follow the basic principles outlined above. In fact, the only requirement which must be observed is this: the terminal equations of any ports which are connected in series must be explicit in an across variable, while the terminal equations of any ports which are connected in parallel must be explicit in a through variable. This is a simple requirement.

Example 11.9. Derive a two-port representation of the hydraulic servo-mechanism whose schematic is shown in Figure 11.18.

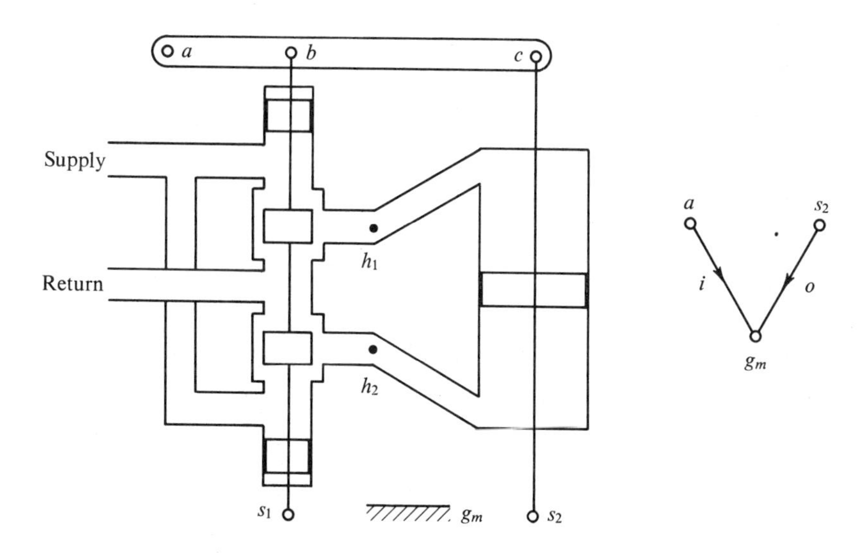

Fig. 11.18. *Hydraulic servo-mechanism and equivalent terminal graph.*

A hydraulic valve is connected to a cylinder with a three-point lever acting as input and feedback linkage. A deflection at point a will result in a proportional deflection at point b, c being momentarily stationary. Fluid will then flow through the valve into the cylinder, moving point c such that point b will be restored to its original position. The servo action is derived from the fact that a small deflection at low power at the input will cause a large deflection at a greatly amplified power level at the output.

Two stages are involved in the derivation of the two-port representation. First, a cascade connection of the valve and cylinder; then, a series-parallel connection between the result and the lever.

The terminal representations of the valve and cylinder (linear models are assumed) are given as follows. Valve:

$$\begin{bmatrix} F_1 \\ \dot{G}_2 \end{bmatrix} = \begin{bmatrix} Y_1(s) & 0 \\ k_v & Q_2 \end{bmatrix} \begin{bmatrix} \Delta_1 \\ P_2 \end{bmatrix}$$

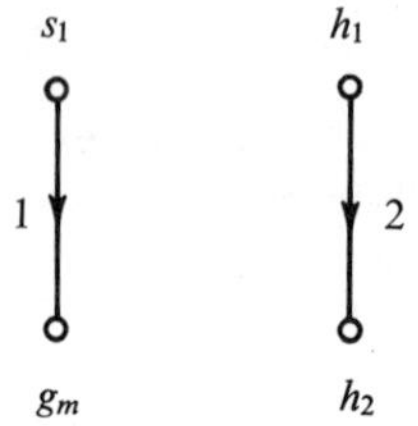

where

$$Y_1(s) = M_1 s^2 + B_1 s + k_1$$

k_v is the valve constant, and Q_2 is the flow constant. Cylinder:

$$\begin{bmatrix} \dot{G}_3 \\ F_4 \end{bmatrix} = \begin{bmatrix} 0 & As \\ -A & Y_4(s) \end{bmatrix} \begin{bmatrix} P_3 \\ \Delta_4 \end{bmatrix}$$

where

$$Y_4(s) = M_4 s^2 + B_4 s$$

We combine the valve and the cylinder such that

$$P_2 = P_3$$

and

$$\dot{G}_2 + \dot{G}_3 = 0$$

The resulting two-port has the terminal representation

$$\begin{bmatrix} F_1 \\ F_4 \end{bmatrix} = \begin{bmatrix} Y_1(s) & 0 \\ \dfrac{Ak_v}{Q_2} & \dfrac{A^2 s}{Q_2} + Y_4(s) \end{bmatrix} \begin{bmatrix} \Delta_1 \\ \Delta_4 \end{bmatrix}$$

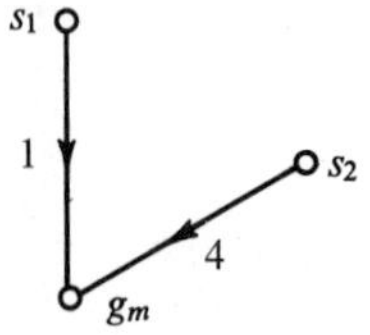

Now, the model of the lever is given as an ideal transducer

$$\begin{bmatrix} \Delta_5 \\ F_6 \\ F_7 \end{bmatrix} = \begin{bmatrix} 0 & N_{56} & -N_{57} \\ -N_{56} & 0 & 0 \\ N_{57} & 0 & 0 \end{bmatrix} \begin{bmatrix} F_5 \\ \Delta_6 \\ \Delta_7 \end{bmatrix}$$

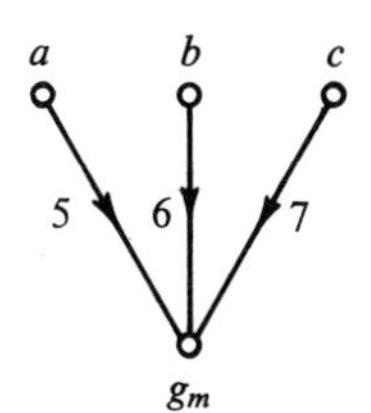

To view the combination of the lever with the valve cylinder subassembly as a series-parallel configuration, we modify the mathematical model for the latter to include a fictitious third port such that

$$\begin{bmatrix} \Delta_8 \\ F_1 \\ F_4 \end{bmatrix} = \begin{bmatrix} 0 & 0 & 0 \\ 0 & Y_1(s) & 0 \\ 0 & \dfrac{Ak_v}{Q_2} & \dfrac{A^2s}{Q_2} + Y_4(s) \end{bmatrix} \begin{bmatrix} F_8 \\ \Delta_1 \\ \Delta_4 \end{bmatrix}$$

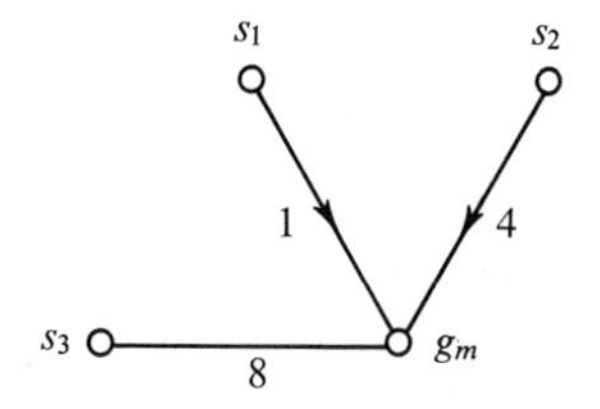

The series-parallel connection thus realized is indicated by the system graph of Figure 11.19. For the two three-ports we obtain an equivalent three-port

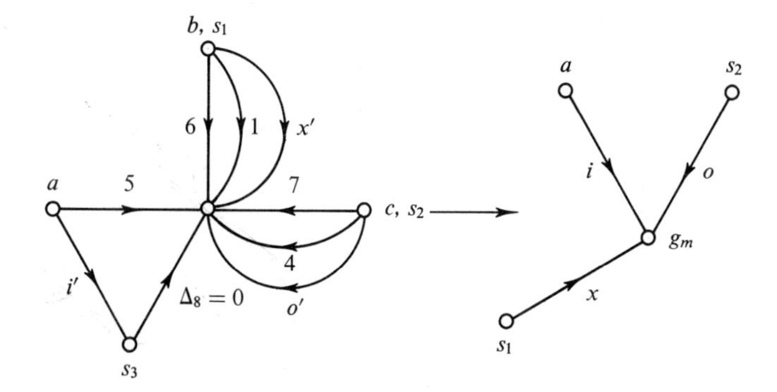

Fig. 11.19. *System graph and intermediate terminal graph of hydraulic servo-mechanism.*

representation by addition of the corresponding matrices.

$$\begin{bmatrix} \Delta_i \\ F_x \\ F_o \end{bmatrix} = \begin{bmatrix} 0 & N_{56} & -N_{57} \\ -N_{56} & Y_1(s) & 0 \\ N_{57} & \dfrac{Ak_v}{Q_2} & \dfrac{A^2s}{Q_z} + Y_4(s) \end{bmatrix} \begin{bmatrix} F_i \\ \Delta_x \\ \Delta_o \end{bmatrix}$$

However, since the pair of p variables F_x and Δ_x associated with port x is not required for the final model, it is eliminated by requiring that

$$F_x = 0$$

Therefore, from the center equation,

$$-N_{56}F_i + Y_1(s)\Delta_x = 0$$

or

$$\Delta_x = \frac{N_{56}}{Y_1(s)}F_i$$

Substituting this expression into the three-port model yields

$$\begin{bmatrix} \Delta_i \\ F_o \end{bmatrix} = \begin{bmatrix} N_{56}^2/Y_1(s) & -N_{57} \\ N_{57} + \dfrac{N_{56}Ak_v}{Q_2 Y_1(s)} & \dfrac{A^2 s}{Q_2} + Y_4(s) \end{bmatrix} \begin{bmatrix} F_i \\ \Delta_o \end{bmatrix}$$

These are the terminal equations associated with the desired terminal graph.

11.5 Interconnection of Components in the *t*-Domain

We have investigated systematic procedures for deriving s-domain models of subassemblies of components which are connected in typical two-port interconnection patterns. Let us now direct our attention to similar procedures which apply to component models given by state equations.

Although formal procedures may be specified, they tend to be impractical due to the large number of equations that have to be carried along. It will be shown that a more informal, direct approach will lead to a desired result more quickly and efficiently.

Formal Approach

As an introduction, consider the cascade connection of two components given in state space model form. Let the state models for two two-port components, a and b, be give respectively by

$$\begin{bmatrix} \dfrac{d}{dt}\mathbf{x}_a \\ \hdashline y_1 \\ x_2 \end{bmatrix} = \begin{bmatrix} \mathbf{A}_a & \mathbf{B}_{a_1} & \mathbf{B}_{a_2} \\ \hdashline \mathbf{C}_{a_1} & d_{a_1} & d_{a_{12}} \\ \mathbf{C}_{a_2} & d_{a_{21}} & d_{a_2} \end{bmatrix} \begin{bmatrix} \mathbf{x}_a \\ \hdashline x_1 \\ y_2 \end{bmatrix} \tag{11.34}$$

and

$$\begin{bmatrix} \dfrac{d}{dt}\mathbf{x}_b \\ \cdots \\ y_3 \\ x_4 \end{bmatrix} = \begin{bmatrix} \mathbf{A}_b & \mathbf{B}_{b_1} & \mathbf{B}_{b_2} \\ \cdots & \cdots & \cdots \\ \mathbf{C}_{b_1} & d_{b_1} & d_{b_{12}} \\ \mathbf{C}_{b_2} & d_{b_{21}} & d_{b_2} \end{bmatrix} \begin{bmatrix} \mathbf{x}_b \\ \cdots \\ x_3 \\ y_4 \end{bmatrix} \tag{11.35}$$

a_2, 3, b_2; c_2, 4, d_2

When the components are cascaded these constraint equations apply:

$$\begin{aligned} y_2 + y_3 &= 0 \\ x_2 - x_3 &= 0 \end{aligned} \tag{11.36}$$

The interconnection will involve the algebraic equations of the component model together with Equations 11.36. We first combine Equations 11.34 with Equations 11.35 and arrange them in a form suitable for the final model.

$$\begin{bmatrix} \dfrac{d}{dt}\mathbf{x}_a \\ \dfrac{d}{dt}\mathbf{x}_b \\ y_1 \\ x_4 \end{bmatrix} = \begin{bmatrix} \mathbf{A}_a & 0 & \mathbf{B}_{a_1} & 0 \\ 0 & \mathbf{A}_b & 0 & \mathbf{B}_{b_2} \\ \mathbf{C}_{a_1} & 0 & d_{a_1} & 0 \\ 0 & \mathbf{C}_{b_2} & 0 & d_{b_2} \end{bmatrix} \begin{bmatrix} \mathbf{x}_a \\ \mathbf{x}_b \\ x_1 \\ y_4 \end{bmatrix} + \begin{bmatrix} 0 & -\mathbf{B}_{a_2} \\ \mathbf{B}_{b_1} & 0 \\ 0 & -d_{a_2} \\ d_{b_{21}} & 0 \end{bmatrix} \begin{bmatrix} x_2 \\ y_3 \end{bmatrix} \tag{11.37}$$

What remains is the solution for x_2 and y_3. Using Equations 11.34 and 11.35 and the constraint relations, we obtain

$$\begin{bmatrix} x_2 \\ y_3 \end{bmatrix} = \begin{bmatrix} \mathbf{C}_{a_2} & 0 \\ 0 & \mathbf{C}_{b_1} \end{bmatrix} \begin{bmatrix} \mathbf{x}_a \\ \mathbf{x}_b \end{bmatrix} + \begin{bmatrix} 0 & -d_{a_2} \\ d_{b_1} & 0 \end{bmatrix} \begin{bmatrix} x_2 \\ y_3 \end{bmatrix} + \begin{bmatrix} d_{a_{21}} & \\ 0 & d_{b_{12}} \end{bmatrix} \begin{bmatrix} x_1 \\ y_4 \end{bmatrix}$$

Solving for x_2 and y_3 yields

$$\begin{bmatrix} x_2 \\ y_3 \end{bmatrix} = \frac{1}{1 + d_{a_2} d_{b_1}} \left\{ \begin{bmatrix} \mathbf{C}_{a_2} & -d_{a_2}\mathbf{C}_{b_1} \\ d_{b_1}\mathbf{C}_{a_2} & \mathbf{C}_{b_1} \end{bmatrix} \begin{bmatrix} \mathbf{x}_a \\ \mathbf{x}_b \end{bmatrix} + \begin{bmatrix} d_{a_2} & -d_{a_2} d_{b_{12}} \\ d_{b_1} d_{a_{21}} & d_{b_{12}} \end{bmatrix} \begin{bmatrix} x_1 \\ y_4 \end{bmatrix} \right\} \tag{11.38}$$

The desired equations in the final state model are then the combination of Equations 11.37 and 11.38. Inasmuch as the result will be bulky, the procedure will be illustrated by a number of examples. The desired equations in the final state model are then obtained by substituting Equations 11.38 into 11.37. Note that the procedure outlined above will be successful only for state models whose algebraic equations are explicit in an across variable and a through variable, but not both of the same kind.

As an illustration of a case where the terminal variables of the ports to be connected are both of the same kind, consider the derivation of a state model for a Ward-Leonard system. The system is shown for reference in Figure 11.9. The terminal equations for the two machines are obtained from Equations 8.136. First machine:

$$\begin{bmatrix} \frac{d}{dt}i_f \\ i_{a_1} \\ \hdashline i_1 \\ i_2 \end{bmatrix} = \left[\begin{array}{cc:cc} -R_f/L_f & 0 & 1/L_f & 0 \\ -k_g/L_a & -R_a/L_a & 0 & 1/L_a \\ \hdashline 1 & 0 & 0 & 0 \\ 0 & 1 & 0 & 0 \end{array}\right] \begin{bmatrix} i_f \\ i_{a_1} \\ \hdashline v_1 \\ v_2 \end{bmatrix}$$

Second machine:

$$\begin{bmatrix} \frac{d}{dt}i_{a_2} \\ \dot{\varphi}_m \\ \hdashline i_3 \\ \dot{\varphi}_4 \end{bmatrix} = \left[\begin{array}{cc:cc} -R_a/L_a & -k_m/L_a & 1/L_a & 0 \\ k_m/J & -B/J & 0 & 1/J \\ \hdashline 1 & 0 & 0 & 0 \\ 0 & 1 & 0 & 0 \end{array}\right] \begin{bmatrix} i_{a_2} \\ \dot{\varphi}_m \\ \hdashline v_3 \\ \tau_4 \end{bmatrix}$$

From the component models we pull out the equations

$$\frac{d}{dt}i_{a_1} = -\frac{k_m}{L_a}i_f - \frac{R_a}{L_a}i_{a_1} + \frac{1}{L_a}v_2$$

$$\frac{d}{dt}i_{a_2} = -\frac{R_a}{L_a}i_{a_2} - \frac{k_m}{L_a}\dot{\varphi}_m + \frac{1}{L_a}v_3$$

Since

$$v_2 = v_3$$

we solve for v_2 and v_3 and equate the result

$$L_a\frac{d}{dt}i_{a_1} + k_m i_f + R_a i_{a_1} = L_a\frac{d}{dt}i_{a_2} + R_a i_{a_2} + k_m\dot{\varphi}_m$$

Since also

$$i_2 = -i_3$$

we have

$$i_{a_1} = -i_{a_2} = i_a$$

so that

$$2L_a\frac{d}{dt}i_a + 2R_a i_a + k_m i_f - k_m\dot{\varphi}_m = 0$$

Solving for the derivative

$$\frac{d}{dt}i_a = -\frac{R_a}{L_a}i_a - \frac{k_m}{2L_a}i_f + \frac{k_m}{2L_a}\dot{\varphi}_m$$

and recombining with the remaining state equations yields the final state model,

$$\begin{bmatrix} \dfrac{d}{dt}\begin{Bmatrix} i_f \\ i_a \end{Bmatrix} \\ \dot{\varphi}_m \\ \hdashline i_1 \\ \dot{\varphi}_4 \end{bmatrix} = \left[\begin{array}{ccc:cc} -R_f/L_f & 0 & 0 & 1/L_f & 0 \\ -k_m/2L_a & -R_a/L_a & k_m/2L_a & 0 & 0 \\ 0 & -k_m/J & -B/J & 0 & 1/J \\ \hdashline 1 & 0 & 0 & 0 & 0 \\ 0 & 0 & 1 & 0 & 0 \end{array}\right] \begin{bmatrix} i_f \\ i_a \\ \dot{\varphi}_m \\ \hdashline v_1 \\ \tau_4 \end{bmatrix}$$

Characteristic of this case is the fact that the state models are explicit in i_2 and i_3. Since these variables are also identical to a state variable, both of which could not be eliminated, a successful procedure requires that the fact that $v_2 = v_3$ be used first.

Note also that all direct transmission terms, the "d" coefficients, are zero in this example. This is a frequent occurrence in state models of two-ports, and results in a significant simplification of the work involved in combining two components in cascade.

Informal Approach

In contrast to the formal procedures outlined above, the development of a state model of a hydraulic transmission system will be informally approached. Shown in Figure 11.20 are two hydraulic cylinders connected to one another by means of two hydraulic lines. Terminals s_1 and s_2 constitute the input and output, respectively. A hydraulic line has capacitance due to elastic deformation of line walls and compres-

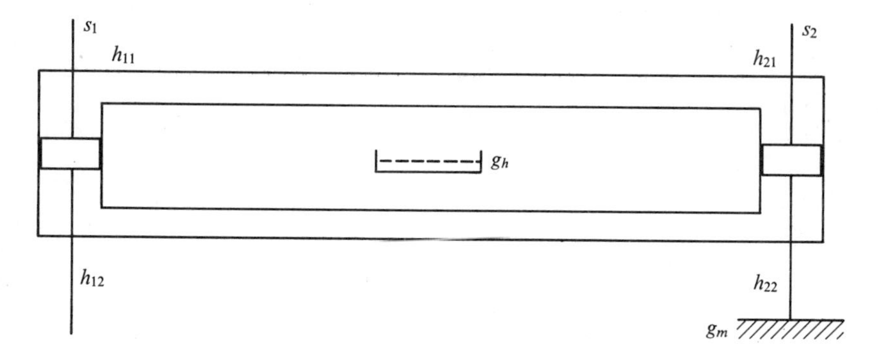

Fig. 11.20. *Schematic of a hydraulic transmission.*

sibility of the fluid. To represent this capacitance properly we choose a lumped-parameter approximation of the line which is analogous to an assembly of two capacitors and one resistor as shown in Figure 11.21. With this assumption regarding the modeling of the hydraulic line we may then draw the system graph of the transmission as shown in Figure 11.22. Our objective is to derive a terminal representation in state model form.

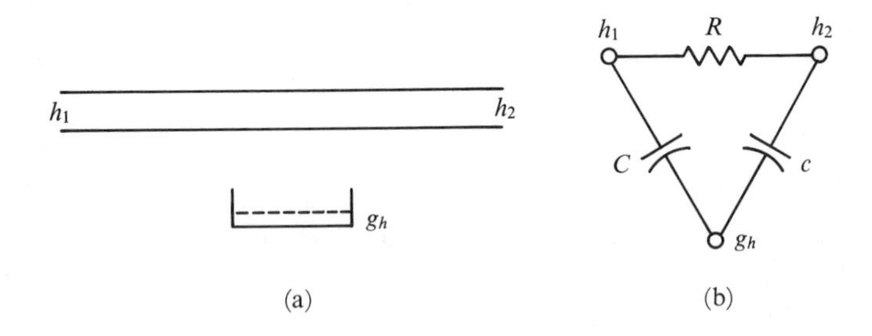

Fig. 11.21. (a) *Schematic of a hydraulic line and* (b) *its lumped-parameter analog.*

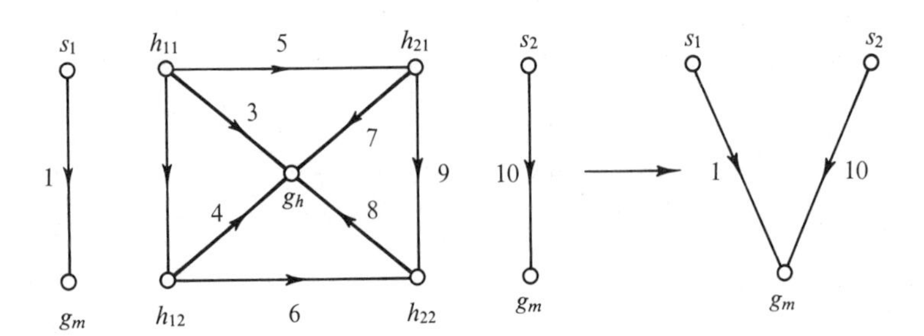

Fig. 11.22. *System graph of transmission and final terminal graph.*

The formal approach would require that the two cylinders and the two lines each be represented as a two-port. The resulting interconnection would then first view the two lines as a series combination which in turn would be cascaded on either end with the two cylinders. An approach thus described would require a great deal of equation wielding. A much simpler development is now shown. The equations of the components follow. Cylinder 1:

$$\frac{d}{dt}\dot{\delta}_1 = -\frac{B}{M}\dot{\delta}_1 + \frac{1}{M}f_1 + \frac{A}{M}p_2$$

$$\dot{g}_2 = A\dot{\delta}_1$$

Line elements:

$$\frac{d}{dt}p_3 = \frac{1}{C}\dot{g}_3$$

$$\frac{d}{dt}p_4 = \frac{1}{C}\dot{g}_4$$

$$\frac{d}{dt}p_7 = \frac{1}{C}\dot{g}_7$$

$$\frac{d}{dt}p_8 = \frac{1}{C}\dot{g}_8$$

$$p_5 = R\dot{g}_5$$
$$p_6 = R\dot{g}_6$$

Cylinder 2:

$$\dot{g}_9 = -A\dot{\delta}_{10}$$

$$\frac{d}{dt}\dot{\delta}_{10} = -\frac{B}{M}\dot{\delta}_{10} + \frac{1}{M}f_{10} - \frac{A}{M}p_9$$

Following the rules of Section 6.11 we select the four elements corresponding to the capacitors as the tree. Hence

$$\dot{g}_3 = -\dot{g}_2 - \dot{g}_5$$
$$\dot{g}_4 = \dot{g}_2 - \dot{g}_6$$
$$\dot{g}_7 = -\dot{g}_9 + \dot{g}_5$$
$$\dot{g}_8 = \dot{g}_9 + \dot{g}_6$$

also

$$p_2 = p_3 - p_4$$
$$p_5 = p_3 - p_7$$
$$p_6 = p_4 - p_8$$
$$p_9 = p_7 - p_8$$

When the last eight equations are substituted into the terminal equations and the algebraic equations are eliminated we obtain

$$\frac{d}{dt}\dot{\delta}_1 = -\frac{B}{M}\dot{\delta}_1 + \frac{1}{M}f_1 + \frac{A}{M}(p_3 - p_4)$$

$$\frac{d}{dt}p_3 = -\frac{1}{C}\left[A\dot{\delta}_1 + \frac{1}{R}(p_3 - p_7)\right]$$

$$\frac{d}{dt}p_4 = \frac{1}{C}\left[A\dot{\delta}_1 - \frac{1}{R}(p_4 - p_8)\right]$$

$$\frac{d}{dt}p_7 = \frac{1}{C}\left[A\dot{\delta}_{10} - \frac{1}{R}(p_7 - p_3)\right]$$

$$\frac{d}{dt}p_8 = -\frac{1}{C}\left[A\delta_{10} + \frac{1}{R}(p_8 - p_4)\right]$$

$$\frac{d}{dt}\dot{\delta}_{10} = -\frac{B}{M}\dot{\delta}_{10} + \frac{1}{M}f_{10} - \frac{A}{M}(p_7 - p_8) \tag{11.39}$$

or in matrix format as a complete state model,

$$\begin{bmatrix} \frac{d}{dt}\begin{matrix} \dot{\delta}_1 \\ p_3 \\ p_4 \\ p_7 \\ p_8 \\ \dot{\delta}_{10} \end{matrix} \\ \hdashline \dot{\delta}_1 \\ \dot{\delta}_0 \end{bmatrix} = \left[\begin{array}{cccccc:cc} -\frac{B}{M} & \frac{A}{M} & -\frac{A}{M} & 0 & 0 & 0 & \frac{1}{M} & 0 \\ -\frac{A}{C} & -\frac{1}{RC} & 0 & \frac{1}{RC} & 0 & 0 & 0 & 0 \\ \frac{A}{C} & 0 & -\frac{1}{RC} & 0 & \frac{1}{RC} & 0 & 0 & 0 \\ 0 & \frac{1}{RC} & 0 & -\frac{1}{RC} & 0 & \frac{A}{C} & 0 & 0 \\ 0 & 0 & \frac{1}{RC} & 0 & -\frac{1}{RC} & -\frac{A}{C} & 0 & 0 \\ 0 & 0 & 0 & -\frac{A}{M} & \frac{A}{M} & -\frac{B}{M} & 0 & \frac{1}{M} \\ \hdashline 1 & 0 & 0 & 0 & 0 & 0 & 0 & 0 \\ 0 & 0 & 0 & 0 & 0 & 1 & 0 & 0 \end{array}\right] \begin{bmatrix} \dot{\delta}_1 \\ p_3 \\ p_4 \\ p_7 \\ p_8 \\ \dot{\delta}_{10} \\ \hdashline f_1 \\ f_0 \end{bmatrix} \tag{11.40}$$

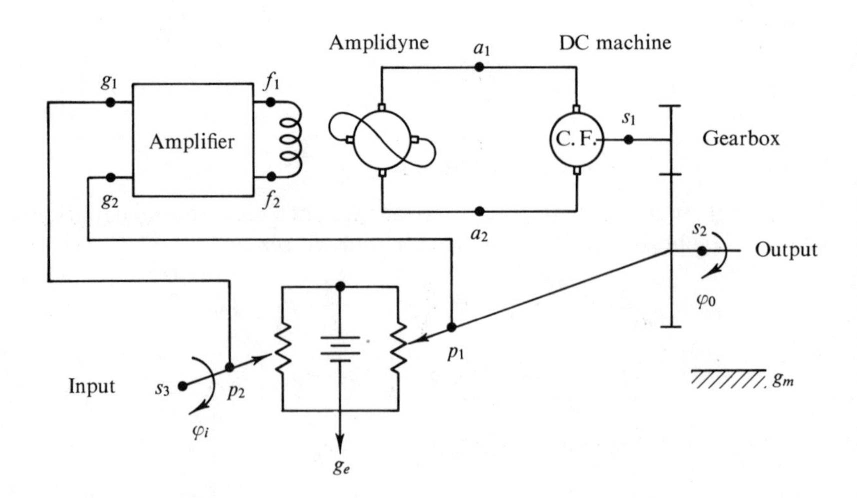

Fig. 11.23. *Rotational position control system.*

There are six differential equations and two terminal equations involved in the state model of the hydraulic transmission. The result is obtained in a straightforward manner, essentially following the procedures of Section 6.11. The informal approach will prove successful in essentially all applications.

As a final illustration of the informal approach, let us develop a state model for the position control system shown in Figure 11.23. A dc machine is used as the output actuator. Its armature current is supplied by the amplidyne whose field is driven by the output of the amplifier. The amplifier is a high-impedance input operational amplifier acting as a summer with the two potentiometer voltages as inputs.

The component equations are given in first-order differential equation or algebraic form. Amplifier:

$$v_2 = k_a v_1$$

$$i_1 = 0$$

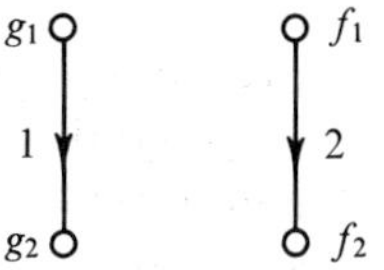

Amplidyne: The state model component equations are obtained from Equations 8.140,

$$\frac{d}{dt}i_3 = -\frac{R_3}{L_3}i_3 + \frac{1}{L_3}v_3$$

$$\frac{d}{dt}i_4 = -\frac{R_4}{L_4}i_4 + \frac{1}{L_4}v_4 - \frac{k_{am_1}}{L_4}i_q$$

$$\frac{d}{dt}i_q = -\frac{R_q}{L_q}i_q - \frac{k_{am_2}}{L_q}i_3$$

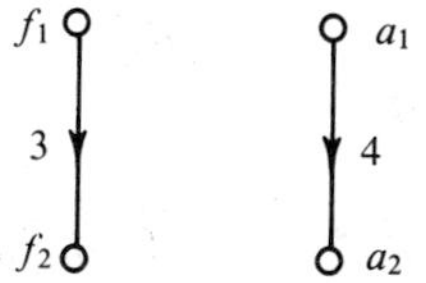

where i_q is the quadrature current and

$$k_{am_1} = \dot{\Phi}k_{dg}$$
$$k_{am_2} = \dot{\Phi}k_{df}$$

dc machine:

$$\frac{d}{dt}i_5 = -\frac{R_5}{L_5}i_5 + \frac{1}{L_5}v_5 + \frac{k_m}{L_5}\dot{\varphi}_6$$

$$\frac{d}{dt}\dot{\varphi}_6 = \frac{k_m}{J_6}i_5 - \frac{B_6}{J_6}\dot{\varphi}_6 + \frac{1}{J_6}\tau_6$$

$$\frac{d}{dt}\varphi_6 = \dot{\varphi}_6$$

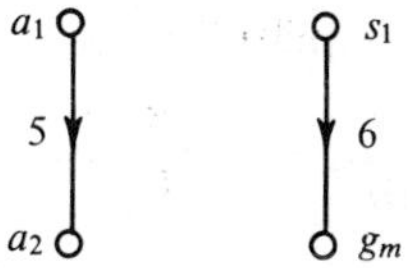

Gearbox:

$$\varphi_8 = -\frac{1}{n}\varphi_7$$

$$\tau_8 = n\tau_7$$

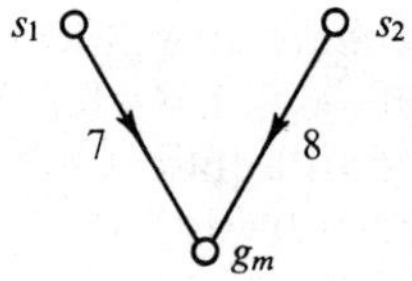

Double potentiometer.

$$v_9 = k_p(\varphi_1 - \varphi_{10}) + R(\varphi_i, \varphi_{10})i_9$$

$$\tau_i = \tau_{10} = 0$$

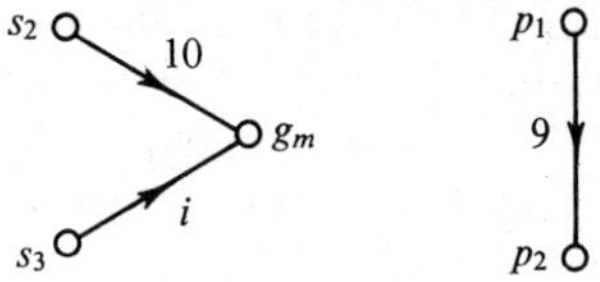

In deriving the overall state model of the control system we recognize that basically a series-parallel configuration exists; one two-port is composed of four components, the amplifier plus amplidyne plus dc machine plus gearbox, and the double potentiometer represents the other one. Therefore we first cascade the four components.

The combination of the amplidyne and dc machine results in

$$\frac{d}{dt}i_3 = -\frac{R_3}{L_3}i_3 + \frac{1}{L_3}v_3$$

$$\frac{d}{dt}i_q = -\frac{R_q}{L_q}i_q - \frac{k_{am_2}}{L_q}i_3$$

$$\frac{d}{dt}i_a = -\frac{(R_4 + R_5)}{(L_4 + L_5)}i_a - \frac{k_{am_1}}{(L_4 + L_5)}i_q - \frac{k_m}{(L_4 + L_5)}\dot{\varphi}_6$$

$$\frac{d}{dt}\dot{\varphi}_6 = \frac{k_m}{J_6}i_a - \frac{B_6}{J_6}\dot{\varphi}_6 + \frac{1}{J_6}\tau_6$$

where use has been made of the relations $v_4 = v_5$ and $i_4 = -i_5 = i_a$. By virtue of the relations $v_3 = v_2$ and $i_3 = -i_2$ the amplifier may be added. Also, to add the gearbox, we have $\varphi_7 = \varphi_6$ and $\tau_7 = -\tau_6$ as the constraint equations between the dc machine and the gearbox. However, since $\tau_0 = 0$, we have $\tau_8 = 0$, $\tau_7 = 0$, and $\tau_6 = 0$.

Thus the entire group of feedforward components is represented by the equations

$$\frac{d}{dt}i_3 = -\frac{R_3}{L_3}i_3 + \frac{k_a}{L_3}k_a v_1$$

$$\frac{d}{dt}i_q = -\frac{R_q}{L_q}i_q - \frac{k_{am_2}}{L_q}i_3$$

$$\frac{d}{dt}i_a = -\frac{(R_4 + R_5)}{(L_4 + L_5)}i_a - \frac{k_{am_1}}{(L_4 + L_5)}i_q + \frac{nk_m}{(L_4 + L_5)}\dot{\varphi}_8$$

$$\frac{d}{dt}\dot{\varphi}_2 = -\frac{B_6}{J_6}\dot{\varphi}_2 - \frac{k_m}{nJ_6}i_a$$

$$\frac{d}{dt}\varphi_6 = \dot{\varphi}_6 \qquad \textbf{(11.41)}$$

The remaining connections are established by the relations

$$v_1 = v_9$$

$$i_1 = -i_9 = 0^*$$

and

$$\varphi_{10} = \varphi_8 = \varphi_o$$

$$\tau_{10} = 0$$

Thus the final state model is given by

$$\frac{d}{dt}i_3 = -\frac{R_3}{L_3}i_3 + \frac{k_a k_p}{L_3}(\varphi_i - \varphi_o)$$

$$\frac{d}{dt}i_q = -\frac{R_q}{L_q}i_q - \frac{k_{am_2}}{L_q}i_3$$

$$\frac{d}{dt}i_a = -\frac{(R_4 + R_5)}{(L_4 + L_5)}i_a - \frac{k_{am_1}}{(L_4 + L_5)}i_q + \frac{nk_m}{(L_4 + L_5)}\dot{\varphi}_o$$

$$\frac{d}{dt}\dot{\varphi}_o = -\frac{B_6}{J_6}\dot{\varphi}_o - \frac{k_m}{nJ_6}i_a$$

$$\frac{d}{dt}\varphi_o = \dot{\varphi}_o \qquad \textbf{(11.42)}$$

Note that the series-parallel connection of the feedforward components and the feedback components is almost trivial because of the fact that the through variables at the point of interconnection are zero. Therefore only the equations involving across variables are necessary in the development. The components involved, the amplifier and the feedback potentiometers, are said to be isolation components in the sense that no power is being transferred across their terminals. Isolation components play an important role in the design of control systems. This subject and the general problem of formulating mathematical models of feedback control systems will be the topic of the next section.

* The fact that $i_9 = 0$ is of great benefit since the nonlinear resistance term in the feedback potentiometer can be ignored.

11.6 The Formulation of Feedback Control Systems

Several examples of feedback control systems have been presented in the preceding sections. They were introduced as illustrations of series-parallel combinations of two-port or three-port components. Those examples point out a pattern that holds in general for all simple feedback systems in that they may be viewed as series-parallel connections of components. Thus feedback systems are generally structured as shown by the schematic of Figure 11.24. They typically consist of a number of cascaded two-ports forming the feedforward component and a single two-port representing the feedback component. Feedback systems so structured would be analyzed according to the formal formu-

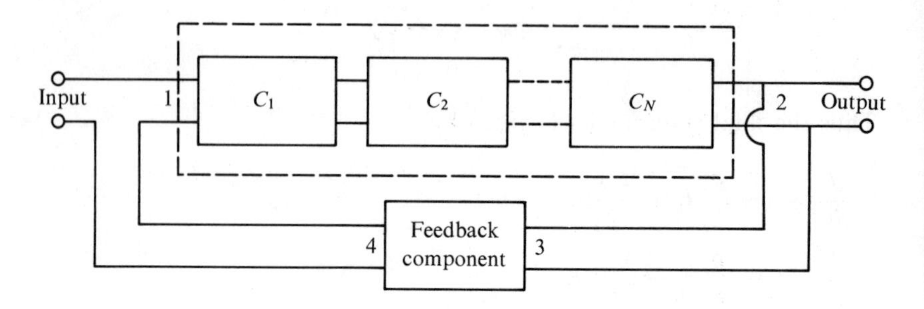

Fig. 11.24. *General structure of feedback system.*

lation procedures of series-parallel connections. However, fortunately for the person faced with the task of analyzing and designing control systems, derivation procedures usually need not be quite as formal as a series-parallel combination requires for the following reason.

It is usually an inherent requirement in the design of a control system that the input side be operated at a low power level while the output operates at a high power level. Consequently, the components in the first stage of the feedforward components and the feedback component itself are essentially instrumentation components such as amplifiers and transducers, respectively. The last stage, on the other hand, is usually a high-power actuation or control component.

The instrumentation components may be modeled as ideal unilateral components with "lots" of zeros in the terminal equations. Their terminal equations usually consist only of transfer functions defining the ratio of two across variables, such as voltages or displacements. The instrumentation components are isolation components which do not introduce inter-component loading. It is convenient to represent these components by a mathematical model which may be classified as a degenerate two-port. Consider, for instance, a two-port with the terminal equations

$$\begin{bmatrix} I_1 \\ V_2 \end{bmatrix} = \begin{bmatrix} 0 & 0 \\ K_{21} & R_2 \end{bmatrix} \begin{bmatrix} V_1 \\ I_2 \end{bmatrix} \tag{11.43}$$

It would be completely sufficient to represent the component by the schematic of Figure 11.25. It is called a block diagram. It is simply

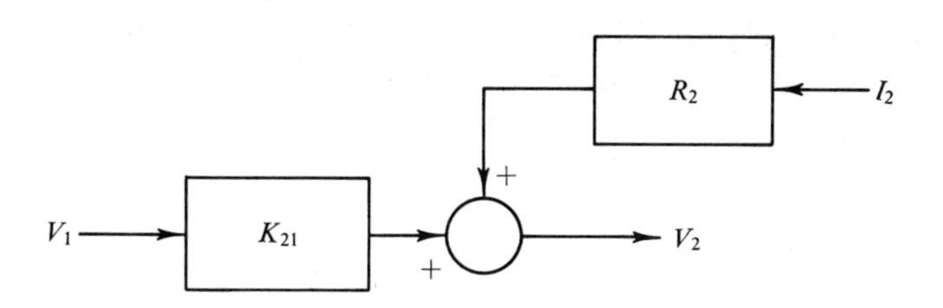

Fig. 11.25. *Block diagram of Equation 11.43.*

a graphical representation of the equation, and completely self-explanatory.

Block diagrams of Control Systems

Block diagrams assume an important part in the formulation and analysis of control systems. For instance, the general series-parallel structure as indicated by Figure 11.25 may be readily converted into a block diagram, provided the feedback component and the first stage of the feedforward group are ideal unilateral components. Then we can model the system by the following subassemblies. Feedforward components:

$$\begin{bmatrix} Y_1 \\ X_2 \end{bmatrix} = \begin{bmatrix} 0 & 0 \\ G_{21}(s) & G_2(s) \end{bmatrix} \begin{bmatrix} X_1 \\ Y_2 \end{bmatrix} \tag{11.44}$$

Feedback components:

$$\begin{bmatrix} Y_3 \\ X_4 \end{bmatrix} = \begin{bmatrix} 0 & 0 \\ G_{43}(s) & G_4(s) \end{bmatrix} \begin{bmatrix} X_3 \\ Y_4 \end{bmatrix} \tag{11.45}$$

where the variables correspond to the ports of Figure 11.24.

Representing these equations as block diagrams, we construct the schematics of Figure 11.26. The two subassemblies are combined according to the constraint equations

$$\begin{aligned} X_i &= X_1 + X_4 \\ Y_i &= Y_1 = Y_4 = 0 \end{aligned} \tag{11.46}$$

and

$$Y_o = Y_2 + Y_3$$
$$X_o = X_2 = X_3 \qquad (11.47)$$

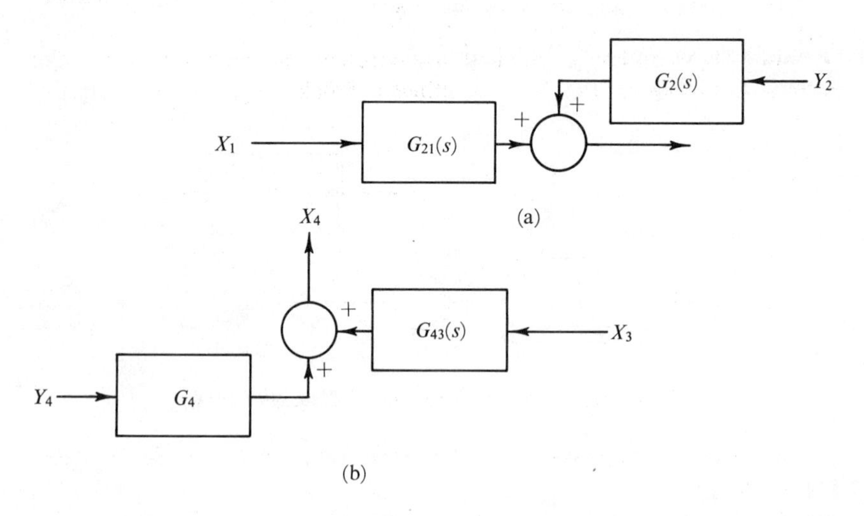

Fig. 11.26. *Block diagrams of control system subassemblies.*

The equations are used to combine the block diagrams of Figure 11.27. The combination is the desired block diagram of a typical feedback control system. The transfer function $G_4(s)$ is eliminated due to the fact that $Y_1 = 0$.

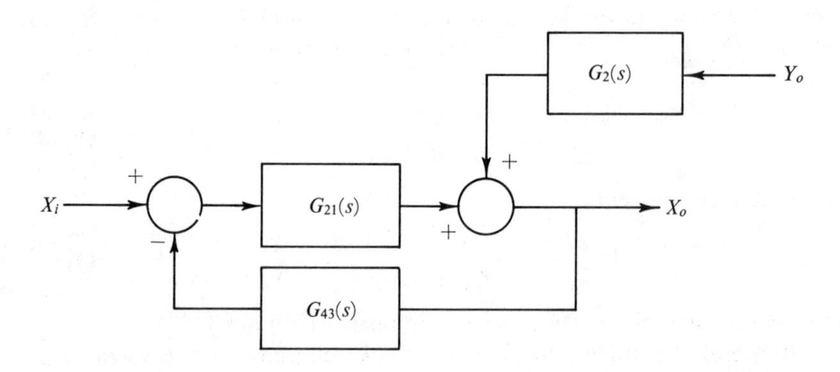

Fig. 11.27. *Block diagram of typical feedback control system.*

Although transfer functions and, consequently, s-domain nomenclature are normally preferred in constructing block diagrams, it is perfectly legitimate and feasible to construct a block diagram in terms of time-domain equations. Naturally, the state equations are most suitable for this purpose.

Example 11.10. Formulate a block diagram representation of the control system shown in Figure 11.28. The block diagram will be developed in terms of both transfer functions and state equations.

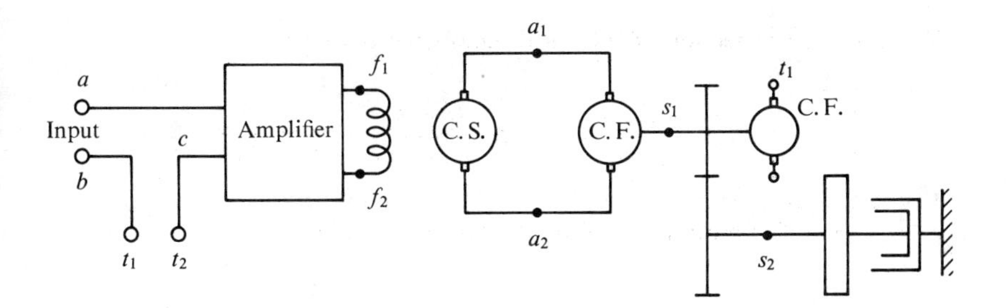

Fig. 11.28. *Speed control system.*

1. Transfer function model. We first develop the block diagram for the feedforward components consisting of the amplifier, Ward-Leonard system, gearbox, and load. For these four components the terminal equations are as follows.

Amplifier:

$$\begin{bmatrix} V_1 \\ V_2 \end{bmatrix} = \begin{bmatrix} 0 & 0 \\ K_a & 0 \end{bmatrix} \begin{bmatrix} V_1 \\ I_2 \end{bmatrix}$$

Ward-Leonard system:

$$\begin{bmatrix} V_3 \\ T_2 \end{bmatrix} = \begin{bmatrix} R_3 + L_3 s & 0 \\ -\dfrac{k_{mg}^2 I\dot{\Phi}}{z_a(s)} & Js + B + \dfrac{k_{mg}^2 I^2}{z_a(s)} \end{bmatrix} \begin{bmatrix} I_3 \\ \dot{\Phi}_4 \end{bmatrix}$$

where $z_a(s) = 2(R_a + L_a s)$.

Gearbox:

$$\begin{bmatrix} T_5 \\ \dot{\Phi}_6 \end{bmatrix} = \begin{bmatrix} 0 & n \\ -n & 0 \end{bmatrix} \begin{bmatrix} \dot{\Phi}_5 \\ T_6 \end{bmatrix}$$

Load:

$$T_7 = (J_7 s + B_7)\dot{\Phi}_7$$

s_2, 7, g_m

The cascade connection of these four components yields

$$\begin{bmatrix} I_1 \\ T_o \end{bmatrix} = \begin{bmatrix} 0 & 0 \\ \dfrac{k_{mg}^2 I\dot{\Phi}}{z_3 z_a n} & \dfrac{1}{n^2}\left(Js + B + \dfrac{k_{mg}^2 I^2}{z_a}\right) + J_7 s + B_7 \end{bmatrix} \begin{bmatrix} V_1 \\ \dot{\Phi}_o \end{bmatrix}$$

where $z_3 = R_3 + L_3 s$:

To simplify notation, we write the last equation as

$$\begin{bmatrix} I_1 \\ T_o \end{bmatrix} = \begin{bmatrix} 0 & 0 \\ -Y_{o1} & Y_{oo}(s) \end{bmatrix} \begin{bmatrix} V_1 \\ \dot{\Phi}_o \end{bmatrix}$$

f_1, 1, f_2 s_2, 0, g_m

These equations may be expressed as a block diagram as shown in Figure 11.29.

It is now a simple matter to combine this result with the feedback component, the tachometer. We model the tachometer as

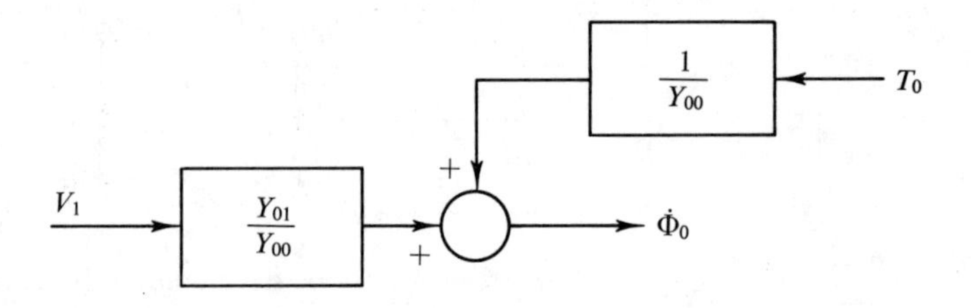

Fig. 11.29. *Block diagram of feedforward components.*

$$\begin{bmatrix} T_8 \\ V_9 \end{bmatrix} \begin{bmatrix} 0 & +k_t \\ -k_t & R_9 + L_9 s \end{bmatrix} \begin{bmatrix} \dot{\Phi}_8 \\ I_o \end{bmatrix}$$

t_1, 9, t_2 s_1, 8, g_m

From the interconnection constraints we have

$$\dot{\Phi}_8 = \dot{\Phi}_4 = -\frac{1}{n}\dot{\Phi}_o$$

$$V_i = V_1 + V_9$$
$$I_i = I_1 = I_9 = 0$$

Therefore the final block diagram is given by Figure 11.30.

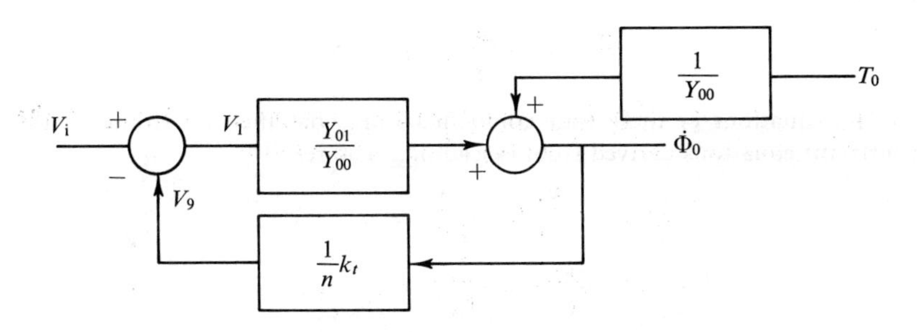

Fig. 11.30. *Final block diagram with provision for additional load.*

If no further load additions to the system are expected, we set $T_o = 0$ and reduce the block diagram to what is shown in Figure 11.31.

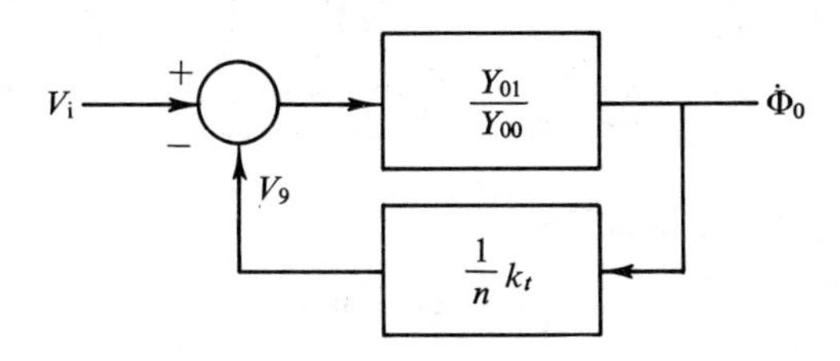

Fig. 11.31. *Final block diagram for system under no-load.*

2. State equation model. We repeat the above development by carrying the formulation out in the t-domain and by preparing a corresponding block diagram. We begin by formulating the state equations for the feedforward components. Amplifier:

$$v_2 = K_a v_1$$
$$i_1 = 0$$

Ward-Leonard system (see equations):

$$\frac{d}{dt}i_3 = -\frac{R_3}{L_3}i_3 + \frac{1}{L_3}v_3$$

$$\frac{d}{dt}i_a = -\frac{k_m}{2L_a}i_3 - \frac{R_a}{L_a}i_a + \frac{k_m}{2L_a}\dot{\varphi}_4$$

$$\frac{d}{dt}\dot{\varphi}_4 = -\frac{k_m}{J_4}i_a - \frac{B_4}{J_4}\dot{\varphi}_4 + \frac{1}{J_4}\tau_4$$

Gear box:

$$\tau_5 = n\tau_6$$
$$\dot{\varphi}_6 = -n\dot{\varphi}_5$$

Load:

$$\frac{d}{dt}\dot{\varphi}_7 = -\frac{B_7}{J_7}\dot{\varphi}_7 + \frac{1}{J_7}\tau_7$$

The equations of these four components are combined according to the constraint equations derived from cascading. The result is

$$\frac{d}{dt}i_3 = -\frac{R_3}{L_3}i_3 + \frac{1}{L_3k_a}v_1$$
$$\frac{d}{dt}i_a = \frac{-k_m}{2L_a}i_3 - \frac{R_a}{L_a}i_a - \frac{k_m}{2nL_a}\dot{\varphi}_o$$
$$\frac{d}{dt}\varphi_o = \frac{nk_m}{J_4 + n^2J_7}i_a = \frac{B_4 + n^2B_7}{J_4 + p^2J_7}\dot{\varphi}_o$$

We write this in matrix form

$$\frac{d}{dt}\begin{bmatrix} i_3 \\ i_a \\ \dot{\varphi}_o \end{bmatrix} = \begin{bmatrix} -\dfrac{R_3}{L_3} & 0 & 0 \\ -\dfrac{k_m}{2L_a} & -\dfrac{R_a}{L_a} & -\dfrac{k_m}{2nL_a} \\ 0 & \dfrac{nk_m}{J_4 + n^2J_7} & \dfrac{B_4 + n^2B_7}{J_4 + n^2J_7} \end{bmatrix}\begin{bmatrix} i_3 \\ i_a \\ \dot{\varphi}_o \end{bmatrix} + \begin{bmatrix} 1/L_3k_a \\ 0 \\ 0 \end{bmatrix} v_1 \qquad \textbf{(11.48)}$$

and adopt the symbolic notation

$$\frac{d}{dt}\mathbf{x} = \mathbf{A}\mathbf{x} + \mathbf{B}v_1$$
$$\dot{\varphi}_o = \mathbf{C}\mathbf{x} \qquad \textbf{(11.49)}$$

The matrix block diagram in Figure 11.32 represents the matrix differential equations.

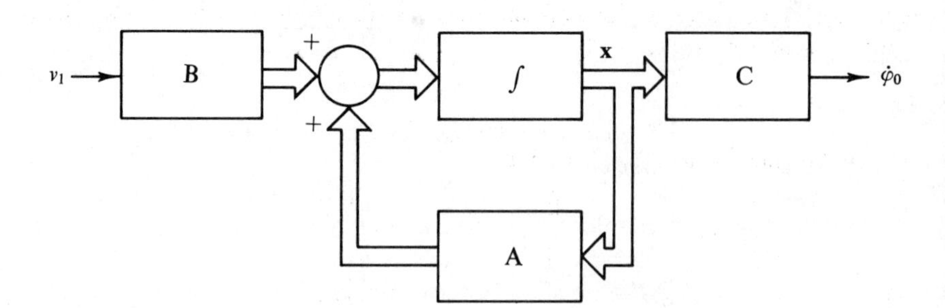

Fig. 11.32. *Matrix block diagram of feedforward components.*

The following symbols are identified for clarification.

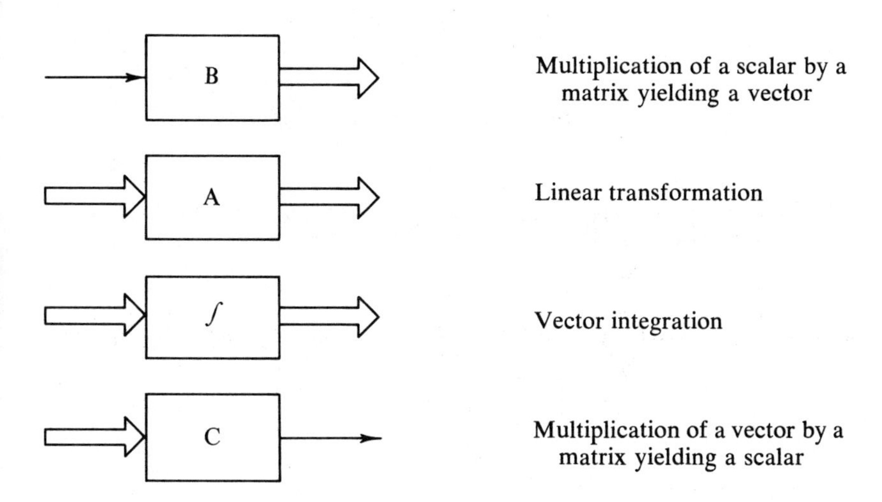

The addition of the feedback component by the equation

$$v_1 = v_i - \frac{k_t}{n}\dot{\varphi}_o \tag{11.50}$$

completes the formulation of the system equations in the t-domain.

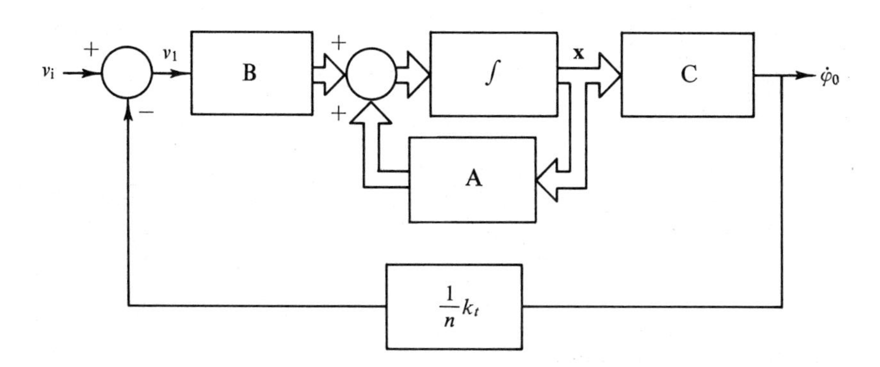

Fig. 11.33. *T-domain block diagram of speed control system.*

The above example demonstrates how s-domain and state variable techniques may be employed in developing block diagrams of linear control systems. A block diagram presents the mathematical model of a system in compact form while effectively retaining the topological outline of the system. Block diagrams have therefore been widely accepted as the official language of the control systems engineer.

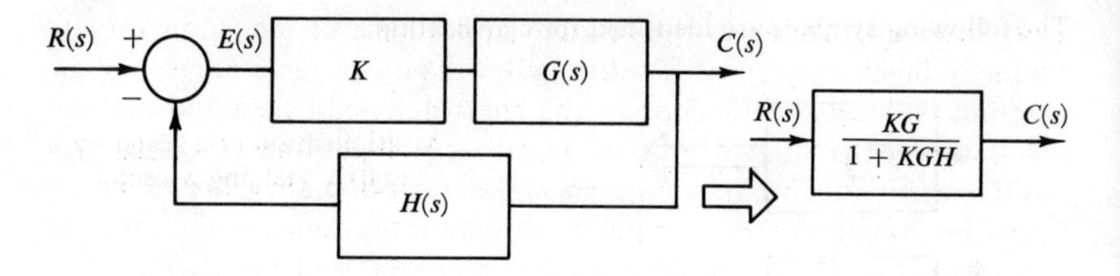

Fig. 11.34. *Feedback identity.*

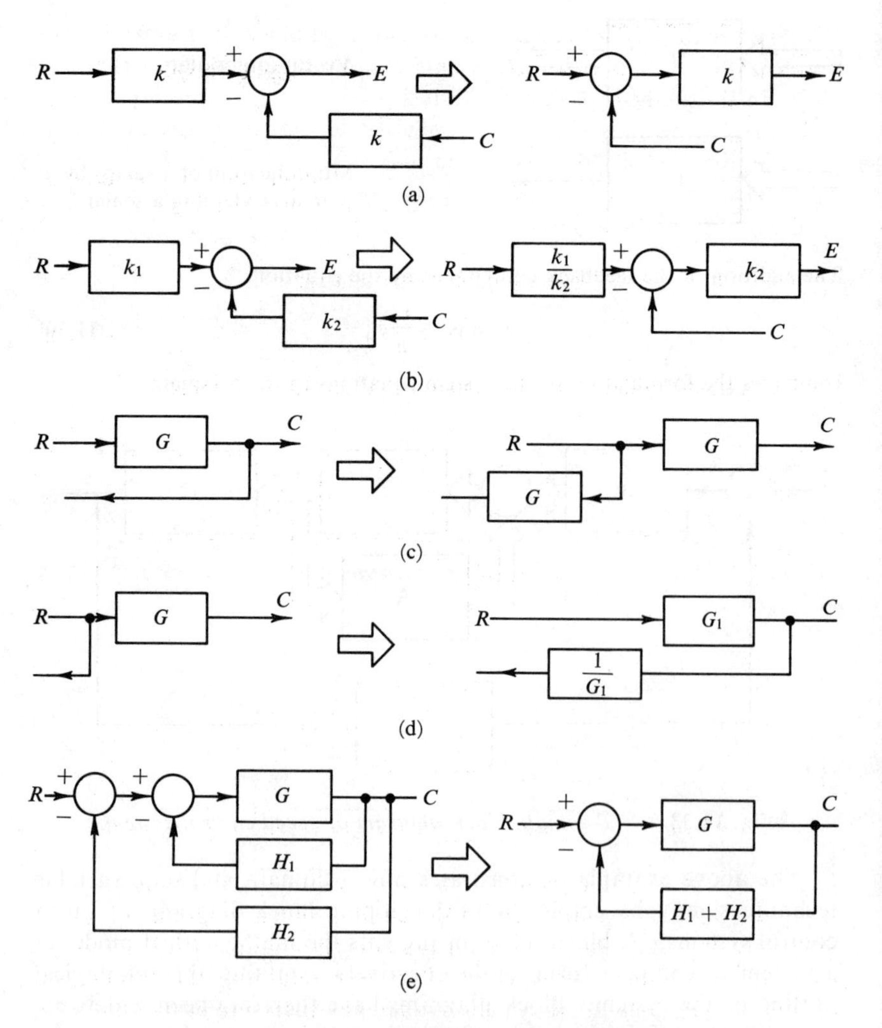

Fig. 11.35. *Several block diagram identities.*

It is difficult to assess the relative importance of the s-domain and t-domain block diagrams. Traditionally, the use of the s-domain block diagram is deeply entrenched in the control systems field and the user has developed a high degree of familiarity with transfer functions. But the recent advance in computers makes the t-domain more attractive from the standpoint of computer programming and simulation since state equations are prerequisite to almost any kind of programming.

Block Diagram Manipulation

Quite frequently it is expedient to rearrange block diagrams to effect simplification. This section presents a number of identities that are useful in the analysis of control systems.

Probably the most important identity is shown in Figure 11.34. This identity is easily derived. The output is

$$C(s) = kG(s)E(s)$$

but

$$E(s) = R(s) - H(s)C(s)$$

so that

$$C(s) = kG(s)R(s) - H(s)C(s)$$

or

$$C(s) = \frac{kG(s)}{1 + kG(s)H(s)} \tag{11.51}$$

Other identities are shown in Figure 11.35.

Example 11.11. Simplify the block diagram of the system shown in Figure 11.36.

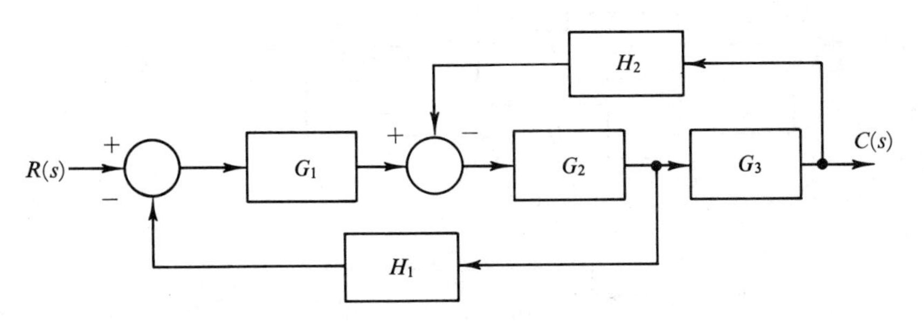

Fig. 11.36. *Example of block diagram.*

The block diagram will be simplified in two ways, as shown by the schematics in Figures 11.37 and 11.38.

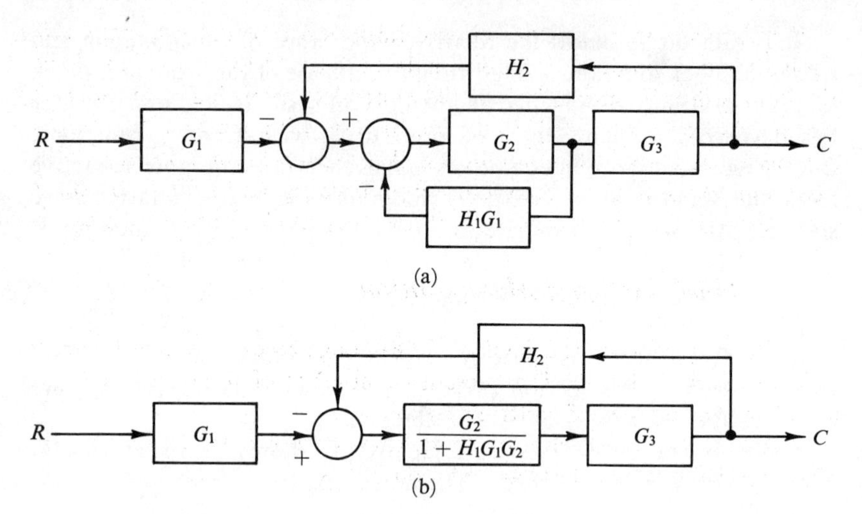

Fig. 11.37. *Simplification to eliminate lower feedback loop.*

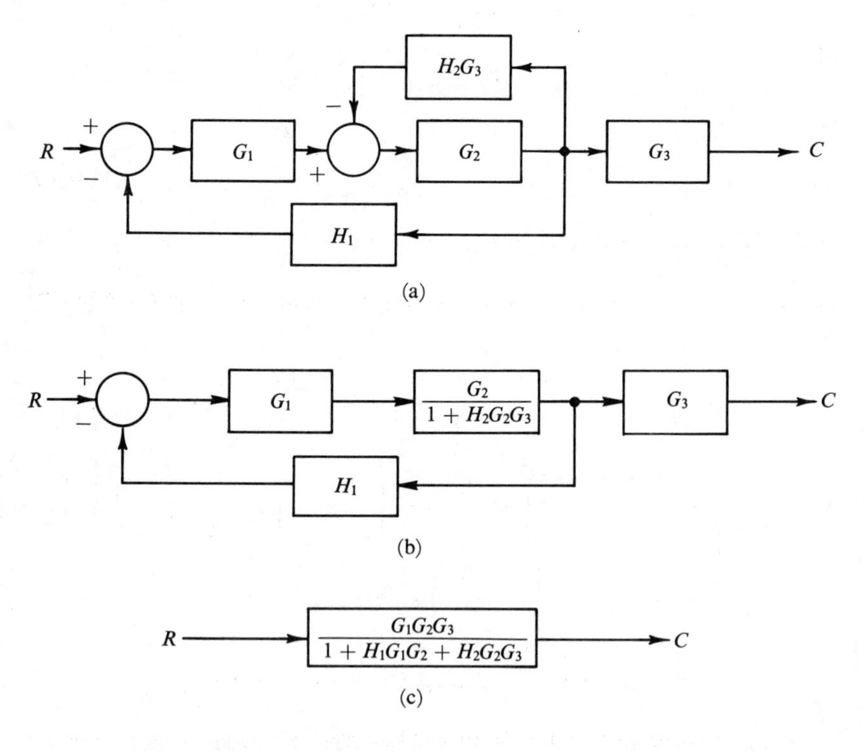

Fig. 11.38. *Simplification to eliminate upper feedback loop and final closed-loop transfer function.*

Summary

This chapter presents systematic procedures, both formal and informal, for the development of mathematical models for systems involving a relatively large number of components, particularly multiterminal components. Both s-domain and t-domain models can be generated with equal case.

As was demonstrated in earlier chapters, the development of state equations of large-scale systems is considerably more efficient through a direct approach into the t-domain than through first developing a transfer function model which is converted into a corresponding state model. Large-scale systems very often possess feedback. A systematic approach in the development of equations for a feedback system relies on viewing such a system as subassemblies of feedforward components and feedback components which are interconnected in series-parallel configuration.

ADDITIONAL READINGS

Harman, W. W., and D. W. Lytle, *Electrical and Mechanical Networks*, New: York: McGraw-Hill Book Co., 1962.

Huelsman, L., *Circuits, Matrices, and Linear Vector Spaces*, New York: McGraw-Hill Book Co., 1963.

Koenig, Herman E., Y. Tokad, and H. K. Kesavan, *Discrete Physical Systems*, New York: McGraw-Hill Book Co., 1966.

Schwarz, R. J., and B. Friedland, *Linear Systems*, New York: McGraw-Hill Book Co., 1965.

Seshu, S., and N. Balabanian, *Linear Network Analysis*, New York: John Wiley & Sons, Inc., 1959.

PROBLEMS

11.1. Two hydraulic cylinders are connected in cascade by means of hydraulic lines. If the component equations are

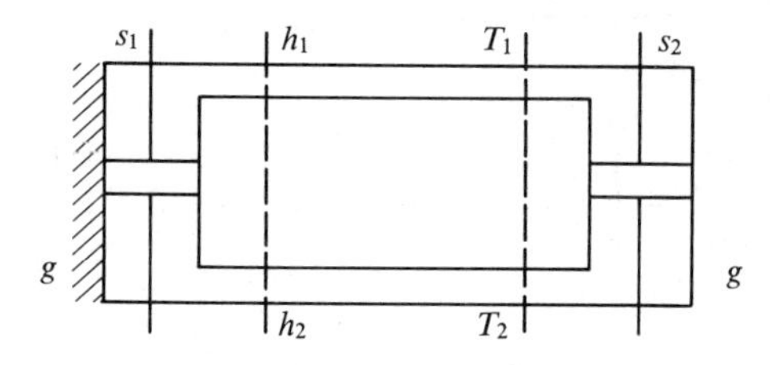

Fig. P 11.1.

hydraulic cylinder,

$$\begin{bmatrix} f \\ \dot{g} \end{bmatrix} = \begin{bmatrix} Ms + B & -A \\ A & 0 \end{bmatrix} \begin{bmatrix} \dot{\delta} \\ p \end{bmatrix}$$

hydraulic line,

$$p = R\dot{g}$$

derive the following terminal representation:

$$\begin{bmatrix} f_1 \\ \\ \delta_2 \end{bmatrix} = \begin{bmatrix} \quad & \quad \\ & \end{bmatrix} \begin{bmatrix} \delta_1 \\ \\ f_2 \end{bmatrix}$$

s_1 s_2 g

11.2. Repeat Problem 11.1 but derive a state model with f_1 as input and δ_2 as output.

11.3. The rear axle of a truck is driven by two hydraulic motors, one on each end, as schematically indicated in Figure P 11.3. The hydraulic motors

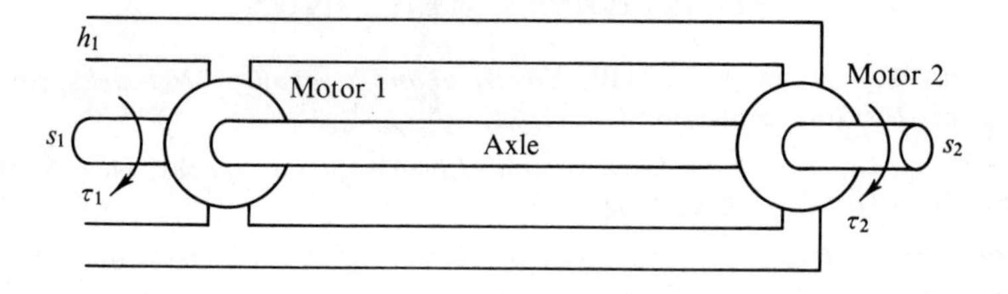

Fig. P 11.3.

are driven by the same pressure supply. A wheel is connected to each end of the axle. The axle is considered a flexible shaft with rotational spring constant k. Develop a mathematical model to study the torque loading of the axle as a function of the independent load torques τ_1 and τ_2.

11.4. Derive a set of state equations to study the stress loading in the flexible shaft which connects the hydraulic motor to an inertial load as shown in Figure P 11.4. Assume that the motor is connected to a sinusoidally varying pressure source.

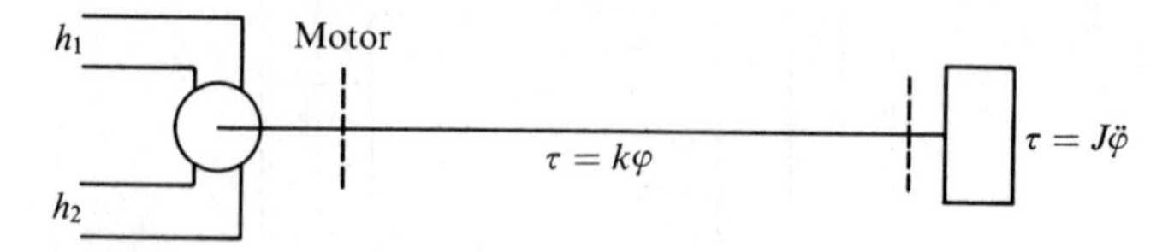

Fig. P 11.4.

11.5. For the problems discussed in Example 11.9, develop a state variable model where δ_i is the input and δ_o is the output.

11.6. For the problem discussed in Example 11.9, connect a spring between the center pivot of the lever and ground and derive the hybrid parameters according to the equation form

$$\begin{bmatrix} F_i \\ \Delta_o \end{bmatrix} = \begin{bmatrix} \quad & \quad \\ \quad & \quad \end{bmatrix} \begin{bmatrix} \Delta_i \\ F_o \end{bmatrix}$$

11.7. Show what simplification in component equations must result for the problem of Example 11.9 if the lever at point *a* can be moved without application of any force, that is, the input power to the system is zero.

11.8. Two components, *A* and *B*, are characterized as follows:

$$A: \begin{bmatrix} x_1 \\ y_2 \end{bmatrix} = \begin{bmatrix} g_1 & 0 \\ g_{21} & g_{22} \end{bmatrix} \begin{bmatrix} y_1 \\ x_2 \end{bmatrix} \qquad B: \begin{bmatrix} y_3 \\ x_4 \end{bmatrix} = \begin{bmatrix} 0 & 0 \\ h_{43} & h_4 \end{bmatrix} \begin{bmatrix} x_3 \\ y_4 \end{bmatrix}$$

Connect these components in the following ways: cascade, series, parallel, and series-parallel, and derive equivalent mathematical models.

11.9. A three-terminal component is characterized by the following mathematical model:

$$\begin{bmatrix} x_1 \\ x_2 \end{bmatrix} = \begin{bmatrix} Z_1 & Z_{12} \\ Z_{21} & Z_2 \end{bmatrix} \begin{bmatrix} y_1 \\ y_2 \end{bmatrix}$$

A two-terminal component is connected between *a* and *b*. Derive an equivalent three-terminal representation by use of a parallel connection. Hint: View the two-terminal component as a three-terminal component.

11.10. Derive the equations of the amplidyne.

11.11. The system shown in Figure P 11.11 consists of a filter network, an amplifier, and an acoustical transducer. Develop an equivalent representation for the three components in cascade.

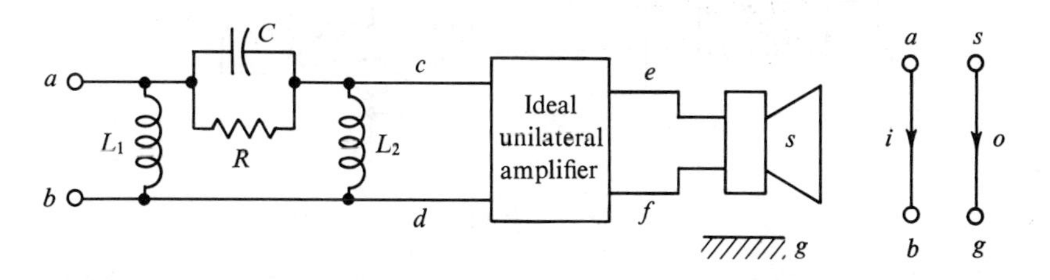

Fig. P 11.11.

11.12. Develop a state variable model for a Ward-Leonard system in which the input voltage, the generator shaft speed, and the motor field voltage are considered as input variables.

11.13. Develop a block diagram for the control system shown in Figure P 11.13.

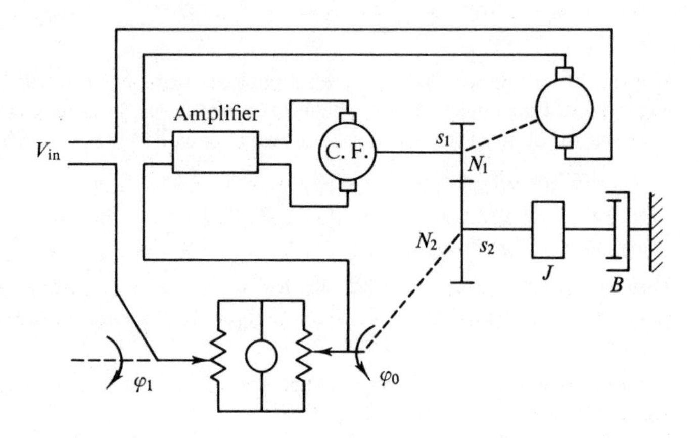

Fig. P 11.13.

11.14. What are the state variable equations for the system of Figure P 11.13?

11.15. Figure P 11.15 shows a differential speed control system. The operation is briefly described. The shaft speed of the dc motor, $\dot{\varphi}_{out}$, is to be matched to the reference speed $\dot{\varphi}_{ref}$. A differential gear measures the speed error and feeds an electrical signal proportional to the error to an integrating amplifier.

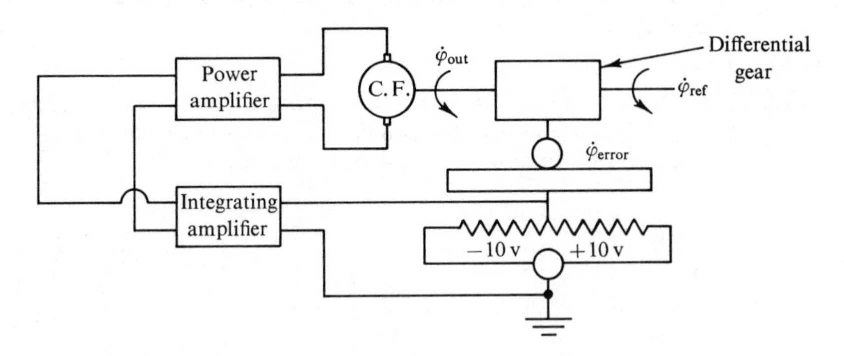

Fig. P 11.15.

11.16. Find the transfer function $C(s)/R(s)$ for the system described by the block diagram of Figure P 11.16.

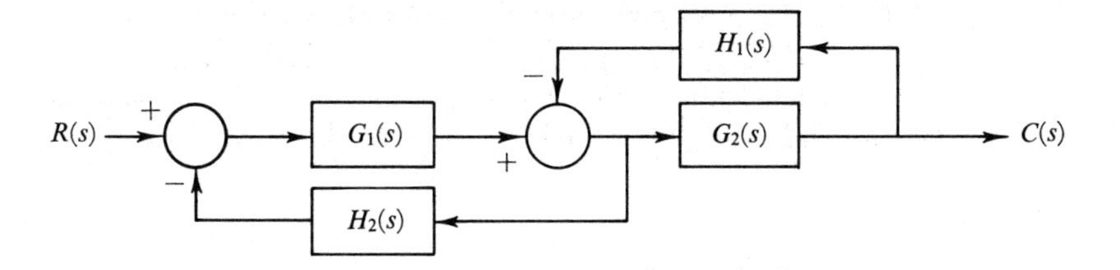

Fig. P 11.16.

11.17 A constant field operated dc motor drives a load of the characteristics $I = (Js^2 + Bs)\varphi$ through a flexible shaft as shown schematically in Figure P 11.17. Determine a mathematical model suitable for computer study with V_{ab} as input and $\dot{\varphi}_{load}$ as output.

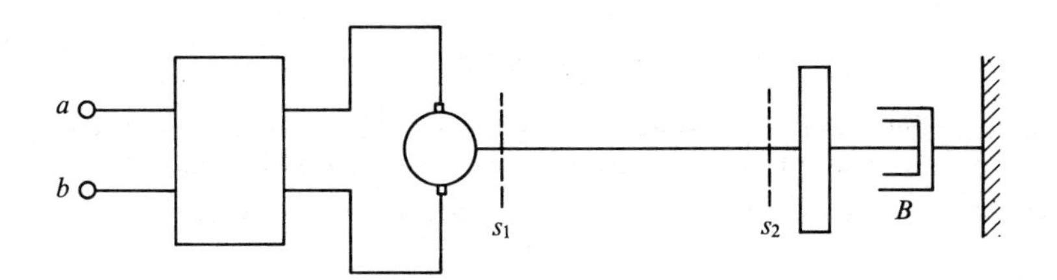

Fig. P 11.17.

11.18. Derive a set of equations suitable for the performance study of the system shown in Figure P 11.18. The form of the equations sought is given as

$$\begin{bmatrix} \dot{g}_1 \\ \delta_o \end{bmatrix} = \begin{bmatrix} \quad \end{bmatrix} \begin{bmatrix} P_i \\ f_o \end{bmatrix}$$

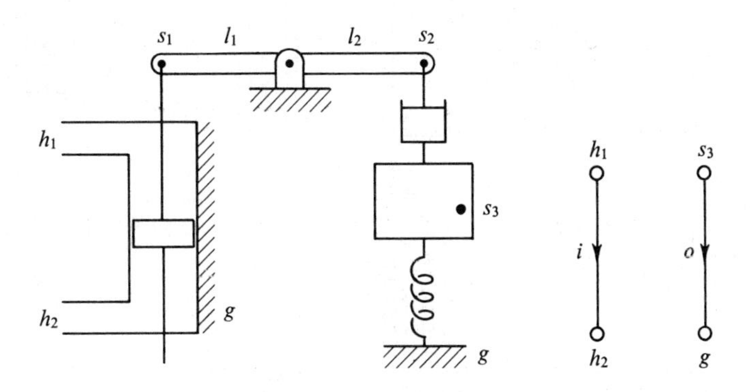

Fig. P 11.18.

Hint: View the system as a combination of three subassemblies.

11.19. Figure P 11.19 shows the schematic of an electrical system designed to mix two inputs into a single signal. Develop both an s-domain and t-domain model showing V_a and V_b as inputs and V_c as output.

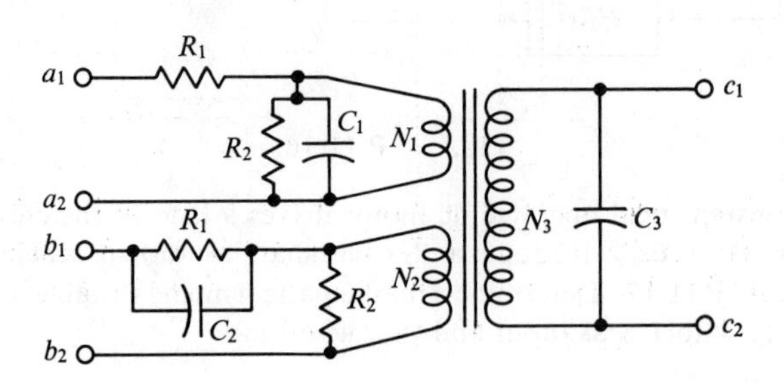

Fig. P 11.19. *Ideal transformer.*

11.20. Show that if the system of Problem 11.19 is used in reverse it separates a signal into a high-frequency and a low-frequency signal.

11.21. Find state variable equations for the systems in Figure P 11.21.

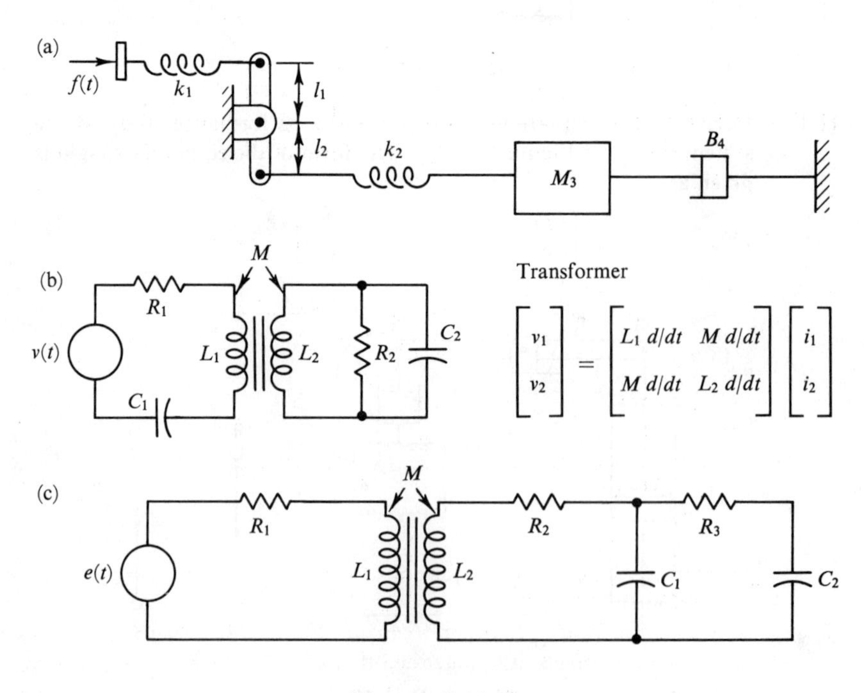

Fig. P 11.21.

11.22.

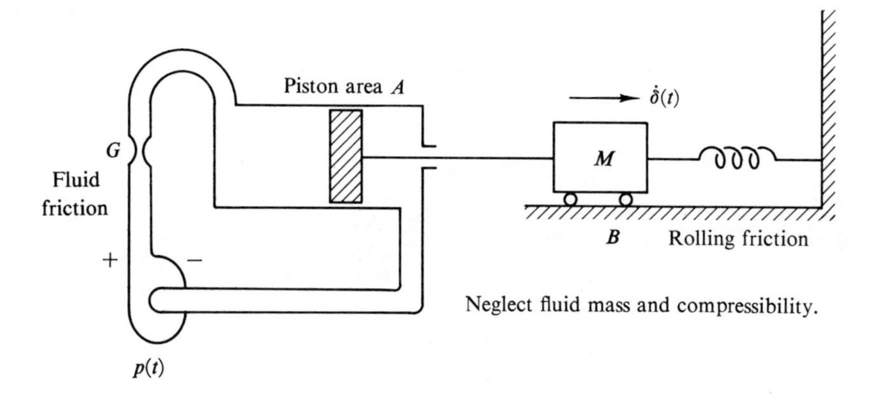

Fig. P 11.22.

Develop a state space model of the system of Figure P 11.22; $\dot{\delta}(t)$ = output, $p(t)$ = drive.

11.23.

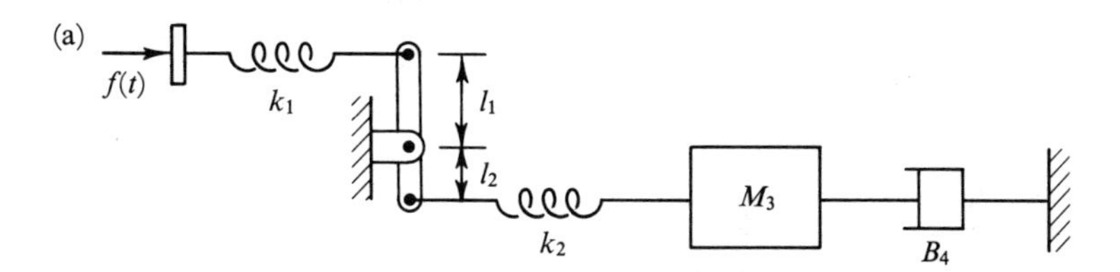

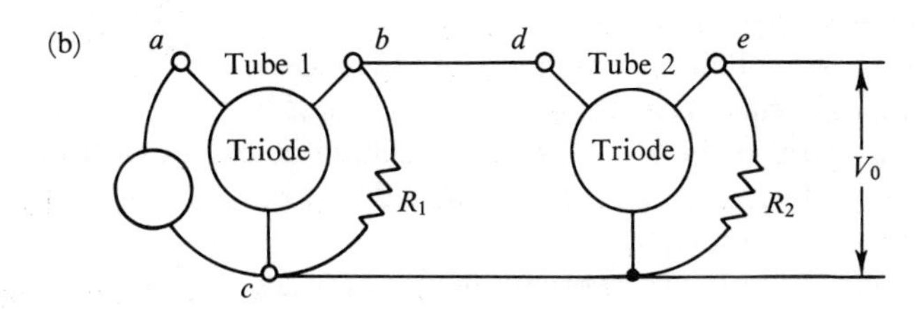

Fig. P 11.23.

a) Find the state variable equations for the systems of Figure P 11.23 (a) and (b).

b) Calculate V_o/V_i. In order to maintain control over the order of inverses involved, it is suggested that the systems be solved in two steps.

Computer Methods in System Analysis

12

In recent years an important tool has been made available to the scientific community. It is the electronic computer. With the aid of a computer, man can realize objectives today which were considered fantastic only a few years ago. The achievements of the modern computer (really of man with the aid of the modern computer) can easily leave the layman in a state of bewilderment, or perhaps in a state of carefree ignorance. But the scientist cannot afford to be ignorant of the computer.

The trend of the modern curriculum is to involve the engineering student in the use of a computer to solve his problems. This chapter offers some insight into the utilization of both analog and digital computers as tools in the analysis of circuits and systems. Part of the objective is to develop background fundamentals in the area of system analysis by computer. And in part the objective is to present some of the knowledge and techniques needed in approaching the solution of an analysis problem by use of the computer.

Both the analog and digital computer are of equal importance in the field of system analysis. Both types of computers are, in a manner of speaking, processors of mathematical models to generate solutions. The analog computer is particularly successful in the solution of differential equations, both linear and nonlinear. On the other hand, the strength of the digital computer (one of many, to be sure) is its ability to perform a large amount of computation with high precision in the determination of performance aspects such as frequency response, transient response, characteristic roots, etc.

By and large, both types of computers serve well for a wide range of objectives. For some it matters little which computer is used. For others it makes a big difference, not just because of the nature of the problems, but also because of the basic differences in the physical design of the computer. The two types of computers represent tools of system analysis of tremendous potential, the full range of which can only be realized with a substantial effort. The full picture in computer utilization should be supported with a basic understanding and fortified with a reasonable amount of experience in the following aspects:

1. Generation of mathematical models for computer processing,
2. Analog computer programming,
3. Digital computer programming,
4. Fundamentals of numerical analysis,
5. Basic machine characteristics of the analog computer,
6. Basic machine characteristics of the digital computer,
7. Knowledge of application programs.

Background in these areas should best be built in the order shown. We aim to cover some aspects of the first four.

12.1 Equations for Computer Solution

One of the factors to be considered in the employment of a computer for the analysis of a system is the form of the mathematical model derived. We have studied several formulation procedures in the preceding chapters. They can be categorized according to whether they generate an s-domain model or a t-domain model, or whether the end product is a transfer function or a set of state equations. It will be shown in this chapter that a state model is the most suitable form in which to derive equations for computer processing.

State equations as we have learned to use them are a set of simultaneous first-order differential equations, linear and nonlinear, of the general form

$$\frac{d}{dt}x_i = f_i(x_1, x_2, \cdots, x_n, t) \qquad i = 1, 2, \cdots, n \tag{12.1}$$

$$x_{\text{out}} = \sum_{i=1}^{n} c_i x_i \tag{12.2}$$

These equations describe the time dependent relationships of a given system. The independent variable in these equations is time, which is a continuous variable. The analog computer is basically an electronic analog whose dynamics are adjusted to be mathematically identical to the system described by Equations 12.1. Since it is therefore a continuous time system, equations of the form 12.1 and 12.2 are directly processable by the analog computer.

In contrast to the analog computer, which functions as a *continuous* time system, the digital computer is a *discrete* time processor. It is restricted to receiving input information and generating output results only at discrete time instants. Consequently, the most suitable form in which mathematical models should be prepared for solution by digital computer is a set of simultaneous first-order *difference* equations. Difference equations, as was pointed out in the first chapter, are the proper mathematical language for describing the interrelationship of discrete event systems. Thus a model for the digital computer is given by the equation

$$x_i(k+1) = f_i[x_1(k), x_2(k), \cdots, x_n(k), k] \quad i = 1, 2, \cdots, n \tag{12.3}$$

where the $x_i(k)$ are the state variables of a system describing the system at event or time k. Equations of the type 12.3 may be derived according to formal procedures similar to those presented in this book.

The discussion so far indicates that differential equations are solved by the analog computer, while the digital computer can only handle difference equations. Strictly speaking, that is true. However, if difference equation approximations of differential equations are considered, the usefulness of the digital computer is significantly expanded. As an illustration of this approach, consider the following.

Let the state equations be given

$$\frac{d}{dt}\begin{bmatrix} x_1 \\ x_2 \end{bmatrix} = \begin{bmatrix} -1 & -2 \\ 1 & 0 \end{bmatrix}\begin{bmatrix} x_1 \\ x_2 \end{bmatrix} + \begin{bmatrix} 1 \\ 0 \end{bmatrix} r(t) \tag{12.4}$$

If the derivatives are approximated by a first order difference such that

$$\frac{d}{dt}x = \frac{x(k+1) - x(k)}{t_{k-1} - t_k} = \frac{x(k+1) - x(k)}{h} \tag{12.5}$$

then Equations 12.4 may be approximated by the difference equations

$$\begin{aligned} x_1(k+1) &= x_1(k) + h[-x_1(k) - 2x_2(k) + r(k)] \\ x_2(k+1) &= x_2(k) + h[x_1(k)] \end{aligned} \tag{12.6}$$

These equations are now in a form suitable for the digital computer.

A relatively simple computer program will suffice to evaluate them recursively. The solution will then consist of two sequences of numbers, each one associated with one value of the state variables and all of them spaced h units of time apart.

An approximation of a continuous variable by a discrete variable is involved in the above development in two ways. For one thing, the derivatives are approximated by finite differences; second, the input, which is a continuous function, is represented by a staircase approximation such as is shown in Figure 12.1. The quality of this approxi-

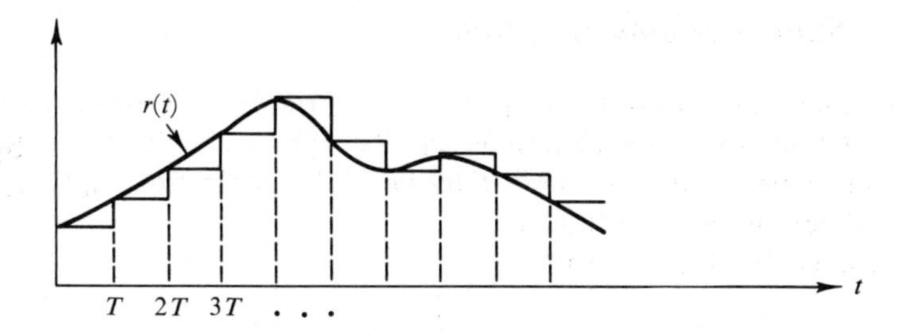

Fig. 12.1. *Staircase approximation of continuous function.*

mation obviously depends upon the selection of the time interval h and the " rapidity " with which the function $r(t)$ varies.

Approximations of differential equations by difference equations introduce errors into the solution. The magnitude of these errors must be carefully understood in order to assess the reliability of the solution. More will be said about this later. For approximating the solutions of differential equations, a subject which is generally referred to as numerical integration, the digital computer becomes a powerful tool in system analysis in general.

12.2 Generation of State Equations from Transfer Functions

Linear systems are very frequently described by transfer functions. In order to perform a computer analysis of the response characteristics of transfer functions, it is necessary to convert the representation of the system from a transfer function into a set of state equations. Basically, the objective is to convert an input-output relationship of the form

$$x_{\text{out}}(s) = \frac{a_0 s^m + a_1 s^{m-1} + \cdots + a_{m-1} s + a_m}{s^n + b_1 s^{n-1} + \cdots + b_{n-1} s + b_n} x_{\text{in}}(s) \quad m \leq n \qquad \textbf{(12.7)}$$

into the form

$$\frac{d}{dt}\mathbf{x} = \mathbf{A}\mathbf{x} + \mathbf{B}x_{\text{in}} \tag{12.8}$$

$$x_{\text{out}} = \mathbf{C}\mathbf{x} + dx_{\text{in}} \tag{12.9}$$

We will see how this problem can be handled in a straightforward systematic procedure. This will be accomplished by a clever application of a topological reduction formula, called Mason's gain formula, and the use of state variable diagrams.

State Variable Diagrams

The interrelationship between the state variables of a linear system as defined by the state equations can be effectively displayed by a diagram, called a *state variable diagram*. The generation and use of such a diagram will be illustrated.

Consider the state equations

$$\frac{d}{dt}\begin{bmatrix} x_1 \\ x_2 \end{bmatrix} = \begin{bmatrix} -1 & -2 \\ 1 & 0 \end{bmatrix}\begin{bmatrix} x_1 \\ x_2 \end{bmatrix} + \begin{bmatrix} 1 \\ 0 \end{bmatrix} x_{\text{in}} \tag{12.10}$$

$$x_{\text{out}} = [5 \quad 1]\begin{bmatrix} x_1 \\ x_2 \end{bmatrix} \tag{12.11}$$

A state variable diagram is formulated in the following steps.

1. Write the differential equations as integrating equations.

$$x_1 = \int_0^t (-x_1 - 2x_2 + x_{\text{in}})\, d\tau$$

$$x_2 = \int_0^t x_1\, d\tau$$

2. View the state variables as outputs of integrators.

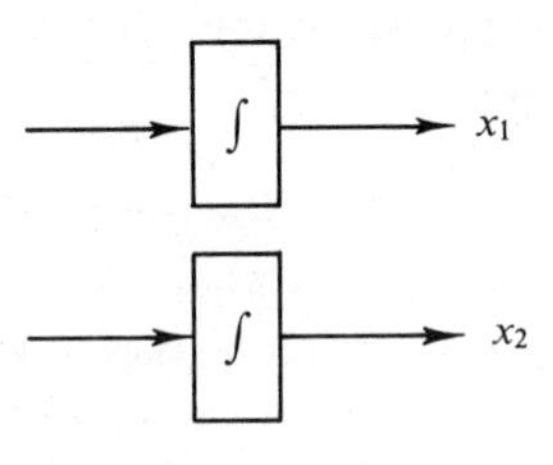

3. Draw the necessary interconnection to generate the inputs to the integrators.

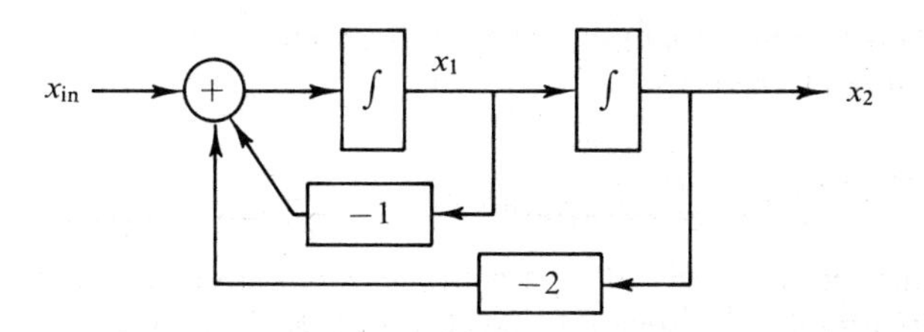

4. Generate the output as a linear combination of state variables.

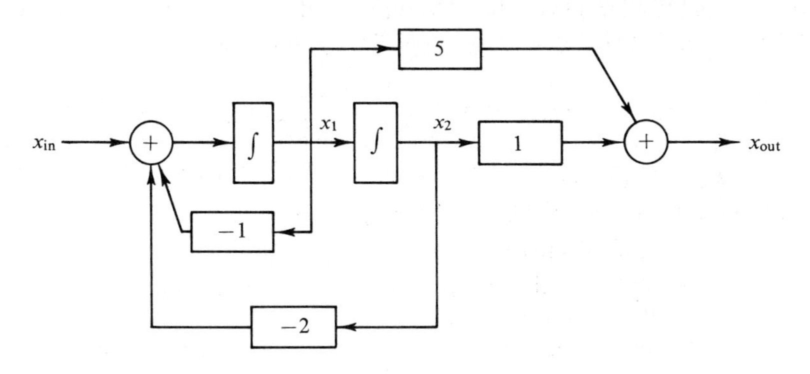

Fig. 12.2. *State variable diagram of Equations 12.10 and 12.11.*

It is easily seen that the construction of a state variable diagram is a relatively uncomplicated process.

On occasion it is convenient to use a different set of symbols, as indicated by the diagram of Figure 12.3. Such a diagram is called a flow-graph.

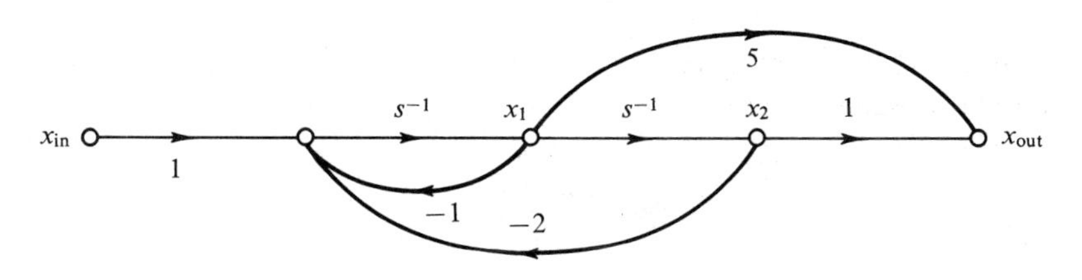

Fig. 12.3. *Flow-graph of state equations.*

In a state variable diagram, basic linear operators such as summers, integrators, and multipliers are indicated by block diagram symbols in an input-output manner. Flow graphs use operator-weighted oriented line elements, while the nodes represent variables. Both types of graphs are used interchangeably.

*Mason's Gain Formula**

An important topological formula, called Mason's gain formula, can be effectively employed to compute transfer functions between any two points of a state variable diagram. This technique is efficient and rapid, permitting the determination of input-output transforms from a state variable diagram or flow graph. According to Mason, the transfer function between two nodes in a flow-graph is given by

$$\frac{x_1(s)}{x_2(s)} = T(s) = \frac{\sum_k M_k(s)\,{}_k\Delta k(s)}{\Delta(s)} \tag{12.12}$$

where $M_k(s)$ is the gain of the kth forward path, $\Delta(s)$ is the system determinant or characteristic equation equal to

1 − (sum of all individual loop gains)
+ (sum of gain products of all possible combinations of two non-touching loops)
− (sum of gain products of all possible combinations of three non-touching loops)
+ · · ·

and $\Delta_k(s)$ is the value of $\Delta(s)$ for that part of the graph not touching the kth forward path. The method is probably quite complex if all possible combinations of topological configurations are present—but normally this is not the case. In connection with our objective, the topological complexities are minimum. The method is best illustrated by an example.

Example 12.1. Compute the transfer function $X_{\text{out}}(s)/X_{\text{in}}(s)$ for the state variable diagram of Figure 12.2.

There are two forward paths:

$$M_1 = 5s^{-1}$$

and

$$M_2 = s^{-2}$$

In both cases the $\Delta_k(s)$ is equal to unity, since both paths touch all loops. There are two loops touching each other; hence

$$\begin{aligned}\Delta(s) &= 1 - (-s^{-1} - 2s^{-2})\\ &= 1 + s^{-1} + 2s^{-2}\end{aligned}$$

* S. J. Mason, "Feedback Theory—Further Properties of Signal Flow Graphs," *Proc. IRE.*, Vol. 44, No. 7 (July 1956), pp. 920–926.

The overall transfer function is

$$T(s) = \frac{M_1 + M_2}{\Delta(s)}$$
$$= \frac{5s^{-1} + s^{-2}}{1 + s^{-1} + 2s^{-2}}$$
$$= \frac{5s + 1}{s^2 + s + 2}$$

Generation of State Equations by Use of Mason's Formula

By reversing the process just demonstrated so that we begin with a transfer function, generate a corresponding flow-graph and then read off the state equations by inspection, we have a rapid and direct approach to determining the state equations from a transfer function. The key to the success of applying Mason's gain formula to the generation of state equations from a transfer function lies in determining flow-graphs (or state variable diagrams) that are topologically minimum such that

$$\Delta(s) = 1 - (\text{sum of all loop gains of all individual loops}) \quad \textbf{(12.13)}$$
$$\Delta_k(s) = 1 \quad \textbf{(12.14)}$$

Thus the flow-graphs to be generated must have all their loops touch one another, and all forward paths must touch all loops. This technique will be demonstrated for the transfer function

$$G(s) = \frac{s^2 + 5s + 2}{s^3 + 2s^2 + 4s + 10} \quad \textbf{(12.15)}$$

In order to apply Mason's gain formula conveniently, we write this transfer function in powers of s^{-1},

$$G(s) = \frac{s^{-1} + 5s^{-2} + 2s^{-3}}{1 + 2s^{-1} + 4s^{-2} + 10s^{-3}} \quad \textbf{(12.16)}$$

Now the objective of this method is to generate a flow-graph (state variable diagram) which represents a direct realization of the transfer function by application of Mason's formula. To look at it another way, we wish to generate a flow-graph which will yield the above transfer function by application of Mason's formula in the simplest manner.

Unfolding the development step by step, our first objective will be the synthesis of the denominator

$$1 + 2s^{-1} + 4s^{-2} + 10s^{-3}$$

According to Equation 12.13, we write this as

$$1 - (-2s^{-1} - 4s^{-2} - 10s^{-3})$$

and stipulate that the flow-graph should contain three loops with gains equal to

$$-2s^{-1} \qquad -4s^{-2} \qquad -10s^{-3}$$

Furthermore, these loops must be touching such that $\Delta(s)$ is indeed given by Equation 12.14. A flow-graph satisfying these requirements is shown in Figure 12.4.

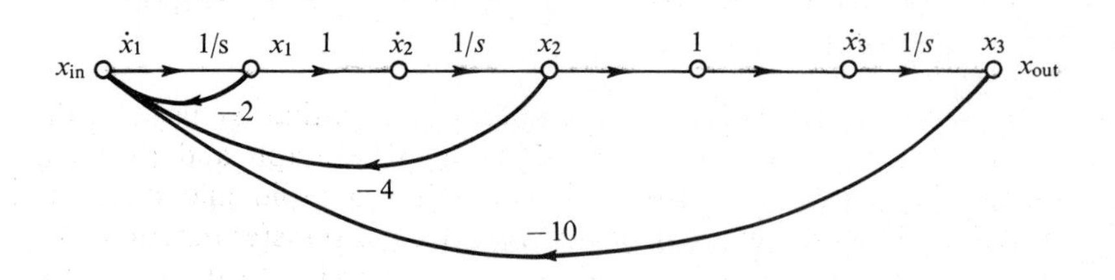

Fig. 12.4. *Flow graph to realize denominator.*

Although a simpler flow-graph (eliminating nodes x_2 and x_3) yielding the same denominator could be found, we must keep in mind that we want to generate state equations and hence introduce three state variables into the diagram.

We next turn to the numerator of the transfer function. By Mason's formula this must correspond to

$$\sum_k M_k \Delta_k(s)$$

According to Equation 12.14, $\Delta_k(s) = 1$; hence

$$\sum_k M_k = s^{-1} + 5s^{-2} + 2s^{-3}$$

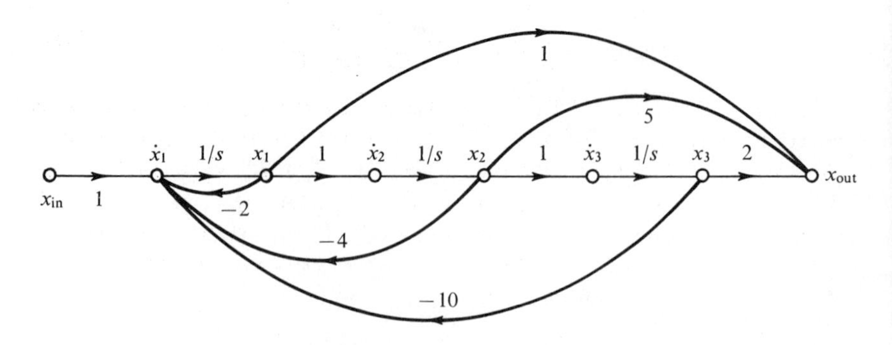

Fig. 12.5. *Complete flow-graph synthesis of transfer function.*

Thus we look for three forward paths between x_{in} and x_{out} with gains, respectively, of

$$s^{-1} \qquad 5s^{-2} \qquad 2s^{-3}$$

Figure 12.5 shows these forward paths in addition to the first graph. Notice that three state variables are provided. It is now an easy matter to generate the state model corresponding to the flow graph. These are

$$\frac{d}{dt}\begin{bmatrix} x_1 \\ x_2 \\ x_3 \end{bmatrix} = \begin{bmatrix} -2 & -4 & -10 \\ 1 & 0 & 0 \\ 0 & 1 & 0 \end{bmatrix}\begin{bmatrix} x_1 \\ x_2 \\ x_3 \end{bmatrix} + \begin{bmatrix} 1 \\ 0 \\ 0 \end{bmatrix} x_{in}$$

$$x_{out} = [1 \quad 5 \quad 2]\begin{bmatrix} x_1 \\ x_2 \\ x_3 \end{bmatrix} \tag{12.17}$$

These state equations are not unique. An alternate configuration for a state variable diagram may be readily constructed, as shown in Figure 12.6

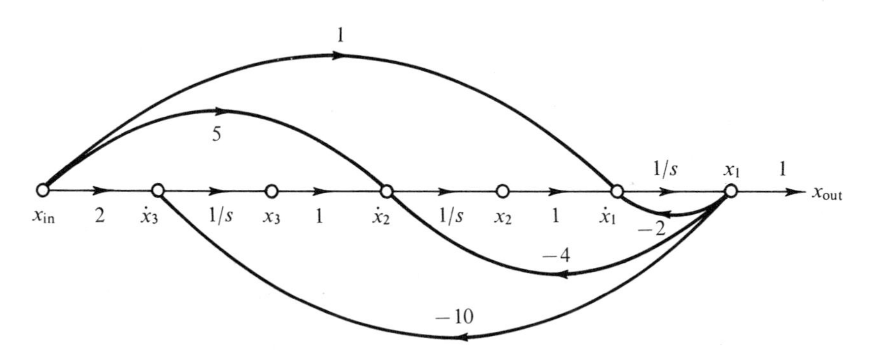

Fig. 12.6. *Alternate flow-graph.*

The state equations for this flow-graph are

$$\frac{d}{dt}\begin{bmatrix} x_1 \\ x_2 \\ x_3 \end{bmatrix} = \begin{bmatrix} -2 & 1 & 0 \\ -4 & 0 & 1 \\ -10 & 0 & 0 \end{bmatrix}\begin{bmatrix} x_1 \\ x_2 \\ x_3 \end{bmatrix} + \begin{bmatrix} 1 \\ 5 \\ 2 \end{bmatrix} x_{in}$$

$$x_{out} = x_1 \tag{12.18}$$

Both approaches find equal application in the development of state equations from transfer functions. Because of the manner in which the input and output functions affect the form, the equations of these two methods are called *single-input programming* (Equation 12.17) and *single-output programming* (Equation 12.18). The two methods are closely related, a fact which is easily recognized through inspection of the respective state equations.

General Properties of State Equation Programming Techniques

It is interesting to investigate the general properties of single-input and single-output programming. For this purpose, consider the flow-graphs corresponding to the transfer function given by Equation 12.7, which is repeated here for $n = m$;

$$X_{\text{out}}(s) = \frac{a_0 s^n + a_1 s^{n-1} + \cdots + a_{n-1}s + a_n}{s^n + b_1 s^{n-1} + \cdots + b_{n-1}s + b_n} X_{\text{in}}(s) \tag{12.19}$$

The two possible flow-graphs are shown in Figures 12.7 and 12.8.

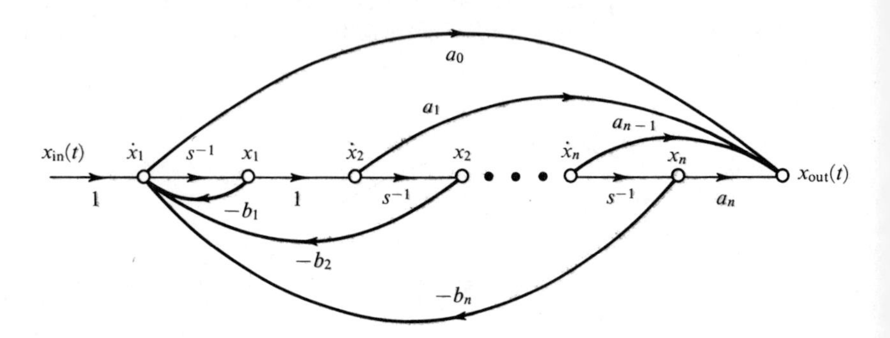

Fig. 12.7. *Single-input programming flow-graph.*

The state equations for the single-input realization are

$$\frac{d}{dt}\begin{bmatrix} x_1 \\ x_2 \\ \cdot \\ \cdot \\ \cdot \\ x_n \end{bmatrix} = \begin{bmatrix} -b_1 & -b_2 & \cdots & 0 & -b_n \\ 1 & 0 & \cdots & 0 & 0 \\ 0 & 1 & \cdots & 0 & 0 \\ \cdot & & & & \cdot \\ \cdot & & & & \cdot \\ 0 & 0 & \cdots & 1 & 0 \end{bmatrix} \begin{bmatrix} x_1 \\ x_2 \\ \cdot \\ \cdot \\ \cdot \\ x_n \end{bmatrix} + \begin{bmatrix} 1 \\ 0 \\ \cdot \\ \cdot \\ \cdot \\ 0 \end{bmatrix} x_{\text{in}}(t) \tag{12.20}$$

$$x_{\text{out}}(t) = [a_1 - b_1 a_0 \quad a_2 - b_2 a_0 \quad \cdots \quad a_n - b_n a_0] \begin{bmatrix} x_1 \\ x_2 \\ \cdot \\ \cdot \\ \cdot \\ x_n \end{bmatrix} + a_0 x_{\text{in}}(t) \tag{12.21}$$

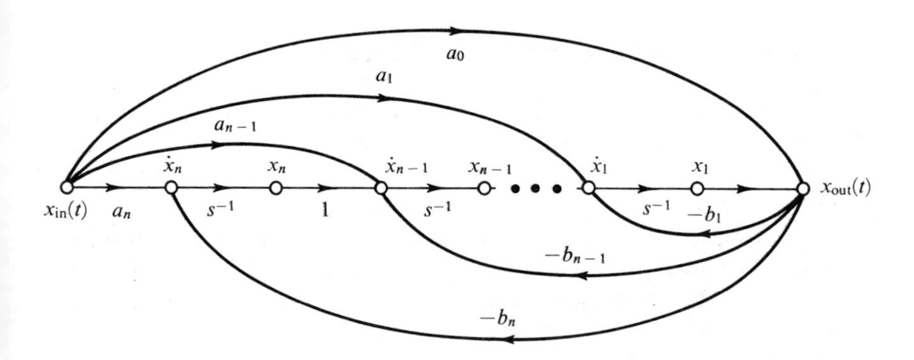

Fig. 12.8. *Single-output programming flow-graph.*

The corresponding state equations are

$$\frac{d}{dt}\begin{bmatrix} x_1 \\ x_2 \\ \cdot \\ \cdot \\ \cdot \\ x_n \end{bmatrix} = \begin{bmatrix} -b_1 & 1 & 0 & \cdots & 0 \\ -b_2 & 0 & 1 & \cdots & 0 \\ \cdot & & & & \\ \cdot & & & & \\ \cdot & & & & 1 \\ -b_n & 0 & 0 & \cdots & 0 \end{bmatrix}\begin{bmatrix} x_1 \\ x_2 \\ \cdot \\ \cdot \\ \cdot \\ x_n \end{bmatrix} + \begin{bmatrix} a_1 - b_1a_0 \\ a_2 - b_2a_0 \\ \cdot \\ \cdot \\ \cdot \\ a_n - b_na_0 \end{bmatrix} x_{in}(t) \quad \textbf{(12.22)}$$

$$x_{out}(t) = [1 \quad 0 \quad \cdots \quad 0]\begin{bmatrix} x_1 \\ x_2 \\ \cdot \\ \cdot \\ \cdot \\ x_n \end{bmatrix} + a_0x_{in}(t) \quad \textbf{(12.23)}$$

A comparison of the two models reveals that if the single-input programming model is

$$\frac{d}{dt}\mathbf{x}_1 = \mathbf{A}\mathbf{x}_1 + \mathbf{B}x_{in}(t)$$
$$x_{out}(t) = \mathbf{C}\mathbf{x}_1 + dx_{in}(t) \quad \textbf{(12.24)}$$

then the single-output programming model is

$$\frac{d}{dt}\mathbf{x}_2 = \mathbf{A}'\mathbf{x}_2 + \mathbf{C}'x_{in}(t)$$
$$x_{out}(t) = \mathbf{B}'\mathbf{x}_2 + dx_{in}(t) \quad \textbf{(12.25)}$$

Note that the state variables are *not* the same in the two cases.

12.3 Analog Computer Techniques

Analog computers are extensively employed in the analysis, simulation, and design of systems. As the name of this type of computer implies, solutions are provided as a direct analog to the system under study. Problem variables are represented by voltages, while the solution may progress at a time scale directly proportional to the actual problem solution. As was pointed out earlier, a mathematical model in terms of state variables is most suitable for using an analog computer in investigating performance characteristics of dynamic systems.

In this section we will consider some of the more elementary techniques of preparing an analog computer solution. It is, of necessity, a brief introduction and the reader is referred to numerous texts on analog computer techniques.

Basic Analog Computer Components

An analog computer solution consists of the interconnection of a number of functional components into a system whose dynamics represents an analog to the real system. The components have characteristics which are by and large identical to those indicated by the operational blocks in a state variable diagram. The analog computer components essential to the solution of linear state equations follow.

1. Integrator-summer.

Symbol: Equation:

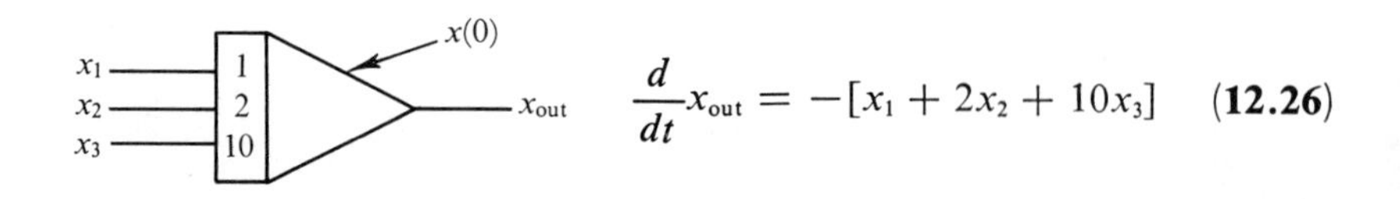

$$\frac{d}{dt}x_{\text{out}} = -[x_1 + 2x_2 + 10x_3] \quad \mathbf{(12.26)}$$

$x(0)$ is the initial condition.

An example for three inputs is shown, with fixed gains of 1, 2, and 10, respectively, which are usually available as standard. A fixed characteristic of an integrator is the sign inversion as indicated by Equation 12.26. This is an inherent design feature of all amplifiers.

The initial value of an integrator may be set equal to the initial condition of a state variable by providing a fixed voltage equal or proportional to the initial condition.

2. Amplifier-summer.

Symbol: Equation:

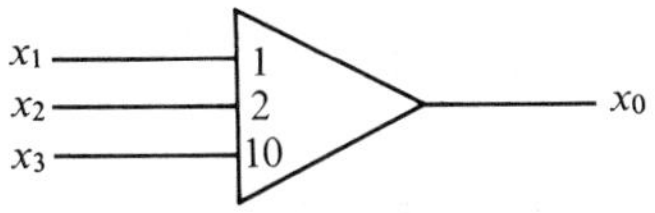

x_1, x_2, x_3 — 1, 2, 10 — x_0

$$x_{out} = -[x_1 + 2x_2 + 10x_3] \tag{12.27}$$

Again an example of three inputs is shown, with fixed gains of 1, 2, and 10, respectively. Note again the sign of inversion.

3. Potentiometer (attenuator).

Symbol: Equation:

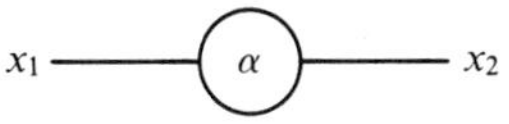

x_1 — α — x_2

$$x_2 = \alpha x_1, \qquad 0 \leq \alpha \leq 1 \tag{12.28}$$

Solution of Linear State Equations

The three analog computer components so far introduced are sufficient to solve linear state equations. A first step essential to the programming of an analog computer is the preparation of an analog computer diagram. This diagram serves then as a blueprint for the interconnection of the computer elements.

Let the state equations corresponding to a linear system be given as

$$\frac{d}{dt}\begin{bmatrix} x_1 \\ x_2 \\ \cdot \\ \cdot \\ \cdot \\ x_n \end{bmatrix} = \begin{bmatrix} a_{11} & a_{12} & \cdots & a_{1n} \\ a_{21} & & \cdots & a_{2n} \\ \cdot & & & \\ \cdot & & & \\ \cdot & & & \\ a_{n1} & & \cdots & a_{nn} \end{bmatrix}\begin{bmatrix} x_1 \\ x_2 \\ \cdot \\ \cdot \\ \cdot \\ x_n \end{bmatrix} + \begin{bmatrix} b_1 \\ b_2 \\ \cdot \\ \cdot \\ \cdot \\ b_n \end{bmatrix} x_{in}(t) \tag{12.29}$$

$$x_{out}(t) = [c_1 \quad c_2 \quad \cdots \quad c_n]\begin{bmatrix} x_1 \\ x_2 \\ \cdot \\ \cdot \\ \cdot \\ x_n \end{bmatrix} \tag{12.30}$$

A single-input single-output system will be assumed. Each state equation requires one integrator-summer with exactly $n + 1$ inputs, n inputs of state variables and one input of the driving function. Since an integrator introduces an automatic sign inversion, it is best to rewrite Equations 12.29 to reflect this sign inversion. Thus

$$\frac{d}{dt}\begin{bmatrix} x_1 \\ x_2 \\ \cdot \\ \cdot \\ \cdot \\ x_n \end{bmatrix} = -\left\{\begin{bmatrix} -a_{11} & -a_{12} & \cdots & -a_{1n} \\ -a_{21} & -a_{22} & \cdots & -a_{2n} \\ \cdot & & & \\ \cdot & & & \\ \cdot & & & \\ -a_{n1} & & \cdots & -a_{nn} \end{bmatrix}\begin{bmatrix} x_1 \\ x_2 \\ \cdot \\ \cdot \\ \cdot \\ x_n \end{bmatrix} + \begin{bmatrix} -b_1 \\ -b_2 \\ \cdot \\ \cdot \\ \cdot \\ -b_n \end{bmatrix} x_{\text{in}}(t)\right\} \tag{12.31}$$

In addition, the programming of each equation requires the use of $n + 1$ potentiometers, one for each input. A given state equation, therefore, is programmed by a diagram as shown in Figure 12.9.

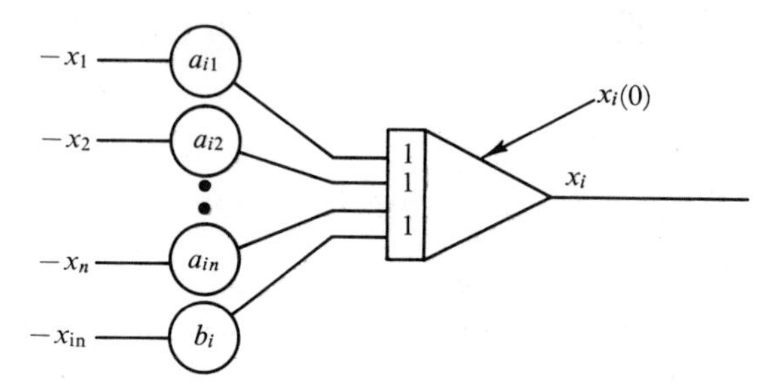

Fig. 12.9. *Analog computer implementation of a state equation.*

Similar diagrams are prepared for other state equations. A complete diagram is best demonstrated by an example.

Example 12.2. Set up an analog computer diagram for the state equations

$$\frac{d}{dt}\begin{bmatrix} x_1 \\ x_2 \end{bmatrix} = \begin{bmatrix} -1 & -0.2 \\ 1 & 1 \end{bmatrix}\begin{bmatrix} x_1 \\ x_2 \end{bmatrix} + \begin{bmatrix} 1 \\ 4 \end{bmatrix} x_{\text{in}}(t)$$

To include the sign inversion of the analog computer amplifiers we rewrite the equations

$$\frac{d}{dt}\begin{bmatrix} x_1 \\ x_2 \end{bmatrix} = \begin{bmatrix} 1 & 0.2 \\ -1 & 0 \end{bmatrix}\begin{bmatrix} x_1 \\ x_2 \end{bmatrix} - \begin{bmatrix} -1 \\ -4 \end{bmatrix} x_{\text{in}}(t)$$

The analog computer diagram then follows directly, and is shown in Figure 12.10.

Analog computer diagrams have a remarkable similarity to state diagrams. If it were not for the inherent sign inversion in analog computer components and different symbols, the two types of diagrams would be identical.

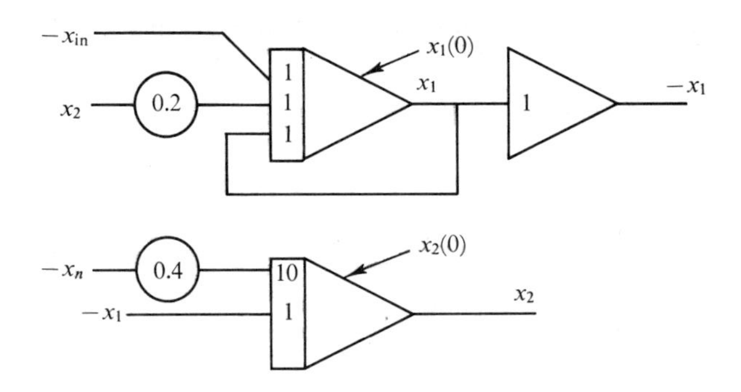

Fig. 12.10. *Analog computer diagram.*

The solution of state equations by analog computer is represented by voltages. Therefore, solutions are recorded as a function of time. When scales of magnitude and sign are properly recorded on the graph paper, numerical values may be read off for any point in time of any variable.

Solution of Nonlinear State Equations

Analog computers provide to a moderate degree for the solution of nonlinear state equations. Some of the typical nonlinearities which may be accommodated are multiplication and division of two variables; square root; sine, cosine, and log; absolute value; certain discontinuities such as relay functions; and arbitrary single-valued functions. Prerequisite, however, to the successful programming of nonlinear differential equations, is the ability to develop a set of state equations. In other words, any nonlinear function involved in the mathematical model can be evaluated only in terms of state variables.

Example 12.3. Develop an analog computer diagram to solve the nonlinear differential equation

$$\ddot{x} + f(\dot{x}) + x = x_{in}(t)$$

where

$$\begin{aligned} f(\dot{x}) &= x\dot{x} \text{ for } \dot{x} > 0 \\ &= -x\dot{x} \text{ for } \dot{x} < 0. \end{aligned}$$

The corresponding state equations are

$$\frac{d}{dt}\dot{x} = -[f(\dot{x}) + x - x_{in}(t)]$$

$$\frac{d}{dt}x = -[-\dot{x}]$$

The nonlinear function $f(\dot{x})$ may be generated by use of a multiplier which will form the product $x\dot{x}$ and a differential relay which will sense the sign of $\dot{x}$. Thus a diagram is constructed as shown in Figure 12.11.

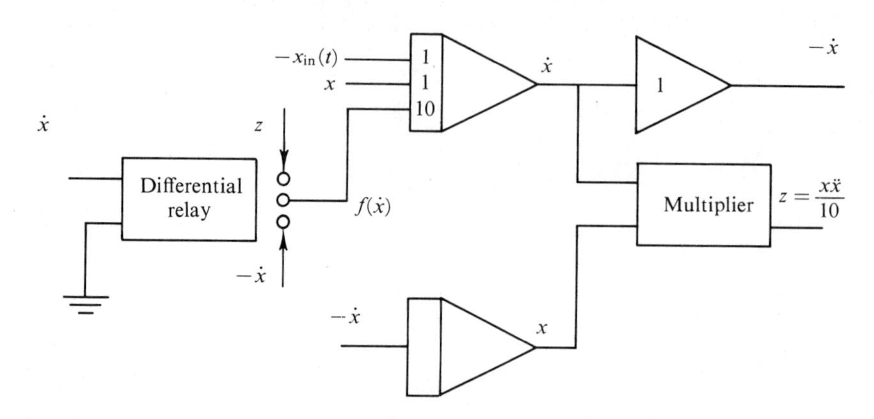

Fig. 12.11. *Analog computer diagram for nonlinear problem.*

To explain the diagram, we introduce the two additional analog computer components.

5. Multiplier.

Symbol: Equation:

$$x_o = \frac{x_1 x_2}{10} \qquad \textbf{(12.32)}$$

The factor 10 in Equation 12.32 is a scale factor which is introduced to maintain the amplitude of the output within operational bounds of ± 10 volts.

6. Differential relay.

Symbol: Equation:

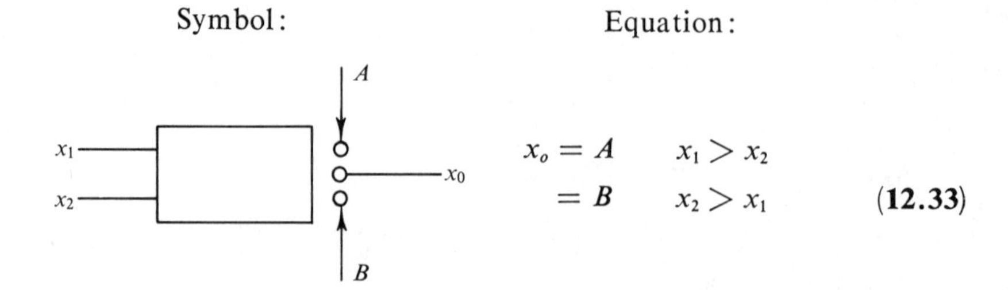

$$\begin{aligned} x_o &= A \qquad x_1 > x_2 \\ &= B \qquad x_2 > x_1 \end{aligned} \qquad \textbf{(12.33)}$$

The task of developing workable and efficient analog computer diagrams requires experience. Many reference texts are available discussing useful analog computer techniques. A further elaboration on the solution of nonlinear problems is beyond the scope of this book.

Analog Computer Scaling

Magnitude Scaling

The magnitude that problem variables may assume during an analog computer solution is limited by the linear range of the components. This linear range corresponds to ± 10 volts on one type of computer and ± 100 volts on another type of computer. It is desirable to establish a correspondence between problem variables and computer voltages; for instance, 1 meter = 1 volt on the computer or 1 ampere = 0.1 volt on the computer or 1 cubic meter per second = 10 volts on the computer or, in general, 1 problem unit = s volts on the computer where s is a scaling factor. This scaling factor, if suitably selected, will permit the range of voltage variation of all variables on the computer to be maintained within the allowable voltage range of ± 10 volts or ± 100 volts. Not only is it essential that no voltage exceed the allowable range, but it is also desirable to avoid voltages of small magnitude. Thus some variables must be scaled down for the first reason, while others must be scaled up for the second. An example will best illustrate this.

Example 12.4. Draw a computer diagram to obtain a solution to the differential equation

$$\dddot{y} + 10\ddot{y} + 80\dot{y} + 700y = 0$$

$$y(0) = 0$$

$$\dot{y}(0) = 10$$

$$\ddot{y}(0) = 0$$

The corresponding state equations are

$$\frac{d}{dt}\begin{bmatrix} \ddot{y} \\ \dot{y} \\ y \end{bmatrix} = -\begin{bmatrix} 10 & 80 & 700 \\ -1 & 0 & 0 \\ 0 & -1 & 0 \end{bmatrix}\begin{bmatrix} \ddot{y} \\ \dot{y} \\ y \end{bmatrix}$$

Amplitude scaling is advised because of the presence of terms like $10\ddot{y}$ and $700y$ in the same equation. The selection of the proper scale factors can be made systematic by the following guide line: all coefficients of the **A**-matrix should be made as nearly equal as possible. Thus we wish to reduce the coefficients of the first row and increase the coefficients of the second and third rows.

We divide the first row by 10. Then the equations are

$$\frac{d}{dt}\begin{bmatrix} \dfrac{\ddot{y}}{10} \\ \dot{y} \\ y \end{bmatrix} = -\begin{bmatrix} 1 & 8 & 70 \\ -1 & 0 & 0 \\ 0 & -1 & 0 \end{bmatrix}\begin{bmatrix} \ddot{y} \\ \dot{y} \\ y \end{bmatrix}$$

But the state vector must be identical. Thus

$$\frac{d}{dt}\begin{bmatrix} \dfrac{\ddot{y}}{10} \\ \dot{y} \\ y \end{bmatrix} = -\begin{bmatrix} 10 & 8 & 70 \\ -10 & 0 & 0 \\ 0 & -1 & 0 \end{bmatrix}\begin{bmatrix} \dfrac{\ddot{y}}{10} \\ \dot{y} \\ y \end{bmatrix}$$

If we also multiply the last row by 10, we obtain

$$\frac{d}{dt}\begin{bmatrix} \dfrac{\ddot{y}}{10} \\ \dot{y} \\ 10y \end{bmatrix} = -\begin{bmatrix} 10 & 8 & 70 \\ -10 & 0 & 0 \\ 0 & -10 & 0 \end{bmatrix}\begin{bmatrix} \dfrac{\dot{y}}{10} \\ \dot{y} \\ y \end{bmatrix}$$

Equalizing the state vectors

$$\frac{d}{dt}\begin{bmatrix} \dfrac{\ddot{y}}{10} \\ \dot{y} \\ 10y \end{bmatrix} = -\begin{bmatrix} 10 & 8 & 7 \\ -10 & 0 & 0 \\ 0 & -10 & 0 \end{bmatrix}\begin{bmatrix} \dfrac{\ddot{y}}{10} \\ \dot{y} \\ 10y \end{bmatrix}$$

If we now let

$$x_1 = \frac{\ddot{y}}{10}$$
$$x_2 = \dot{y}$$
$$x_3 = 10y$$

we have the proper scale factors for a satisfactory computer solution. The equations to be programmed are

$$\frac{d}{dt}\begin{bmatrix} x_1 \\ x_2 \\ x_3 \end{bmatrix} = -\begin{bmatrix} -10 & 8 & 7 \\ -10 & 0 & 0 \\ 0 & -10 & 0 \end{bmatrix}\begin{bmatrix} x_1 \\ x_2 \\ x_3 \end{bmatrix}$$

The computer diagram is given in Figure 12.12

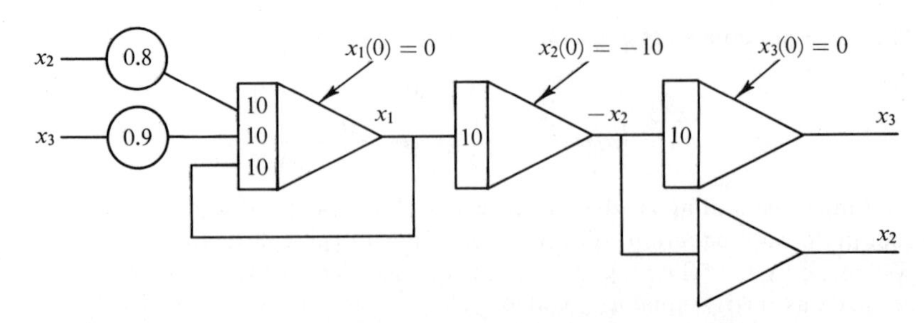

Fig. 12.12. *Analog computer diagram for differential equations.*

Time Scaling

In addition to amplitude scaling, the solution of an analog computer problem may be controlled in terms of time required for the solution. Adjustments made in the state equations to affect a change in solution time is called time scaling. Time scaling is readily accomplished by making the substitution

$$t = \alpha\tau \tag{12.34}$$

in the state equations. When $\alpha > 1$, the solution is speeded up; when $\alpha < 1$, the solution is slowed down. Given the state equations

$$\frac{d}{dt}\mathbf{x} = \mathbf{A}\mathbf{x} \tag{12.35}$$

and using Equation 12.34 yields the time scaled state equations

$$\frac{d}{d\tau}\mathbf{x} = \alpha\mathbf{A}\mathbf{x} \tag{12.36}$$

Thus in a time scale change *all* state variables are altered by the same factor.

Example 12.5. Reduce the speed of solution of the problem of Example 12.4 by a factor of 10.

Starting with the state equations

$$\frac{d}{dt}\begin{bmatrix} x_1 \\ x_2 \\ x_3 \end{bmatrix} = -\begin{bmatrix} 10 & 8 & 7 \\ -10 & 0 & 0 \\ 0 & -10 & 0 \end{bmatrix}\begin{bmatrix} x_1 \\ x_2 \\ x_3 \end{bmatrix}$$

we perform the time scale change with $\alpha = 0.1$ and obtain

$$\frac{d}{d\tau}\begin{bmatrix} x_1 \\ x_2 \\ x_3 \end{bmatrix} = -\begin{bmatrix} 1 & 0.8 & 0.7 \\ -1 & 0 & 0 \\ 0 & -1 & 0 \end{bmatrix}\begin{bmatrix} x_1 \\ x_2 \\ x_3 \end{bmatrix}$$

Time scaling with $\alpha = 100$ or $\alpha = 1000$ is available as a standard feature on today's analog computers to provide high-speed repetitive solutions of the same problem.

Analog Computer Simulation of Systems

The analog computer is widely employed in the simulation of complex dynamic systems. Simulation is closely related to the solution of state variable equations by analog computer. However, simulation implies the solution of dynamic systems in a broader sense: it involves the solution of the state equations representing appropriately chosen subsystems of the system with interconnections that are in a one-to-one correspondence with the topology of the system. Let us consider the simulation of a feedback control system shown in Figure 12.13 as a block diagram.

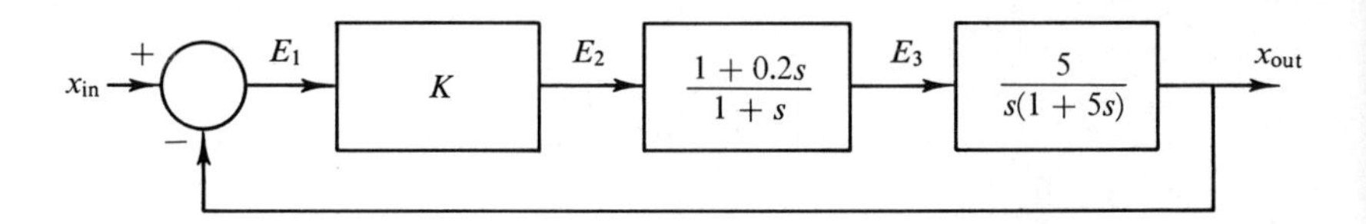

Fig. 12.13. *Block diagram of a control system.*

We can dissect the system into four subassemblies.

1.

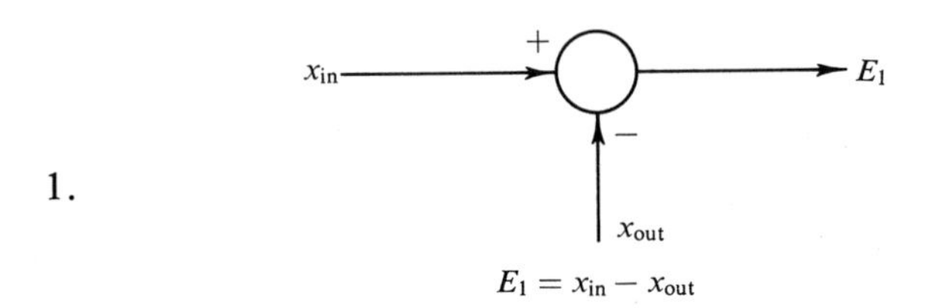

In terms of a computer diagram,

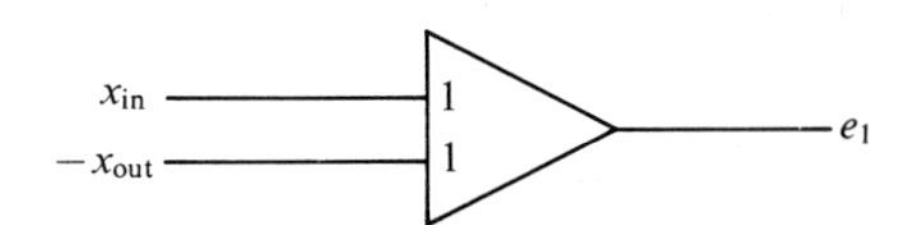

2.

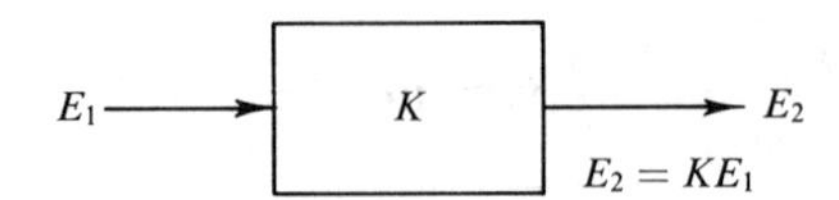

and

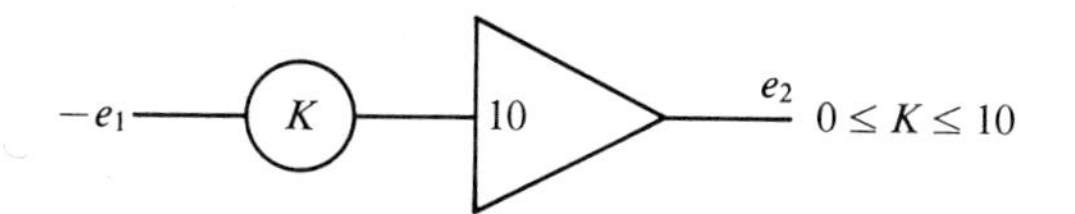

3.

$$E_2 \longrightarrow \boxed{\frac{1+0.2s}{1+s}} \longrightarrow E_3$$

The state equations for this subassembly are, by Equations 12.20 and 12.21,

$$\frac{d}{dt}x_3 = -[-x_3 - e_2(t)]$$

$$e_3(t) = -[-0.8x_3 - 0.2e_2(t)]$$

Therefore the corresponding analog diagram is

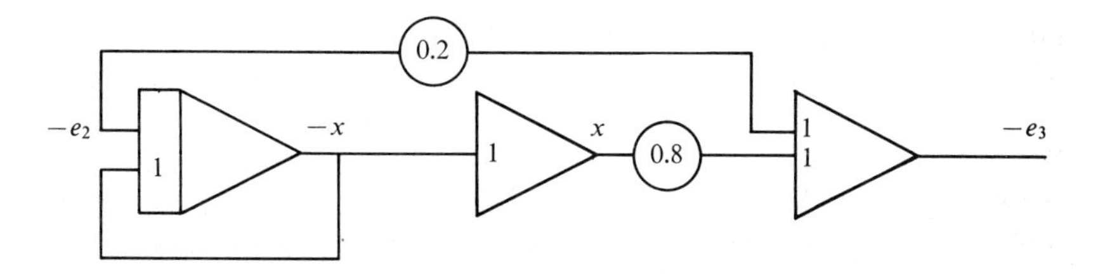

4.

$$E_3 \longrightarrow \boxed{\frac{5}{s(1+5s)}} \longrightarrow x_{\text{out}}$$

The state equations are

$$\frac{d}{dt}\begin{bmatrix} x_1 \\ x_2 \end{bmatrix} = -\left\{\begin{bmatrix} +0.2 & 0 \\ -1 & 0 \end{bmatrix}\begin{bmatrix} x_1 \\ x_2 \end{bmatrix} - \begin{bmatrix} 1 \\ 0 \end{bmatrix} e_3(t)\right\}$$

$$x_0 = x_2$$

and the diagram is

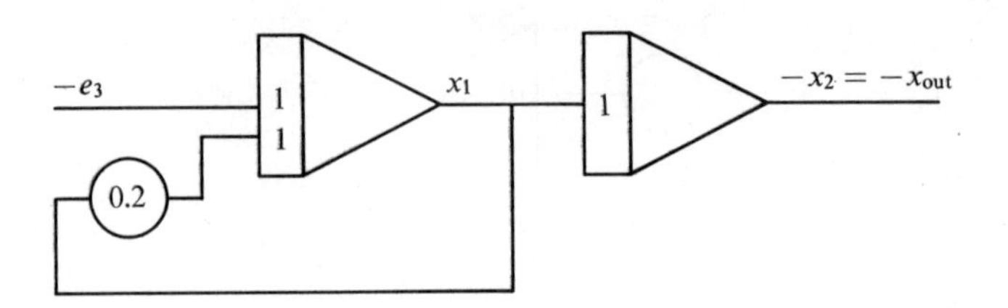

These four subassemblies may now be integrated into a single diagram representing the entire system. The result is shown in Figure 12.14. The analog computer program thus obtained is a simulation of the feed-

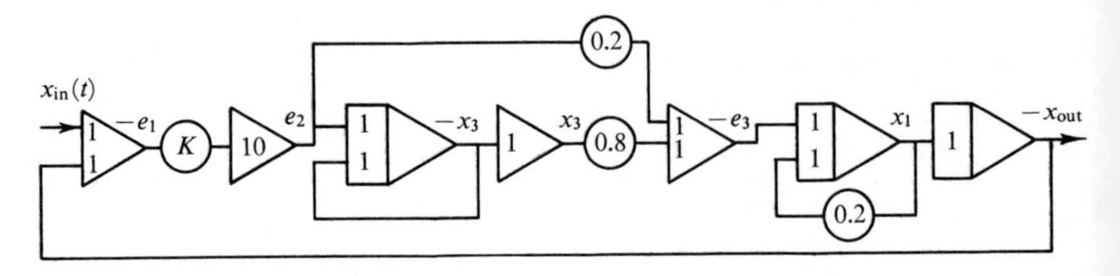

Fig. 12.14. *Analog computer diagram for feedback system.*

back system. The structural correspondence between the computer diagram and the block diagram of the system is easily recognized. The diagram may be simplified by removing the second and fifth summer-amplifier and combining their functions with those adjacent to them. Figure 12.15 shows the simplified diagram. Although this simplification requires the elimination of the variables e_2 and e_3, it is consistent with good analog computer practice of constructing a diagram of minimum complexity. The main structure is still preserved.

In contrast to the simulation approach outlined above, we will consider a straight state equation solution of the same problem. The combined " closed loop " transfer function is given by

$$X_o(s) = \frac{K(0.2s + 1)}{s^3 + 1.2s^2 + 0.2(K + 1)s + K} X_i(s)$$

Fig. 12.15. *Simplified computer diagram.*

The corresponding state equations by single-input programming are

$$\frac{d}{dt}\begin{bmatrix} x_1 \\ x_2 \\ x_3 \end{bmatrix} = \begin{bmatrix} -1.2 & -0.2(K+1) & -K \\ 1 & 0 & 0 \\ 0 & 1 & 0 \end{bmatrix}\begin{bmatrix} x_1 \\ x_2 \\ x_3 \end{bmatrix} + \begin{bmatrix} 1 \\ 0 \\ 0 \end{bmatrix} x_{\text{in}}(t)$$

$$x_{\text{out}}(t) = K[0 \quad 0.2 \quad 1]\begin{bmatrix} x_1 \\ x_2 \\ x_3 \end{bmatrix}$$

The analog computer diagram corresponding to these equations is shown in Figure 12.16.

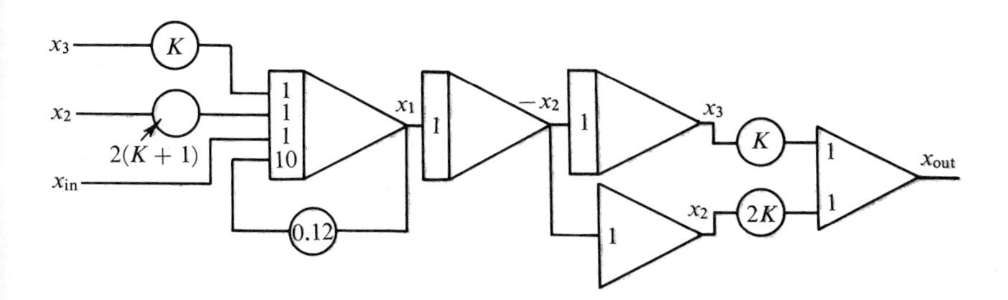

Fig. 12.16. *Direct approach of feedback system.*

Figures 12.15 and 12.16 show computer diagrams which represent two approaches to the solution of a dynamic system. Although both will yield identical results in terms of the solution, the simulation approach is usually preferred. Not only is the structure of the system preserved in the computer diagram, but also it is much more readily adaptable for design considerations. For instance, if the parameter K, which represents the gain of the system, is to be selected according to some response specifications, only one potentiometer has to be adjusted in the simulation diagram against three in the state equation approach.

The simulation of systems is particularly useful when the system contains isolated nonlinearities. Some subassemblies will be characterized by linear state equations, while others may contain typical nonlinearities which are much more easily dealt with on a subassembly basis than on a complete system approach.

Examples of Analog Computer Circuits

We will consider here the construction of analog computer diagrams for a number of typical linear systems. Each example is characterized by a particular analysis objective.

Example 12.6. In the electrical circuit of Figure 12.17, determine the value of R_2 for which the output voltage is in phase with the input which is a sinusoidal voltage. An analytical check will quickly reveal that this condition is met when $R_5 = 20{,}000$ ohms. Thus the analog computer circuit must be constructed to permit an adjustment of R_5 in the range 1,000 ohms $\leq R_5 \leq$ 1,000,000 ohms.

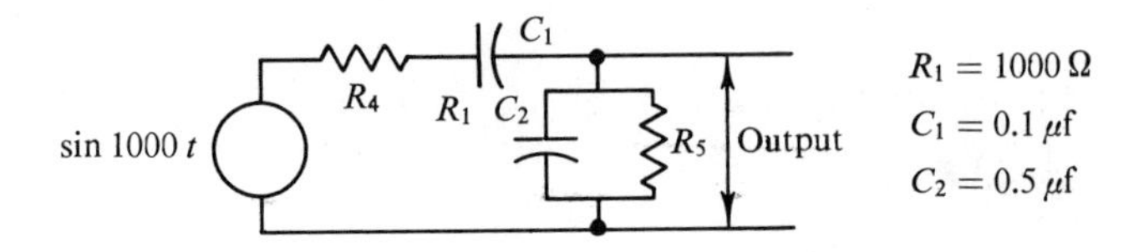

Fig. 12.17. *Electric circuit.*

The first step in this problem is the development of a state variable model for the circuit. A system graph with a tree is show in Figure 12.18. The tree includes the voltage source and the two capacitors.

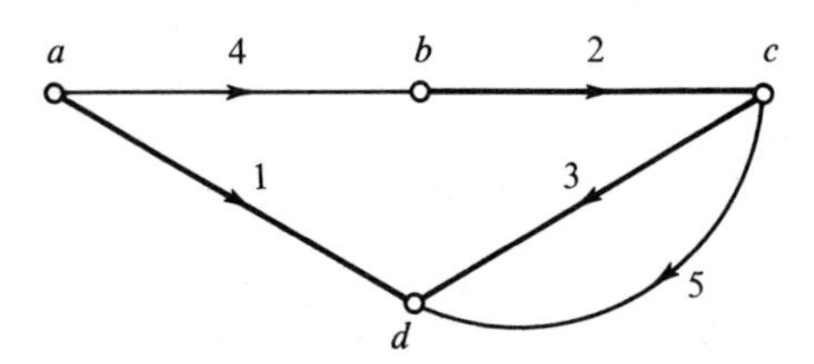

Fig. 12.18. *System graph of circuit.*

Beginning with the capacitors we write

$$\frac{d}{dt}v_2 = \frac{1}{C_2}i_2$$

$$\frac{d}{dt}v_3 = \frac{1}{C_3}i_3$$

But since

$$i_2 = i_4$$

$$i_3 = i_4 - i_5$$

and

$$i_4 = \frac{v_4}{R_4} = \frac{v_1 - v_2 - v_3}{R_4}$$

$$i_5 = \frac{v_5}{R_5} = \frac{v_3}{R_5}$$

we have the state variable equations

$$\frac{d}{dt}v_2 = \frac{1}{C_2R_4}(v_1 - v_2 - v_3)$$

$$\frac{d}{dt}v_3 = \frac{1}{C_2}\left(\frac{v_1}{R_4} - \frac{v_2}{R_4} - \frac{v_3}{R_4} - \frac{v_3}{R_5}\right)$$

We now substitute the numerical values and obtain

$$\frac{d}{dt}v_2 = 10^4(v_1 - v_2 - v_3)$$

$$\frac{d}{dt}v_3 = 20 \times 10^3\left(v_1 - v_2 - v_3 - \frac{1000}{R_5}v_3\right)$$

To determine the desired value of R_5 for which the input and output are in phase (note the output is given by v_3) we solve these two differential equations on the analog computer with v_1 derived from a sinusoidal function generator adjusted to 1000 radians/second. The resistor R_5 is then adjusted until recorded or scope displayed waveforms of $v_1(t)$ and $v_3(t)$ are in phase.

In order to keep the frequency range of the solution within range of an analog computer we time scale the solution by a factor of 10,000. Note that this time scale also changes the frequency of the voltage v_1 by the same factor. Thus the equations to be programed are

$$\frac{d}{dt}v_2' = 1(v_1' - v_2' - v_3') \qquad v_1'(t) = \sin 0.1t$$

$$\frac{d}{dt}v_3' = 2\left(v_1' - v_2' - v_3' - \frac{1000}{R_5}v_3'\right)$$

The corresponding analog computer circuit is shown in Figure 12.19. The coefficient potentiometer K represents the gain $1000/R_5$. In order to vary the

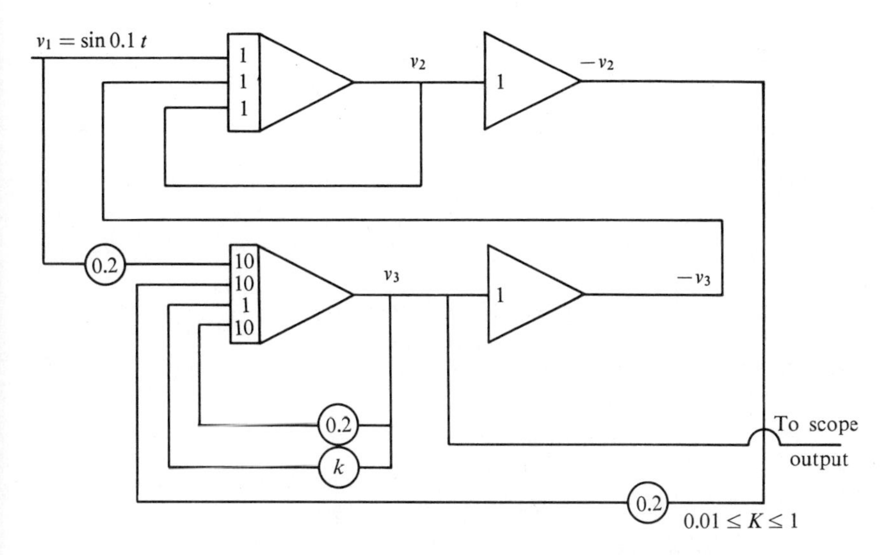

Fig. 12.19. *Analog computer circuit.*

value of R_5 through the specified range, K must vary according to the range $0.01 \leq K \leq 1$. The value $K = 0.05$ should give the desired in-phase response of the circuit.

Example 12.7. By use of an analog computer simulation, determine suitable springs for the accelerometer such that the device will respond to acceleration signals with a critically damped deflection. For this purpose we simulate the

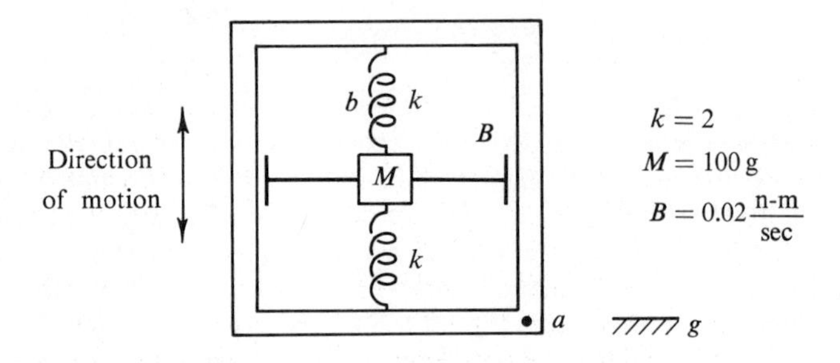

Fig. 12.20. *Schematic of an accelerometer.*

motion of the accelerometer as being subjected to a step displacement or step velocity of the reference frame. During the resultant response it will be possible to adjust the value of the spring constant for critical damping.

The state variable equation might be derived by choosing the velocity and displacement of the indicator mass as state variables. A system graph is shown in Figure 12.21 with a tree as indicated.

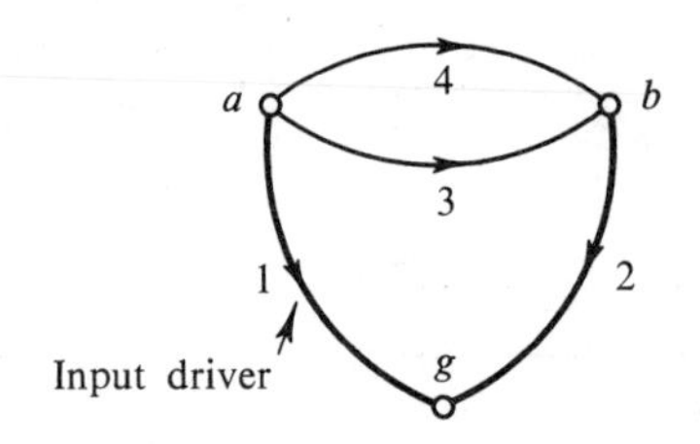

Fig. 12.21. *System graph.*

Accordingly, we obtain the state equations

$$\frac{d}{dt}\dot{\delta}_2 = \frac{1}{M} f_2 = \frac{1}{M}\left[f_3 + f_4 \right]$$

$$= \frac{1}{M}\left[2k(\delta_1 - \delta_2) + B(\dot{\delta}_1 - \dot{\delta}_3) \right]$$

$$\frac{d}{dt}\delta_2 = \dot{\delta}_2$$

Although these equations are valid state equations, they contain as input variables both the displacement and velocity of the reference mass. This will prove to be awkward if one considers that a step input does not have a properly defined derivative at the time of application.

A better model for the simulation of the accelerometer may be found by considering $\dot{\delta}_2$ and f_3 as state variables. We obtain then

$$\frac{d}{dt}\dot{\delta}_2 = \frac{1}{M}\left[f_3 + B(\dot{\delta}_1 - \dot{\delta}_2)\right]$$

$$\frac{d}{dt}f_3 = 2k(\dot{\delta}_1 - \dot{\delta}_2)$$

Only the reference velocity is present in these state equations. Furthermore, the spring coefficient appears all by itself, which makes its adjustment a simple matter. With the numerical values substituted, these equations become

$$\frac{d}{dt}\dot{\delta}_2 = 10f_3 + 0.2(\dot{\delta}_1 - \dot{\delta}_2)$$

$$\frac{d}{dt}f_3 = 2k(\dot{\delta}_1 - \dot{\delta}_2)$$

An analog computer circuit is shown in Figure 12.22. No scaling is indicated. For convenience an extra amplifier is employed to generate the term $\dot{\delta}_2 - \dot{\delta}_1$. This way the input is applied only at one place.

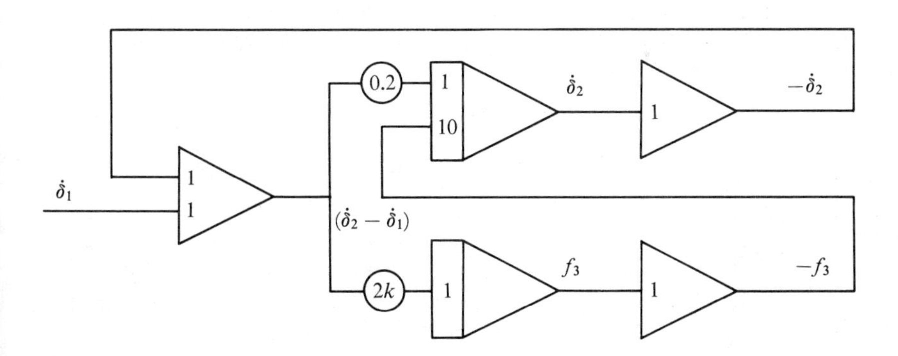

Fig. 12.22. *Analog computer circuit for accelerometer.*

An alternate approach to this problem is available through deriving the transfer function relating δ_2 to δ_1. From a node equation for vertex b we obtain

$$Ms^2\Delta_2 + 2k(\Delta_2 - \Delta_1) + Bs(\Delta_2 - \Delta_1) = 0$$

from which

$$\Delta_2 = \frac{2k + Bs}{Ms^2 + Bs + 2k}\Delta_1$$

and using the numerical values

$$\Delta_2 = \frac{20k + 0.2s}{s^2 + 0.2s + 20k}\Delta_1$$

This transfer function may be transformed into a set of state equations by use of one of the programming techniques. Using the single input technique we have

$$\frac{d}{dt}\begin{bmatrix} x_1 \\ x_2 \end{bmatrix} = \begin{bmatrix} -0.2 & -20k \\ 1 & 0 \end{bmatrix}\begin{bmatrix} x_1 \\ x_2 \end{bmatrix} + \begin{bmatrix} 1 \\ 0 \end{bmatrix}\delta_1$$

$$\delta_2 = [0.2 \quad 20k]\begin{bmatrix} x_1 \\ x_2 \end{bmatrix}$$

This may be programmed for an analog computer solution. However, adjustments of k are not as simple as in the previous solution since it appears in two places in the equations. It is left to the reader to construct the analog computer diagram.

Example 12.8. Figure 2.3 shows the schematic of a galvanometer movement. It is a basic ingredient of a wide variety of instruments such as voltmeters, ammeters, and ink-pen recorders. This example shows an analog computer simulation demonstrating the dynamic response of the galvanometer movement. An interesting characteristic is investigated. As experimental observation during applications of this instrument for measurement purposes will verify, the dynamic response of the galvanometer may vary from an overdamped to an underdamped response depending upon application.

A typical application is illustrated in Figure 12.23. Shown is a voltage or current source, which may have an internal resistance, driving a galvanometer.

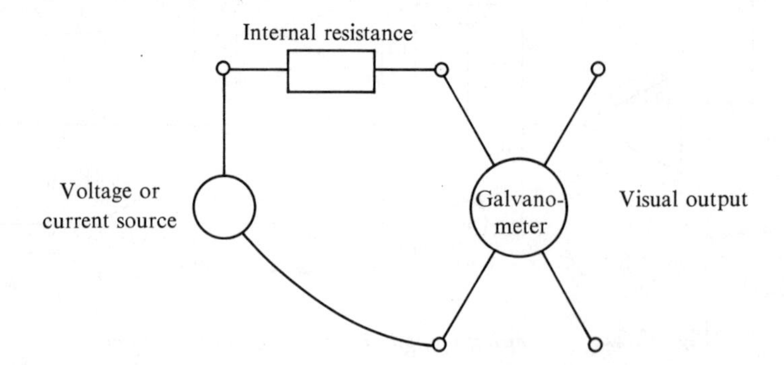

Fig. 12.23. *Connection schematic of galvanometer circuit.*

The mathematical model for a galvanometer is obtained by using Equation 8.123 describing a dynamometer. A galvanometer is derived from a dynamometer by connecting a rotational spring and a mechanical damper to the mechanical movement. The torque of this spring provides for an angular displacement of the moving coil which is proportional to the current in the coil when the galvanometer is damped out.

A system graph of the entire galvanometer circuit is shown in Figure 12.24.

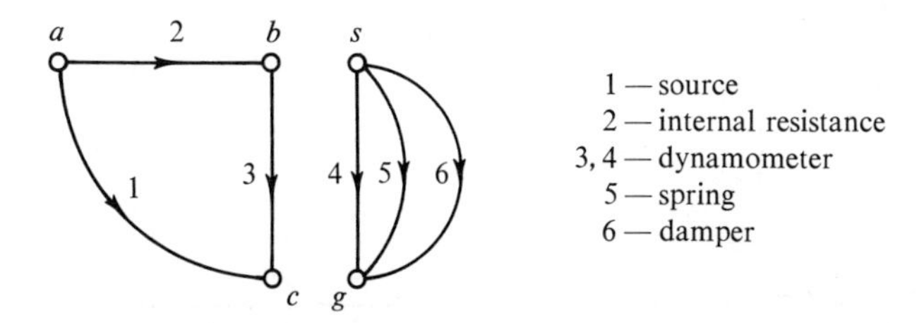

Fig. 12.24. *System graph of galvanometer circuit.*

The component equations of the individual components are

$$v_1(t) \quad \text{or} \quad i_1(t)$$

$$v_2 = R_2 i_2$$

$$\begin{bmatrix} v_3 \\ \tau_4 \end{bmatrix} = \begin{bmatrix} R_3 + L\dfrac{d}{dt} & k_g \\ -k_g & J\dfrac{d}{dt} \end{bmatrix} \begin{bmatrix} i_3 \\ \varphi_4 \end{bmatrix}$$

$$\tau_5 = k\varphi_5$$

$$\tau_6 = B\varphi_6$$

The state equations (with a voltage driver applied) are

$$\frac{d}{dt}i_3 = -\frac{R_2 + R_3}{L_3}i_3 + \frac{1}{L_3}v_1 - \frac{k_g}{L_3}\varphi_4$$

$$\frac{d}{dt}\dot{\varphi}_4 = -\frac{B}{J}\dot{\varphi}_4 - \frac{k}{J}\varphi_4 + \frac{k_g}{J}i_3$$

$$\frac{d}{dt}\varphi_4 = \dot{\varphi}_4$$

These equations describe the dynamics of the galvanometer when a voltage is measured. When the voltage driver is removed from the terminals, the galvanometer dynamics are described by the simpler equations

$$\frac{d}{dt}\dot{\varphi}_4 = -\frac{B}{J}\dot{\varphi}_4 - \frac{k}{J}\varphi$$

$$\frac{d}{dt}\varphi_4 = \dot{\varphi}_4$$

Note that the input circuit is left open.

Both modes of operation can be conveniently simulated by a single computer circuit which can be alternated between modes of operation by two switches, s_1 and s_2. The switches are closed when the voltage source is measured, and opened when the voltage source is removed. The circuit which is shown in Figure 12.25 shows no numerical values. They may be inserted for a particular application.

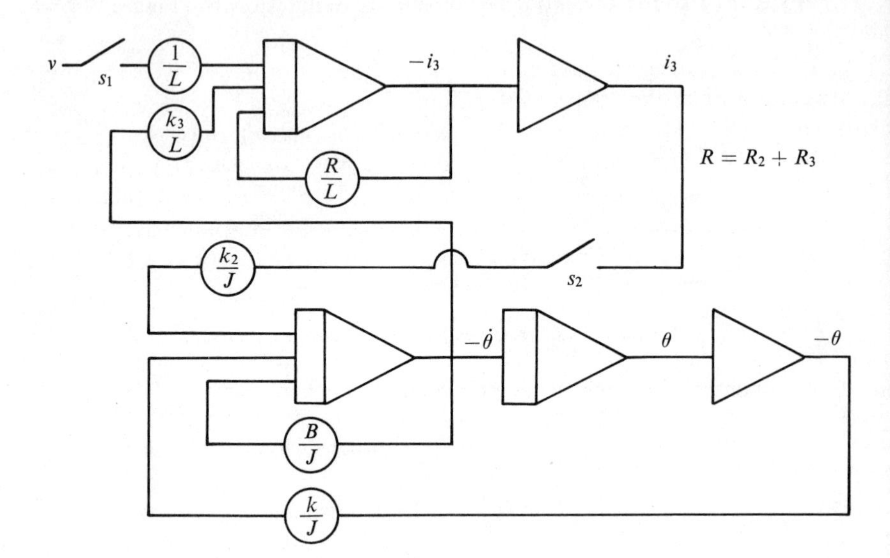

Fig. 12.25. *Analog computer circuit for voltage measurement.*

The interesting feature of the galvanometer operation is the difference in damping between the measuring and free modes of operation. A time response for a typical measurement is shown in Figure 12.26. In the measurement mode the meter is more damped than during the free mode. It is demonstrated very clearly that the closing of the electrical loop of the galvanometer circuit pro-

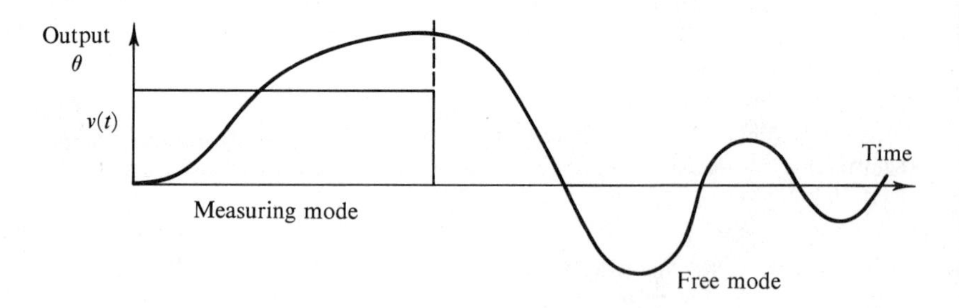

Fig. 12.26. *Time response of galvanometer.*

vides additional "electrical" damping. Other effects on the damping characteristics of the galvanometer are noticeable when the internal resistance of the voltage driver is changed: the higher the internal resistance the greater the damping.

12.4 Digital Computer Techniques

In almost every digital computer analysis of dynamic systems, the programming of the solution of differential and/or difference equations is required. These equations characterize the dynamics of the system under study. The digital machine performs its basic operations involving arithmetic, memory, and logic in terms of variables which are always represented in discrete form. All continuous mathematical operations must therefore be converted into a corresponding discrete form before they can be processed by the computer. Subject to this requirement are the frequently occurring operations such as integration and differentiation, for example.

To handle these and a great many other tasks, suitable digital programs called *subroutines* are available for use by the systems analyst. This section will examine a number of such techniques which are frequently used in the solution of differential equations. We will direct our attention to a presentation of the discrete approximation technique and errors that are incurred by it. Briefly, two basic types of errors are introduced: the truncation error, which is due to finite approximations of infinite series expansions, and round-off error, which is due to finite bit capacity of the digital computer. Furthermore, consideration has to be given to the possibility of an unstable discrete equivalent.

In the solution of differential equations by a digital computer it is assumed that the system to be simulated is characterized in first-order differential equation form, or state space equations, that is,

$$\frac{d}{dt}x_i = f_i(x_1, x_2, \cdots, x_n, t) \quad i = 1, 2, \cdots, n \tag{12.37}$$

or, in the case of a linear system,

$$\dot{\mathbf{x}} = \mathbf{Ax} + \mathbf{Br} \tag{12.38}$$

Techniques dealing with the derivation of these equations were presented in earlier chapters.

Numerical integration of these equations is based upon a recursive evaluation of their discrete equivalent which may be of the form

$$x_i(t_k + h) = f_i[x_1(t_k), x_2(t_k), \cdots, k_n(t_k), t_k] \quad i = 1, 2, \cdots, n \tag{12.39}$$

where the $x_i(t_k)$ denotes the ith state variable of the simulated system at time $t = t_k$, and h is the time increment to determine the next state.

This form of a discrete equivalent is the most desirable. It is simple because the next state $x_i(k + 1)$ is determined from a knowledge of the present state $x_i(k)$ only, and it involves only one evaluation of the derivatives. More frequently, however, the discrete equivalents of differential equations are structured in a more complicated fashion, primarily in these two aspects: The determination of the next system state involves (1) an algorithm operating on a predictor-corrector basis requiring the use of the present state and previous states $x_i(k-1)$, $x_i(k-2)$ etc; and (2) a multistep procedure requiring the use of the present state and several intermediate values of the state variables.

In the analysis of dynamic systems, it is a matter of some concern to the user of numerical integration techniques to determine what method represents the most suitable choice. The principle factors to consider are speed, accuracy, stability, and convenience. In addition, and directly coupled to these four factors, is the choice of the time increment employed in the processing of the discrete model. Advantage in speed is obviously desirable in every case—this requires a fast method and a large time increment. On the other hand, good accuracy can be obtained only from the relatively more sophisticated methods which in general are time consuming. Convenience becomes a factor in consideration of input-output timing, ease of initialization, and overall synchronization with other parts of the computer analysis.

In this section, then, we concern ourselves with a brief study of some of the more widely used digital computer methods of solving differential equations.

Selected Methods of Numerical Integration

Euler Method

Probably the simplest approximation to Equation 12.37 is obtained from a first-order Taylor Series expansion of the state variables $x_i(t)$. Such an expansion yields

$$x_i(t+h) = x_i(t) + h\dot{x}_i(t) \tag{12.40}$$

If we let

$$x_i(t+h) = x_i(k+1)$$

and

$$x_i(t) = x_i(k)$$

where k denotes the kth evaluation, actually corresponding to $t = kh$, and also substitute Equation 12.37 into Equation 12.40, we obtain

$$x_i(k+1) = x_i(k) + hf_i(x_1, x_2, \cdots, x_n, k) \tag{12.41}$$

This approximation is generally referred to as the Euler approximation.

It is simple and can be programmed in a straightforward fashion. As an illustration, consider the following differential equation.

Example 12.9. Determine the Euler approximation of the differential equation

$$\ddot{x} + a\dot{x} + bx = 1 \qquad t \geq 0 \tag{12.42}$$

First, the state equations are

$$\begin{aligned} \dot{x}_1 &= -ax_1 - bx_2 + 1 \\ \dot{x}_2 &= x_1 \end{aligned} \tag{12.43}$$

Consequently, the Euler approximation is

$$\begin{aligned} x_1(k+1) &= x_1(k) + h(-ax_1(k) - bx_2(k) + 1) \\ x_2(k+1) &= x_2(k) + hx_1(k) \end{aligned} \tag{12.44}$$

The Euler approximation works both for linear and nonlinear system models. Despite its attractive features, however, it suffers serious shortcomings and is therefore rarely used. Discussion of these drawbacks will serve well to point out some of the important considerations that go into the selection of a numerical technique in general. This discussion will be presented summarily at the end of this section.

Runge-Kutta Method

The Runge-Kutta method and its various modifications are the most widely employed of the single step methods. These are methods of a class for which $x_i(k)$ alone and the differential equations are required for each iteration. The methods are selfstarting and are not difficult to program. The basic Runge-Kutta method is partially an extension of the Euler method which, as was mentioned, is based upon the first-order Taylor series (Equation 12.40). This series expansion suggests inclusion of higher-order terms to reduce the truncation error. While the first derivative is available from the differential equation, higher-order derivatives must be evaluated separately, possibly by difference methods. This would result in an effective method except that the evaluation of the higher-order derivatives can be very tedious. The Runge-Kutta method makes use of the higher-order Taylor approximations indirectly to avoid this problem.

The Runge-Kutta methods used in practice are based on fourth-order Taylor approximations. Although these are simple in their use, their derivations entail complicated developments.* It will suffice here to present only the computational algorithm.

Let the system of equations to be solved be given in the familiar form

* See, for example, F. B. Hildebrand, *Introduction to Numerical Analysis*, New York: McGraw-Hill Book Co., 1956, p. 233.

$$\dot{x}_i = f_i(x_1, x_2, \cdots, x_n, t) = f_i(\mathbf{x}, t)$$
$$x_i(t_0) = x_{i0} \qquad i = 1, 2, \cdots, n \tag{12.45}$$

Let $x_i(k)$ be the value of x_i at $t = t_k$, and $f_i(k)$ the derivative of x_i at $t = t_k$. If k is the increment (step-size) of the time variable t, the Runge-Kutta fourth-order method uses the formulas

$$K_{i1} = hf_i[\mathbf{x}(k), t_k]$$
$$K_{i2} = hf_i[\mathbf{x}(k) + 0.5\mathbf{K}_1, t_k + 0.5h]$$
$$K_{i3} = hf_i[\mathbf{x}(k) + 0.5\mathbf{K}_2, t_k + 0.5h]$$
$$K_{i4} = hf_i[\mathbf{x}(k) + \mathbf{K}_3, t_k + h]$$
$$x_i(k + 1) = x_i(k) + \frac{1}{6}(K_{i1} + 2K_{i2} + 2K_{i3} + K_{i4})$$
$$i = 1, 2, \cdots, n \tag{12.46}$$

For each step of integration in Equations 12.46 the Runge-Kutta method requires four evaluations of the differential equations $f_i(x_1, x_2, \cdots, x_n, t)$, thus requiring a considerable amount of machine time. Despite this additional time requirement, the Runge-Kutta method is characterized by a high degree of accuracy which compares well with analytical methods of solution.

A Runge-Kutta solution to the problem of a harmonic oscillator is presented later in this chapter. The results for various step sizes are shown and compared with other techniques.

Tustin Method

A technique of great appeal in the simulation of linear systems is the Tustin method. It is basically a derivative approximation by a difference equation using a delay operator. Consider the following relationships. The definition of the delay operator z is given by

$$z = e^{sT}* \tag{12.47}$$

Solving for s yields

$$s = \frac{1}{T}\ln z \tag{12.48}$$

The logarithmic term may be approximated by the series

$$\ln z = 2\left(u + \frac{1}{3}u^3 + \frac{1}{5}u^5 + \cdots\right) \tag{12.49}$$

where
$$u = \frac{1 - z^{-1}}{1 + z^{-1}}$$

* T is used here in place of h to denote integration time interval.

Truncating the series after the first term and substituting into Equation 12.48 yields the so-called Tustin approximation for the derivative

$$s \approx \frac{2}{T}\frac{1 - z^{-1}}{1 + z^{-1}} \tag{12.50}$$

This relationship is used in converting the continuous time models of linear systems into difference equations. These difference equations may be readily solved recursively on a digital computer, yielding a fairly accurate digital simulation of the linear system.

The substitution of Equation 12.50 may be applied to an nth-order linear differential equation, n first-order linear differential equations, or an nth-order transfer function. The result can usually be arranged into the form of an nth-order difference equation. This may best be illustrated by an example.

Example 12.10. Derive a difference equation for a harmonic oscillator using the Tustin approximation.

The differential equations of the harmonic oscillator are given here in state model form,

$$\dot{x}_1 = -\omega^2 x_2$$

$$\dot{x}_2 = x_1$$

Using Equation 12.50,

$$\frac{2}{T}\frac{1 - z^{-1}}{1 + z^{-1}} x_1 = -\omega^2 x_2$$

and

$$\frac{2}{T}\frac{1 - z^{-1}}{1 + z^{-1}} x_2 = x_1$$

Converting into difference equations,

$$x_1(k) = x_1(k-1) - \frac{\omega^2 T}{2}[x_2(k) + x_2(k-1)] \tag{12.51}$$

$$x_2(k) = x_2(k-1) + \frac{T}{2}[x_1(k) + x_1(k-1)] \tag{12.52}$$

In order to evaluate these difference equations recursively we must eliminate $x_2(k)$ from the first equation. This yields

$$x_1(k) = \left(\frac{4 - \omega^2 T^2}{4 + \omega^2 T^2}\right) x_1(k-1) + 2\left(\frac{2 - \omega^2 T}{4 + \omega^2 T^2}\right) x_2(k-1) \tag{12.53}$$

The digital simulation of the harmonic oscillator now involves Equations 12.53 and 12.52 to be recursively evaluated, in that order. This simulation is carried out for various values of T and is compared with the results of other methods later in this chapter.

State Transition Method

A numerical technique of simulating linear systems which is rapidly gaining widespread acceptance by systems designers is based upon state variable techniques. A linear system may be described by the equations

$$\frac{d}{dt}\mathbf{x} = \mathbf{A}\mathbf{x} + \mathbf{B}r \tag{12.54}$$

$$c = \mathbf{C}\mathbf{x} + dr \tag{12.55}$$

When the input $r(t)$ can be adequately represented by a piecewise constant equivalent

$$r(t) : r(kT + \tau) = r(kT) \qquad 0 < \tau \leq T \tag{12.56}$$

it is possible to determine $c(t)$ at the discrete times $t = 0, T, 2T, \cdots$ by means of the discrete state equations

$$\mathbf{x}[(k+1)T] = e^{\mathbf{A}T}\mathbf{x}(kT) + \int_0^T e^{\mathbf{A}\tau} d\tau \mathbf{B} r(kT) \tag{12.57}$$

$$c(kT) = \mathbf{C}\mathbf{x}(kT) + dr(kT) \tag{12.58}$$

These equations may be easily derived from the relationships of Appendix C by evaluating the general state space solution repeatedly over a fixed interval.

The most remarkable feature of the state transition method is that it offers a discrete simulation of a continuous time system which is almost completely exact. There are only two sources of error. One is introduced by the discretization of the input. The other is caused by the iterative procedure for evaluating the matrices

$$e^{\mathbf{A}T} \quad \text{and} \quad \int_0^T e^{\mathbf{A}t} dt$$

which we will discuss shortly. Note that no error is introduced by the actual discrete model—it is exact.

The matrices

$$e^{\mathbf{A}T} \quad \text{and} \quad \int_0^T e^{\mathbf{A}t} dt \mathbf{B}$$

are matrices of constants and are called the state transition matrix and the input transition matrix, respectively. Both may be evaluated by a computer algorithm based upon a power series expansion. Thus the transition matrix is expressed by the infinite series

$$e^{\mathbf{A}T} = \sum_{i=0}^{\infty} \frac{(\mathbf{A}T)^i}{i!} \qquad \mathbf{A}^0 = \mathbf{I} \tag{12.59}$$

This series is uniformly convergent. It is therefore possible to evaluate $e^{\mathbf{A}T}$ within a prescribed accuracy. If the series is truncated at $i = L$ then we may write

$$e^{\mathbf{A}T} = \sum_{i=0}^{L} \frac{(\mathbf{A}T)^i}{i!} + \text{remainder} \qquad \mathbf{(12.60)}$$

The value of L determines the accuracy of the series approximation.

By integrating the series given by Equation 12.59 term by term, one can develop a formula for the evaluation of the input transition matrix. This is

$$\int_0^T e^{\mathbf{A}\tau} d\tau \, \mathbf{B} \cong T \sum_{i=0}^{L} \frac{(\mathbf{A}T)^i}{(i+1)} \mathbf{B} \qquad \mathbf{(12.61)}$$

Because of the great similarity between Equations 12.60 and 12.61, the evaluation of the two series may be easily combined into a single computer routine. In applying the state transition in the evaluation of system dynamics one simply uses Equation 12.57 recursively.

The four methods presented here represent a cross section of numerical integration techniques ranging from a very simple (Euler) to a relatively sophisticated (Runge-Kutta) technique, also covering techniques for linear systems only (state transition, Tustin).

Solution Errors

Solutions as they would be carried out by these techniques suffer in varying degree from truncation error and round-off error. They are also subject to instability. The following is a brief discussion of these factors.

Truncation Error

Truncation error is the most fundamental problem affecting the accuracy of a numerical solution of a differential equation. It results as a direct consequence of truncating an infinite series expansion. It will be most prominent in the Euler method, since the series expansion upon which it is based consists of only one term. It can be shown that the truncation error is proportional to the time increment for the Euler method.* On the other hand, the truncation error in the Runge-Kutta method is of considerably less significance, since this method is essentially based upon a fourth-order Taylor series expansion. The truncation error for a fourth-order method is proportional to the fifth power

* H.E. Hamming, *Numerical Methods for Scientists and Engineers*, New York: McGraw-Hill Bcok Co., 1962.

of the time increment. Truncation error is also present in the Tustin method, but not in the state transition method because the matrix e^{AT} can be evaluated to any accuracy desired.

The significance of the truncation error can be further emphasized by the fact that it tends to accumulate with time. However, differential equations which characterize stable dynamic systems contain built-in feedback which is preserved in modified form in their discrete approximation. This feedback acts in support of the accuracy of the solution. The numerical approximation solution will seek the same steady-state as the original continuous model provided, of course, that the stability of the equivalent discrete model is not adversely affected. Example 12.9 illustrates this problem.

Example 12.11. Investigate the steady-state of the Euler approximation of Example 12.1. It is quite clear that the steady-state of Equation 12.42 is $1/b$ with no problems of stability, provided both a and b are positive. From Equation 12.44 it can be seen that as $k \to \infty$ $x_1(k) \to 0$ and $x_2(k) \to 1/b$. This verifies that the discrete approximation has the same steady-state value.

Truncation error may be partially controlled by making the time interval sufficiently small. This is accompanied, however, by an increase in the number of steps in the solution, requiring more computer time and eventually making another type of error, round-off error, prominent.

The step size may be adjusted automatically during a calculation provided there exists an explicit expression for the upper bound of the truncation error. The typical dynamic transient is associated with large values of derivatives during the early stages which rapidly decrease during the final stages. Considerable computer time may be saved if the step is adjusted to be small when the derivatives are large and vice versa.

With an explicit knowledge of the instantaneous, or local, truncation error one can always select that step size which keeps the truncation error just below an acceptable upper bound. Although it is known that local truncation error is roughly proportional to the fifth power of the step size for a fourth-order Runge-Kutta integration method, it is not easy to obtain a running estimate of the truncation error during the course of an integration.

A modification of the basic fourth-order Runge-Kutta method which has a slightly smaller truncation error and provides an estimate of the truncation error is the Runge-Kutta-Merson method.* It has been

* G. N. Lance, *Numerical Methods for Highspeed Computers*, London: Iliffe & Sons, 1960.

shown to provide excellent accuracy and speed under a variety of conditions when compared with other integration techniques.†

Round-Off Error

Round-off error is a basic error encountered in digital computation. It results as a consequence of the finite number of digits with which a digital computer can carry out arithmetic operations. This number may range from 4 digits for digital machines with 12 bit words to 15 digits for digital machines with 60 bit words. Round-off affects the last digit of a given digital word. For instance, in a word with 8 digits, the first 7 digits are exact while the last digit is rounded off. By this process it is possible to represent approximately a real number which conceivably could have an infinite number of digits for exact definition by an 8-digit word. The first 7 digits match, while the 8th digit is adjusted up if the 9th digit is larger than 0.5; otherwise it stays the same.

Round-off error affects every digital computation. In numerical integration it assumes particular importance when the integration step has to be selected to be very small. Under this condition the significant changes in the values of dynamic systems variables occur more and more in the last few digits of the computer words. Round-off error is normally controlled by performing all computer calculation in double precision, which effectively doubles the word length of the computer.

Numerical Stability

Essentially, the only parameter left to the user's discretion is the time increment h. For obvious reasons this should be selected to be as large as possible. If the truncation error is kept small, in most cases the only risk incurred by making the step size too large is the possibility of numerical instability. For most applications, numerical instability is a more predominant problem than inaccuracy caused by truncation error. The analytical complexity of the method prohibits a direct stability analysis, even for the simplest case. A good rule of thumb is to keep the step size at approximately a tenth of the value of the smallest time constant of the differential equations to be solved.

A stability analysis, when tractable, is carried out according to the principles of discrete time systems which stipulate that stability is assured as long as the eigenvalues of the discrete transition matrix are less than unity in absolute value.*

---

† H. R. Martens, "A Comparative Study of Digital Integration Methods," (Eastern Simulation Council Meeting, Buffalo, New York, Oct. 17–18, 1967).

* See, for instance, H. Freeman, *Discrete-Time Systems*, New York: John Wiley and Sons, 1965, p. 163.

Example 12.12. We wish to examine the stability of the discrete appoximation. For this purpose we determine eigenvalues of the characteristic matrix of Equation 12.44. In matrix format we have

$$\begin{bmatrix} x_1(k+1) \\ x_2(k+1) \end{bmatrix} = \begin{bmatrix} 1-ah & -bh \\ h & 1 \end{bmatrix} \begin{bmatrix} x_1(k) \\ x_2(k) \end{bmatrix} + \begin{bmatrix} h \\ 0 \end{bmatrix} \tag{12.62}$$

The eigenvalues are

$$\lambda_{1,2} = 1 - \frac{ah}{2} \pm \sqrt{1 + h^2\left(\frac{a^2}{4} - b\right)}$$

It is easily seen that $|\lambda_{1,2}| > 1$ for h sufficiently large. Hence the solution will become unstable if h exceeds a certain value, thus making any feedback corrective action ineffective.

Comparison of Numerical Integration Techniques

In the preceding paragraphs a number of numerical methods which are typically used in the digital simulation of dynamic systems have been presented. They are principally methods which are based upon the recursive evaluation of difference equations which represent discrete equivalents of the differential equations describing the dynamics of the continuous systems. As was pointed out, there exists a multitude of ways of deriving a set of difference equations representing an equivalent. These differ in several respects, principally in method, convenience of application, speed of computation, and accuracy. In this section the methods previously discussed will be compared with respect to the last three factors. The comparison will be limited to these four methods: (1) Euler Method (EM), (2) Runge-Kutta Method (RKM), (3) Tustin Method (TM), (4) State-Transition Method (STM).

Convenience of Application

Methods EM and RKM are applicable to nonlinear systems, while TM and STM are restricted to linear systems. EM and RKM require the preparation of an identical sub-program for the evaluation of derivatives; this sub-program is used concurrently with the execution of the integration programs. TM and STM require intermediate programs for the preparation of the difference equations, TM a program to implement the Tustin substitution and STM to determine the exponential matrices $e^{\mathbf{A}T}$ and $\int e^{\mathbf{A}T}$. These programs are run prior to the integration program. To use TM, the description of the dynamic system must be available in transfer function form, while STM requires a state model.

It is probably fair to state that with respect to convenience of application no method is particularly disadvantageous, as long as the digital computer is effectively exploited to do the computational chores.

Speed of Computation

The relative speed of computation of the four methods depends entirely upon the total number of instructions that require execution during the course of the program. Table 12.1 shows a listing of computer time elapsed during compile, load, and execution stages for identical problems* for which the four methods were used. Time is given in minutes and seconds.** It is easily seen that EM is the fastest and RKM is the slowest, while TM and STM rank second and third. Since RKM requires four times as many calculations (it is a four-step method) as EM, it is easily explained that roughly four times as much time is required. The total time for TM is approximately 25 per cent longer than EM, while STM requires about 75 per cent more time than EM.

TABLE 12.1.

Time in min-sec	EM	RKM	TM	STM
Compile time	0–57	1–40	0–59	1–46
Execution time	2–55	12–53	4–26	5–34
Load time	0–19	0–21	0–19	0–22
Total time	4–16	15–18	5–49	7–42

To draw any meaningful conclusion from this time summary, one must also take into consideration the accuracy factor, for a method may require little time for implementation but may be marked by poor accuracy.

Accuracy

It goes without saying that accuracy is the most important factor in considering the selection of a numerical method for system simulation. In the earlier paragraphs of this section we considered the solution of the differential equation

$$\ddot{x} + \omega^2 x = 0$$

via the four methods under consideration. The results will now be compared.

---

* See next item (accuracy).

** These numbers are representative of computations carried out on an IBM 7044 computer.

The solution of this equation represents a circle (for $\omega = 1$) when $\dot{x}$ is plotted versus x. The period of this circle is 2π seconds. Plotting the result as a circle can offer a quick visual check on the quality of the solution.

Of interest here are the effects of truncation and round-off error on the accuracy of the solution. For this purpose we show the solution $x(t)$ for seven choices of h in Table 12.2. The initial conditions are chosen as $x(0) = 10.0$ and $\dot{x}(0) = 0.0$ so that a circle of radius 10.0 results. The solution is run for roughly 10 seconds of time sufficient to cover one full period. Solution values are shown at full second intervals and for $h \leq 0.01$, and also for $t = 3.14$ and $t = 6.28$, which correspond to half and full periods of the circle.

We recall that error due to truncation of series approximation is present in the methods EM, RKM, and TM, but not in STM. Reviewing Table 12.2(a) we see that EM produces an unstable solution, RKM and TM produce stable solutions with considerable truncation error, and the STM solution is accurate to within the decimal places shown. We recall that the accuracy of the last method depends in this case only on the accuracy to which the series expansion of $e^{\mathbf{A}T}$ is computed; each entry in the matrix $e^{\mathbf{A}T}$ is accurate to within 10^{-6}. Thus the solution generated by STM may serve as a reference.

When the increment of integration is reduced 0.1 the RKM becomes exact and the TM is improved considerably, but is not as good as the RKM. The solution generated by EM now appears stable, but still suffers considerable truncation error.* These results are shown in Table 12.2(b).

When h is further reduced to $h = 0.01$ the RKM and TM are identical to STM. EM, however, still shows truncation error effects. See Table 12.2(c). Also shown are values of the solution at $t = 3.14$ and $t = 6.28$, for which the exact solution is -10.00 and $+10.00$, respectively.

Table 12.2(d) shows the solutions for $h = 0.001$. The results indicate no error for RKM, TM, and STM. EM is now accurate to within two places.

A further reduction in the time increment to $h = 0.0001$ permits the generation of an exact solution (four significant figures) by the EM. On the other hand, the other three methods are beginning to show the effects of round-off. See Table 12.2(e).

When the increment is selected as small as $h = 0.00001$, round-off error becomes a significant influence in determining the quality of the solution. Table 12.2(f) demonstrates this. The results further indicate

* Actually the EM solution of the oscillator problem is always unstable independent of the value of h, but the growth rate is very small.

TABLE 12.2. *Numerical results of four methods*

Time	R-K	Euler	Tustin	State transition
1	5.417	10.00	6.0	5.403
2	−4.010	0.00	−2.8	−4.161
3	−9.695	−20.00	−9.36	−9.900
4	−6.542	−40.00	−8.432	−6.536
5	2.491	−40.00	−7.584	2.837
6	9.161	0.00	7.522	9.602
7	7.463	80.00	9.785	7.540
8	−9.638	160.00	4.220	−1.455
9	−8.417	160.00	−4.721	−9.111
10	−8.166	0.00	−9.885	−8.40

(a) $h = 1$ second

Time	R-K	Euler	Tustin	State transition
1	5.403	5.708	5.410	5.403
2	−4.161	−4.530	−4.146	−4.161
3	−9.900	−1.148	−9.896	−9.900
4	−6.536	−8.097	−6.562	−6.536
5	2.837	3.434	2.797	2.837
6	9.602	1.286	9.588	9.602
7	7.539	1.089	7.577	7.540
8	−1.455	−1.775	−1.389	−1.455
9	−9.111	−1.406	−9.080	−9.111
10	−8.391	−1.409	−8.436	−8.391

(b) $h = 0.1$ second

Time	R-K	Euler	Tustin	State transition
1	5.403	5.43	5.403	5.403
2	−4.161	−4.203	−4.161	−4.161
3	−9.900	−10.05	−9.900	−9.900
3.14	−10.000	−10.16	−10.00	−10.00
4	−6.669	−6.536	−6.536	−6.536
5	2.837	2.907	2.836	2.836
6	9.602	9.893	9.602	9.602
6.28	10.000	10.32	10.00	10.00
7	7.539	7.809	7.539	7.539
8	−1.455	−1.512	−1.454	−1.454
9	−9.111	−9.529	−9.111	−9.111
10	−8.391	—	—	—

(c) $h = 0.01$ second

TABLE 12.2. *Numerical results of four methods*

Time	R-K	Euler	Tustin	State transition
1	5.403	5.405	5.403	5.403
2	−4.161	−4.165	−4.161	−4.161
3	−9.900	−9.915	−9.900	−9.900
3.14	−10.00	−10.02	−10.00	−10.00
4	−6.536	−6.549	−6.536	−6.536
5	2.837	2.844	2.837	2.837
6	9.601	9.630	9.601	9.601
6.28	10.00	10.03	10.00	10.00
7	7.539	7.565	7.539	7.539
8	−1.455	−1.461	−1.455	−1.455
9	−9.111	−9.152	−9.111	−9.111
10	−8.390	—	−8.390	−8.390

(d) $h = 0.001$ second

Time	R-K	Euler	Tustin	State transition
1	5.403	5.403	5.403	5.403
2	−4.161	−4.161	−4.160	−4.160
3	−9.898	−9.900	−9.897	−9.896
3.14	−9.998	−10.00	−9.997	−9.996
4	−6.535	−6.536	−6.534	−6.533
5	2.836	2.836	2.835	2.835
6	9.598	9.601	9.596	9.594
6.28	9.996	9.999	9.994	9.991
7	7.536	7.539	7.534	7.532
8	−1.454	−1.455	−1.454	−1.454
9	−9.106	−9.111	−9.104	−9.100
10	—	—	—	—

(e) $h = 0.0001$ second

Time	R-K	Euler	Tustin	State transition
1	5.400	5.400	5.401	5.393
2	−4.157	−4.157	−4.147	−4.147
3	−9.882	−9.882	−9.864	−9.848
3.14	−9.983	−9.982	−9.963	−9.945
4	−6.521	−6.521	−6.510	−6.490
5	2.828	2.828	2.815	2.812
6	9.568	9.568	9.533	9.501
6.28	9.963	9.963	9.926	9.889
7.00	7.508	7.508	7.481	7.446

(f) $h = 0.00001$ second

that the RKM and EM generate identical solutions. This supports the fact that the truncation error for $h = 0.00001$ is completely negligible in both these methods and they provide equally good Taylor series approximations.

Of the four numerical integration methods tested, one can rate the state transition method as the most accurate. For the simulation of linear systems it is the most appropriate. If the system is nonlinear, the best choice is the Runge-Kutta method. Although it is four times slower than the Euler method for equal increments, the Euler method requires a time increment approximately 10,000 times smaller to attain comparable accuracy. Although the Euler method must be ruled out as a method of simulation because of poor accuracy, it may still be used during check-out phases of large-scale simulations in order to save time. The Tustin method compares relatively well as a method of simulating linear systems; however, it requires more time than the Runge-Kutta method to achieve comparable accuracy.

The brief summary given above is almost exclusively based upon the results of the case at hand. The reader is cautioned that, given a different differential equation, particularly one of considerably higher order, the balance may shift. It is known, for instance, that the matrix $e^{\mathbf{A}T}$ becomes more difficult to evaluate as the order of $\mathbf{A}$ increases. Therefore it is entirely possible that for large systems a method like the Runge-Kutta is the best choice.

12.5 Digital Computer Solution of a Nonlinear Circuit

In this section we consider the digital computer solution of a nonlinear circuit. This circuit, as shown in Figure 12.27, is a dc power supply which generates a dc voltage from an ac voltage source. The diodes pass current only in one direction, producing a rectified sine wave at point e (with no further component connected). This rectified sine wave is filtered and smoothed. The purpose of the resistor is to simulate a load. A digital computer study is to be performed to determine suitable values for the filter network. The component equations for the transformer are given as

$$\begin{bmatrix} i_0 \\ v_1 \\ v_2 \end{bmatrix} = \begin{bmatrix} 0 & -N & N \\ N & 0 & 0 \\ -N & 0 & 0 \end{bmatrix} \begin{bmatrix} v_0 \\ i_1 \\ i_2 \end{bmatrix}$$

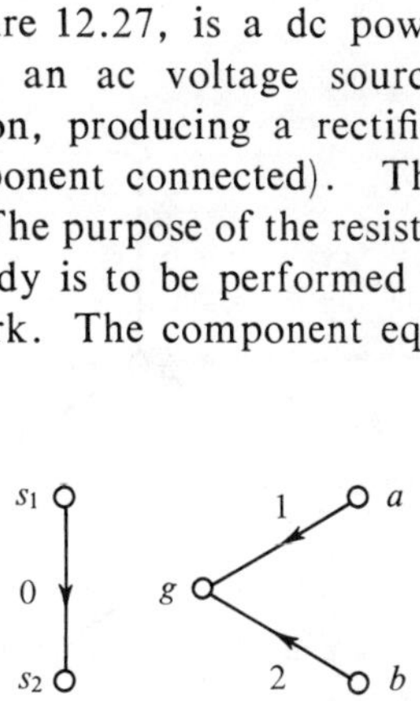

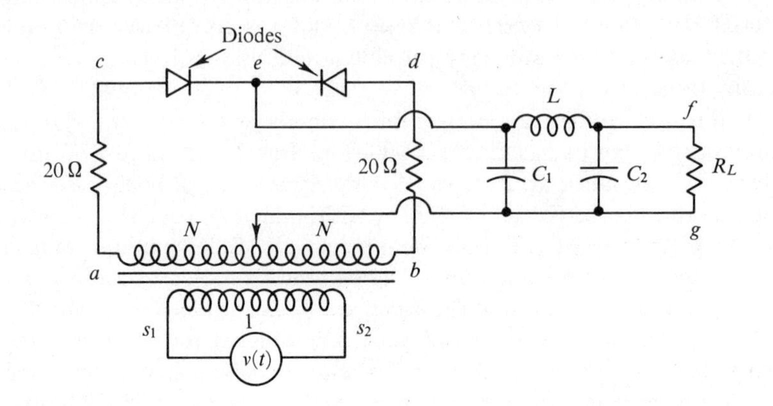

Fig. 12.27. *dc power supply.*

A diode is characterized by the *v-i* plot of Figure 12.27. It may be viewed as a nonlinear resistor with the component equation

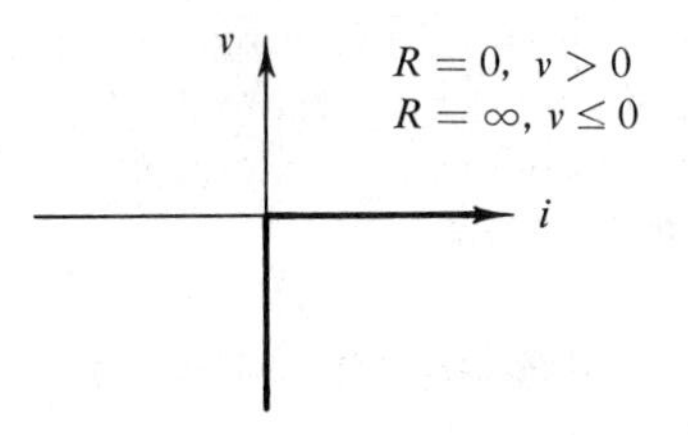

Fig. 12.28. *v-i characteristic of a diode.*

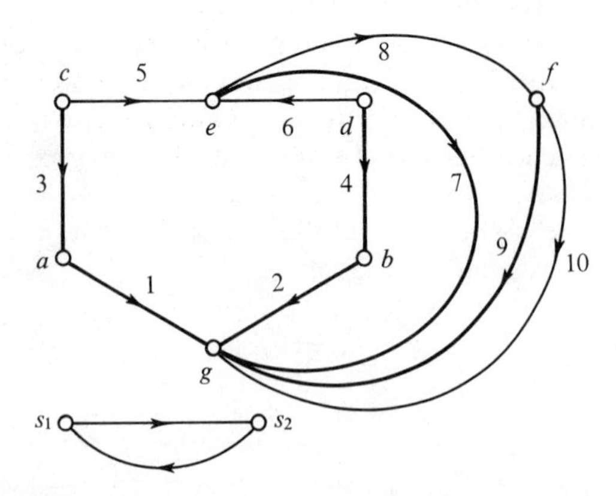

Fig. 12.29. *System graph of power supply.*

A state variable model is required in order to perform a digital computer study. For the development of the state equation we determine a system graph and select a tree as shown in Figure 12.29
For the three storage components we write the following equations:

$$\frac{d}{dt}v_7 = \frac{1}{C_1}(i_5 + i_6 - i_8)$$

$$\frac{d}{dt}i_8 = \frac{1}{L}(v_7 - v_9)$$

$$\frac{d}{dt}v_9 = \frac{1}{C_2}\left(i_8 - \frac{1}{R}v_9\right) \qquad \textbf{(12.63)}$$

The currents i_5 and i_6 represent the diode currents. From two simple circuit equations it can be determined that

$$i_5 = \frac{v_1 - v_7}{R + R_5} \qquad v_1 = Nv_0$$

and

$$i_6 = \frac{v_2 - v_7}{R + R_6} \qquad v_2 = -Nv_0$$

From the diode characterization we require that when $v_5 > 0$ then $R_5 = 0$ and when $v_6 > 0$ then $R_6 = 0$. However, when $v_5 \leq 0$ then $i_5 = 0$ and when $v_6 \leq 0$ then $i_6 = 0$. The voltages v_5 and v_6 are given by

$$v_5 = Nv_0 + i_5R - v_7$$

and

$$v_6 = -Nv_0 + i_6R - v_7$$

In summary, the diode currents are determined by the following equations:

$$i_5 \begin{cases} = \dfrac{Nv_0 - v_7}{R} \\ = \quad 0 \end{cases}$$

$$i_6 \begin{cases} = \dfrac{-Nv_0 - v_7}{R} \\ = \quad 0 \end{cases} \qquad \textbf{(12.64)}$$

when $v_5 > 0$, $v_5 < 0$, $v_6 > 0$, and $v_6 < 0$, respectively.

Equations 12.63 and 12.64 represent the state variable model for the dc power supply. As can be seen, they constitute a piecewise linear model. Since the mathematical model consists of three linear first-order differential equations at any one time, the analysis of the dc power supply is therefore carried out by solving three linear differential equations by any of the techniques discussed in the preceding section.

If, for example, the Runge-Kutta method is chosen, the execution of the program will require four evaluations of the derivatives (the right sides of the differential equations) per integration step. In the interest of program efficiency it would be best to prepare a subroutine for this purpose. A Fortran program implementing the necessary calculations is listed below.

```
SUBROUTINE SYSTEM (X, DX, C, T)
DIMENSION X(3), DX(3), C(3)
REAL I5, I6
VO= 167.* SIN (377.* T)
Y1 = N* VO - X(1)
Y2 = -N*VO - X(1)
V5 = Y1 + 50* I5
V6 = Y2 + 50* I6
I5 = 0.0
IF    (V5. GT. 0.0) I5 = Y1
I6 = 0.0
IF    (V6. GT. 0.0) I6 = Y2
DX(1) = C(1)* (I5 + I6 - X(2))
DX(2) = C(2)* (X(1) - X(3))
DX(3) = C(3)* (X(2) - 1000.)* X(3)
RETURN
END
```

The following Fortran variables have been used.

X (3)—Array of state variables
DX(3)—Array of derivatives
C (3)—Array of filter coefficients
T —Time

This subroutine completely describes the system. It will be called four times for each integration step from the main program which implements the Runge-Kutta algorithm. The main program may be a library routine already available to the user from a peripheral storage location such as magnetic tape or disk.

12.6 Computer Analysis of Systems and Networks

The last section demonstrated the use of the digital computer as a means of analyzing the response characteristics of a nonlinear filter network. It was shown that such an approach is feasible as long as one is able to derive a state variable model describing the particular system, for all that is necessary for a computer solution of a dynamic system is that the system be characterized as a set of first-order differental equations which may then be readily solved by numerical integration routines.

Although for most systems the systematic procedures developed in this text for the formulation of state variable equations can be readily utilized to develop a set of equations for computer study, this is still a considerable effort. In recent years an important new development in the mode of utilization of the digital computer has been developed. This is the time-shared digital computer. Basically, in this mode of operation a large centrally located digital computer can be remotely accessed through typewriter or visual display input and output terminals. A typical user would communicate with the digital computer directly through such a remote access terminal. He enters his program or execution instructions through the typewriter keyboard and then the computer processes these instructions or the data that the user has entered through programs that are permanently stored in the central digital computer and returns the processed information either through the typewriter as printed output or through the visual display as visual output. Since the user will have an almost instantaneous return of processed information, the time-shared facility will permit a high degree of interaction between user and computer through a rapid succession of input-output responses. It is this feature which makes a time-shared computing facility an immensely valuable tool for the person involved in system analysis and system design. This section will consider the applicability of a time-shared computer system to the analysis of electrical circuits and systems in general.

One of the basic requirements in the use of a time-shared system for system analysis is the ability to describe the system to the computer in as simple and straightforward a manner as possible. Specifically, the user should not be required to derive a set of state equations. This task should be left to the computer. Since the development of state models is based upon some rigorous topological concepts leading to systematic procedures, a circuit description in terms of components and structure is sufficient. In addition, the user specifies the types of performance tests to be carried out and the manner in which the results are to be returned to him. Although both the teletypewriter and the cathode ray tube may be used for this purpose, it is readily appreciated that the visual display is more desirable because of the increased speed of return as well as the smoother display of time responses.

Although the user never need concern himself with the actual details of the program, it is interesting to investigate some of the principles upon which the formulation of the computer model is based. It is clear that whatever the dynamic description of the system is, the digital computer must follow a numerical integration approach in order to solve the ensuing differential equations. This may be carried out in two basic ways. In one approach, the computer program views the entire system and develops a state model involving all components at the same time. Subsequent to the formulation stage, the computer takes the differential equations and solves them by a standard numerical integration routine such as those discussed in Section 12.4. Alternatively, the computer program takes all the dynamic components that normally give rise to the choice of a state variable such as capacitors, inductors, and other storage type components and converts them into a discrete equivalent model. Subsequently, the discrete component models are combined into an overall system model which is then solved as an algebraic set of equations. The second modeling approach offers greater flexibility, especially when repeated modifications of network topology are required, by simulating the energy storage components first as algebraic discrete models. If the system to be studied is modified and the first approach is used, a completely new state model will have to be derived. On the other hand, the second would require a small modification in the overall system model pertaining only to those parts which have been changed.

A fundamental advantage realized by the utilization of a time-shared computer system in the analysis of a system is the high degree of flexibility available to the user in specifying a large variety of system configurations which may be studied by the computer program with an equal amount of difficulty. A time-shared computer analysis program which has been described above in its gross details has recently been developed and perfected.* This program is, at the present, restricted to the analysis of electrical circuits; however, there is no fundamental reason why it cannot be expanded to include other types of systems as well as multiterminal components of multi-discipline systems. This program, called CIRCAL (meaning circuit analysis), has been provided with a special keyboard to permit the entering of coded information useful in the description of an electrical circuit such as a resistor or a capacitor, inductor, or various types of configurations involving passive and active components. With this special keyboard the efficiency in describing a particular circuit to the computer is improved considerably. The user of CIRCAL has at his disposal a teletypewriter terminal and a graphical input-output terminal consisting of a graphical output cathode ray tube and a light pen for graphical input. The computer

* M. L. Dertouzos, "CIRCAL: On-line Circuit Design," *Proc. IEEE*, LV, No. 5, (May, 1967).

system is equipped with the necessary software to permit mixed communication through the typewriter terminal as well as through the graphical input-output in connection with the specially prepared input keyboard.

Obviously, a time-shared computer analysis system offers great attractions to the user. Its combined speed, flexibility, and accuracy contain a tremendous potential for the future of circuit analysis and design, particularly when it is realized that one can develop a design procedure that is based upon a repeated application of an analysis program, and by means of an iterative approach one can realize a great variety of desired circuit performance characteristics. In view of the tremendous progress that computer utilization has made in recent years, it is probably not difficult to imagine that a time-shared computer analysis program will be available in the near future to anybody who needs it, students and practicing engineers alike.

ADDITIONAL READINGS

Hamming, H. E., *Numerical Methods for Scientists and Engineers*, New York: McGraw-Hill Book Co., 1964.

Hildebrand, F. B., *Introduction to Numerical Analysis*, New York: McGraw-Hill Book Co., 1958.

Johnson, *Analog Computer Techniques*, 2nd ed., New York: McGraw-Hill Book Co., 1965.

Korn and Korn, *Analog and Hybrid Computers*, New York: McGraw-Hill Book Co., 1965.

Kovach, *Computer—Oriented Mathematics*, San Francisco: Holden-Day, Inc., 1964.

PROBLEMS

12.1 Derive state equations by both single-input and single-output programming techniques for the following transfer functions:

a) $G(s) = \dfrac{s+5}{s(s^2+s+1)}$ c) $G(s) = \dfrac{10s+5}{20s^2+5s+1}$

b) $G(s) = \dfrac{s^2}{s^2+s+1}$ d) $G(s) = \dfrac{0.5(s+1)}{s+1}$

12.2. Synthesize flow diagrams by direct application of Mason's gain formula for the transfer functions of Problem 12.1.

12.3. Form state variable diagrams for the state equations developed in Problem 12.1.

12.4. Develop an analog computer diagram for the transfer functions of Problem 12.1.

12.5. On occasion it is useful to develop a set of state equations from a transfer function by a procedure called parallel programming. It is based upon a partial fraction expansion of the transfer function and is of the following general form for the transfer functions with distinct poles.

$$\frac{d}{dt}\begin{bmatrix} x_1 \\ x_2 \\ \vdots \\ x_n \end{bmatrix} = \begin{bmatrix} p_1 & & & 0 \\ & p_2 & & \\ & & \ddots & \\ 0 & & & p_n \end{bmatrix}\begin{bmatrix} x_1 \\ x_2 \\ \vdots \\ x_n \end{bmatrix} + \begin{bmatrix} 1 \\ 1 \\ \vdots \\ 1 \end{bmatrix} x_{\text{in}}(t)$$

$$x_{\text{out}} = [k_1 \quad k_2 \cdots k_n]\begin{bmatrix} x_1 \\ x_2 \\ \vdots \\ x_n \end{bmatrix} + d x_{\text{in}}(t)$$

where $p_1, p_2, \cdots p_n$ are the poles, $k_1, k_2, \cdots, k_n$ are partial fraction expansion coefficients, and d is the direct transmission term which is non-zero only when the numerator and denominator are of equal degree. For the transfer functions of Problem 12.1, determine the state equations applicable to parallel programming.

12.6. Determine an analog computer solution for the system problems shown in Figure P 12.6. Employ amplitude or time scaling where appropriate.

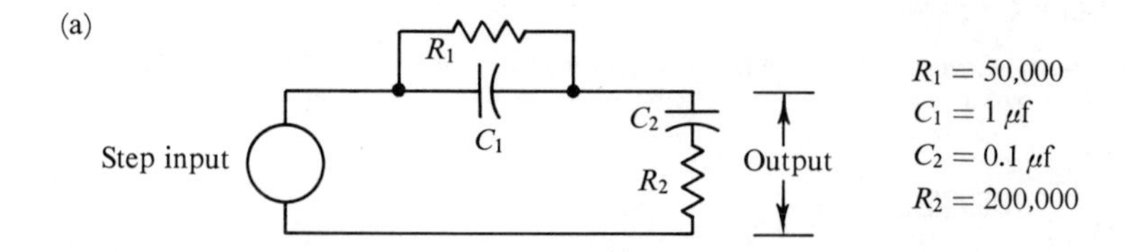

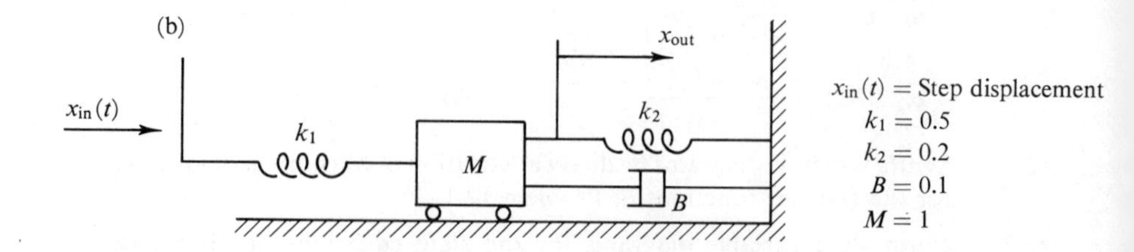

Obtain response as indicated. For the twin-tee network obtain a frequency response by use of an analog computer simulation. Compare the measured frequency response with a Bode plot.

(c)

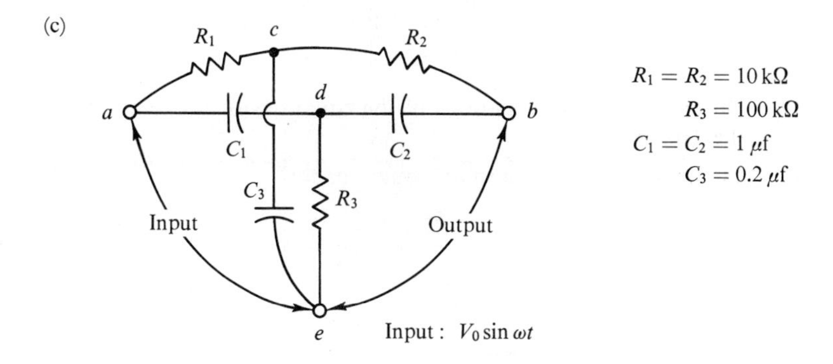

Fig. P 12.6.

12.7. Perform an amplitude scaling on the following equations so that they become suitable for analog computer solution.

$$\frac{d}{dt}\begin{bmatrix} x_1 \\ x_2 \\ x_3 \\ x_4 \end{bmatrix} = \begin{bmatrix} -57 & -10 & 0 & 0 \\ 1 & 0 & 0 & 0 \\ 0 & 400 & -20 & -5 \\ 0 & -200 & 0 & -10 \end{bmatrix} \begin{bmatrix} x_1 \\ x_2 \\ x_3 \\ x_4 \end{bmatrix} + \begin{bmatrix} -3 \\ +30 \\ 0 \\ 0 \end{bmatrix} x_{in}(t)$$

12.8. Determine the transfer function relating x_{out} to x_{in} from the analog computer diagram given in Figure P 12.8.

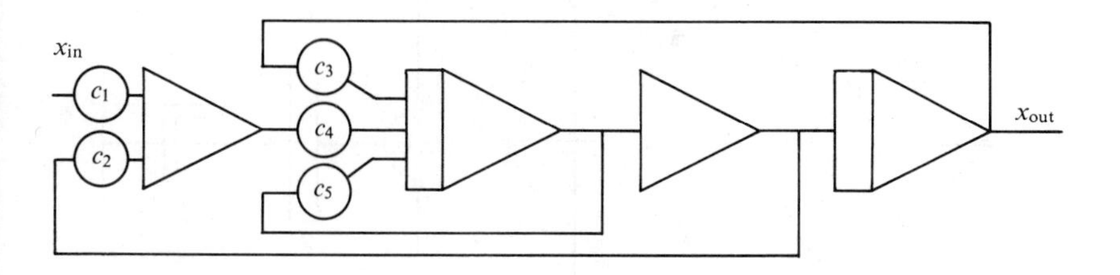

Fig. P 12.8.

12.9. Develop a set of difference equations for the numerical integration by the Euler method of the following relations.

a) $$x_{out}(s) = \frac{s^2 + s + 1}{s^3 + s^2 + 2s + 1} x_{in}(s)$$

b) $$5\ddot{x} + 2x + 10x = \sin \omega t$$

c)
$$\frac{d}{dt}\begin{bmatrix} x_1 \\ x_2 \\ x_3 \end{bmatrix} = \begin{bmatrix} -5 & 1 & 6 \\ 0 & -1 & 5 \\ 1 & 0 & -2 \end{bmatrix}\begin{bmatrix} x_1 \\ x_2 \\ x_3 \end{bmatrix} + \begin{bmatrix} 1 \\ 0 \\ 1 \end{bmatrix} x_{in}(t)$$
$$x_{out} = [1 \quad 2 \quad 3]\begin{bmatrix} x_1 \\ x_2 \\ x_3 \end{bmatrix}$$

12.10. Develop recursion equations of the equations of Problem 12.9 using the Tustin method.

12.11. Compute the state transition equations for

a)
$$G(s) = \frac{1}{s(s+2)}$$

b)
$$\frac{d}{dt}\begin{bmatrix} x_1 \\ x_2 \end{bmatrix} = \begin{bmatrix} -1 & -2 \\ 1 & -4 \end{bmatrix}\begin{bmatrix} x_1 \\ x_2 \end{bmatrix} + \begin{bmatrix} 1 \\ 0 \end{bmatrix} x_{in}$$
$$x_{out} = x_2$$

12.12. Develop the state equations and prepare a FORTRAN program to study the performance of the systems shown in Figure P 12.12 by digital computer.

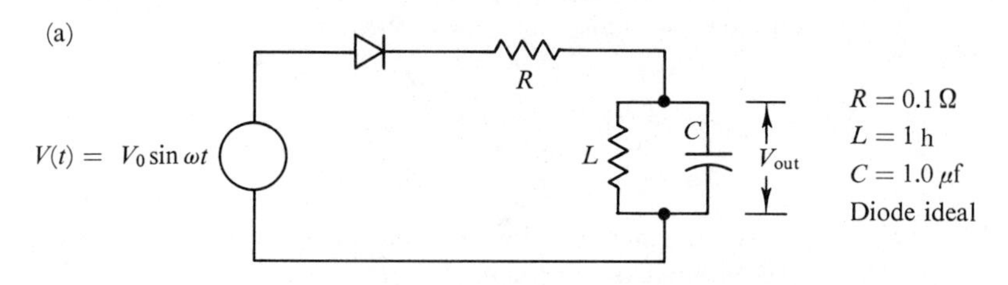

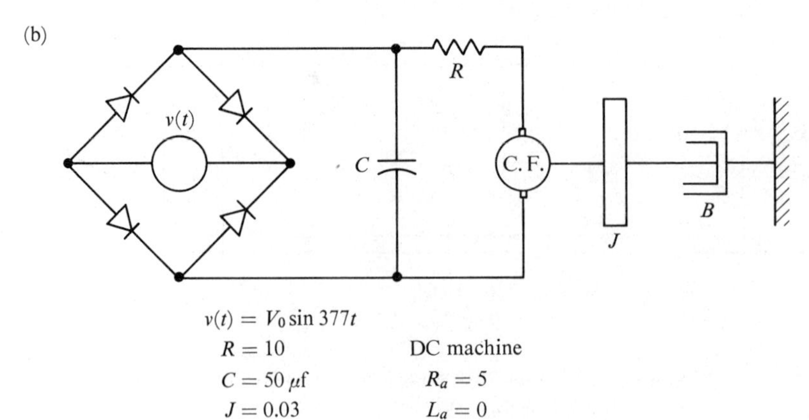

Fig. P 12.12.

Appendix

A. Selected Topics in Matrix Algebra

Part A of the appendix is designed as a quick reference on frequently-used matrix operations. It is not an introduction to matrix algebra, but rather assumes that the reader has a basic understanding of matrix concepts.

A.1 Determinant of a Square Matrix

The determinant of a square matrix $\mathbf{A}$ is denoted by det $\mathbf{A}$. If $\mathbf{A}$ is a matrix of real numbers, then det $\mathbf{A}$ is a real number; if $\mathbf{A}$ is a matrix of rational functions, then det $\mathbf{A}$ is a rational function.

Determinants are evaluated by the following formula:

$$\det \mathbf{A} = \sum_{i=1}^{n} a_{ij} \mathbf{A}_{ij} \tag{A.1}$$

for any $j = 1, 2, \cdots, n$ where a_{ij} are the elements of a given row or column and where

$$\mathbf{A}_{ij} = (-1)^{i+j}\mathbf{M}_{ij} \tag{A.2}$$

is called the cofactor of the element a_{ij} and

$$\mathbf{M}_{ij} = \det \tag{A.3}$$

(submatrix of **A** with i^{th} row and j^{th} column deleted).

Determinants of order two and three:

$$\begin{vmatrix} a_{11} & a_{12} \\ a_{21} & a_{22} \end{vmatrix} = a_{11}a_{22} - a_{12}a_{21}$$

$$\begin{vmatrix} a_{11} & a_{12} & a_{13} \\ a_{21} & a_{22} & a_{23} \\ a_{31} & a_{32} & a_{33} \end{vmatrix} = a_{11}\begin{vmatrix} a_{22} & a_{23} \\ a_{32} & a_{33} \end{vmatrix} - a_{12}\begin{vmatrix} a_{21} & a_{23} \\ a_{31} & a_{33} \end{vmatrix} + a_{13}\begin{vmatrix} a_{21} & a_{22} \\ a_{31} & a_{32} \end{vmatrix}$$

A.2 Rank of a Matrix

A matrix **A**, not necessarily square, is said to have rank r if at least one of its r-square minors is different from zero while every $(r + 1)$-square minor, if any, is zero. An n-square matrix is called non-singular if its rank $r = n$. The determinant of a non-singular matrix is non-zero.

A.3 Elementary Matrix Operations

The following operations on a matrix, called elementary matrix operations, do not change either its rank or its order:

1. The interchange of any two rows or columns;
2. The multiplication of every element of a row or column by a non-zero scalar;
3. The addition to the elements of a row or column a scalar multiple of the elements of any other row or column.

Elementary matrix operations may be referred to as *elementary row transformations* or *elementary column transformations*, depending on whether rows or columns are involved.

When elementary matrix operations are performed on a unit matrix, *elementary matrices* result. The pre-multiplication (post-multiplication) of a matrix by an elementary matrix will implement an elementary row (column) operation.

Example A.1. Examples of elementary matrices.

$$\begin{bmatrix} 0 & 1 \\ 1 & 0 \end{bmatrix}$$

interchange of rows or columns.

$$\begin{bmatrix} 1 & 0 \\ 0 & \rho \end{bmatrix}$$

multiplication of second row or column by ρ.

$$\begin{bmatrix} 1 & \rho \\ 0 & 1 \end{bmatrix}$$

addition of ρ times the second row or column to first row or column.

A.4 Equivalent Matrices

Two matrices **A** and **B** are equivalent, $\mathbf{A} \sim \mathbf{B}$, if one can be obtained from the other by a sequence of elementary matrix operations. If two matrices are equivalent, this implies that they have the same rank.

A.5 Adjoint

The adjoint of an n-square matrix **A**, denoted by adj **A**, is also an n-square matrix. It is given by

$$\text{adj}\,\mathbf{A} = \begin{bmatrix} \mathbf{A}_{11} & \mathbf{A}_{21} & \cdots & \mathbf{A}_{n1} \\ \mathbf{A}_{12} & \mathbf{A}_{22} & \cdots & \mathbf{A}_{n2} \\ - & - & - & - \\ \mathbf{A}_{1n} & \mathbf{A}_{2n} & \cdots & \mathbf{A}_{nn} \end{bmatrix} \quad (\mathbf{A.4})$$

where the $\mathbf{A}_{ij}$ are the cofactors of a_{ij}. Note that the elements of the ith row of adj **A** are the cofactors of the ith column of **A**.

Example A.2. Given

$$\mathbf{A} = \begin{bmatrix} 1 & 2 & 3 \\ 2 & 3 & 2 \\ 3 & 3 & 4 \end{bmatrix}$$

then

$$\text{adj}\,\mathbf{A} = \begin{bmatrix} 6 & 1 & -5 \\ -2 & -5 & 4 \\ -3 & 3 & -1 \end{bmatrix}$$

A.6 Inverse of a Matrix

The inverse of a non-singular matrix may be calculated by the relation

$$\mathbf{A}^{-1} = \frac{\text{adj}\,\mathbf{A}}{\det \mathbf{A}} \quad (\mathbf{A.5})$$

Example A.3. Given

$$\mathbf{A} = \begin{bmatrix} 1 & 2 & 3 \\ 2 & 3 & 2 \\ 3 & 3 & 4 \end{bmatrix}$$

$$\det \mathbf{A} = -7$$

and using the results of Example A.2,

$$\mathbf{A}^{-1} = -\frac{1}{7}\begin{bmatrix} 6 & 1 & -5 \\ -2 & -5 & 4 \\ -3 & 3 & -1 \end{bmatrix}$$

A.7 Linear Equations

A system of m linear equations in n unknowns $x_1, x_2, \cdots, x_n$ may be written in the matrix format

$$\begin{bmatrix} a_{11} & a_{12} & \cdots & a_{1n} \\ a_{21} & a_{22} & \cdots & a_{2n} \\ - & - & - & - \\ a_{m1} & a_{m2} & \cdots & a_{mn} \end{bmatrix}\begin{bmatrix} x_1 \\ x_2 \\ \vdots \\ x_n \end{bmatrix} = \begin{bmatrix} b_1 \\ b_2 \\ \vdots \\ b_m \end{bmatrix} \tag{A.6}$$

or

$$\mathbf{Ax} = \mathbf{B} \tag{A.7}$$

If the matrices **A** and [**A B**] are of the same rank r then the system of Equation A.6 is said to be consistent.

In a consistent system (Equation A.6) of rank r, $n - r$ of the unknown may be chosen so that the coefficient matrix of the remaining r unknown is of rank r.

Example A.4. Find a solution for the system

$$\begin{bmatrix} 1 & -1 & 2 & 4 \\ 1 & 2 & 1 & -1 \\ -1 & 3 & -3 & 1 \end{bmatrix}\begin{bmatrix} x_1 \\ x_2 \\ x_3 \\ x_4 \end{bmatrix} = \begin{bmatrix} 1 \\ 6 \\ -2 \end{bmatrix}$$

We determine the rank of **A** and [**AB**] by successive elementary opererations:

$$[\mathbf{AB}] = \begin{bmatrix} 1 & -1 & 2 & 4 & 1 \\ 1 & 0 & 1 & -1 & 6 \\ -1 & 3 & -3 & 1 & -2 \end{bmatrix} \sim \begin{bmatrix} 1 & -1 & 2 & 4 & 1 \\ 0 & 1 & -1 & -5 & 5 \\ 0 & 2 & -1 & 5 & -1 \end{bmatrix}$$

$$\sim \begin{bmatrix} 1 & -1 & 2 & 4 & 1 \\ 0 & 1 & -1 & -5 & 5 \\ 0 & 0 & 1 & -5 & -11 \end{bmatrix} \sim \begin{bmatrix} 1 & -1 & 0 & 14 & 23 \\ 0 & 1 & 0 & -10 & -6 \\ 0 & 0 & 1 & -5 & -11 \end{bmatrix}$$

$$\sim \begin{bmatrix} 1 & 0 & 0 & 4 & 17 \\ 0 & 1 & 0 & -10 & -6 \\ 0 & 0 & 1 & -5 & -11 \end{bmatrix}$$

It is seen that both **A** and [**A B**] are of rank 3. Furthermore, the first three variables are chosen as unknowns. Letting $x_4 = a$, we find that

$$\begin{bmatrix} x_1 \\ x_2 \\ x_3 \end{bmatrix} = \begin{bmatrix} 17 - 4a \\ -6 + 10a \\ -11 + 5a \end{bmatrix}$$

These r unknowns are uniquely determined in terms of the arbitrarily chosen solutions for the $n - r$ unknowns.

A.8 Non-Homogeneous Equations

If the number of unknowns equals the number of equations, the system is called non-homogeneous. This system has the unique solution

$$\mathbf{x} = \mathbf{A}^{-1}\mathbf{B} \qquad \textbf{(A.8)}$$

provided **A** is non-singular.

In addition to the solution by inverse Equation A.8, one may use several other methods to solve Equation A.7 when $m = n$. One of these methods is Cramer's Rule, or solution by determinants.

Denoting by $\mathbf{A}_i$ ($i = 1, 2, \cdots, n$) the matrix obtained from **A** and replacing its ith column with the column matrix **B**, then if det $\mathbf{A} \neq 0$, the system has the unique solution

$$x_i = \frac{\det \mathbf{A}_i}{\det \mathbf{A}} \qquad i = 1, 2, \cdots, n \qquad \textbf{(A.9)}$$

A.9 Homogeneous Equations

The system of linear Equations A.7 is called homogeneous when $\mathbf{B} = 0$, that is,

$$\mathbf{Ax} = 0 \qquad \textbf{(A.10)}$$

If the matrix **A** is non-singular then no solution exists except the trivial solution $x_1 = x_2 = \cdots = x_n = 0$.

If the rank is $r < n$ then the system has exactly $n - r$ linearly independent solutions. Every other solution is a linear combination of these $n - r$ solutions.

If the system of Equation A.10 has n unknowns and n equations, a solution exists if and only if det $\mathbf{A} \neq 0$.

A.10 Eigenvectors and Eigenvalues

Any vector **x** which when multiplied by an n-square matrix **A** yields a scalar multiple of the vector according to the equation

$$\mathbf{A}\mathbf{x} = \lambda\mathbf{x} \tag{A.11}$$

is called an *eigenvector* of the matrix **A**. The scalar λ is called an eigenvalue of matrix **A**. An n-square matrix **A** has n eigenvalues and n eigenvectors, not all of which are necessarily distinct.

The eigenvalues are determined by solving Equation A.11, from which we obtain

$$\lambda\mathbf{x} - \mathbf{A}\mathbf{x} = [\lambda\mathbf{U} - \mathbf{A}]\mathbf{x} = \begin{bmatrix} \lambda - a_{11} & -a_{12} & \cdots & -a_{1n} \\ -a_{21} & \lambda - a_{22} & \cdots & -a_{2n} \\ \cdot & \cdot & \cdot\ \cdot\ \cdot & \cdot \\ -a_{n1} & -a_{n2} & & \lambda - a_{nn} \end{bmatrix} \begin{bmatrix} x_1 \\ x_2 \\ \vdots \\ x_n \end{bmatrix} = \mathbf{0} \tag{A.12}$$

Equation A.12 is a system of n homogeneous equations in n unknowns with the nontrivial solution

$$[\lambda\mathbf{U} - \mathbf{A}] = \mathbf{0} \tag{A.13}$$

Equation A.13 is an nth degree polynomial in λ whose n roots are the eigenvalues of the matrix **A**. It is called the characteristic equation.

Example A.5. Determine the eigenvalues and eigenvectors of the matrix

$$\mathbf{A} = \begin{bmatrix} -3 & -2 \\ 1 & 0 \end{bmatrix}$$

$$|\lambda\,\mathbf{U} - \mathbf{A}| = \begin{vmatrix} \lambda + 3 & +2 \\ -1 & \lambda \end{vmatrix} = (\lambda + 3)\lambda + 2 = \lambda^2 + 3\lambda + 2$$
$$= (\lambda + 1)(\lambda + 2)$$

$$\lambda_1 = -1 \qquad \lambda_2 = -2$$

To determine the eigenvectors

$$\mathbf{x}_1 = \begin{bmatrix} x_{12} \\ x_{21} \end{bmatrix} \quad \text{and} \quad \mathbf{x}_2 = \begin{bmatrix} x_{12} \\ x_{22} \end{bmatrix}$$

we use Equation A.11,

$$\begin{bmatrix} -3 & -2 \\ 1 & 0 \end{bmatrix} \begin{bmatrix} x_{11} \\ x_{21} \end{bmatrix} = -1 \begin{bmatrix} x_{11} \\ x_{21} \end{bmatrix}$$

which yields $x_{11} = \alpha$ and $x_{12} = -\alpha$. Thus

$$\mathbf{x}_1 = \begin{bmatrix} \alpha \\ -\alpha \end{bmatrix}$$

Similarly,

$$\mathbf{x}_2 = \begin{bmatrix} 2\alpha \\ -\alpha \end{bmatrix}$$

where α is an arbitrary constant.

ADDITIONAL READINGS

Bellman, R., *Introduction to Matrix Analysis*, New York: McGraw-Hill Book Co., 1960.

Pipes, L., *Matrix Methods for Engineering*, Englewood Cliffs, New Jersey: Prentice-Hall, Inc., 1963.

Tropper, A. M., *Matrix Theory for Electrical Engineers*, Reading, Mass.: Addison-Wesley Publishing Co., Inc., 1963.

B. The Laplace Transform

Part B is intended to serve as a quick and convenient reference to some of the more elementary properties of the Laplace transform and the associated process of partial fraction expansion. It will not suffice as a basis for the study of the Laplace transform and its application to the solution of linear differential equations. The student is referred to any number of more complete and detailed texts devoted to the Laplace transform.

B.1 Definition

The Laplace transform is defined as

$$\mathscr{L}\{f(t)\} = \int_0^\infty f(t)e^{-st}dt \tag{B.1}$$

Functions resulting from this integration are dependent upon s and denoted by $F(s)$. Although the variable s is a complex variable expressible as $s = \alpha + j\omega$, it is sufficient to consider s a parameter taking on real and/or complex values, provided the application of the Laplace transform is limited to elementary operations. The function $F(s)$ is then subject to the rules of algebra only. By application of the definition of Equation B.1, the following table may be established.

TABLE B.1

	$f(t)$	$F(s)$
1.	$u(t)$	$1/s$
2.	t	$1/s^2$
3.	e^{-at}	$\frac{1}{s+a}$
4.	$\sin \omega t$	$\frac{\omega}{s^2+\omega^2}$
5.	$\cos \omega t$	$\frac{s}{s^2+\omega^2}$
6.	$e^{-\alpha t} \sin \omega t$	$\frac{\omega}{(s+\alpha)^2+\omega^2}$
7.	$te^{-\alpha t}$	$\frac{1}{(s+\alpha)^2}$
8.	$\delta(t)$	1

B.2 Transform of a Derivative

$$\mathscr{L}\{\dot{f}(t)\} = \int_0^\infty \frac{df}{dt} e^{-st} dt \tag{B.2}$$

The integral is evaluated by integration by parts,

$$\mathscr{L}\{\dot{f}(t)\} = f(t)e^{-st}\Big|_0^\infty + s\int_0^\infty f(t)e^{-st}dt = -f(0) + sF(s) \tag{B.3}$$

The Laplace transform of higher order derivatives may be easily established through repeated application of Equation B.3 to yield

$$\mathscr{L}\{\ddot{f}(t)\} = s^2F(s) - \dot{f}(0) - sf(0) \tag{B.4}$$

and

$$\mathscr{L}\{\dddot{f}(t)\} = s^3F(s) - \ddot{f}(0) - s\dot{f}(0) - s^2f(0) \tag{B.5}$$

and so forth.

B.3 Transform of an Integral

$$\mathscr{L}\left\{\int_0^t f(\tau)d\tau\right\} = \int_0^\infty \int_0^t f(\tau)d\tau e^{-st}dt \tag{B.6}$$

Again, this integral is evaluated by parts

$$\mathscr{L}\left\{\int_0^t f(\tau)d\tau\right\} = -\frac{1}{s}e^{-st}\int_0^t f(\tau)d\tau\Big|_0^\infty + \frac{1}{s}\int_0^\infty f(t)e^{-st}dt$$

so that

$$\mathcal{L}\left\{\int_0^t f(\tau)\,d\tau\right\} = \frac{F(s)}{s} \qquad \textbf{(B.7)}$$

B.4 Initial and Final Values

Consider the transform of a derivative. From Equation B.3 we have

$$\int_0^\infty \dot{f}\, e^{-st}dt = -f(0) + sF(s)$$

We write the left side as

$$\lim_{t\to\infty}\int_0^t \dot{f}(\tau)e^{-s\tau}d\tau = -f(0) + sF(s) \qquad \textbf{(B.8)}$$

Now if we let $s \to \infty$ then Equation B.8 becomes

$$f(0) = \lim_{s\to\infty} sF(s) \qquad \textbf{(B.9)}$$

This is the initial value theorem. And if we let $s \to 0$, then Equation B.8 becomes

$$\lim_{t\to\infty}[f(t) - f(0)] = \lim_{s\to 0}[-f(0) + sF(s)]$$

or

$$f(\infty) = \lim_{s\to 0} sF(s) \qquad \textbf{(B.10)}$$

This is the final value theorem.

B.5 Partial Fraction Expansion

In order to determine the t-domain function corresponding to an s-domain function

$$X_o(s) = G(s)\cdot X_i(s)\cdot \qquad \textbf{(B.11)}$$

where $X_i(s)$ is the transform of the input function and $G(s)$ is the transfer function, it is most expedient to express the right side by a partial fraction expansion of a simple transform whose t-domain function is easily recognized. In general, $X_o(s)$ is expressible as the ratio of two polynomials,

$$\frac{P(s)}{Q(s)}$$

For a partial fraction expansion, the polynomial $Q(s)$ is expressed as the product of the factors corresponding to the roots of the equation

$$Q(s) = 0 \qquad \textbf{(B.12)}$$

When only elementary input functions are applied, these factors are normally of the following type:

a. $s, s^2, s^3, \cdots$
b. $s + a, (s + a)^2, \cdots$
c. $s^2 + 2\zeta\omega_n s + \omega_n^2$

The expansion process is best defined by treating certain important cases.

Partial Fraction Expansion When All Roots Are of Simple Order

If all the roots of Equation B.12 are simple, we may write Equation B.11 as

$$X_o(s) = \frac{P(s)}{Q(s)} = \frac{P(s)}{(s + s_1)(s + s_2) \cdots (s + s_n)}$$

$$X(s) = \frac{K_1}{s + s_1} + \frac{K_2}{s + s_2} + \cdots + \frac{K_n}{s + s_n} \tag{B.13}$$

The expansion coefficients are evaluated by

$$K_j = (s + s_j)X_o(s) \Big|_{s = -s_j} \tag{B.14}$$

$$= \frac{P(-s_j)}{(s + s_1)(s + s_2) \cdots (s + s_{j-1})(s + s_{j-1}) \cdots (s + s_n)}$$

and

$$x_o(t) = K_1 e^{-s_1 t} + K_2 e^{-s_2 t} + \cdots + K_n e^{-s_n t} \tag{B.15}$$

When one of the roots is zero, the expansion will contain the term

$$\frac{K}{s}$$

This expansion coefficient is evaluated as above. The corresponding time function is simply K.

Partial Fraction Expansion When Some Roots Are of Multiple Order

If not all roots of Equation B.12 are simple, we may express Equation B.11 as

$$X_o(s) = \frac{P(s)}{(s + s_1)(s + s_2) \cdots (s + s_i)^m \cdots (s + s_n)} \tag{B.16}$$

The partial fraction expansion then is

$$X_o(s) = \frac{K_1}{s+s_1} + \frac{K_2}{s+s_2} + \cdots + \frac{K_{i1}}{s+s_i} + \frac{K_{i2}}{(s+s_i)^2} + \cdots$$
$$+ \frac{K_{im}}{(s+s_i)^m} + \cdots + \frac{K_n}{s+s_n} \quad \textbf{(B.17)}$$

The expansion coefficients, K_{ij}, are evaluated by

$$K_{im} = (s+s_i)^m X_o(s)\Big|_{s=-s_i} \quad \textbf{(B.18a)}$$

$$K_{im-1} = \frac{d}{ds}[(s+s_i)^m X_o(s)]\Big|_{s=-s_i} \quad \textbf{(B.18b)}$$

$$K_{i1} = \frac{1}{(m-1)!}\frac{d^{m-1}}{ds^{m-1}}[(s+s_i)^m X_o(s)]\Big|_{s=-s_i} \quad \textbf{(B.18c)}$$

so that

$$X_o(t) = K_1 e^{-s_1 t} + K_2 e^{-s_2 t} + \cdots + K_{i1} e^{-s_i t} + K_{i2} t e^{-s_i t}$$
$$+ \cdots + K_{im}\frac{t^{m-1}}{(m-1)!}e^{-s_1 t} + \cdots + K_n e^{-s_n t} \quad \textbf{(B.19)}$$

Partial Fraction Expansion of Complex Conjugate Roots

Let $Q(s)$ contain a pair of complex roots

$$s_{1,2} = -\zeta\omega_n \pm j\omega_n\sqrt{1-\zeta^2} \quad \textbf{(B.20)}$$
$$= -\alpha \pm j\beta$$

Since these roots are simple, their expansion coefficients are

$$K_1^+ = (s+\alpha-j\beta)\frac{P(s)}{Q(s)}\Big|_{s=-\alpha+j\beta} \quad \textbf{(B.21)}$$
$$K_1^- = \hat{K}_1^+$$

Consider, for example, the function

$$X_o(s) = \frac{\omega_n^2}{s^2+2\zeta\omega_n s+\omega_n^2}\cdot X_i(s) \qquad X_i(s) = \frac{1}{s}$$
$$= \frac{K_0}{s} + \frac{K_1}{s+\alpha-j\beta} + \frac{\hat{K}_1}{s+\alpha+j\beta} \quad \textbf{(B.22)}$$

where $\alpha = \zeta\omega_n$ and $\beta = \omega_n\sqrt{1-\zeta^2}$.

$$K_0 = sX_o(s)\Big|_{s=0} = 1 \quad \textbf{(B.23a)}$$

$$K_1 = (s+\alpha-j\beta)\,X_o(s)\Big|_{s=-\alpha+j\beta}$$

$$= \frac{\omega_n^2}{(-\alpha + j\beta)2j\beta} = \frac{\omega_n}{2j\beta} e^{-j\phi} \tag{B.23b}$$

$$\phi = \tan^{-1} \frac{\beta}{-\alpha}$$

$$\hat{K}_1 = -\frac{\omega_n}{2j\beta} e^{j\phi} \tag{B.23c}$$

The t-domain function is then

$$X_o(t) = 1 + \frac{\omega_n}{\beta} e^{-\alpha t} \frac{[e^{j(\beta t - \phi)} - e^{-j(\beta t - \phi)}]}{2j}$$

$$= 1 + \frac{e^{-\zeta\omega_n t}}{\sqrt{1-\zeta^2}} \sin(\omega_n \sqrt{1-\zeta^2}\, t - \phi) \tag{B.24}$$

$$\phi = \tan^{-1} \frac{\sqrt{1-\zeta^2}}{-\zeta}$$

TABLE B.2 *Selected Laplace transform pairs.*

	Laplace transform $F(s)$	Time function $f(t)$
1.	$\frac{1}{s}$	$u(t)$ (unit step function)
2.	$\frac{1}{s^2}$	t
3.	$\frac{1}{s+a}$	e^{-at}
4.	$\frac{1}{(s+a)^n}$	$\frac{t^{n-1}}{(n-1)!} e^{-at}$
5.	$\frac{1}{(s+a)(s+b)}$	$\frac{e^{-at} - e^{-bt}}{b-a}$
6.	$\frac{1}{s(1+Ts)}$	$1 - e^{-t/T}$
7.	$\frac{\omega_n^2}{s^2 + 2\zeta\omega_n s + \omega_n^2}$	$\frac{\omega_n}{\sqrt{1-\zeta^2}} e^{-\zeta\omega_n t} \sin \omega_n \sqrt{1-\zeta^2}\, t$
8.	$\frac{s + \zeta\omega_n}{s^2 + 2\zeta\omega_n s + \omega_n^2}$	$e^{-\zeta\omega_n t} \cos \omega_n \sqrt{1-\zeta^2}\, t$
9.	$\frac{\omega_n^2}{s(s^2 + 2\zeta\omega_n s + \omega_n^2)}$	$1 + \frac{1}{\sqrt{1-\zeta^2}} e^{-\zeta\omega_n t} \sin(\omega_n \sqrt{1-\zeta^2}\, t - \phi)$ where $\phi = \tan^{-1} \frac{\sqrt{1-\zeta^2}}{-\zeta}$

Laplace transform $F(s)$	Time function $f(t)$
10. $\dfrac{\omega_n^2}{(1+Ts)(s^2+2\zeta\omega_n s+\omega_n^2)}$	$\dfrac{T\omega_n^2 e^{-t/T}}{1-2\zeta T\omega_n+T^2\omega_n^2} + \dfrac{\omega_n e^{-\zeta\omega_n t}\sin(\omega_n\sqrt{1-\zeta^2}t-\phi)}{\sqrt{(1-\zeta^2)(1-2\zeta T\omega_n-T^2\omega_n^2}}$ where $\phi=\tan^{-1}\dfrac{T\omega_n\sqrt{1-\zeta^2}}{1-T\zeta\omega_n}$
11. $\dfrac{\omega_n^2}{s(1+Ts)(s^2+s\zeta\omega_n s+\omega_n^2)}$	$1-\dfrac{T^2\omega_n^2}{1-2T\zeta\omega_n+T^2\omega_n^2}e^{-t/T} + \dfrac{e^{-\zeta\omega_n t}\sin(\omega_n\sqrt{1-\zeta^2}t-\phi)}{\sqrt{1-\zeta^2(1-2\zeta T\omega_n+T^2\omega_n^2}}$ where $\phi=\tan^{-1}(\sqrt{1-\zeta^2}/-\zeta + \tan^{-1}T\omega_n\sqrt{1-\zeta^2}/(1-T\zeta\omega_n)$
12. $\dfrac{\omega_n^2(1+as)}{s^2+2\zeta\omega_n s+\omega_n^2}$	$\omega_n\sqrt{\dfrac{1-2a\zeta\omega_n+a^2\omega_n^2}{1-\zeta^2}}e^{-\zeta\omega_n t}$ $\sin(\omega_n\sqrt{1-\zeta^2}t+\phi)$ where $\phi=\tan^{-1}\dfrac{a\omega_n\sqrt{1-\zeta^2}}{1-a\zeta\omega_n}$
13. $\dfrac{\omega_n^2(1+as)}{s(s^2+2\zeta\omega_n s+\omega_n^2)}$	$1+\dfrac{1}{\sqrt{1-\zeta^2}}\sqrt{1-2a\zeta\omega_n+a^2\omega_n^2}\,e^{-\zeta\omega_n t}$ $\sin(\omega_n-\sqrt{1-\zeta^2}t+\phi)$ where $\phi=\tan^{-1}\dfrac{a\omega_n\sqrt{1-\zeta^2}}{1-a\zeta\omega_n} - \tan^{-1}\dfrac{\sqrt{1-\zeta^2}}{-\zeta}$

ADDITIONAL READINGS

Aseltine, J. A., *Transform Methods in Linear System Analysis*, New York: McGraw-Hill Book Co., 1958.

Churchill, R. V., *Modern Operational Methods in Engineering*, New York: McGraw-Hill Book Co., 1944.

Gardner, M. F., and J. L. Barnes, *Transients in Linear Systems*, New York: John Wiley & Sons, Inc., 1942.

Kaplan, W., *Operational Methods for Linear Systems*, Reading, Mass.: Addison-Wesley Publishing Co., Inc., 1962.

Lepage, W. R., *Complex Variables and the Laplace Transform for Engineers*, New York: McGraw-Hill Book Co., 1961.

Roberts, G. E., and H. Kaufman, *Table of Laplace Transforms*, Philadelphia: W. B. Saunders Co., 1966.

Widder, P. V., *The Laplace Transform*, New Jersey: Princeton University Press, 1941.

C. The Transition Matrix

The solution of state equations requires the evaluation of the transition matrix

$$\boldsymbol{\phi}(t) = e^{\mathbf{A}t}$$

There are two essentially different methods of evaluating this matrix. They are methods using (1) Laplace transforms, and (2) functions of a matrix. They will be explored here for a matrix **A** with distinct eigenvalues.*

C.1 Solution by Laplace Transform

It has been shown in Section 6.13 that the following relation exists between the Laplace transform and the transition matrix:

$$\boldsymbol{\phi}(t) = \mathscr{L}^{-1}\{s\mathbf{U} - \mathbf{A}]^{-1}\} \tag{C.1}$$

This equation indicates a solution process which is entirely defined in terms of Laplace transform techniques. Required in this process are two steps: (1) the determination of $[s\mathbf{U} - \mathbf{A}]^{-1}$ and (2) the inverse Laplace transform $\mathscr{L}^{-1}\{[s\mathbf{U} - \mathbf{A}]^{-1}\}$. Both steps are cumbersome and involve considerable work.

The inverse of the matrix $[s\mathbf{U} - \mathbf{A}]$ may be obtained in a number of ways. Two methods which follow a systematic procedure are presented here. The first is analytical, while the second is topological in approach.

The first method is based upon matrix algebra and involves a procedure which is given here without proof.† This procedure makes use of the property

$$[s\mathbf{U} - \mathbf{A}]^{-1} = \frac{1}{D(s)} \text{ adjoint } [s\mathbf{U} - \mathbf{A}] \tag{C.2}$$

where $D(s)$ is the determinant of $[s\mathbf{U} - \mathbf{A}]$. From the expansion into minors the determinant $|s\mathbf{U} - \mathbf{A}|$ may be evaluated by

---

* For cases where **A** contains repeated eigenvalues the reader is referred to F. R. Gantmacher, *The Theory of Matrices*, New York: Chelsea Publishing Co., 1960.

† See H. E. Koenig, Y. Tokad, and H. K. Kesavan, *Analysis of Discrete Physical Systems*, New York: McGraw-Hill Book Co., 1966.

$$D(s) = s^n - p_1 s^{n-1} - p_2 s^{n-2} - \cdots - p_n \qquad \text{(C.3)}$$

where $p_1, p_2, \cdots, p_n$ are defined below. The adjoint may be evaluted by

$$\text{adjoint } [s\mathbf{U} - \mathbf{A}] = \mathbf{U}s^{n-1} + \mathbf{H}_1 s^{n-2} + \mathbf{H}_2 s^{n-3} + \cdots + \mathbf{H}_{n-1} \qquad \text{(C.4)}$$

where

$$\mathbf{H}_1 = \mathbf{A} - p_1\mathbf{U} \qquad p_1 = \text{trace } \mathbf{A}$$

$$\mathbf{H}_2 = \mathbf{A}\mathbf{H}_1 - p_2\mathbf{U} \qquad p_2 = \frac{1}{2} \text{ trace } (\mathbf{A}\mathbf{H}_1)$$

$$\mathbf{H}_3 = \mathbf{A}\mathbf{H}_2 - p_3\mathbf{U} \qquad p_3 = \frac{1}{3} \text{ trace } (\mathbf{A}\mathbf{H}_2)$$

$$\vdots \qquad \qquad \vdots$$

$$\mathbf{H}_{n-1} = \mathbf{A}\mathbf{H}_{n-2} - p_{n-1}\mathbf{U} \qquad p_{n-1} = \frac{1}{n-1} \text{ trace } (\mathbf{A}\mathbf{H}_{n-2})$$

$$\mathbf{H}_n = \mathbf{A}\mathbf{H}_{n-1} - p_n\mathbf{U} = \mathbf{0} \qquad p_n = \frac{1}{n} \text{ trace } (\mathbf{A}\mathbf{H}_{n-1})$$

The trace of a matrix is given by

$$\text{trace } \mathbf{A} = \sum_{i=1}^{n} a_{ii} \qquad \text{(C.5)}$$

Example C.1. Determine the inverse and the determinant of $[s\mathbf{U} - \mathbf{A}]$ when

$$\mathbf{A} = \begin{bmatrix} 2 & -1 & 0 \\ 1 & 1 & 2 \\ -1 & 0 & 1 \end{bmatrix}$$

From Equation C.5 we have

$$p_1 = \text{trace } \mathbf{A} = 4$$

and from Equation C.4 we have

$$\mathbf{H}_1 = \mathbf{A} - p_1\mathbf{U} = \begin{bmatrix} -2 & -1 & 0 \\ 1 & -3 & 2 \\ -1 & 0 & -3 \end{bmatrix}$$

Continuing, we evaluate

$$p_2 = \frac{1}{2}\text{trace } (\mathbf{A}\mathbf{H}_1) = \frac{1}{2}\text{trace} \begin{bmatrix} -5 & 1 & -2 \\ -3 & -4 & -4 \\ 1 & 1 & -3 \end{bmatrix} = -6$$

$$\mathbf{H}_2 = \mathbf{A}\mathbf{H}_1 + 6\mathbf{U} = \begin{bmatrix} 1 & 1 & -2 \\ -3 & 2 & -4 \\ 1 & 1 & 3 \end{bmatrix}$$

$$\text{trace }(\mathbf{AH}_2) = \frac{1}{3}\text{trace}\begin{bmatrix} 5 & 0 & 0 \\ 0 & 5 & 0 \\ 0 & 0 & 5 \end{bmatrix} = 5$$

and

$$\mathbf{H}_3 = 0$$

Thus

$$\begin{aligned} \text{adjoint }[s\mathbf{U} - \mathbf{A}] &= \mathbf{U}s^2 + \mathbf{H}_1 s + \mathbf{H}_2 \\ &= \begin{bmatrix} s^2 - 2s + s & -s + 1 & -2 \\ s - 3 & s^2 - 3s + 2 & 2s - 4 \\ -s + 1 & 1 & s^2 - 3s + 3 \end{bmatrix} \end{aligned}$$

Also

$$D(s) = s^3 - 4s^2 + 6s - 5$$

This procedure for determining the inverse of $[s\mathbf{U} - \mathbf{A}]$ may be programmed as a numerical routine and made available as a standard library program. The inverse Laplace transform of $[s\mathbf{U} - \mathbf{A}]^{-1}$ is obtained by applying the procedures of partial fraction expansion.

A second method of evaluating the inverse of $[s\mathbf{U} - \mathbf{A}]$ is based upon the use of Mason's gain formula.* This formula may be effectively employed for state variable diagrams to calculate transfer functions between any state variable and the initial condition of any other state variable.

The transition matrix may be viewed as relating the state variable vector to the initial condition vector, *i. e.*,

$$\begin{bmatrix} x_1(t) \\ x_2(t) \\ \cdot \\ \cdot \\ \cdot \\ x_n(t) \end{bmatrix} = \begin{bmatrix} a_{11}(t) & a_{12}(t) & \cdots & a_{1n}(t) \\ a_{21}(t) & a_{22}(t) & \cdots & a_{2n}(t) \\ \cdot & & & \\ \cdot & & & \\ \cdot & & & \\ a_{n1}(t) & & \cdots & a_{nn}(t) \end{bmatrix} \begin{bmatrix} x_1(0) \\ x_2(0) \\ \cdot \\ \cdot \\ \cdot \\ x_n(0) \end{bmatrix} \tag{C.6}$$

where the functions $a_{ij}(t)$ are the components of $\boldsymbol{\phi}(t)$. Thus the function $a_{ij}(t)$ can be interpreted as representing the transfer relationship

$$x_i(t) = a_{ij}(t) \cdot x_j(0) \qquad \begin{aligned} x_1(0) = x_2(0) \cdots &= x_n(0) = 0 \\ x_j(0) &\neq 0 \end{aligned}$$

More appropriately, in the s-domain $a_{ij}(s)$ represents the transfer function

$$X_i(s) = a_{ij}(s) \cdot x_j(0) \qquad \begin{aligned} x_1(0) = x_2(0) = \cdots &= x_n(0) = 0 \\ x_j(0) &\neq 0 \end{aligned}$$

The individual transfer functions may be readily obtained from the state variable diagram by the use of Mason's gain formula.

---

* See Chapter 12.

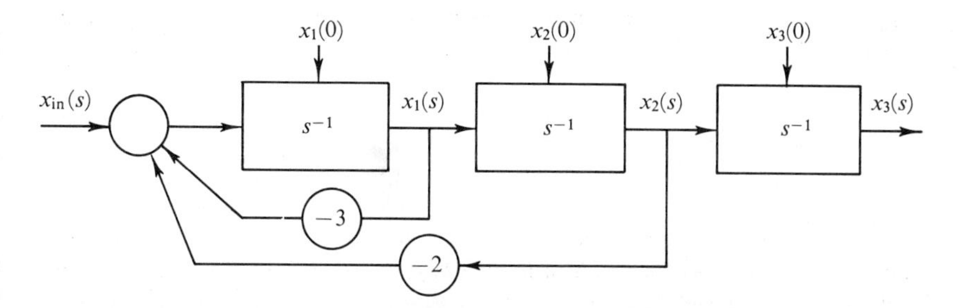

Fig. C.1. *State variable diagram for Example C.2.*

Example C.2. For each transfer function there is only one possible path as evidenced by the diagram. We write

$$x_1(s) = a_{11}(s)x_1(0) + a_{12}(0)x_2(0) + a_{13}(s)x_3(0)$$

$$a_{11}(s) = \frac{s^{-1}\Delta_1(s)}{\Delta(s)}$$

$$a_{11}(s) = \frac{-2s^{-2}\Delta_2(s)}{\Delta(s)}$$

$$a_{13}(s) = 0$$

where

$$\Delta(s) = 1 + 3s^{-1} + 2s^{-2}$$
$$\Delta_1(s) = 1$$
$$\Delta_2(s) = 1$$

Therefore we have

$$X_1(s) = \frac{sx_1(0)}{s^2 + 3s + 2} + \frac{-2x_2(0)}{s^2 + 3s + 2}$$

Similarly, we have

$$X_2(s) = \frac{x_1(0)}{s^2 + 3s + 2} + \frac{-s + 3}{s^2 + 3s + 2}x_2(0)$$

and

$$X_3(s) = \frac{x_1(0)}{s(s^2 + 3s + 2)} + \frac{s + 3}{s(s^2 + 3s + 2)}x_2(0) + \frac{x_3(0)}{s}$$

Upon assembling this into a matrix, we have

$$\begin{bmatrix} X_1(s) \\ X_2(s) \\ X_3(s) \end{bmatrix} = \begin{bmatrix} \dfrac{s}{d(s)} & \dfrac{-2}{d(s)} & 0 \\ \dfrac{1}{d(s)} & \dfrac{s+3}{d(s)} & 0 \\ \dfrac{1}{sd(s)} & \dfrac{s+3}{sd(s)} & \dfrac{1}{s} \end{bmatrix} \begin{bmatrix} x_1(0) \\ x_2(0) \\ x_3(0) \end{bmatrix}$$

Taking the inverse Laplace transformation of the matrix of transfer functions yields the state transition matrix

$$\boldsymbol{\phi}(t) = \begin{bmatrix} -e^{-t} + 2e^{-2t} & -2e^{-t} + 2e^{-2t} & 0 \\ e^{-t} - e^{-2t} & 2e^{-t} - e^{-2t} & 0 \\ \frac{1}{2} - e^{-t} + \frac{1}{2}e^{-2t} & \frac{3}{2} - 2e^{-t} + \frac{1}{2}e^{-2t} & 1 \end{bmatrix}$$

It should be pointed out that by the topological method three additional transfer functions can be determined. They relate the state variables to the input, $x_i(s)$. Although they are not required in the evaluation of the transition, they may be used in determining the complete solution to the non-homogeneous state equations.

C.2 Solutions by Functions of a Matrix

The transition matrix may be evaluated by means of a number of important results from the study of the functions of a matrix.

Cayley-Hamilton Theorem*

The characteristic equation of the matrix **A** is

$$d(\lambda) = |\mathbf{A} - \lambda\mathbf{U}| = 0$$

This equation yields the polynomial

$$d(\lambda) = \lambda^n + a_{n-1}\lambda^{n-1} + \cdots + a_1\lambda + a_0 = 0$$

whose zeros are the eigenvalues of **A**.

If we replace λ by **A** in the above equations, we establish a function of a matrix. We obtain

$$d(\mathbf{A}) = |\mathbf{A} - \mathbf{A}\mathbf{U}| = 0 \tag{C.7}$$

which implies that the matrix **A** satisfies its own characteristic equation. Indeed, this is true for every square matrix. This result is called the Cayley-Hamilton theorem.

We restrict our attention to those functions of matrices which can be represented as a series of powers of the matrix. This restriction is appropriate in the study of linear systems. Thus, for a function of a matrix, one may write the expansion

$$f(\mathbf{A}) = c_0\mathbf{U} + c_1\mathbf{A} + c_2\mathbf{A}^2 + c_3\mathbf{A}^3 + \cdots + c_n\mathbf{A}^n + c_{n+1}\mathbf{A}^{n+1} + \cdots \tag{C.8}$$

The Cayley-Hamilton theorem, however, says that

* J. S. Frame, "Matrix Functions and Applications," *I. E. E. E. Spectrum*, I, No. 6 (June, 1964).

$$d(\mathbf{A}) = \mathbf{A}^n + a_{n-1}\mathbf{A}^{n-1} + \cdots + a_1\mathbf{A} + a_0\mathbf{U} = 0 \tag{C.9}$$

or

$$\mathbf{A}^n = -a_{n-1}\mathbf{A}^{n-1} - \cdots - a_1\mathbf{A} - a_0\mathbf{U} \tag{C.10}$$

Upon multiplying both sides by **A**, the last equation becomes

$$\mathbf{A}^{n+1} = -a_{n-1}\mathbf{A}^n - \cdots - a_1\mathbf{A}^2 - a_0\mathbf{A} \tag{C.11}$$

If we substitute Equation C.10 into Equation C.11, we get

$$\mathbf{A}^{n+1} = -a_{n-1}(-a_{n-1}\mathbf{A}^{n-1} - \cdots - a_1\mathbf{A} - a_0\mathbf{U}) - a_1\mathbf{A}^2 - a_0\mathbf{A} \tag{C.12}$$

Equation C.11 implies that $\mathbf{A}^n$, $\mathbf{A}^{n+1}$, $\cdots$, or in general, all powers of **A** greater than $n-1$ can be expressed as linear combinations of $\mathbf{A}^0$, $\mathbf{A}^1$, $\cdots$, $\mathbf{A}^{n-1}$. We use this result in Equation C.8 to obtain a finite power series expansion for the function of a matrix,

$$f(\mathbf{A}) = \alpha_0\mathbf{U} + \alpha_1\mathbf{A} + \cdots + \alpha_{n-1}\mathbf{A}^{n-1} = \sum_{i=0}^{n-1}\alpha_i\mathbf{A}^i \tag{C.13}$$

where the α_i's are linear combinations of the c's and a's used in Equations C.8 and C.9.

Example C.3. Given

$$\mathbf{A} = \begin{bmatrix} -3 & -1 \\ 2 & 0 \end{bmatrix}$$

calculate $e^{\mathbf{A}t}$ by use of the Cayley-Hamilton theorem.

From Equation C.13 we get

$$f(\mathbf{A}) = e^{\mathbf{A}t} = \alpha_0\mathbf{U} + \alpha_1\mathbf{A}$$

To determine the coefficients α_0 and α_1 we calculate the eigenvalues of **A**. Thus

$$d(\lambda) = |\mathbf{A} - \lambda\mathbf{U}| = \begin{vmatrix} -3-\lambda & -1 \\ 2 & -\lambda \end{vmatrix} = \lambda^2 + 3\lambda + 2 = 0$$

giving

$$\lambda_1 = -1 \quad \text{and} \quad \lambda_2 = -2$$

By the Cayley-Hamilton theorem, $f(A)$ must be satisfied by λ_1 and λ_2. Hence

$$f(\lambda_1) = \alpha_0 + \alpha_1\lambda_1 \quad \text{and} \quad f(\lambda_2) = \alpha_0 + \alpha_1\lambda_2$$

or

$$e^{-t} = \alpha_0 - \alpha_1 \quad \text{and} \quad e^{-2t} = \alpha_0 - 2\alpha_1$$

from which we solve for α_0 and α_1:

$$\alpha_1 = e^{-t} - e^{-2t}$$
$$\alpha_0 = 2e^{-t} - e^{-2t}$$

Finally,

$$e^{\mathbf{A}t} = (2e^{-t} - e^{-2t})\mathbf{U} + (e^{-t} - e^{-2t})\mathbf{A}$$
$$= \begin{bmatrix} -e^{-t} + 2e^{-2t} & -e^{-t} + e^{-2t} \\ 2e^{-t} - 2e^{-2t} & 2e^{-t} - e^{-2t} \end{bmatrix}$$

The Sylvester Expansion Theorem*

This important theorem states that a function of a matrix may be expanded by the series

$$f(\mathbf{A}) = \sum_{i=1}^{n} \mathbf{A}_i f(\lambda_i) \tag{C.14}$$

where

$$\mathbf{A}_i = \prod_{\substack{j=1 \\ j \neq i}}^{n} \frac{[\mathbf{A} - \lambda_j \mathbf{U}]}{\lambda_i - \lambda_j} \tag{C.15}$$

The matrices $\mathbf{A}_1, \mathbf{A}_2, \cdots, \mathbf{A}_n$ are called the constituent matrices of **A** and are dependent only on **A** and its n eigenvalues. This is a significant property inasmuch as it permits the use of the same constituent matrices for any function of a matrix.

Example C.4. For the matrix **A** of the previous example, evaluate $e^{\mathbf{A}t}$ and $\mathbf{A}^n$.

$$\mathbf{A} = \begin{bmatrix} -3 & -1 \\ 2 & 0 \end{bmatrix} \qquad \lambda_1 = -1 \qquad \lambda_2 = -2$$

We determine

$$\mathbf{A}_1 = \frac{\begin{bmatrix} -3 & -1 \\ 2 & 0 \end{bmatrix} - \begin{bmatrix} -2 & 0 \\ 0 & -2 \end{bmatrix}}{-1-(-2)} = \begin{bmatrix} -1 & -1 \\ 2 & 2 \end{bmatrix}$$

$$\mathbf{A}_2 = \frac{\begin{bmatrix} -3 & -1 \\ 2 & 0 \end{bmatrix} - \begin{bmatrix} -1 & 0 \\ 0 & -1 \end{bmatrix}}{-2-(-1)} = \begin{bmatrix} 2 & 1 \\ -2 & -1 \end{bmatrix}$$

Therefore

$$e^{\mathbf{A}t} = \mathbf{A}_1 e^{\lambda_1 t} + \mathbf{A}_2{}^{\lambda_2 t}$$
$$= \begin{bmatrix} -1 & -1 \\ 2 & 2 \end{bmatrix} e^{-t} + \begin{bmatrix} 2 & 1 \\ -2 & -1 \end{bmatrix} e^{-2t}$$

This result agrees with the previous example. For $\mathbf{A}^n$ we use the same constituent matrices to obtain

$$\mathbf{A}^n = \mathbf{A}_1 \lambda_1{}^n + \mathbf{A}_2 \lambda_2{}^n$$
$$= \begin{bmatrix} -1 & -1 \\ 2 & 2 \end{bmatrix} (-1)^n + \begin{bmatrix} 2 & 1 \\ -2 & -1 \end{bmatrix} (-2)^n$$

---

* Ibid.

Three Properties of Constituent Matrices

$\mathbf{A}$ has distinct eigenvalues.

1. Constituent matrices are mutually orthogonal:

$$\mathbf{A}_i\mathbf{A}_j = \mathbf{0} \tag{C.16}$$

2. A complete set of constituent matrices sum to the unit matrix:

$$\sum_{i=1}^{n} \mathbf{A}_i = \mathbf{U} \tag{C.17}$$

This property serves as a convenient numerical check on calculations.

3. A constituent matrix is an idempotent matrix:

$$\mathbf{A}_i^r = \mathbf{A}_i \tag{C.18}$$

The technique of evaluating constituent matrices by the Sylvester Expansion theorem is systematic. It may be programmed as a subroutine in a program library. This routine may be efficiently employed to evaluate functions of a matrix in connection with a routine which determines the eigenvalues of the matrix.

Other Properties of Exponential Matrices

The study of functions of a matrix has a much broader scope than is indicated. The principal objective here is to present convenient and practical techniques of evaluating $e^{\mathbf{A}t}$, which is just one special case. Several important properties of $e^{\mathbf{A}t}$ are now developed by use of the Sylvester Expansion theorem.

1.

$$\mathbf{A}e^{\mathbf{A}t} = e^{\mathbf{A}t}\mathbf{A} \tag{C.19}$$

Consider

$$e^{\mathbf{A}t} = \sum_{i=1}^{n} \mathbf{A}_i e^{\lambda_i t}$$

and

$$\mathbf{A} = \sum_{j=1}^{n} \mathbf{A}_j \lambda_j$$

Then

$$\begin{aligned} \mathbf{A}e^{\mathbf{A}t} &= \sum_{j=1}^{n} \mathbf{A}_j \lambda_j \sum_{i=1}^{n} \mathbf{A}_i e^{\lambda_i t} \\ &= \sum_{j=1}^{n} \sum_{i=1}^{n} \mathbf{A}_j \mathbf{A}_i \lambda_j e^{\lambda_i t} \\ &= \sum_{i=1}^{n} \mathbf{A}_i \mathbf{A}_i \lambda_i e^{\lambda_i t} \end{aligned}$$

by Equation C.16

$$= \sum_{i=1}^{n} \mathbf{A}_i \lambda_i e^{\lambda_i t}$$

by Equation C.18. Similarly,

$$e^{\mathbf{A}t}\mathbf{A} = \sum_{i=1}^{n} \mathbf{A}_i \lambda_i e^{\lambda_i t}$$

Hence

$$\mathbf{A}e^{\mathbf{A}t} = e^{\mathbf{A}t}\mathbf{A}$$

This property is extendable for all functions of a matrix, such that in general

$$f_1(\mathbf{A})f_2(\mathbf{A}) = f_2(\mathbf{A})f_1(\mathbf{A}) \tag{C.20}$$

2.

$$\frac{d}{dt}e^{\mathbf{A}t} = \mathbf{A}e^{\mathbf{A}t} \tag{C.21}$$

This result follows a procedure identical to that of the last property.

3.

$$(e^{\mathbf{A}t})^{-1} = e^{-\mathbf{A}t} \tag{C.22}$$

Consider

$$e^{\mathbf{A}t} = \sum_{i=1}^{n} \mathbf{A}_i e^{\lambda_i t}$$

$$(e^{\mathbf{A}t})^{-1} = \sum_{i=1}^{n} \mathbf{A}_i (e^{\lambda_i t})^{-1}$$

$$= \sum_{i=1}^{n} \mathbf{A}_i e^{-\lambda_i t}$$

$$= e^{-\mathbf{A}t}$$

4.

$$e^{\mathbf{A}t}\Big]_{t=0} = \mathbf{U} \tag{C.23}$$

Consider

$$e^{\mathbf{A}t}\Big]_{t=0} = \sum_{i=1}^{n} \mathbf{A}_i e^0 = \mathbf{U}$$

by Equation C.17.

The functions of a matrix provide two techniques for the evaluation of the transition matrix without requiring the use of the Laplace transform. In addition, several useful properties of $e^{\mathbf{A}t}$ are readily derived.

ADDITIONAL READINGS

Belliman, R., *Introduction to Matrix Analsis*, New York: McGraw-Hill Book Co., 1960.

Pipes, L., *Matrix Methods for Engineering*, Englewood Cliffs, New Jersey: Prentice-Hall, Inc., 1963.

D. Complex Numbers

A complex number is defined by two coordinates. It represents a point on the plane in precisely the same manner as a real number represents a point on the line. The two coordinates of the complex plane are called the *real* and the *imaginary* axis. A complex number may be represented mathematically in two ways, as shown in Figure D.1.

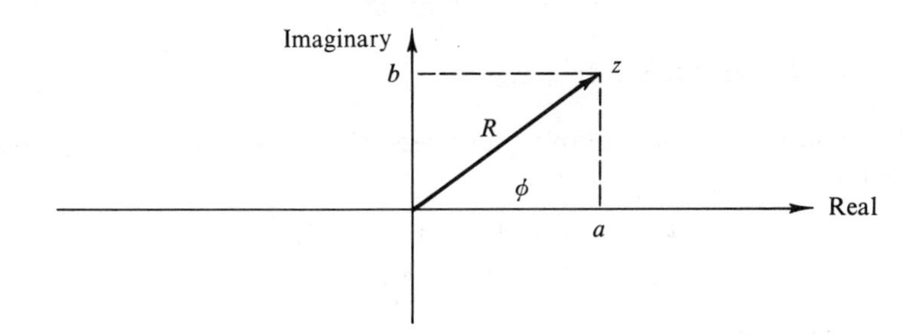

Fig. D.1. *Representation of complex number on plane.*

a. Rectangular coordinates:

$$z = a + jb \tag{D.1}$$

a is called the real part of z denoted by Re $\{z\}$ and b is called the imaginary part of z denoted by Im $\{z\}$.

b. Polar coordinates:

$$z = Re^{j\varphi} \tag{D.2}$$

R is called the magnitude of z denoted by $|z|$ and ϕ is called the argument of z denoted by Arg $\{z\}$. The two representations are shown to be equivalent by considering the simple trigonometric relationship

$$\left.\begin{aligned} a &= R\cos\phi \\ b &= R\sin\phi \end{aligned}\right] \tag{D.3}$$

$$a + jb = R(\cos\phi + j\sin\phi) \tag{D.4}$$

But from Euler's identity, one has

$$e^{jx} = \cos x + j \sin x \tag{D.5}$$

so that Equation D.4 then will yield

$$a + jb = Re^{j\phi} \tag{D.6}$$

Equation D.6 states the rule by which a complex number may be transformed from rectangular to polar coordinates, or vice versa. In addition to the relations given by Equation D.3, where a and b are specified in terms of R and ϕ, the inverse relations are

$$R = \sqrt{a^2 + b^2}$$
$$\phi = \tan^{-1}\frac{b}{a} \tag{D.7}$$

Consider now two complex numbers,

$$z_1 = a_1 + jb_1 = R_1e^{j\phi_1}$$
$$z_2 = a_2 + jb_2 = R_2e^{j\phi_2}$$

D.1 Addition $z_1 + z_2$

For addition of two complex numbers, the rectangular form is most convenient;

$$z_1 + z_2 = a_1 + jb_1 + a_2 + jb_2$$
$$= (a_1 + a_2) + j(b_1 + b_2)$$

D.2 Subtraction $z_1 - z_2$

For subtraction of two complex numbers, the rectangular form is most convenient;

$$z_1 - z_2 = a_1 + jb_1 - a_2 - jb_2$$
$$= (a_1 - a_2) + j(b_1 - b_2)$$

D.3 Multiplication $z_1 \cdot z_2$

For multiplication of two complex numbers, the polar form is most convenient;

$$z_1 \cdot z_2 = (R_1e^{j\phi_1})(R_2e^{j\phi_2})$$
$$= R_1R_2e^{j(\phi_1+\phi_2)}$$

D.4 Division z_1/z_2

For division of two complex numbers, the polar form is the most convenient:

$$z_1/z_2 = (R_1 e^{j\phi_1})/(R_2 e^{j\phi_2})$$
$$= R_1/R_2 e^{j(\phi_1 - \phi_2)}$$

If two complex numbers are to be added or subtracted and are given in polar form, they should first be converted to rectangular form; similarly, if two complex numbers are to be multiplied or divided, and are given in rectangular form, they should first be converted to polar form. The required conversions are specified by Equations D.3 and D.7. They may be readily accomplished by a simple operation on the slide rule.

Quite frequently, calculations are required where the operations of addition, subtraction, multiplication, and division are combined. The following example illustrates this.

Example D.1. Calculate

$$z = \frac{(3 + 4j)(-5 - 12j)}{5e^{-j36.8} + 13e^{j157.4}}$$

We first convert

$$3 + 4j = 5e^{j53.2}$$
$$-5 - 12j = 13e^{-112.6}$$
$$5e^{-j36.8} = 4 - 3j$$
$$13e^{j157.4} = -12 + 5j$$
$$z = \frac{65e^{-j59.4}}{-8 + 2j}$$

Again, we convert

$$-8 + 2j = 8.23e^{j165.9}$$
$$z = 7.9e^{-j225.3}$$

Since a complex number may be in any of the four quadrants, it is extremely helpful in the process of converting a number from one form into another to draw a little sketch of the complex plane to reduce the chance of numerical errors.

Index